PROTEIN FOLDING

Deciphering the Second Half of the Genetic Code

Edited by
Lila M. Gierasch and Jonathan King

AMERICAN ASSOCIATION FOR THE ADVANCEMENT OF SCIENCE

Library of Congress Cataloging-in-Publication Data

Gierasch, Lila M. and King, Jonathan
    Protein Folding: Deciphering the Second Half of the Genetic Code / Lila M. Gierasch and Jonathan King
       p.   cm.
    Includes bibliographic references.
    ISBN 0-87168-353-9
    1. Protein folding—Congresses.   2. Protein engineering—Congresses.

I. Gierasch, Lila M.   II. King, Jonathan

QP551.P69582   1989
574.87'328—dc20   89-29567
                                                             CIP

Publication No. 89-18S

© 1990 by the American Association for the Advancement of Science
1333 H Street, N.W., Washington, D.C. 20005

Contents

Preface

The catalytic activity of enzymes, the unique properties of structural proteins, and the biophysical sophistication of contractile and membrane-channel proteins all depend on the precise folding of their polypeptide chains. From the seminal work of Christian Anfinsen and co-workers in the 1960s, we know that the amino acid sequence of a polypeptide chain in the appropriate solvent environment can fully determine its folding into its native conformation. Clearly, there are rules that determine how a given sequence of amino acid side chains directs its chain into a discrete conformation. Yet, given the amino acid sequence of a protein of unknown structure and function, it is still not possible to predict reliably or even to understand how the sequence of the amino acids determines the spatial organization of the chain.

The triplet genetic code by which the nucleotide sequence determines the amino acid sequence of polypeptide chains is well understood. However, unfolded polypeptide chains lack most of the properties needed for biological function and, therefore, gene expression. The chains must be folded into native three-dimensional conformations in order to function. The rules through which the sequence determines the folding represent an undeciphered aspect of the genetic code: the need to break this part of the code is increasingly urgent for several reasons.

First, the solution to this problem is of pressing practical importance. With recent breakthroughs in genetic engineering technology, the speed at which the nucleotide sequences of genes can be determined has far outstripped the rate at which the protein products can be isolated and characterized. Yet much of the information in these sequences — most notably the three-dimensional structure of the gene product — can not presently be reliably extracted. The Human Genome Project will rapidly increase the appearance of such sequences.

Second, polypeptide chain folding within cells has emerged as a bottleneck in the production and analysis of the proteins of genes cloned from their natural host into another host organism. Instead of folding with the efficiency and fidelity found in their native cell, such polypeptide chains frequently fail to reach the native state. This failure has called attention to the intracellular processes of protein folding. The misfolded states or inclusion bodies can frequently be solubilized by strong denaturants and then refolded in vitro. The need to refold a much larger and diverse range of proteins, often on a large scale, has also increased interest in the mechanism of in vitro refolding.

Third, the ability to design proteins from scratch will require an understanding of what the sequence determinants of folding and assembly are. It is currently possible to modify existing proteins and also to recover a variety of hybrids. A great deal of progress will thus be made empirically. But the ability to design proteins to carry out novel functions requires a fuller understanding of how sequences control folding.

The chapters in this volume address key aspects of polypeptide chain behavior that have been barriers to the solution of the folding problem: solvation and peptide structural principles, protein folding pathways, and intermediates. In addition, attention is given to in vivo folding mechanisms and to recent successes in design and in mutagenesis approaches. Together these papers represent an overview of the status of the protein folding problem and the prospects for its solution. We have tried to organize the volume so that it will be useful as a tutorial or textbook. The chapters are presented as continuous narratives in lecture format for ease of reading. Each section of papers has a brief introduction to provide orientation.

This volume grew out of a very successful symposium organized under the auspices of the American Association for the Advancement of Science. Thanks are due to Dan Kemp, Peter Kim, Barry Nall, Jiri Novotny, Jane Richardson, George Rose, and Martha Teeter for help in organizing the original program. Our editor, Susan McMurray, was instrumental in bringing the book from conception to completion. Susan M. O'Connell and Kathy Doucette prepared the camera-ready pages, and Susan Cherry prepared the art.

The coming decade promises to be a period of the blossoming of the applications of basic medical research. We believe that the emergence of the missing answers with respect to the protein folding rules will be one of the particularly exciting developments in this period. This should yield new possibilities in biotechnology and deeper understanding of the healthy and diseased functions of organisms.

Lila M. Gierasch and
Jonathan King

Part I

Structural Themes in Native Proteins

George D. Rose

Protein folding is a mature discipline in the midst of an exuberant second childhood. The field dates back at least half a century to work of Mirsky and Pauling (1936). Yet, today, with hundreds of complete protein structures at our disposal – elucidated by both x-ray and nuclear magnetic resonance (NMR) – we still lack predictive understanding of how even the simplest structural motifs are determined by the amino acid sequence.

In the last decade, our failure to "crack the code" after so much effort took its toll and interest in the field began to dwindle. But now there has been a rebirth, engendered in large part by our new-found ability to replace essentially any residue in a protein of interest and to overexpress the resulting mutant protein. The structural effect of a residue can then be assessed simply by substituting other residues (often, all 19 other residues) and measuring the consequences.

While we cannot yet reliably predict structural motifs from sequence alone, the motifs themselves are clear and are the topic of this first section. At the level of secondary structure, α-helix, β-sheet, reverse turns, and Ω-loops account for more than 90 percent of proteins. These units pack together into larger assemblages – supersecondary structure – which, in turn, participate in yet larger composites, in interactive fashion, resulting ultimately in the observed hierarchic architecture of protein molecules (Rose, 1979). These *structural themes* found in native proteins comprise the first six chapters of this volume.

In the first chapter, Richardson and Richardson draw an extended analogy between origami and protein folding and inform us about each. This paper, prepared initially as a plenary lecture for a diversified audience, had the dual and difficult task of stimulating both laymen and practitioners alike. It succeeds brilliantly. A casual familiarity with origami is sufficient background to grasp topics that include the folding transition, convergent evolution, the cooperative behavior of intermediates, domains, packing arrangements between units of secondary structure, and protein engineering and design. Specific examples are taken from the authors' contributions in many of these areas. In addition, a new approach to conformational analysis using carbonyl oxygen directions is presented.

The chapter by Fetrow (Leszczynski) and Rose, reprinted from an earlier publication (Leszczynski and Rose, 1986), describes the Ω-loop, a novel category of secondary structure. Ω-loops are so named because their main chain circumscribes a central cavity, bringing the two chain ends into spatial proximity, like a capital Greek omega. Loops are abundant in globular proteins. They are situated at the molecular surface, poised to interact with other molecules. Often, they are found at or near sites of functional interest. Surprisingly, Ω-loops are highly compact, despite the fact that they lack the regular patterns of hydrogen bonding that are characteristic of helix and sheet. The stability of isolated loops remains to be assessed.

The chapter by Presta and Rose, also reprinted from an earlier publication (1988), is concerned with the helix. Thirty-eight years ago, the α-helix was first proposed as a model structure by Pauling *et al.* (1951). Experimental confirmation was quick to follow, and the helix has since become a familiar landmark in proteins. The key feature of the Pauling-Corey-Branson helical model is a pattern of iterated backbone hydrogen bonding between each N-H donor and the C=O acceptor located four residues previously. Much effort has been directed toward understanding which sequences form stable helices (Marqusee *et al.*, 1989). The hypothesis introduced here was prompted by the observation that the initial four N-H groups and final four C=O groups of the helix lack intrahelical partners, and it states that a necessary condition for helix formation is the presence of residues flanking the helix termini that supply hydrogen-bond partners for these otherwise unsatisfied main-chain polar groups. This simple hypothesis implies the existence of a stereochemical code at helix boundaries.

The solvent that surrounds proteins is then analyzed by Teeter, using crambin as a model. The importance of solvent water cannot be overemphasized (Edsall and McKenzie, 1983). Proteins are macromolecules, large enough to have a buried interior in which many apolar groups can be sequestered upon being driven from the aqueous surround in consequence of the hydrophobic effect. Indeed, anhydrous environments are known to disrupt protein folding (Waks, 1986). The crambin structure reveals highly ordered water within the crystal. Since protein crystals are well hydrated (typically 40–50 percent water, by weight), the crystalline form is thought to be a good model for the protein in solution. Not all apolar groups are buried, particularly in the case of the hydrophobic protein crambin. At the protein surface, Teeter finds ordered water clusters (clathrates) that enclose exposed hydrophobic groups, and, to some extent, reproducible patterns of hydrogen bonding between water and exposed polar groups. Further analysis and additional proteins may well lead to a set of coordination rules for water localized at the protein surface.

Fibrous proteins are introduced by Brodsky, who emphasizes the coiled coil and the triple-helix. Fibrous or structural proteins often are neglected in discussions of folding, although they account for the majority of total protein in larger vertebrates. There is a widespread (and misguided) feeling that fibrous proteins are less interesting than globular proteins, somewhat akin perhaps to the pre-Watson and Crick notion that DNA would prove uninteresting in comparison to molecules of greater complexity. At the moment, more than 400 proteins have been solved at essentially atomic resolution in single-crystal x-ray studies, with not a fibrous protein among them. The issue has become especially pressing in view of recent studies indicating that "leucine zipper" peptide products of the *fos* and *jun* proto-oncogenes associate into a coiled coil (O'Shea *et al.*, 1989). Brodsky's chapter is a fine summary of this important area.

In the final chapter of this section, Urry turns to the topic of energetics. The free energy difference between the native and denatured states of globular proteins is small, typically on the order of 10–15 kcal/mol (i.e., the equivalent of two or three water:water hydrogen bonds). This small free energy change results from comparatively large changes in both enthalpy and entropy, as first pointed out by Brandts (1964). Modest errors in measurement easily can become major problems in such a delicately balanced system, and attempts to sum energetic contributions arising from hydrogen bonding, electrostatics, hydrophobic interactions, and so forth have been inconclusive. Urry has developed a polymer system to amplify small changes of interest to such a degree that interaction energies can be converted to mechanical work.

References

Brandts, J. F., *J. Am. Chem. Soc.* **86**, 4302 (1964).

Edsall, J. T., and H. A. McKenzie, *Adv. Biophys.* **16**, 53 (1983).

Leszczynski (Fetrow), J. F., and G. D. Rose, *Science* **234,** 849 (1986).

Marquesee, S., V. H. Robbins, R. L. Baldwin, *Proc. Natl. Acad. Sci. U.S.A.***86,** 5286 (1989).

Mirsky, A. E., and L. Pauling, *Proc. Natl. Acad. Sci. U.S.A.* **22,** 439 (1936).

O'Shea, E. K., R. Rutkowski, P. S. Kim, *Science* **243,** 538 (1989).

Pauling, L., R. B. Corey, H. R. Branson, *Proc. Natl. Acad. Sci. U. S. A.* **37,** 205 (1951).

Presta, L. G., and G. D. Rose, *Science* **240,** 1632 (1988).

Rose, G. D., *J. Mol. Biol.* **134,** 447 (1979).

Waks, M., *Proteins: Struct., Funct. & Genet.* **1,** 4 (1986).

1

The Origami of Proteins

Jane S. Richardson and David C. Richardson

The purpose of this chapter is to develop what is more properly a metaphor, rather than an analogy, between origami paper folding and the folding of protein molecules. While far from perfect, the correspondence can help illuminate the subject. As an analogy, the most obvious flaw is that someone must fold the paper, while proteins typically can fold up by themselves, as suggested by Fig. 1. The usefulness of the metaphor lies in the suggestion of scientifically fruitful attitudes and approaches that are different from those offered by the dominant paradigm of folding as a stepwise accretion of bits and pieces.

Color Plate I introduces the metaphor by showing, on the left, a pair of origami flowers and, on the right, the structure of γ crystallin, one of the major proteins in the lens of the eye. That protein is made up of two very similar domains, each of which looks a bit like a flower. The arrows in the schematic drawing represent β-strands; those are where the polypeptide chain is extended, with hydrogen bonds across between the strands. Nonrepetitive loop regions are just shown as ropes. Some of the proteins depicted later in this chapter show spiral ribbons representing α-helices, which are the other major repeating structure in proteins.

Similarities Between Origami and Protein Folding

What is of interest here is not the final protein structures or the final pieces of origami but the process by which they are formed. Origami is an appropriate metaphor for protein folding because the process itself is a centrally important aspect of paper folding, and, in trying to understand protein folding, it is the process with which we are concerned. Another major point of the metaphor is that both activities begin with a very uninteresting object. For origami it is a single piece of paper, normally square (the one in Color Plate IIa just happens to be a triangle), two dimensional, flat, and unmarked. A protein starts off as a one-dimensional amino acid sequence, which has a lot of potential but no remarkable chemical or biological properties in the unfolded state. In both cases, however, the final result of folding is a meaningful, functional object: a paper lobster in Color Plate IIa and a protease inhibitor in Color Plate IIb.

The amino acid sequence shown in Color Plate IIb folds up into the complex looking, three-dimensional structure of bovine pancreatic trypsin inhibitor, familiarly known as BPTI. But this is actually a very small, simple protein as such things go; a more typical one might be ten times the size. BPTI has been called the "hydrogen atom" of protein folding. It is probably the protein whose folding has been most thoroughly studied both by physical experiments and by calculations. Yet, until recently, we still had very few clues about exactly how that specific sequence folded up into this particular protein. Now we are beginning to understand something of how BPTI

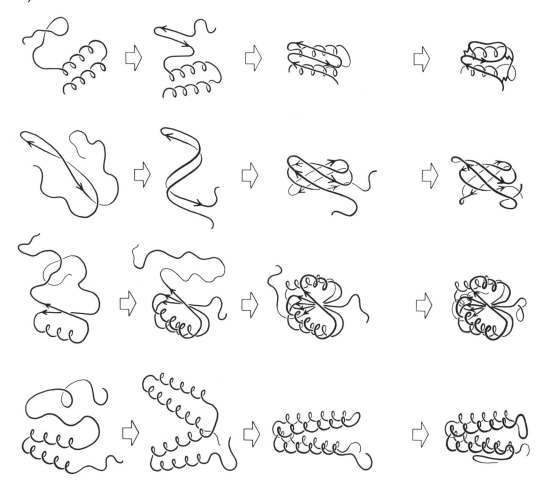

Fig. 1. A schematic illustration of hypothetical steps in the folding of various types of protein structures (Richardson, 1977). In most cases, the final stage of small rearrangements must occur before the protein is active.

folds up (see, for instance, chapter 12, by Oas and Kim, this volume), and in a few more years, it might indeed be central to a fundamental understanding of protein folding.

There are a number of specific resemblances between origami pieces and proteins, many of which have to do with how the proteins fold. One common observation about proteins is that, even for single polypeptide chains like the p-hydroxybenzoate hydroxylase in Color Plate IIIb, they often fold up into what have been called domains, where a region that is contiguous in the amino acid sequence folds up locally together in space. In many cases, a domain has been shown to fold independently and then later to associate with the other parts of the protein. Also, in origami,

there are "domains" that are folded separately and then put together, for example, the little black and gray kitten in Color Plate IIIa. Origami can even have multisubunit assemblies that show concerted movements. The mobile ornament in Color Plate IVa is like an allosteric enzyme or like the immunoglobulin structure in Color Plate IVb, where a multisubunit and multidomain assembly has cooperative motions that are a principal part of its biological function.

Another interesting likeness between origami and proteins is that origami also frequently illustrates convergent evolution. Color Plate Vb shows one of the classic examples of convergent evolution in protein structures. It is a comparison of trypsin, a "serine-protease" digestive enzyme, and subtilisin, another digestive enzyme with very similar function, slightly different specificity, and with active-site serine, histidine, and aspartate side chains that almost perfectly superimpose on the ones from trypsin. However, there simply is nothing in common in the rest of the two protein folds, showing fairly conclusively that trypsin and subtilisin must have invented this same mechanism of proteolysis quite independently. Similarly, it is difficult to find an example of the same origami figure that is folded up the same way in two different instruction books. For instance, Color Plate Va shows two pieces that are recognizably both swans, but the folding patterns are quite unrelated. They start off differently, and most steps along the way differ, except perhaps for formation of the head.

As folding research has shown for some proteins such as BPTI, there can be very substantial rearrangements during folding. The process is not necessarily a stepwise affair where first one piece folds, and then another is added to it, and then another—like building a house. Proteins are very loose; they fold by a balance between relatively weak forces. Origami, too, is a subtle matter of friction and timing rather than glue and staples; a piece is constructed, and it may not necessarily stay in that position while one does something else. In BPTI, such rearrangements can be followed because the three disulfide links (the "lightning bolts" in Fig. 2) allow intermediate forms to be trapped and identified. Tom Creighton (1977) has shown that the favored folding pathway for BPTI goes through an intermediate where an end of the right-hand disulfide is fastened to an end of one of the ones at the left, which must involve a structure very different from the native protein. Thus, part of the protein folds up, and then it must turn inside out and rearrange. This also happens very frequently in origami. One of the early steps in folding many paper figures is to start off with an arrangement like Color Plate VI with flaps sticking up. Then one pulls out the part on top, turns it inside out, and flattens it down in the opposite arrangement, so that now the parts of the paper that lie next to each

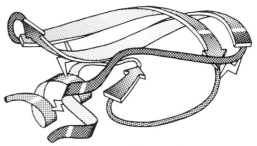

Pancreatic Trypsin Inhibitor

Fig. 2. Schematic ribbon drawing of BPTI with the disulfide bridges shown as lightning bolts. A major folding intermediate (Creighton, 1977) has one end of the disulfide at the right end of the molecule attached to one at the left end, so that its overall structure must be quite different from this.

other have changed. There really is no viable way to get to some final origami figures without going through such a rearrangement.

Another interesting feature of the paper-folding process is that the object (such as the swan of Color Plate VII) is seldom recognizable until the very end. The last small folds around the head are the ones that give it personality, so that one knows this is a swan and not some other bird or beast. Similarly in protein folding (symbolized hypothetically in Fig. 1), one of the late steps in the process is an approximately correct structure that still does not work. Only the final readjustments actually put the side chains in quite the right position to do the job this particular protein is supposed to do.

In a way, the most relevant similarity of all between the two folding processes is that both are subtle and mysterious. In other words, there is still a protein folding problem. Color Plate VIIIb shows the amino acid sequence of staphylococcal nuclease laid out to highlight hydrophobic versus hydrophilic residues. From such a layout, even assuming that the helices and β-strands can all be correctly located, no one knows how to gather it up into the three-dimensional, functional molecule shown in Color Plate IXb. Again with an origami figure, if it is carefully unfolded, the end result is a crinkled sheet like the ones in Color Plate VIIIa. It shows some evidence about how the thing went together, but it is extremely difficult from this starting point to figure out what the final figure was and how to duplicate it. It turns out that these four were a swan, a canary, a flower, and a square box (Color Plate IXa).

The exercise of taking a final origami piece and unfolding it points up another similarity with proteins, which is that very careful work is required to make proteins unfold and refold reversibly. It is easy to get irreversible denaturation in proteins and, of course, one can easily tear or crumple origami. In biology, proteins depend on being formed, being functional for a certain length of time, and then being degraded again. Like origami, proteins are an evanescent art form.

A visitor in our house observing the two of us and our two children playing with origami would find lots of examples of flat pieces of origami paper and lots of examples of little swans, balloons, and paper flowers lying around. However, very few intermediate forms would be found. People do not make origami by folding six different examples halfway along and leaving them to sit there for a while, then later finishing them all (except for multipiece assemblies like Color Plate IVa). Again, one of the major difficulties in studying protein folding is that, for single domains, it is almost always a highly cooperative two-state process in which only rarely do true intermediates accumulate. One line of research that has been very active recently is a new set of tricks to trap and study such intermediates.

Current Developments

At the present time, two things contribute to increased excitement and progress in the field of protein folding. One is the change that has come from the revolution in molecular biology and, to some extent, also from improvements in such techniques as peptide synthesis and nuclear magnetic resonance (NMR) spectroscopy. We now can go in and manipulate proteins much more easily. Besides being able to mutate native proteins, we can also synthesize or obtain from gene expression new

model systems, which we can then change and play with in turn. All of this has made an enormous difference to the whole field. Sometimes a mutation has the result we expected, which is comforting, and sometimes it does not, which gives us a chance to learn something new. Although the easiest thing to study is stability in the final structure, these methods are increasingly being applied to folding kinetics and pathways as well.

The other thing that has happened is a change in motivation. The snake in the cartoon in Fig. 3 seems to be perplexed; nevertheless, he is working extremely hard at folding properly. Like the snake, people these days have stronger motivation and increased resources for studying "the art of globular protein origami." There are immediate practical reasons why people need to know how to fold up proteins well, in order to express and recover high levels of proteins made by biotechnology. An even more fundamental understanding of folding will be needed to design entirely new, functioning proteins — a prospect which sounded wildly utopian just a few years ago but which now seems increasingly imminent.

β-Barrel Proteins

Some examples from our own research illustrate the power of this origami metaphor, either because, in hindsight, they seem illuminated by that viewpoint or because the line of inquiry was actually first suggested by the paper-folding metaphor. Color Plate XI shows Cu, Zn superoxide dismutase (SOD), which is a protein structure we determined by x-ray crystallography at Duke University (Richardson *et al.*, 1975). Its main feature is an eight-stranded barrel of β-sheet structure. The arrows showing the N- to C-terminal direction of the polypeptide chain point in opposite directions on adjacent strands, so this is what is known as antiparallel β structure. Very often the chain goes from one β-strand through a tight hairpin and down into the neighboring strand. It is a very common theme in proteins for pieces of structure that are ad-

- NOW COLLAPSE DOWN HYDROPHOBIC CORE, AND FOLD
OVER HELIX 'A' TO DOTTED LINE, BRINGING CHARGED
RESIDUES OF 'A' INTO CLOSE PROXIMITY TO IONIC
GROUPS ON OUTER SURFACE OF HELIX 'B' ---

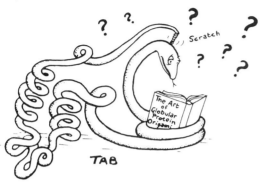

Fig. 3. Cartoon illustrating the subtleties of protein origami. Reprinted from T.A.B., in *Trends in Biochem. Sci.* **12**, 312 (1987), with permission.

jacent in the sequence to lie next to each other in the final protein. What intrigues us so much about the β-strand organization found in SOD is that it represents one of the major exceptions to that rule. The SOD type of β structure involves connections that skip over a couple of intervening strands rather than joining near-neighbor strands. One such connection curves smoothly across the top of the SOD barrel, and another one skips across the bottom with a little curly loop.

The SOD kind of barrel topology actually turns out to be very common — much more so than β-cylinders that have all near-neighbor connections. It was at first unclear why that should be true, because connections that skip two strands are not very common in other places in proteins. The reason is not that skipping over two strands is a favorable way to make a connection; there must be some factor that relates to the overall organization of β-barrels. We discovered that if you imagine breaking open the β-barrel and laying it out flat so that you can make a diagram of the strand topology, what you produce is the sort of pattern shown at the bottom in Fig. 4, with the vertical bars representing the β-strands and the horizontal ones representing the connections. I presume this pattern looks familiar; it is the sort of design that is used as a border decoration on Greek vases, like the one in

Color Plate X. It is called the "Greek key" pattern, so we have called these structures Greek key β-barrels. As well as in superoxide dismutase, it is also found in immunoglobulin domains and in very many other proteins. It is the second most common protein structure. One of the interesting features is that either on a protein or on a Greek vase, the inside is different from the outside, so it makes a difference whether the pattern swirls in a clockwise or counterclockwise direction. It turns out that all of the proteins swirl in the counterclockwise direction. This, however, is one detail the Greeks did not understand: they used both swirl directions on their vases.

We have some idea now of why this Greek key structure is so common, and we believe

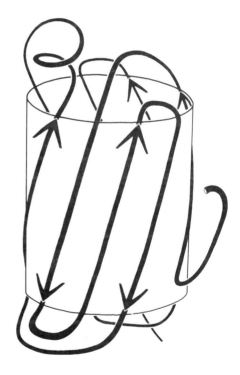

Fig. 4. Simplified backbone drawing of the β barrel from prealbumin (Oatley and Blake, 1978) shown on the surface of a cylinder. At the bottom, the β strand connectivity has been further simplified as a repeating pattern.

that it has to do with the way β-barrel proteins fold up (Richardson, 1977; Salemme 1983; Richardson and Richardson, 1987). β-sheets never are completely flat unless they are in a very constrained environment in the protein. They always have a nice, graceful, right-handed twist, as seen for the two twisted β strands at the top in Fig. 2. One can imagine in the Greek key proteins that an early intermediate in folding may involve forming a very long two-stranded β-ribbon, which would twist because they always twist. Figure 5 shows such a ribbon smoothly curling up into a β-barrel. The right-handed twist in the original ribbon gets converted into a counterclockwise swirl of the strand-connection pattern in the final structure. This is a consistent handedness preference for a very large piece of structure: a Greek key involves at least four and often as

many as eight strands, which may be well over a hundred residues, all of which are apparently folding as a concerted unit. Here we have an example where the polypeptide chain apparently goes into two dimensions like a long strip of paper, and then that strip folds up to form the final protein. Going through this kind of an intermediate can explain why β-barrels do not have the usual strong preference for near-neighbor connections in the final structure.

Figure 6 shows one of the domains of the CAP repressor protein in which the hypothetical two-stranded ribbon has been shaded for emphasis. There is a hairpin in the middle in front, and these two strands can be followed along next to one another, back through the β-barrel to the two helices at the top. There are now quite a number of β-barrel proteins whose connectivity strongly suggests this kind of two-stranded organization rather than a one-stranded organization during folding.

Fold Points

Another approach to protein structures that was suggested to us by the origami metaphor is inquiring what the "fold points" or corners are actually doing in the protein. Some origami pieces end up almost flat, but the ones that are truly three dimensional, like the little blue cube in Color Plate XIIa, involve both perpendicular folds and 180° creases. One can imagine in a final protein structure that features like α-helices and β-strands represent the flat parts of the paper in an origami piece, and that the creases are the change points between features—the points, for instance, where the chain comes to the end of a helix and goes out into a loop. Those change points, for similar reasons, must involve some kind of perpendicular corner. We looked at those corners again in some detail, particularly emphasizing the sense in which there is an intermediate two-dimensional organization of the polypeptide chain between the one dimensionality of the sequence and the three dimensionality of the complete structure. Each peptide is planar—the carbonyl oxygen sticks out in one

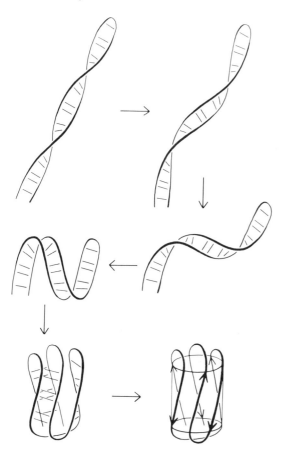

Fig. 5. Steps in a hypothetical scheme by which a Greek key β barrel could fold up from a long, twisted, two-strand β ribbon (from Richardson, 1981).

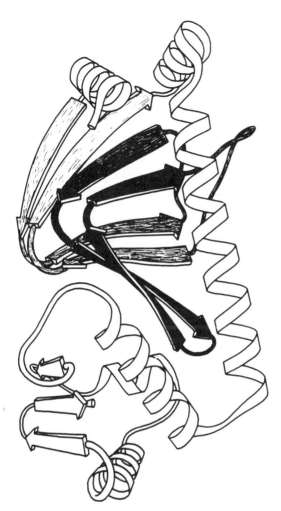

Fig. 6. A schematic drawing of CAP repressor protein (McKay and Steitz, 1981), with the Greek key β barrel domain at the top. The hypothetical 2-stranded β ribbon from which the β barrel is thought to fold has been shaded, darkest near its central hairpin.

direction along the plane and the amide NH in the other direction. (The NH cannot be seen because the hydrogens are left off. It is difficult to see the hydrogens when doing x-ray crystallography, and so people typically leave them out of the pictures.) Thus, the polypeptide chain is locally two dimensional, like a narrow strip of paper, which may twist or may stay flat.

We can use the carbonyl oxygen direction as an indication of peptide orientation and use the angle between successive carbonyls as a measure of how the chain twists. In an α-helix

like the one in Color Plate XIII, all of the carbonyl oxygens point in the same direction: toward the C-terminal end. The peptide planes are all parallel to each other, which generates the familiar representation of a helix as a spiral ribbon.

In β-sheet, as in the center of Color Plate XIIb, the carbonyl oxygens point alternately one to the left and one to the right. Again, the chain may be thought of as planar, except that the rule is different for relating successive units along the β-strand. In loops and at the ends of helices or strands, there are sometimes conformations with successive carbonyls nearly perpendicular, as at the top in Color Plates XIV and XIIIb.

We calculated the angle between successive carbonyls, either as a function of ϕ and ψ (see Fig. 7) or within specific proteins. As already noted, in α-helix that carbonyl angle is near 0° and in β-sheet, near 180°. The ϕ, ψ values that have an angle near 90° are the 3_{10} helix (near α) and polyproline conformation (near extended β). For left-handed conformations (with $\phi > 0$) there is a left-handed version of the α-helix with parallel carbonyls, and

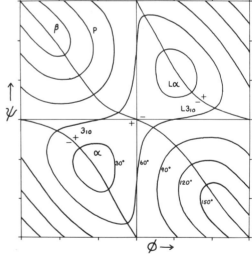

Fig. 7. The angle between successive carbonyl groups along the polypeptide chain, plotted as a function of the backbone conformational angles ϕ and ψ. Labeled contours show the scalar angle between CO vectors, while the major diagonals divide regions of positive versus negative CO torsion angles.

there is a left-handed version of 3_{10} helix with approximately perpendicular carbonyls. Therefore, the 3_{10}, the left-handed 3_{10}, and the polyproline conformations are the main cases with nearly perpendicular carbonyls.

Figure 8 shows the backbone of flavodoxin, with only those residues highlighted that are surrounded by perpendicular carbonyls. At least one occurs at each end of almost every strand and helix, plus a few scattered in the loops and one in a β bulge. These conformations do really seem to represent "fold points" that turn the chain in or out of a straight piece of secondary structure. A hairpin turn, also, needs at least two of those 90° conformations.

The residues that prefer to be at perpendicular fold points are glycine, proline, serine, and asparagine. These are already known as turn-formers and helix-breakers, but it has not been noted before that they do it by making conformations with perpendicular carbonyls. Glycine and proline are straightforward because Pro prefers the polyproline conformation and Gly, the lefthanded 3_{10}. We decided

to look at asparagine and see what it is actually doing in perpendicular corners. One very interesting place is at the N-terminus of a helix.

Figure 9 shows relative preferences for how often asparagine occurs in each specific position along an α-helix (Richardson and Richardson, 1988a). Between the two vertical dotted lines there is an α-helix in the protein. For the most part asparagine is not very good in helices — at best neutral, with a preference of 1, and generally much lower. But right at the specific interface residue at the helix start, or "N-cap" (the one which is half in and half out of the helix), there is an almost 4:1 preference for asparagine.

Two things are apparent about these asparagines: most of them do, indeed, have perpendicular carbonyls, like the residue at the upper right in Color Plate XIII. However, asparagines in the N-cap position can also form a hydrogen bond to one of the exposed NH groups in the first turn of the helix (see Color Plate XIV). They actually mimic a peptide in this position, so, in one sense, they are especially designed for confusing the chain.

Fig. 8. The backbone of flavodoxin (Smith *et al.*, 1977), with perpendicular carbonyls (angles between 60° and 120°) highlighted. One is in a β bulge on the front strand and several are in loops, but the majority are at the beginning or end of a helix or strand. Conversely, almost all such ends have at least one residue surrounded by perpendicular carbonyls (Richardson and Richardson, 1989).

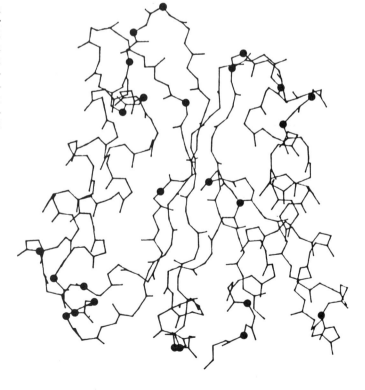

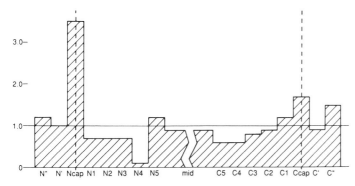

Fig. 9. Relative preference values for asparagine in each individual position within α-helices (Richardson and Richardson, 1988a). The dotted vertical lines represent the transitional residues ("N-cap" or "C-cap") that are half in and half out of the helix. Asn has a very strong and sharply localized preference for the N-cap position.

They can pretend that they are continuing the helix for one more turn and let the polypeptide chain go off and do something else. This makes asparagines a very good way of starting and ending things. Their preference for conformations with 90° carbonyls is presumably a result of favorable H-bond geometry in such arrangements.

We also looked at right-angle corners on a larger scale, particularly at right-angled joints between adjacent α-helices (Richardson and Richardson, 1988b). Most adjacent, perpendicular α-helices have intersecting axes and ends that point at each other. They look as though they could have started off as a single helix and then simply been bent in the middle. The helix-turn-helix motifs found in DNA-binding proteins are quite different: the helix ends do not point at each other but are offset by about one helix diameter, which is a handed arrangement. Color Plate XV shows λ repressor binding to DNA, and Fig. 10 shows a close-up superposition of five of the DNA-binding helix corners plus one very similar structure

from another protein. The view is directly down the second helix, while the first helix is in the plane of the page, so it can be seen that they are both perpendicular and offset. There are positive charges near these corners, both from side chains and from the partial charge of the helix dipole, that interact with the negatively charged phosphates in the DNA. (The helix dipole is generated by all the individual peptide dipoles pointing in the same direction.)

Although this type of offset helix corner (which we call a "lap-joint") is generally quite rare, there is one other category of protein that has them: the "E-F hands" of calcium-binding loops, first seen in carp Ca-binding protein (Fig. 11). Several of these Ca-binding lap-joints are superimposed in Fig. 12. In this case, the reader is looking down the first helix, and the second one is in the plane of the paper. The loop excursion in between contains most of the negatively charged side chains, mainly glutamate and aspartate, that bind the positively charged calcium. Now if we

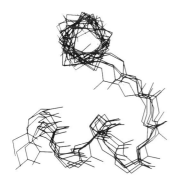
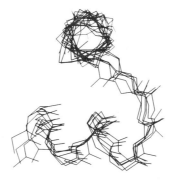

Fig. 10. Superposition of DNA-binding helix-turn-helix motifs from cro (1CRO: Anderson *et al.*, 1981), CAP (1GAP: McKay and Steitz, 1981), trp (2WRP: Schevitz *et al.*, 1985), and λ repressor (1LRP: Pabo and Lewis, 1982) proteins and a lap-joint with the same conformation from cytochrome C peroxidase (2CYP: Finzel *et al.*, 1984).

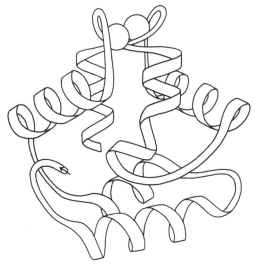

Carp Muscle Calcium-binding Protein

Fig. 11. Schematic drawing of Carp Ca-binding protein (Kretsinger and Nockolds, 1973), with the two calciums shown as balls.

put the DNA-binding and the Ca-binding corners on top of each other (as in Color Plate XVI), one can see that they really have the same backbone structure in terms of the relationship of the helices, although there is a different conformation in the loop. However, a computer search will not find these as similar structures because they go in opposite directions in the sequence. One type of lap-joint binds positively charged ligands, the other type binds negatively charged ligands. Reversing the direction of the chain also reverses the direction of the dipole along the helix, thus changing which charge it is suitable for binding. These two types of lap-joints are like two origami figures: in one case, folding with the white side of the paper out and, in the other case, with the colored side out.

Model Systems

A major effort has been under way in our lab for quite a number of years to try to make model systems with which we could study protein folding. That is, we have been trying to learn how to design and fold up our own protein origami pieces, rather than just watching the native protein masters of the art. This project is reminiscent of the example in Color Plate XVIIa, where someone has managed to fold up a symmetrical five-pointed star out of an uncut, square piece of paper. One can perhaps do such things, but it is not straightforward. One of the molecules that we are working on is a four-helix cluster protein called felix (see Color Plate XVIIb), which is a bit like the one described in chapter 17 (Regan *et al.,* this volume). Ours has a non-repetitive sequence using 19 different amino acids:

MPEVAENFQQCLERWAKLSVG
GELAHMANQAAEAILKGG
NEAQLKNAQALMHEAMKTRKY
SEQLAQEFAHCAYKARASQ.

It is made all in one piece, using genetic methods, by Michael Hecht in our lab and Richard Ogden at the Agouron Institute. At this point, felix has been successfully expressed as a fusion protein with dihydrofolate reductase. There are indications that it has helical structure, but we can not really tell in the fusion protein.[1]

The second invented protein that we have been working on is a β-sheet structure known as betabellin (Richardson *et al.,* 1984; Richardson and Richardson, 1987). It is meant to be an antiparallel β barrel, or sandwich structure, as shown in Plate XVIIIb. Each of the sheets has four strands, all in up-and-down connectivity, and the two halves are identical. Betabellin is being made by peptide synthesis methods in Bruce Erickson's laboratory at the University of North Carolina, Chapel Hill.

After deciding to make a specific type of tertiary structure, the next problem is trying to figure out what the sequence ought to be. Figure 13 illustrates the fact that there is a lot of choice: in this case, 4.3×10^{41} possibilities. Thus, we can make the sequence satisfy many

---

1   Felix has since been expressed by itself (Hecht *et al.,* 1989), and it does, indeed, have an α-helical circular dichroism spectrum. It forms the designed intramolecular disulfide bond and is monomeric both covalently and in solution.

The Origami of Proteins / 15

Fig. 12. Superposition (in stereo) of Ca-binding lap-joints from carp Ca-binding protein (1CPV: Moews and Kretsinger, 1975), calmodulin (1CLN: Babu *et al.*, 1985), and troponin C (2TNC: Herzberg and James, 1985).

different constraints at the same time. Of course, it should satisfy all of the various rules that we think we know, both about stability in final structures and about what goes on during folding. This involves many compromises of conflicting criteria, especially in β structure. There are also a lot of extraneous constraints: for instance, it should be easy to synthesize and should not be homologous to any native sequence. Modifying the sequence of a native protein is a wonderful way of asking subtle questions, but it is not a very good way of asking questions like "Why does this bit end up here rather than over on the other side?" We have some notion of what makes a protein β rather than α, but we really do not know why it has a particular, detailed arrangement. In order to answer questions at that level, it would be useful to have model systems that are not as well designed as real proteins. Perhaps we have a reasonable chance of producing that. The sequence finally chosen for the initial trial of betabellin was

STVTARQPNVTYSISPNTATVRLPNΦTLSIG,

where Φ is iodo-Phe.

We now are on version 9 of betabellin. This process seems to take a while, and we have had to make a number of changes in the sequence. Several early changes were for things like improving the yield of the synthesis. β-sheet peptides are notorious for not being very soluble, and the early betabellins have lived up to that reputation. Just recently, with betabellin 9, we have produced a version that likes water significantly better than it likes butanol. In all the earlier forms, betabellin was

made with a cross link so that both sheets were synthesized at once. This was a very clever idea that has been useful elsewhere, but it was apparently not the right strategy for betabellin. Betabellin 9 is synthesized as just the single β-sheet without a cross linker, and the Cys that will later form a disulfide between the sheets is initially sulfonated. This material is easy to purify by normal gel filtration and high performance liquid chromatography (HPLC) methods. It gives clean products that do indeed have the correct sequence, which for betabellin 9 is

HTLTASIPDLTYSIDPNTATCKVPDΦTLSIGA.

The SH is made and then oxidized, and it readily and quantitatively forms a disulfide, as shown schematically in Fig. 14. The resulting betabellin 9 goes into solution quite well at slightly acidic *p*H.

Design of Betabellin

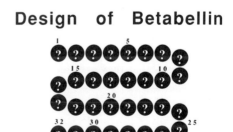

number of sequences = 20^{32} = 4.3 x 10^{41}

Fig. 13. A blank layout of the betabellin sequence, illustrating the problem and opportunity of choosing suitable amino acids. (Scott B. Daniels and Bruce W. Erickson, University of North Carolina)

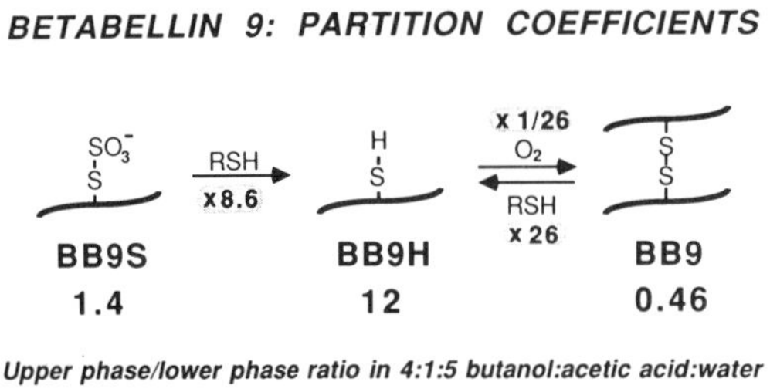

BETABELLIN 9: PARTITION COEFFICIENTS

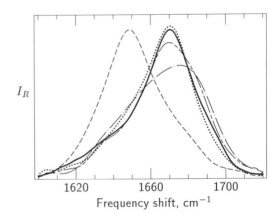

Upper phase/lower phase ratio in 4:1:5 butanol:acetic acid:water

Fig. 14. The progression of betabellin from 9S (sulfonated) to 9H (the free SH form) to 9 (the SS-linked dimer), with partition coefficients indicated at each stage where values below 1 indicate preference for the aqueous phase. (Scott B. Daniels and Bruce W. Erickson, University of North Carolina)

Betabellin 9 has a classic β-sheet circular dichroism spectrum, which changes to random in 6M guanidine hydrochloride. Laser Raman spectra (done by Robert Williams at the Uniformed Services University of the Health Sciences) also indicate extensive β structure (Fig. 15). The Raman amide I band, which represents peptide vibrations sensitive to conformation, looks almost identical to that for antiparallel β proteins like concanavalin A and erabutoxin, and very different from a helical protein like melittin. This is true in solution at low pH, as well as at neutral pH in the precipitate.

Some preliminary NMR experiments have also been done on betabellin 9 (both at Duke University and by Arthur Pardi at the University of Colorado). The peaks for the N-terminal histidine, which should be waving around in the solvent, are indeed very sharp resonances. In contrast, resonances for the tyrosine, which we think is buried in the middle of the protein, are broadened, which probably means that they are tumbling more slowly along with the intact protein. The part in which we are especially interested is the region that represents NMR resonances between Cα protons and, only very occasionally, other types of protons. Betabellin has several through-space cross-peaks in that region which never show up in spectra revealing covalent connectivities. In protein structure, the only time Cα protons are close enough together to produce strong nuclear Overhauser effect spectroscopy (NOESY) peaks is

on adjacent strands of antiparallel β-sheet. Therefore, we believe that by NMR, also, there may be preliminary evidence of β structure in solution for betabellin 9. Such evidence, however, should not be taken too seriously until the resonances can be "assigned" to particular protons in the sequence.

We may perhaps have succeeded in making a betabellin molecule rather like Color Plate XIXb, except without the cross linker. Now should come the really interesting part of this project. We can optimize the solubility and stability and try to get the NMR to look better. Once we determine the three-dimensional structure by NMR or by crystallography, then we can start making intelligent changes to study how betabellin folds up. Perhaps we can eventually do things like making minimal changes at the loops that would actually produce a different topology.

The final message we want to communicate is symbolized by the illustration on the back cover of this volume. First of all, proteins are very elegant. Second, one may now think about proteins productively in terms of the process of their folding, rather than just looking at the final native state.

Fig. 15. Laser Raman spectra in the amide I region for betabellin 9 (solid line) as a gel in dilute HCl at pH 3.1, compared with reference proteins that have mostly β structure (concanavalin A: dotted line), mostly α (melittin: dashed line), or disordered (S peptide: line with dot). The line with dash is for betabellin 7 as a gel at pH 2.1. (Robert W. Williams, Uniformed Services University of the Health Sciences)

Acknowledgments

We would like to thank our collaborators Bruce Erickson, Bob Williams, Michael Hecht, and Richard Ogden for their help with betabellin and felix and with this chapter. This work was supported by NIH grant GM-15000, and in part by the office of Naval Research, the Life Sciences Foundation, and the Mac-Arthur Foundation.

References

Alden, R. A., J. J. Birktoft, J. Kraut, J. D. Robertus, *Biochem. Biophys. Res. Comm.* **45**, 337 (1971).

Anderson, W. F., D. H. Ohlendorf, Y. Takeda, B. W. Matthews, *Nature* **290**, 754 (1981).

Arnone, A., *et al., J. Biol. Chem.* **246**, 2302 (1971).

Babu, Y. S., *et al., Nature* **315**, 37 (1985).

Blundell, T., *et al., Nature* **289**, 771 (1981).

Bode, W., and P. Schwager, *J. Mol. Biol.* **98**, 693 (1975).

Carson, M., and C. E. Bugg, *J. Mol. Graphics* **4**, 121 (1986).

Creighton, T., *J. Mol. Biol.* **113**, 275 (1977).

Finzel, B. C., T. L. Poulos, J. Kraut, *J. Biol. Chem.* **259**, 13027 (1984).

Gray, A., and K. Kasahara, *The Magic of Origami* (Japan Publications, Tokyo, 1977).

Grimm Hobby Co., instruction sheet supplied with *Let's Try Origami* paper (Grimm Hobby, Japan, 1987).

Hecht, M. H., D. C. Richardson, J. S. Richardson, R. Ogden, *J. Cell. Biochem.* **13A**, 86 (1989).

Herzberg, O., and M. N. G. James, *Nature* **313**, 653 (1985).

Honda, Isao, *Origami, the Japanese Art of Paper Folding* (McDowell, Obolensky Inc., New York, 1959.)

Jones, T. A., and L. Liljas, *J. Mol. Biol.* **177**, 735 (1984).

Kasahara, Kunihiko, *Origami Omnibus* (Japan Publications, Tokyo, 1988).

Kretsinger, R. H., and C. E. Nockolds, *J. Biol. Chem.* **248**, 3313 (1973).

McKay, D. B., and T. A. Steitz, *Nature* **290**, 744 (1981).

Moews, P. C., and R. H. Kretsinger, *J. Mol. Biol.* **91**, 201 (1975).

Montroll, John, *Origami for the Enthusiast* (Dover Publications, New York, 1979).

Montroll, John, *Animal Origami for the Enthusiast* (Dover Publications, New York, 1985).

Oatley, S. J., and C. C. F. Blake, *J. Mol. Biol.* **121**, 339 (1978).

Pabo, C. O., and M. Lewis, *Nature* **298**, 443 (1982).

Richardson, J. S., *Nature* **268**, 495 (1977).

_____, *Adv. Protein Chem.* **34**, 167 (1981).

Richardson, J. S., D. C. Richardson, B. W. Erickson, *Biophys. J.* **45**, 25a (1984).

Richardson, J. S., and D. C. Richardson, in *Protein Engineering*, D. L. Oxender and C. F. Fox, Eds. (Alan R. Liss, New York, 1987), p. 149.

_____, *Science* **240**, 1648 (1988a).

_____, *Proteins: Struct. Funct. & Genet.* **4**, 229 (1988b).

_____, *Prediction of Protein Structure and the Principles of Protein Conformation*, G. Fasman, Ed. (Plenum Press, New York, 1898), p. 1.

Richardson, J. S., K. A. Thomas, B. H. Rubin, D. C. Richardson, *Proc. Natl. Acad. Sci. U.S.A.* **72**, 1349 (1975).

Salemme, F. R., *Prog. Biophys. Molec. Biol.* **42**, 95 (1983).

Saul, F. A., L. M. Amzel, R. J. Poljak, *J. Biol. Chem.* **253**, 585 (1978).

Schevitz, R. W., S. Otwinowski, A. Joachimiak, C. L. Lawson, P. B. Sigler, *Nature* **317**, 782 (1985).

Schreuder, H. A., J. M. van der Laan, W. G. J. Hol, J. Drenth, *J. Mol. Biol.* **199**, 637 (1988).

Smith, W. W., R. M. Burnett, G. D. Darling, M. L. Ludwig, *J. Mol. Biol.* **117**, 195 (1977).

Tainer, J. A., E. D. Getzoff, K. M. Beem, J. S. Richardson, D. C. Richardson, *J. Mol. Biol.* **160**, 181 (1982).

Wlodawer, A., J. Walter, R. Huber, L. Sjolin, *J. Mol. Biol.* **180**, 307 (1984).

2

Loops in Globular Proteins

A Novel Category of Secondary Structure

Jacquelyn Fetrow[1] *and George D. Rose*

The secondary structure of proteins falls into three classes: α-helices, β-sheet, and reverse turns (Richardson, 1981; Venkatachalam, 1968; Kuntz, 1972; Lewis *et al.*, 1971; Rose *et al.*, 1985; Smith and Pease, 1980). Helices and sheet are termed "regular" structures because their residues have repeating main-chain torsion angles, and their backbone N-H and C=O groups are arranged in a periodic pattern of hydrogen bonding (Pauling *et al.*, 1951). In contrast, turns are "nonregular" structures with nonrepeating backbone torsion angles and, at most, one internal N-H ... O=C hydrogen bond (Richardson, 1981; Venkatachalam, 1968; Kuntz, 1972; Lewis *et al.*, 1971; Rose *et al.*, 1985; Smith and Pease, 1980). Remaining residues, by subtraction, are often classified as "random coil," although, as Richardson has pointed out, they are neither random nor coil (1981).

In this chapter we examine another category of nonregular secondary structure— the loop. A loop may be described as a continuous chain segment that adopts a "loop-shaped" conformation in three-dimensional space, with a small distance between its segment termini. The main-chain trace of an idealized loop resembles a Greek omega (Ω). Backbone torsion angles for such a structure are nonrepeating, and there are few, if any, backbone hydrogen bonds. A simple loop subsumes no proper subsets that are also loops, while a compound loop contains at least one smaller embedded loop. Only simple loops are considered in the following discussion.

Loops have been discussed in relation to specific structures, such as the conspicuous loops in superoxide dismutase (Tainer *et al.*, 1982) and in immunoglobulin domains (Davies *et al.*, 1975; Richardson *et al.*, 1976), the autolysis loop in serine protease zymogens (Kossiakoff *et al.*, 1977), and the calcium-binding loops in parvalbumin (Kretsinger and Nockolds, 1973). However, there has been no systematic study of these structures. Kuntz alluded to larger loops in his definitive paper on peptide chain turns (1972), and the topic is mentioned briefly in a recent review (Rose *et al.*, 1985). Looped-out regions are also evident in schematic representations of protein structure such as those of Richardson (1981) or Lesk and Hardman (1982). While such examples are clearly "looplike," their description has been only qualitative.

In our study, loops are defined explicitly. Stringent defining criteria are chosen deliberately to exclude those structurally ambiguous examples containing substantial

---

1   This article originally appeared in *Science* **234**, 849 (1986) under the authorship of Jacquelyn F. Leszczynski and George D. Rose.

amounts of regular secondary structure. The definition was implemented in the form of a computer algorithm and used to identify all loops in 67 proteins of known structure. The set of identified loops was then characterized with respect to residue composition, size and shape, compactness, accessibility to solvent, and role in protein taxonomy.

Our survey reveals an abundant population of loops, on the order of four per protein molecule. Almost always, they are situated at the molecular surface; often, they are implicated in molecular function. Most of these loops are highly compact, globular structures, with low x-ray temperature factors and a packing efficiency that rivals that of β-sheet. The observed compactness is a consequence of loop side-chain atoms that pack tightly within the loop core. In view of such characteristics, the description of these chain segments as "random coil" warrants revision.

Loops are choice candidates for protein bioengineering studies. The catalog of loops presented here should be useful for the design of such experiments, as well as in the further study of nonregular protein secondary structure.

Identification of loops from x-ray coordinates

A loop is a continuous segment of polypeptide chain that is defined in terms of its (i) segment length, (ii) absence of regular secondary structure, and (iii) distance between segment termini. These criteria are now specified in detail.

The segment length must be between 6 and 16 residues. The lower length limit serves to eliminate reverse turns. Superficially, it might seem that a turn is merely a small loop, but an important characteristic distinguishes the two. Turns, which range from three to five residues in length, have backbone groups that pack together closely, forcing side chains to project outward (Rose *et al.,* 1985). This stereochemical restriction is relaxed in larger segments where side-chain atoms can pack within the loop's own core. The upper length limit imposes a practical threshold that eliminates most of the compound loops.

A loop may contain no regular secondary structure. This criterion excludes adjacent strands of antiparallel β-sheet as well as structurally ambiguous cases. Secondary structure assignments for the residues were taken from the Kabsch and Sander (K&S) dictionary of protein secondary structure (Kabsch and Sander, 1983). However, two minor exceptions to the K&S classification were adopted: two-residue strands and single turns of helix (four or five residues) are not counted as regular secondary structure. Although they are ignored in most classification schemes, K&S includes β-strands that are just two residues in length. Strand lengths are distributed in a statistically well-behaved fashion, with the exception of these two-residue strands. Four- and five-residue helices are classified as type III reverse turns. Again, the distribution of helical segment lengths is statistically well behaved, except for these single-turn helices.

The distance between segment termini, that is, the end-to-end distance, is measured as the distance from the first α-carbon to the last α-carbon in the segment. The end-to-end distance must be less than 10 angstroms and may not exceed two-thirds the maximum distance between any two α-carbons within the segment under consideration.

This criterion selects as loops those segments with termini that "neck in" like an omega (Ω). The set of discovered loops is not overly sensitive to the coefficient of two-thirds. In practice, the end-to-end distance varies between 3.7 and 10.0 Å.

Loops identified as described above are frequently members of small families. Such families arise whenever a range of segments, all of similar length, satisfies the definition. For example, if residues i through j comprise a loop, then it often happens that residues i through $j + 1$ also comprise a loop. In our study, each family is represented by its most compact member. To choose these individual representatives, we evaluated the compactness of each segment in every family, and the most compact loops were selected.

The coefficient of compactness of Zehfus and Rose (1986) was used to assess compactness. This coefficient, Z, is a sensitive, single-value figure of merit that identifies those segments with the smallest solvent-accessible surface area for their volume. Explicitly,

$$Z = \frac{\text{accessible surface area of segment}}{\text{accessible surface area of sphere of equal volume}}$$

$$(1).$$

Solvent-accessible surface areas and volumes were calculated by the methods of Lee and Richards (1971)[2] and Pavlov and Federov (1983), respectively.

Z is a dimensionless ratio and should show no dependence on unit size. However, the configurational freedom of very small segments is restricted in comparison to larger ones, and is thus biased toward more compact arrangements. To adjust for this apparent size dependency, a compensating correction term was applied to all Z values used in our study. This term,

$$0.488 \times e^{(-.068 \times N_r)} + 0.970$$

(where N_r = number of residues in the segment), is chosen to yield a standard normalized value when multiplied by Z values of the most compact units of all sizes (Zehfus and Rose, 1986).

To identify loops, all continuous segments in 67 proteins from the Brookhaven database (Bernstein *et al.*, 1977) were screened. (The Brookhaven database, a U.S. government–supported resource, maintains atomic coordinates of x-ray elucidated proteins.) Only proteins from the K&S dictionary (Kabsch and Sander, 1983) were used in order to ensure self-consistency in the secondary structure assignments. Those continuous segments 6 to 16 residues in length that satisfied the end-to-end distance criterion were retained, if devoid of regular secondary structure. Coefficients of compactness were then calculated for all survivors and the most compact segment was chosen to represent each family cluster.

Characterization of loops

Compact loops are common structures in proteins. In the 67 proteins included in our survey, 270 loops were found, an average of more than four per molecule. The distribution of loop sizes is shown in Fig. 1 and the full set of loops is listed in Table 1.

Of those examined, only six proteins are without loops entirely: glucagon, insulin, mellitin, ovomucoid, avian pancreatic polypeptide, and pancreatic trypsin inhibitor. These proteins are all less than 60 amino acid residues in length and are among the nine smallest proteins in the database. Three – glucagon, mellitin, and pancreatic polypeptide – are also nonglobular, as determined by their axial ratios (as is discussed below).

Structures perceived intuitively as loops may not satisfy our stringent definition; the calcium-binding loops of parvalbumin (Kret-

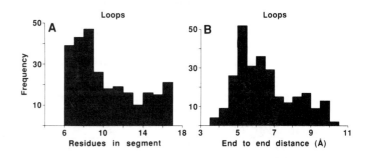

Fig. 1. Histograms showing the distribution of loop sizes for the 270 loops in Table 1 by number of residues (A) and by end-to-end distance (B). The mean values are: (A) 9.8 and (B) 6.4.

---

2   Probe radius that we used was 1.4 Å. The atomic radii, in Å, are: tetrahedral C, 2.0; trigonal carbon, 1.7; carbonyl O, 1.4; hydroxyl O, 1.6; carboxyl O, 1.5; tetrahedral N, 2.0; trigonal N, 1.7; divalent S, 1.85; and sulfhydryl S, 2.0.

Table 1. Summary of 270 omega loops in 67 x-ray–elucidated proteins.*

PROT	FIRST	NUM	SEQUENCE	PROT	FIRST	NUM	SEQUENCE	PROT	FIRST	NUM	SEQUENCE
1ABP	93	7	V N...K P	351C	51	12	G S...M P	1ECD	33	10	S I...F A
1ABP	142	7	A N...T A	155C	21	8	I Q...T D	1ECD	41	9	F A...S I
1ABP	203	6	G M...S T	155C	47	8	A S...K Y	1EST	69	12	G E...T E
1ABP	236	13	A V...G F	155C	83	13	K P...G A	1EST	94	11	W N...Y D
1ABP	289	6	I T...N F	155C	128	6	J J...J J	1EST	112	7	V T...Y V
1ABP	299	6	E K...L G	2C2C	18	16	H T...L F	1EST	142	10	G L...L A
2ACT	8	6	R S...A V	2C2C	30	14	P N...H K	1EST	165	14	Y A...T V
2ACT	58	7	R T...R G	2C2C	41	16	A H...M K	1EST	216	11	V S...R K
2ACT	89	15	Y P...L Q	2C2C	74	16	P K...K S	3FAB	24L	6	G S...N I
2ACT	139	6	A A...A F	2CAB	6	7	G Y...N G	3FAB	122L	11	P S...K A
2ACT	141	16	G D...P C	2CAB	17	8	S K...A N	3FAB	168L	6	K Q...N K
2ACT	182	11	N S...E G	2CAB	78	10	V L...D S	3FAB	182L	6	L T...Q W
2ACT	198	8	R N...G T	2CAB	98	7	G S...H G	3FAB	72H	6	N T...N Q
2ACT	203	7	A G...I A	2CAB	108	7	T V...K Y	3FAB	99H	7	L I...I D
4ADH	14	8	L W...P F	2CAB	128	13	Y S...D G	3FAB	132H	9	S K...T A
4ADH	100	13	C R...C L	2CAB	197	8	S L...L Y	1FDX	12	12	G A...I I
4ADH	115	8	D L...G T	2CAB	230	11	L S...V P	1FDX	30	12	I D...S C
4ADH	122	7	T M...T S	1CAC	5	12	W G...H W	1FDX	39	12	G S...A P
4ADH	282	6	C Q...Y G	1CAC	17	7	H K...I A	3FXN	54	8	S A...V L
2ADK	133	10	G E...D N	1CAC	98	6	G S...G E	2GCH	70	9	E F...S E
1ALP	217	8	N V...N N	1CAC	108	7	T V...K Y	2GCH	94	8	Y N...N N
2APP	41	15	F S...S V	1CAC	128	13	Y G...D G	2GCH	112	7	A S...T V
2APP	129	8	N T...S Q	1CAC	166	7	S I...G K	2GCH	165	12	N T...K I
2APP	139	11	F D...Q P	1CAC	197	8	S L...L L	2GCH	217	8	S S...S T
2APP	184	9	V D...W S	1CAC	232	8	D G...E E	1GPD	47	6	D S...G V
1APR	8	10	T D...Y Y	2CHA	70	9	E F...S E	1GPD	76	7	E M...N I
1APR	18	14	G Q...N L	2CHA	94	9	Y N...N D	1GPD	121	9	P S...F V
1APR	43	16	G S...D K	2CHA	114	6	F S...V S	1GPD	128	10	F V...K Y
1APR	61	9	P S...K A	2CHA	217	8	S S...S T	1GPD	183	16	K T...R G
1APR	76	8	I G...S A	3CNA	13	9	P N...P S	2GRS	83	7	A V...P S
1APR	90	14	D T...G P	3CNA	97	8	T G...T N	2GRS	139	9	T I...K Y
1APR	129	10	D T...S S	3CNA	116	8	K S...Q T	2GRS	162	11	T P...A S
1APR	189	9	I D...W A	3CNA	147	9	T T...L E	2GRS	239	7	E N...E V
1APR	203	9	A T...L G	3CNA	160	6	S S...S P	2GRS	256	6	K T...G L
1APR	216	11	A I...L I	3CNA	199	11	I K...D G	2GRS	268	7	A V...L P
1APR	227	6	L P...A A	†3CNA	222	14	P S...P D	2GRS	300	8	L N...Q T
1APR	233	16	V G...L G	3CNA	229	9	L L...A N	2GRS	315	6	V D...Q N
1APR	243	8	Q D...G F	3CPA	128	14	K T...G V	2GRS	331	7	D V...A L
1APR	261	13	S I...E I	3CPA	142	15	D A...G A	2GRS	404	12	T P...K T
1APR	280	8	A E...C T	3CPA	156	11	A S...Y H	2GRS	465	8	A I...S E
1APR	291	9	G A...A I	3CPA	205	9	P Y...S I	1HIP	20	7	N Q...K S
1AZU	9	7	G N...Q F	3CPA	231	7	K S...T S	1HIP	28	14	R V...E Q
1AZU	35	12	H P...G H	3CPA	244	7	I T...Q A	1HIP	43	7	C A...F M
1AZU	67	6	G L...D Y	3CPA	272	14	R D...S Q	†1HIP	44	16	A D...D E
1AZU	73	11	L K...A H	1CPV	18	6	C K...D S	4LDH	173	16	R Y...G V
1AZU	84	9	T K...E K	1CPV	64	14	K L...A L	4LDH	192	9	I G...V P
1AZU	112	7	C T...H S	1CRN	33	12	I I...D Y	4LDH	203	16	W S...L G
2B5C	32	16	L T...L R	1CTX	1	15	I R...C P	†4LDH	212	14	L H...D W
1BP2	23	8	N N...C G	1CTX	26	10	C D...G K	4LDH	219	8	N K...W K
†1BP2	25	15	Y G...V D	1CYC	18	15	H T...N L	4LDH	239	8	V I...Y T
1BP2	56	11	K K...V D	1CYC	30	14	P N...Q A	4LDH	275	11	V K...N V
2BP2	23	8	N N...C G	1CYC	40	15	T G...K S	1LDX	70	9	S L...K I
†2BP2	25	15	Y G...V D	1CYC	70	15	N P...A G	1LDX	79	8	V G...S L
2BP2	61	8	C K...N P	3CYT	18	15	H T...N L	1LDX	102	7	Q Q...S R
156B	16	10	V I...K A	3CYT	34	10	G L...Q A	1LDX	193	8	G R...G V
156B	47	12	T P...P M	3CYT	40	15	T G...K S	1LDX	207	7	N N...L Q
351C	16	11	H A...P A	3CYT	70	15	N P...A G	1LDX	211	6	N L...G M

Table 1 *continued*

PROT	FIRST	NUM	SEQUENCE			PROT	FIRST	NUM	SEQUENCE			PROT	FIRST	NUM	SEQUENCE	
1LDX	218	7	W E	...E	G	3PGM	98	12	A Q	...K	F	2SGA	93	7	S F	...D	Y
1LDX	236	1	A Y	...Y	E	3PGM	109	12	F N	...P	P	2SGA	218	7	G N	...G	G
1LDX	276	8	K E	...K	E	3PGM	123	8	I D	...F	S	3SGB	16	16	I S	...S	L
†1LH1	41	13	K D	...E	V	3PGM	132	14	K G	...V	L	3SGB	48	8	V R	...Y	Y
1LH1	47	8	L K	...V	P	3PGM	209	16	L V	...S	Y	3SGB	66	9	W A	...T	V
1LHB	46	14	P A	...L	T	2PTN	69	12	G E	...N	E	3SGB	93	7	S F	...D	Y
1LHB	55	10	F K	...E	L	2PTN	94	9	Y N	...N	D	3SGB	118	7	T V	...D	I
7LYZ	18	8	D N	...S	L	2PTN	112	7	A S	...R	V	3SGB	167	14	A T	...G	M
7LYZ	36	7	S N	...Q	A	2PTN	142	11	G N	...Y	P	3SGB	190	12	V C	...P	L
7LYZ	44	9	N R	...T	D	2PTN	184A	8	G Y	...K	D	3SGB	199	9	L Y	...I	G
7LYZ	60	16	S R	...N	L	2PTN	217	8	S G	...N	K	3SGB	235	6	L V	...G	V
1LZM	134	6	A K	...W	Y	1REI	91	6	Y Q	...P	Y	2SNS	43	10	E T	...V	E
1MBN	40	8	L E	...F	K	1RHD	34	10	S W	...E	A	2SNS	114	6	V Y	...N	N
1MBS	37	14	P E	...L	K	1RHD	43	15	A R	...S	F	2SNS	136	6	K L	...W	S
1MBS	49	6	L K	...D	D	1RHD	60	14	I E	...V	M	2SOD	50	9	D N	...S	A
1MBS	78	7	K K	...E	A	1RHD	85	6	G S	...I	S	2SOD	67	12	K K	...R	H
2MHB	40A	9	K T	...D	L	1RHD	99	7	N G	...G	S	2SOD	103	7	S L	...Y	S
2MHB	39B	16	Q R	...A	V	1RHD	185	7	G R	...T	Q	2SOD	122	16	D D	...G	N
2MHB	47B	11	D L	...G	N	1RHD	193	7	E P	...G	L	†2SOD	132	6	S T	...G	N
1NXB	6	8	Q H	...Q	T	1RHD	216	8	L T	...E	K	2SSI	19	7	G V	...T	A
2PAB	49A	6	T S	...G	E	1RHD	284	10	P E	...K	G	1TIM	67A	13	Y K	...I	S
8PAP	8	6	R Q	...A	V	1RNS	36	6	T K	...C	K	1TIM	169A	6	A I	...G	K
8PAP	60	8	S Y	...G	Y	1RNS	87	10	T G	...C	A	3TLN	24	8	Y S	...L	Q
8PAP	86	15	Y P	...E	K	2RXN	18	11	G X	...G	T	3TLN	32	7	D N	...D	G
8PAP	138	16	G K	...P	C	2RXN	38	8	V C	...V	G	3TLN	44	10	A K	...G	S
8PAP	175	11	N S	...N	G	1SBT	17	6	H S	...Y	T	3TLN	55	16	W A	...P	A
8PAP	191	8	R G	...Y	G	1SBT	37	8	S S	...K	V	3TLN	91	7	L S	...N	N
8PAP	198	6	G V	...L	Y	1SBT	74	13	A L	...A	P	3TLN	125	6	G D	...T	F
1PCY	6	8	G A	...L	A	1SBT	96	6	L G	...G	S	3TLN	188	16	I G	...L	R
1PCY	41	16	F D	...I	S	1SBT	157	8	G S	...S	T	3TLN	204	10	S M	...G	D
1PCY	63	6	L N	...G	E	1SBT	181	7	D S	...R	A	3TLN	214	6	P D	...S	K
1PCY	84	9	C S	...G	M	1SBT	257	10	L G	...K	G	3TLN	221	13	Y T	...I	N
3PGM	11	15	S E	...D	V	2SGA	16	16	I A	...S	L	3TLN	248	8	G T	...S	V

Key. PROT, Brookhaven name of protein (Bernstein *et al.,* 1977). FIRST, residue number of loop NH$_2$-terminus; the Brookhaven numbering system, which need not correspond to the numbering in the Kabsch and Sander dictionary (Kabsch and Sander, 1983), was used. NUM, number of residues in loop. SEQUENCE, first, second, penultimate, and ultimate residues in loop. Single letter abbreviations for the amino acid residues are: A, Ala; C, Cys; D, Asp; E, Glu; F, Phe; G, Gly; H, His; I, Ile; K, Lys; L, Leu; M, Met; N, Asn; P, Pro; Q, Gln; R, Arg; S, Ser; T, Thr; V, Val; W, Trp; Y, Tyr; X, Asx; J, unknown. †Indicates a compound loop. Proteins used (and their parenthesized Brookhaven file names) are: 1-arabinose-binding protein (1ABP), actinidin (2ACT), alcohol dehydrogenase (4ADH), adenylate kinase (2ADK), alphalytic protease (1ALP), penicillopepsin (2APP), rhizopuspepsin (1APR), azurin (1AZU), cytochrome b5 (2B5C), phospholipase A2 (1BP2), prophospholipase A2 (2BP2), cytochrome b562 (156B), cytochrome c551 (351C), cytochrome c550 (155C), cytochrome c2 (2C2C), carbonic anhydrase B (2CAB), carbonic anhydrase C (1CAC), alpha chymotrypsin (2CHA), concanavalin A (3CNA), carboxypeptidase (3CPA), calcium-binding parvalbumin (1CPV), crambin (1CRN), alpha cobratoxin (1CTX), ferrocytochrome c (1CYC), cytochrome c (3CYT), erythrocruorin (1ECD), tosylelastase (1EST), lambda immunoglobulin Fab NEW (3FAB), *Peptococcus* ferredoxin (1FDX), flavodoxin (3FXN), gamma chymotrypsin (2GCH), glucagon (1GCN), glyceraldehyde-3-phosphate dehydrogenase (1GPD), glutathione reductase (2GRS), high potential iron protein (1HIP), insulin (1INS), apolactate dehydrogenase (4LDH), lactate dehydrogenase isoenzyme (1LDX), acetate-met-leghemoglobin (1LH1), lamprey methemoglobin cyanide V (1LHB), egg lysozyme (7LYZ), T4 lysozyme (1LZM), whale metmyoglobin (1MBN), seal metmyoglobin (1MBS), horse aquomethemoglobin (2MHB), mellitin (1MLT), neurotoxin B (1NXB), ovomucóid third domain (1OVO), prealbumin (2PAB), papain (8PAP), plastocyanin (1PCY), phosphoglycerate mutase (3PGM), avian pancreatic polypeptide (1PPT), trypsin (2PTN), pancreatic trypsin inhibitor (4PTI), Bence-Jones immunoglobulin REI (1REI), rhodanese (1RHD), ribonuclease S (1RNS), rubredoxin (2RXN), subtilisin BPN (1SBT), Streptomyces proteinase A (2SGA), *Streptomyces* proteinase B (3SGB), staphylococcal nuclease (2SNS), Cu, Zn superoxide dismutase (2SOD), *Streptomyces* subtilisin inhibitor (2SSI), triose phosphate isomerase (1TIM), and thermolysin (3TLN).

singer and Nockolds, 1973) are an example. When the defining criteria are relaxed slightly to avoid elimination of loops containing three-residue β-strands, 22 additional loops are identified (Table 2), including several of these common examples.

Color Plates XIX and XX illustrate typical loops from cytochrome c (Takano and Dickerson, 1980) and thermolysin (Holmes and Matthews, 1982). In each case, the loop main chain surrounds an internal cavity that is packed with side-chain atoms from loop residues. This kind of arrangement results in a highly compact chain fold for the segment. Occasionally, a metal ligand is also included, as shown in the thermolysin loop. In proteins with multiple loops, the individual loops occur frequently in spatial clusters, as they do in superoxide dismutase (Color Plate XXI).

Some loops with irregular tails satisfy our defining criteria both with and without their tail segment; in these cases the most compact representative is chosen, as previously stated. Occasionally, however, the larger version of such a loop, although more compact, is excluded because it exceeds the 16-residue upper limit. For example, the superoxide dismutase loop 67–78 is part of a larger, more compact loop 61–80. Despite this restriction, the upper size limit rarely eliminates a loop entirely; when the threshold is extended to 30 residues, only one de novo loop is found (phosphoglycerate mutase 191–211). As was mentioned above, the 16-residue cutoff serves to eliminate compound loops. If we use this upper bound, only seven compound loops fail to be excluded; these loops are indicated by a dagger in Table 1.

Loops may contain one or more reverse turns; these facilitate the main-chain direction changes needed to bring segment termini together. If loop curvature is sufficiently gradual, the chain direction can be reversed without resorting to an explicit turn, but this is unusual. All of the loops con-

tain at least one turn or bend residue, as defined by Kabsch and Sander (1983), but not every loop contains a complete turn or bend. Because they include reverse turns, loops do not constitute a pure structural category. Nonetheless, a loop and a turn are distinct moieties. While both result in changes in the overall direction of the polypeptide chain, a loop cannot be viewed merely as an "overgrown" turn. A turn, unlike a loop, has backbone groups that pack together closely, forcing side chains to project outward (Rose *et al.,* 1985). For steric reasons, a segment of main chain cannot circumscribe an interior cavity of polyatomic dimensions until it exceeds a length of five residues.

The residue composition of loops was assessed by calculating the normalized frequency of occurrence, f, for each residue type, X, such that

$$f = \frac{X_L/X_T}{N_L/N_T} \quad (2)$$

where X_L is the number of residues of type X in loops, X_T is the total number of residues of type X, N_L is the total number of residues in loops, and N_T is the total number of residues in the database. A value of $f = 1$ implies that X is distributed randomly in loops. Values greater than unity imply that X is found preferentially in loops; conversely, f values less than unity imply a less than average frequency of occurrence of X in loops.

Examination of f values for all residues in

Table 2. Additional loops found in 67 x-ray–elucidated proteins with defining criteria relaxed to allow three-residue strands of β sheet. The key is the same as that for Table 1.

PROT	FIRST	NUM	SEQUENCE	PROT	FIRST	NUM	SEQUENCE
4ADH	130	8	F T...P I	1CPV	51	12	D Q...D E
4ADH	158	16	A K...I G	1CPV	89	9	G D...K I
1ALP	190	12	A C...S W	1GPD	279	15	V S...F D
1ALP	200	8	I T...A Q	2GRS	370	7	V V...P P
2APP	212	11	G I...L L	1HIP	65	15	L F...A S
2APP	290	8	N S...L I	4LDH	289	14	L P...I V
1APR	31	12	L N...W V	3PGM	166	11	I A...M I
1APR	161	7	A A...S D	2RXN	5	8	T C...Y I
1APR	169	11	D F...N K	2SGA	119	7	Y L...S Y
1APR	310	10	V V...I R	2SGB	138	9	R R...T H
155C	36	14	P N...S E	1OVO	23	9	V C...T Y

loops reveals that residues present most often in reverse turns (Richardson, 1981; Venkatachalam, 1968; Kuntz, 1972; Lewis et al., 1971; Rose et al., 1985; Smith and Pease, 1980; Chou and Fasman, 1977; Levitt, 1978) are also found most often in loops (Gly, Pro, Asp, Asn, and Ser) with the notable addition of Tyr (Table 3). All but Tyr have short side chains, and all but Pro are polar; Pro favors turns for steric reasons (Rose et al., 1985). Hydrophobic residues are strongly disfavored in loops; these include Val, Met, Ile, Leu, and Ala with aliphatic side chains, and His, Trp, and Phe with aromatic side chains.

To quantify the accessibility of a loop, we calculated the solvent-accessible surface area (Lee and Richards, 1971) in each of three successive states: in the standard state[3], as an isolated secondary structure, and within the protein (Fig. 2). Approximately half of the area of regular secondary structure is lost upon the formation of the isolated secondary structure, and the remaining half is lost when that secondary structure is buried within the protein (Chothia, 1976; Richards, 1979). In our sample of 67 proteins, the percentage of the area lost when the chain folds into an isolated loop (34 percent) is comparable to the area loss upon formation of an isolated helix (35 percent). However, the subsequent loss when the loop is incorporated into the protein (47 percent) is less than that of the helix (60 percent). These statistics indicate that loops tend to be somewhat more accessible to solvent than helices.

These fractional accessibilities reveal that loops are almost invariably situated at the molecular surface (Color Plate XXI and Fig. 2). It should be noted that the definition of a loop does not require that it be at the surface. Moreover, the data on solvent accessibility are consistent with the residue composition; loops are found at the protein surface and contain a preponderance of hydrophilic residues.

Loops are as compact as the proteins that contain them (Fig. 3). The coefficient of compactness, Z, is used to assess compactness, as described above. The Z values of loop segments range between 1.43 and 1.86, with a mean ($\pm$ standard deviation) of 1.61 ± 0.07. In comparison, Z values for the 67 proteins range between 1.36 and 1.93 (with a single outlier at 2.09); the mean of this distribution is 1.67 ± 0.13.

It is conceivable that the apparent compactness of loops is biased by the use of the most compact segment to represent a loop family. As a control, the largest member of each family was chosen instead and used as the representative member; the coefficient of compactness was then calculated for these largest representatives. The distribution for these largest representatives is similar to that for compact representatives, ranging from 1.48 to 1.86, with a mean ($\pm$ standard deviation) of 1.64 ± 0.07. This control demonstrates that loops are inherently compact structures.

As would be expected from their observed compactness, loops are not flat, but globular. This visual impression is confirmed when we calculate the principal moments of inertia for all loops, helices, strands of sheet, and protein monomers within the set of 67 proteins. Ratios of the largest to the smallest eigenvalues were formed. The axial ratios for loops resemble those for whole proteins (Fig. 4), while ratios for helices and strands are more rodlike.

The free energy change upon closing a

Table 3. Residue frequencies in loops, normalized with the use of equation 2.

Gly	1.35	Glu	1.09	Trp	0.85
Pro	1.28	Thr	1.07	His	0.83
Tyr	1.28	Lys	1.02	Ala	0.77
Asp	1.22	½ Cys	0.94	Leu	0.76
Asn	1.22	Gln	0.93	Ile	0.68
Ser	1.20	Arg	0.91	Met	0.67
Cys	1.16	Phe	0.90	Val	0.64

3   The standard state surface area of a residue, X, is the average area of that residue in a representative ensemble of Gly-X-Gly tripeptides [see table 1 in G. D. Rose, A. R. Geselowitz, G. J. Lesser, R. H. Lee, M. H. Zehfus, *Science* **229**, 834 (1985)]. The standard state surface area of a segment is taken as the sum of its residue standard states.

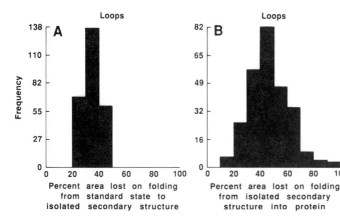

Fig. 2. Histograms showing distribution of the percentage of surface area lost for loops on folding from (A) the standard state (18) to the isolated secondary structure and (B) the isolated secondary structure to the native protein. The mean values (± standard deviation) are: (A) 34.4 percent (± 6.5) and (B) 46.7 percent (± 14.6).

protein segment into a loop consists of an unfavorable entropic contribution and a compensating enthalpic contribution. The enthalpy needed to counterbalance loop-closing entropy may be due to either intrasegment or extrasegment interactions, or both. At one extreme, a loop might be stabilized by interactions within its own core. At the other extreme, the rest of the protein might provide a stable framework that pinches together the termini of an intervening segment, forcing that segment to "loop out." Greater structural autonomy would be expected in the former case.

The number of noncovalent contacts between loops can be used to provide a rough estimate of loop enthalpy. Using united-atom radii (Lee and Richards, 1971), we plotted the number of noncovalent contacts as a function of the number of atoms in the loop, and obtained a line described by the equation (± standard error):

Number of contacts =

$$3.0(\pm 0.03) \times \text{number of atoms} - 11.3(\pm 2.7)$$

$$(3).$$

The equation can be interpreted to mean that loop enthalpy is essentially a linear function of loop length. (The negative intercept is expected upon extrapolation to zero length because a threshold of several atoms would be required to establish any contacts.) If we assume a binding energy of −0.03 kcal/mol per contact, the average loop enthalpy is on the order of −0.6 kcal/mol per residue.

The entropy of loop closure scales linearly with the logarithm of segment length (Flory, 1969), but a confident numerical estimate requires theory that takes into account heterogeneous loops of approximately one statistical segment in length. While such an estimate is beyond the scope of this chapter, it is evident that the loop-closing entropy for these compact loops of 6 to 16 residues is offset, at least

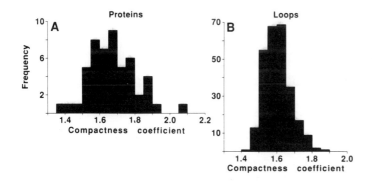

Fig. 3. Histograms showing distribution of the compactness coefficient (Z) for (A) the proteins used in this study and (B) the 270 loops from Table 1. The mean values (± standard deviation) are: (A) 1.67 (± 0.13) and (B) 1.61 (± 0.07).

Fig. 4. Histograms showing the distribution of axial ratios for (A) the proteins used in this study and (B) all loops from Table 1. The mean values (± standard deviation) are: (A) 1.77 (± 0.66) and (B) 2.17 (± 0.51). The three outliers in (A) are glucagon, mellitin, and avian pancreatic polypeptide, three of the six proteins without loops.

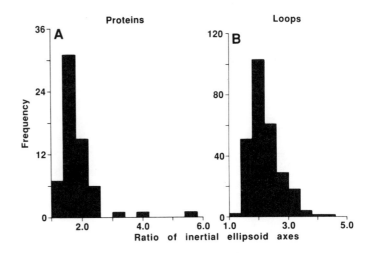

in part, by extensive favorable contacts within the loop.

Protein secondary structure has often been codified into a small number of states on the basis of backbone dihedral angles and hydrogen-bonding patterns. The usual categories include helix, sheet, reverse turn, and random coil. Identification of these categories is not always straightforward, and a given segment may be classified differently by different investigators. Not surprisingly, estimates of the relative abundance within these categories vary somewhat, particularly in the case of turns (Rose *et al.,* 1985). However, a consensus estimate finds that regular secondary structures—helices and sheet—make up slightly less than half of proteins, on average. Chou and Fasman (1977) allocate another third of all residues to turns, although other estimates are closer to a quarter (Kabsch and Sander, 1983; Rose and Seltzer, 1977; Rose and Wetlaufer, 1977).

Two comprehensive studies that codify residues into discrete states based on objective criteria can be found (Kabsch and Sander, 1983; Levitt and Greer, 1977). We used the assignment of Kabsch and Sander (1983) to eliminate regular secondary structure prior to loop identification, as discussed above.

The 67 proteins in our study contain 11,885 residues: 26 percent in helix, 19 percent in sheet, 26 percent in turns, and 21 percent in loops. On the basis of the K&S assignments, calculation of the percentage of residues in

helix and sheet is straightforward, but assignment of residues to turns or loops is confounded because loops contain reverse turns. In that our statistics count such residues among loops, the percentage of residues in reverse turns must be reduced accordingly. When subdivided, 11 percent of all residues are found in turns within loops and 15 percent in turns external to loops. A further correction, although slight, should be made for those two-residue strands and single-turn helices that are counted both in loops and as regular secondary structure; in combination, these two minor categories contain less than 1 percent of all residues. Subject to these adjustments, helices, sheet, reverse turns, and loops account for approximately 80 percent of all residues in the 67 proteins of our study. When our conservative criteria for defining loops are relaxed only slightly, more than 90 percent of all residues are included in the accounting.

Loops as a definitive category for structure analysis

The principal question raised by our findings is whether loops comprise a distinct class of secondary structure. Of course, the classical definition of secondary structure as hydrogen-bonded backbone structure (Linderstrom-Lang, 1952) automatically excludes loops. In practice, however, secondary structure has come to be synonymous with the conformation of continuous segments of the polypeptide chain (Lehninger, 1982).

The fact that loops exist in a range of conformations would seem to argue against their classification as a discrete category. Yet, the situation is not entirely dissimilar to that of reverse turns which can range between three and four residues and adopt multiple conformations (Richardson, 1981; Venkatachalam, 1968; Kuntz, 1972; Lewis *et al.*, 1971; Rose *et al.*, 1985; Smith and Pease, 1980). This range of variability increases exponentially with segment length, and, in loops, it is extremely large.

The conspicuous compactness of most loops is the factor that most convincingly underwrites their classification as a discrete entity. They are autonomously well-folded structures because their observed compactness does not depend on interactions with the rest of the protein. Indeed, were loops amorphous, their location at the molecular surface would render them ready targets for indiscriminate proteolysis (Goldberg and St. John, 1976), leading to rapid protein turnover, but there is no evidence for this.

Because loops contain reverse turns, they should perhaps be viewed as structural composites, akin to supersecondary structure (Richardson, 1981; Levitt and Chothia, 1976). In any event, loops can be identified objectively in x-ray elucidated proteins, and they occur with a frequency comparable to that of the β-sheet. We propose that protein segments which satisfy our defining criteria be called omega (Ω) loops.

The term loop has also been used to describe a chain segment that is cross linked by a disulfide bond. Although one can envision an Ω loop with a disulfide bond between its ends, none are observed among the loops in Table 1. There are interloop disulfide bonds, but these are not situated between loop termini. In addition, the cystines in these omega loops form loop-loop and loop-protein disulfide bridges.

Some loop residues have been implicated in antibody binding. Lysozyme loops 18 to 25, 44 to 52, and 60 to 75 contain antigenic residues 19, 21, 45 to 48 (Smith-Gill, 1982;

Smith-Gill *et al.*, 1984), and 64 to 80 (Arnon, 1977). Since the entire protein surface is thought to be potentially antigenic (Benjamin, 1984; Fanning *et al.*, 1986; Barlow *et al.*, 1986), loop involvement in antigenic sites may be a consequence of the fact that loops are on the protein surface.

It is unclear whether an isolated loop segment will fold independently in solution (Wetlaufer, 1981), but the proposition is testable. The questions are analogous to those raised by Bierzynski *et al.* (1982) and Kim and Baldwin (1982) in their studies of the independent stability of the C-peptide helix from ribonuclease. The isolated segment could be monitored for nativelike interactions by nuclear magnetic resonance. Alternatively, the conformation of loops containing suitable ligands might be probed with metal ions (Horrocks, 1984).

Isolated loop segments are also attractive peptides for use in model studies. They are highly solvated, both within the protein and alone in solution; and they are readily cyclized by addition of cysteines at their termini. An analogous use of cyclized peptides to model reverse turns has been successfully exploited by Gierasch and co-workers (Rose *et al.*, 1985; Smith and Pease, 1980).

Omega loops are appealing candidates for bioengineering studies. From the data in Table 1, experiments could be designed to test the hypothesis that loops function as integral units and have the potential for modular exchange between proteins. Thus, a loop might be "swapped" or excised entirely, and the consequences for protein stability and enzymatic activity can be assessed.

Evolution appears to have established precedents for loop swap experiments. Several protein families in our database such as the cytochromes c and the serine proteases contain loops at homologous locations. Some of those homologous loops are structurally similar, while others have conserved end points, but differing overall structures.

Macromolecular recognition is a hallmark of biological systems. Recognition sites for glycosylation, phosphorylation, supramolecular assembly, and transport all reside on the protein surface. It is plausible that omega loops assume a central role in such processes.

Acknowledgments

We thank Micheal Zehfus for suggestions, Lyndon Hibbard and William Young for discussion during preliminary stages of this work, and an anonymous reviewer for valuable comments. Supported by NIH grants GM29458 and AGO6084.

References

Arnon, R., *Immunochemistry of Enzymes and Their Antibodies*, M. R. J. Salton, Ed. (Wiley, New York, 1977).

Barlow, D. J., M. S. Edwards, J. M. Thornton, *Nature (London)* **322**, 747 (1986).

Benjamin, D. C., *et al., Annu. Rev. Immunol.* **2**, 67 (1984).

Bernstein, F. C., *et al., J. Mol. Biol.* **112**, 535 (1977).

Bierzynski, A., P. S. Kim, R. L. Baldwin, *Proc. Natl. Acad. Sci. U.S.A.* **79**, 2470 (1982).

Chothia, C., *J. Mol. Biol.* **105**, 1 (1976).

Chou, P. Y., and G. D. Fasman, *J. Mol. Biol.* **115**, 135 (1977).

_____, *Annu. Rev. Biochem.* **47**, 251 (1978).

Davies, D. R., E. A. Padlan, D. M. Segal, *Annu. Rev. Biochem.* **44**, 639 (1975).

Fanning, D. W., J. A. Smith, G. D. Rose, *Biopolymers* **25**, 863 (1986).

Flory, P. J., *Statistical Mechanics of Chain Molecules* (Wiley, New York, 1969).

Goldberg, A. L., and A. C. St. John, *Annu. Rev. Biochem.* **45**, 747 (1976).

Holmes, M. A., and B. W. Matthews, *J. Mol. Biol.* **160**, 623 (1982).

Horrocks, W. D., Jr., *Progr. Inorg. Chem.* **31**, 1 (1984).

Kabsch, W., and C. Sander, *Biopolymers* **22**, 2577 (1983).

Kim, P. S., and R. L. Baldwin, *Annu. Rev. Biochem.* **51**, 459 (1982).

Kossiakoff, A. A., J. L. Chambers, L. M. Kay, R. M. Stroud, *Biochemistry* **16**, 654 (1977).

Kretsinger, R. H., and C. E. Nockolds, *J. Biol. Chem.* **248**, 3313 (1973).

Kuntz, I. D., *J. Am. Chem. Soc.* **94**, 8568 (1972).

Lee, B. K., and F. M. Richards, *J. Mol. Biol.* **55**, 379 (1971).

Lehninger, A., *Principles of Biochemistry* (Worth, New York, 1982).

Lesk, A. M., and K. D. Hardman, *Science* **216**, 539 (1982).

Levitt, M., *Biochemistry* **17**, 4277 (1978).

Levitt, M., and C. Chothia, *Nature (London)* **261**, 552 (1976).

Levitt, M., and J. Greer, *J. Mol. Biol.* **114**, 181 (1977).

Lewis, P. N., F. A. Momany, H. A. Scheraga, *Proc. Natl. Acad. Sci. U.S.A.* **68**, 2293 (1971).

Linderstrom-Lang, K., *Lane Memorial Lectures: Proteins and Enzymes* (Stanford University Press, Stanford, CA, 1952), vol. 6, p. 1.

Pavlov, M. Y., and B. A. Federov, *Biopolymers* **22**, 1507 (1983).

Richards, F. M., *Carlsberg Res. Commun.* **44**, 47 (1979).

Richardson, J. S., *Adv. Protein Chem.* **34**, 167 (1981).

Richardson, J. S., D. C. Richardson, K. A. Thomas, E. W. Silverton, D. R. Davies, *J. Mol. Biol.* **102**, 221 (1976).

Rose, G. D., and J. P. Seltzer, *J. Mol. Biol.* **113**, 153 (1977).

Rose, G. D., and D. B. Wetlaufer, *Nature (London)* **268**, 769 (1977).

Rose, G. D., L. M. Gierasch, J. A. Smith, *Adv. Protein Chem.* **37**, 1 (1985).

Smith, J. A., and L. G. Pease, *CRC Crit. Rev. Biochem.* **8**, 315 (1980).

Smith-Gill, S. J., *et al., J. Immunol.* **128**, 314 (1982).

Smith-Gill, S. J., T. B. Lovoie, C. R. Mainhart, *J. Immunol.* **133**, 384 (1984).

Tainer, J. A., E. D. Getzoff, K. M. Beem, J. S. Richardson, D. C. Richardson, *J. Mol. Biol.* **160**, 181 (1982).

Takano, T., and R. E. Dickerson, *Proc. Natl. Acad. Sci. U.S.A.* **77**, 6371 (1980).

Venkatachalam, C. M., *Biopolymers* **6**, 1425 (1968).

Wetlaufer, D. B., *Adv. Protein Chem.* **34**, 61 (1981).

Zehfus, M. H., and G. D. Rose, *Biochemistry* **25**, 5759 (1986).

3

Helix Signals in Proteins

Leonard G. Presta and George D. Rose

The α helix was first proposed as a model structure by Pauling *et al.* (1951). Subsequent experimental support (Perutz, 1951) has made the helix a familiar landmark in proteins. The key feature of the Pauling-Corey-Branson helical model is a pattern of iterated backbone hydrogen bonding between each $>$N–H donor and the $>$C=O acceptor located four residues previously. The resultant structure satisfies the hydrogen-bonding requirements of consecutive main-chain polar groups with a hydrogen-bond geometry that is nearly optimal.

Helices are classified as repetitive secondary structure because their backbone dihedral angles, ϕ and ψ, have repeating values near the canonical value of $(-60°, -40°)$ (Richardson, 1981). When the dihedral angles of a chain segment assume helical values, the backbone polar groups are automatically positioned to form hydrogen bonds with intrasegment partners. The situation is unlike that of β sheet, the other repetitive secondary structure, where backbone hydrogen bonds in each β strand are satisfied by extrasegment partners from an adjacent β strand that may be distant in sequence.

In globular proteins of known structure, approximately one-quarter of all residues are found in helices (Kabsch and Sander, 1983). The frequent occurrence of helices, and the fact that their hydrogen bonds can be localized to intrasegment partners, suggest that α helices may function as autonomous folding units in proteins. Strengthening this suggestion are recent experiments that demonstrate the stability of isolated protein helices in water (Bierzynski *et al.*, 1982; Kim and Baldwin, 1984; Jimenez *et al.*, 1987; Shoemaker *et al.*, 1987).

We now show that the location of helices in water-soluble proteins is dependent on local sequence information alone. This finding is a result of the observation that the Pauling-Corey-Branson model accounts for only about half of the backbone hydrogen bonds in actual protein helices. In particular, the average protein helix, which is 12 residues in length (Schulz and Schirmer, 1979), contains eight intrahelical $>$N–H$\cdots$O=C$<$ bonds, but $>$N–H donors in the first four residues and $>$C=O acceptors in the last four residues lack intrahelical partners (Schellman, 1955) (Color Plate XXII). We hypothesize that a necessary condition for helix formation is the presence of residues flanking the helix termini whose side chains can supply hydrogen-bond partners for unpaired main-chain $>$N–H and $>$C=O groups. These boundary residues would then function as a stereochemical code for helix formation.

Unlike theories derived from statistical correlations, the helix hypothesis is based on simple physical chemistry and provides a

This chapter is reprinted from *Science* **240**, 1632 (1988).

mechanism for many well-known phenomena. For example, the tendency for helices to be situated at the molecular surface (Lee and Richards, 1971; Chothia, 1976) and often to contain amphipathic sequences (DeGrado *et al.*, 1981; Eisenberg *et al.*, 1982) is a consequence of requiring polar residues at the termini and the concomitant desirability of having some apolar residues between the termini to promote hydrophobic association with rest of the protein. The statistical preference for acidic residues at the NH_2-termini of helices and basic residues at the COOH-termini (Chou and Fasman, 1974; Blagdon and Goodman, 1975) results from the Asp and Glu side chains being able to serve as hydrogen-bond acceptors while Lys and Arg can serve as donors; these hydrogen bonds would augment contributions arising from ionic interactions with the helix macrodipole (Shoemaker *et al.*, 1987). The puzzling examples of identical pentapeptides that are helical in one segment but not in another (Kabsch and Sander, 1984) can be reconciled if the segment termini are taken into account.

To test the helix hypothesis in proteins of known structure, we analyzed each sequence for potential helix boundaries and compared the results to the location of observed helices. Although the hypothesis is fundamentally simple, the analysis is complex. Briefly, a complete library of side-chain to main-chain hydrogen-bonding possibilities was compiled. Side chains from each of the 13 polar residues, together with two additional variants of His, were appended to each α carbon of a polyglycyl helix and a representative ensemble of adjacent turns. The conformations of these side chains were then uniformly sampled. Whenever a hydrogen bond could be formed, the residue, together with its conformation and position, was added to the library. The library was then used to evaluate actual protein sequences for sites at which residue side chains could satisfy the four terminal >N–H groups or >C=O groups of a helix. A window of only six consecutive residues turned out to be sufficient to identify such sites. Nevertheless, the enumeration of backbone to side-chain hydrogen bonds in actual

proteins is computationally intensive because, for each six-residue sequence, every permutation of allowed conformations from the library must be assessed, as described below.

Analysis of X-ray–Elucidated Proteins

Our analysis required prior identification of helices and adjacent turns in proteins of known structure. The proteins (Table 1) included 26 high-resolution x-ray structures (resolution ≤ 2.0 Å; R factor ≤ 20 percent) from the Brookhaven protein database (Bernstein *et al.*, 1977).

To identify helices, we determined all intramolecular main-chain to main-chain hydrogen bonds for each protein using criteria enumerated in Fig. 1 (Baker and Hubbard, 1984; Taylor and Kennard, 1984; Vedani and Dunitz, 1985). Backbone segments with $(i, i + 4)$ or $(i, i + 3)$ hydrogen bonds were then inspected for the presence of an α or 3_{10} helix. Helices were terminated at the final residue in which backbone >NH or >C=O groups participate in an $(i, i + 4)$ or $(i, i + 3)$ hydrogen bond while maintaining dihedral angles with helical values ($\varphi \cong -60°$; $\psi \cong -40°$). This strict definition may differ slightly from assignments listed in the header records of the protein database (Bernstein *et al.*, 1977) or those given by Kabsch and Sander (Kabsch and Sander, 1983) because the respective >C=O or >N–H groups in the residue immediately preceding or following a helix form

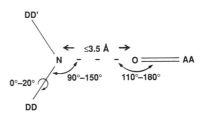

Fig. 1. Hydrogen-bonding criteria for x-ray–elucidated proteins. AA is the acceptor antecedent atom; DD and DD' are the donor antecedent atoms. Torsion angle [N–DD–DD'–O] = 0° to 20°; this angle was used to measure the degree to which the oxygen acceptor is out of plane of the *sp*2 nitrogen donor.

Table 1. Proteins used. All are x-ray structure with resolution ≤ 2.0 Å and crystallographic R factor ≤ 20 percent.

Code[a]	Protein name	Helices[b]
351C	Cytochrome C551	3-9, 27-33, 40-50, 68-79
2ACT	Actinidin	25-42, 51-56, 70-79, 100-103, 121-128, 142-145
1AZA	Azurin (molecule B)	56-64
1BP2	Phospholipase A2	2-12, 18-21, 40-55, 59-63, 90-106
3C2C	Cytochrome C2	{4-10, [11-16]}, 50-58, 64-70, 74-82, 98-108
2CAB	Carbonic anhydrase B	131-134, {[155-157], 158-162, [163-166]}, 220-226
2CDV	Cytochrome C3	65-70, 79-87, 91-98
5CPA	Carboxypeptidase A	15-28, 74-89, 94-100, 113-121, 174-186, 216-230, 254-260, 286-305
1CRN	Crambin	7-16, 23-29
4DFR	Dihydrofolate reductase (molecule B)	25-35, 44-50, 78-83, 97-103
1ECD	Hemoglobin III, *Chironomos thummi thummi*	{3-13, [13-15]}, 20-30, 46-49, 53-71, 77-87, 94-111, 118-132
4FXN	Flavodoxim, semiquinone form	11-25, 66-72, 94-104, 125-135
1GP1	Glutathione peroxidase (molecule B)	48-62, 88-94, 120-128, 185-192
1HMQ	Hemerythrin (molecule D)	19-37, 41-64, 70-84, 91-102
1INS	Insulin, porcine (molecules C and D)	A2-A8, [A13-A18], B9-B19
2LHB	Hemoglobin V, lamprey	{13-24, 24-28, 30-44, [45-51]}, 61-65, 68-86, 91-107, 116-127, 132-145
1LZ1	Lysozyme, human	5-14, 25-35, 90-99, 110-114
1MBO	Myoglobin, sperm whale, oxidized	4-17, {21-35, [37-42]}, 52-56, 59-76, 83-95, 101-118, 125-148
2OVO	Turkey ovomucoid inhibitor	34-43
1PPT	Pancreatic hormone, avian	14-31
5PTI	Pancreatic trypsin inhibitor	48-55
5RSA	Ribonuclease A, bovine	4-12, 25-32, {51-55, [56-57]}
2SGA	*Streptomyces griseus* Protease A	{56-59, [62-63]}, 232-236
1SN3	Scorpion neurotoxin	{23-29, [30]}
3TLN	Thermolysin	68-87, 137-150, 160-179, {[234], 235-246}, 260-273, 281-296, 301-312
1TPP	Trypsin, bovine	165-171, 235-243

[a]Brookhaven protein database four-character name (Bernstein *et al.*, 1977).   [b][ ] denote segments of 3₁₀ helix; { } denote segments considered as 1 helical unit.

one additional intrahelical hydrogen bond with dihedral angles having nonhelical values. Further ambiguity in the precise location of helix boundaries can be occasioned by adjoining type I and type III reverse turns that have dihedral angles near helical values.

Using the foregoing hydrogen-bond criteria and boundary conditions, we found all helical residues in a database of proteins. The average dihedral angles (mean ± SD) are $\phi = -63.8° ± 6.6°$, $\psi = -41.0° ± 7.2°$ for 1062 residues.

Helices and their flanking residues are labeled as follows:

$$N''-N'-N-N1-N2-N3-\ldots-C3-C2-C1-C-C'-C''$$

where N1-N2-N3- ... -C3-C2-C1 participate in the helix backbone hydrogen-bonding network and have helical backbone dihedral angles. Residues N and C participate in the hydrogen-bonding network but have nonhelical dihedral angles. Residues N″, N′, C′, and C″ neither participate in helix backbone hydrogen bonding nor have helical dihedral angles, and they are classified with the preceding or succeeding turns, respectively (Color Plate XXII).

To construct a hydrogen-bond library, we required a representative ensemble of backbone conformations at the N- and C-termini of helices. Six-residue segments consisting of residues N"–N'–N–N1–N2–N3 were tabulated for each helix NH_2-terminus in the 26 proteins. Six-residue COOH-terminal segments consisting of C3–C2–C1–C–C'–C" were also tabulated. These data were then partitioned into classes. Thirteen classes were defined for turns at the NH_2-terminus (representing 60 percent of the observed distribution) (see Table 2), and six classes were defined at the COOH-terminus (representing 50 percent of the observed distribution) (see Table 3). Expansion to seven-residue segments that included the next residue before N" or after C" was attempted, but the variation was too large to be useful.

Construction of a Side-Chain to Main-Chain Hydrogen-Bonding Library

A library of potential hydrogen bonds between side-chain and main-chain groups was compiled for polar residues within helices and flanking turns. The strategy for each residue type was to generate a set of 19 polyglycyl paradigms, including hydrogen atoms, consisting of an eight-residue idealized helix joined to each class of flanking turn (13 at the NH_2-terminus, 6 at the COOH-terminus). All polar side chains, each in turn, were appended separately to each α-carbon position of all paradigms, the side chain was allowed to rotate, and conformations forming hydrogen bonds to the main chain were added to the library.

Amino acid geometries were extracted from the Empirical Conformational Energy Program for Peptides (ECEPP) (Scheraga, 1975), but were modified to assign identical bond lengths and angles to all backbone structures except proline. Backbone dihedral

angles for the idealized helix were set at ($\phi = -63.8°$; $\psi = -41.0°$), the mean value observed in helices of x-ray elucidated structures (Table 1). Backbone dihedral angles assigned to flanking turns are those listed in Tables 2 and 3.

All 13 polar amino acid residues were assessed: Arg, Asn, Asp, Cys, Gln, Glu, His, Lys, Met, Ser, Thr, Trp, and Tyr.[1] Three variants, of His were used: (i) neutral with Nϵ protonated, (ii) neutral with Nδ protonated, and (iii) (+1)-charged with both Nϵ and Nδ protonated. Although the hydrogen-bonding capabilities of Cys and Met are uncertain (Baker and Hubbard, 1984; Srinivasan and Chacko, 1967), both were included for completeness.

Side-chain conformations were sampled uniformly. For practical reasons, the sampling interval increased as side-chain length increased. In particular, side-chain dihedral angles were sampled at rotation increments of 5 degrees for (Ser, Thr, Cys), 10 degrees for (Asp, Asn, His), 15 degrees for (Glu, Gln, Met), and 20 degrees for (Arg, Lys, Tyr, Trp).

Our hydrogen-bonding criteria (Baker and Hubbard, 1984; Taylor and Kennard, 1984, Vedani and Dunitz, 1985) are enumerated in Fig. 2. Conformations were rejected if at least one pair of atoms had an interatomic distance less than 80 percent of the Ramachandran "extreme" limit (Rama-

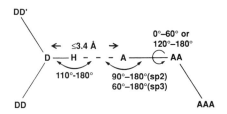

Fig. 2. Hydrogen-bonding criteria for hydrogen-bond library. D is the hydrogen-bond donor, DD and DD' are the donor antecedent atoms; A is the acceptor, AA is the acceptor antecedent atom, AAA is the acceptor penultimate antecedent atom. Torsion angle [H . . . A–AA–AAA] = 0° to 60° or 120° to 180°.

---

1   Single-letter abbreviations for the amino acid residues are: A, Ala; C, Cys; D, Asp; E, Glu; F, Phe; G, Gly; H, His; I, Ile; K, Lys; L, Leu; M, Met; N, Asn; P, Pro; Q, Gln; R, Arg; S, Ser; T, Thr; V, Val; W, Trp; Y, Tyr.

Table 2. Backbone conformations of residues N'', N', and N in observed helices. The magnitude of the respective angle is given in degrees plus or minus the standard deviation (σ) of the respective angle in degrees. The number of residues in the sample is shown as *n*. No standard deviation was computed when $n = 1$.

C[a]	B[b]	N'' (deg $\pm \sigma$)	n	N' (deg $\pm \sigma$)	n	N (deg $\pm \sigma$)	n
A	ϕ	-60 ± 7	8	-91 ± 18	18	-100 ± 24	18
	ψ	-23 ± 12	8	-15 ± 18	18	139 ± 19	18
B	ϕ	-60 ± 6	5	-90 ± 17	5	-75 ± 9	5
	ψ	-27 ± 8	5	-6 ± 18	5	134 ± 17	5
C	ϕ	-108 ± 22	6	-91 ± 18	18	-100 ± 24	18
	ψ	141 ± 22	6	-15 ± 18	18	139 ± 19	18
D	ϕ	-65 ± 14	9	-71 ± 10	13	-94 ± 15	13
	ψ	-26 ± 13	9	-21 ± 16	13	-2 ± 16	13
E	ϕ	-90 ± 47	4	-71 ± 10	13	-94 ± 15	13
	ψ	152 ± 16	4	-21 ± 16	13	-2 ± 16	13
F	ϕ	-84 ± 22	8	-66 ± 11	16	-78 ± 17	16
	ψ	136 ± 25	8	142 ± 10	16	151 ± 20	16
G	ϕ	-93 ± 14	4	-66 ± 11	16	-78 ± 17	16
	ψ	5 ± 14	4	142 ± 10	16	151 ± 20	16
H	ϕ	-94 ± 21	2	-71 ± 11	3	-79 ± 17	3
	ψ	143 ± 25	2	119 ± 8	3	-20 ± 28	3
I	ϕ	-97	1	-71 ± 11	3	-79 ± 17	3
	ψ	12	1	119 ± 8	3	-20 ± 28	3
J	ϕ	-106 ± 25	5	-138 ± 15	8	-91 ± 12	8
	ψ	150 ± 16	5	164 ± 12	8	160 ± 20	8
K	ϕ	-68	1	-89 ± 6	4	-112 ± 8	4
	ψ	136	1	62 ± 10	4	17 ± 15	4
L	ϕ	-67 ± 7	4	-77 ± 8	5	-141 ± 24	5
	ψ	-17 ± 12	4	-17 ± 14	5	72 ± 12	5
M	ϕ	-92 ± 30	3	-73 ± 8	3	-159 ± 2	4
	ψ	141 ± 11	3	-24 ± 5	3	176 ± 9	4

[a]C lists the conformational class.   [b]B is the backbone dihedral angle, ϕ or ψ.

chandran and Sasisekharan, 1968), regardless of hydrogen-bond presence, or if the number of contacts falling between the "extreme" limits and their 80 percent cutoff values exceeded the number of side-chain dihedral angles for the specific amino acid residues. Hydrogen-bond geometry and close-contact constraints were relaxed slightly from accepted values (Taylor and Kennard, 1984; Vedani and Dunitz, 1985; Ramachandran and Sasisekharan, 1968) in order to compensate for the rigid backbone geometry and fixed rotation increments of side chains.

The coefficient of 80 percent is derived from the following useful "rule of thumb." For two atoms with an interatomic distance less than their "extreme" limit, rotation about the subtending dihedral angles by 10 degrees can move each atom by approximately 0.25 Å (Moult and James, 1986), thereby increasing the overall interatomic distance by 0.50 Å (approximately 20 percent of the "extreme" limit). Rotation about distal dihedral angles can cause larger movement.

The resultant library contains allowed hydrogen-bonding conformations for each polar residue at every side-chain position in all 19 paradigms. In practice, two amino acids, Trp and Tyr, cannot form hydrogen bonds at either end of the helix, so they were eliminated.

Table 3. Backbone conformations of C, C', and C'' in observed helices. In conformation N, residue C' is usually a Gly. When ψ for residue C'' is a dash (–), several observed classes have been collapsed into one effective class, since the value of this angle does not affect the conformations of residues in the window [C3–C'']. Conformation R was used only when residue C' is a Pro. In this case, the backbone conformation of residue C1 was $\phi = -75°$, $\psi = -28°$. In conformation S, residue C is usually a Gly.

C	B	C (deg ± σ)	n	C' (deg ± σ)	n	C'' (deg ± σ)	n
N	ϕ	– 92 ± 17	17	71 ± 14	17	– 88 ± 26	13
	ψ	– 2 ± 11	17	27 ± 14	17	—	
O	ϕ	– 74 ± 16	32	– 83 ± 19	32	– 83 ± 14	18
	ψ	– 19 ± 17	32	– 13 ± 19	32	—	
P	ϕ	– 74 ± 16	32	– 83 ± 19	32	54 ± 6	3
	ψ	– 19 ± 17	32	– 13 ± 19	32	55 ± 10	3
Q	ϕ	– 93 ± 13	10	– 73 ± 13	10	– 83 ± 22	6
	ψ	– 6 ± 15	10	134 ± 15	10	– 14 ± 25	6
R	ϕ	– 137 ± 8	7	– 60 ± 11	6	– 74 ± 12	5
	ψ	69 ± 18	7	– 23 ± 12	6	– 19 ± 12	5
S	ϕ	83 ± 9	5	– 119 ± 39	4	– 91 ± 21	4
	ψ	14 ± 11	5	136 ± 22	4	137 ± 13	4

Proline was treated as a special case. Using the 19 polyglycyl paradigms, we modeled both *exo-* and *endo-*Pro at every position having a compatible ϕ value (that is, $\phi \cong -75°$) (Scheraga, 1975). Structures with close contacts were considered sterically forbidden, but an exception was made in positions N'' or C'' where rotation about the Pro ψ dihedral angle can relieve a close-contact involving the Pro without affecting remaining positions.

Searching Protein Sequences for Potential Helix Boundaries

We tested the helix hypothesis by searching the amino acid sequences of x-ray elucidated proteins for potential helix boundaries and comparing the results against the location of observed helices. The search procedure identifies two types of helix boundaries: NH$_2$-terminal bounds (NTB's) and COOH-terminal bounds (CTB's). Such boundaries are identified by moving a six-residue window along the protein sequence from its NH$_2$- to COOH-terminus. When being searched for NTB's, the window contains positions N''–N'–N–N1–N2–N3, and the side chains within the window must provide hydrogen-bond acceptors for at least three of the four main-chain >N–H donors of residues N–N1–N2–N3. When searching for CTB's, the window contains positions C3–C2–C1–C–C'–C'', and the side chains within the window must provide hydrogen-bond donors for at least three of the four main-chain >C=O acceptors of residues C3–C2–C1–C.

Side chains within each window position were appended to each of the six-residue backbone paradigms and coordinates were generated, including hydrogen atoms. All possible hydrogen-bonding arrangements were identified with the use of the hydrogen-bonding library. As the window is advanced, every residue in the sequence is positioned in turn at each locus in all paradigms. This search procedure is not only sequence-dependent but also structure-dependent because residues are assessed in an explicit backbone conformation that depends upon their position in the current window and the paradigm under consideration.

It is necessary to distinguish between hydrogen-bond combinations and conformations. A combination is defined as a distinct pattern of side-chain to main-chain hydrogen bonding for the six residues within the window. In effect, a combination is a hydrogen-bond "wiring diagram." A given six-residue segment could have many possible hydrogen-bond wiring diagrams or none at all. Each combination can assume multiple conformations, all of which preserve its wiring diagram. In effect, a conformation moves the "wires" but not their points of attachment. As the number of combinations, each comprised of an ensemble of conformations, becomes larger, the reduction in chain entropy needed to form the required hydrogen bonds becomes smaller.

The hydrogen-bonding library was used to retrieve all possible conformations with side-chain to main-chain hydrogen bonds for each combination. Since the library is derived from paradigms decorated with solitary residues, some permutations of these individually allowed hydrogen-bonding conformations may be mutually exclusive within the six-residue window. Consequently, all possible hydrogen-bonding conformations for each combination were tested to eliminate steric impossibilities. A conformation was rejected if at least one pair of atoms had an interatomic distance less than 80 percent of the Ramachandran "extreme" limit or if the number of contacts falling between the "extreme" limit and their 80 percent cutoff values exceeded the sum of the number of side-chain dihedral angles for the participating amino acids.

Exhaustive search of conformations is highly computer-intensive, and several approximations were made. Nonhydrogen-bonding residues within the window were approximated by Ala. Specifically, an amino acid residue was represented by Ala unless (i) it was Gly or Pro, (ii) it was Asn, Asp, Gln, Glu, His, Ser, or Thr at an NTB, or (iii) it was Asn, Arg, Gln, His, Lys, Ser, or Thr at a CTB. For example, the sequence Ser-Tyr-Pro-Gly-Asn-Val would be represented by Ser-Ala-Pro-Gly-Asn-Ala. The use of an Ala proxy is based on the assumption that, for any given conformation, the nonhydrogen-bonding side chains can adopt conformations that do not perturb the hydrogen-bonding side chains. In this stage of the analysis, Cys and Met were not treated as hydrogen-bonding residues.

Practical considerations forced the three approximations discussed above: (i) use of an Ala proxy, (ii) relaxation of close contact limits, and (iii) rigid backbone paradigms. Even by resorting to these approximations, the complete search of a small protein such as ribonuclease requires ~30 weeks of VAX 11/780 processor time. In practice, typical proteins take 2 to 3 weeks of processor time with a dedicated CSPI 6430 array processor together with three microVAX II computers. With abundant processor capability, an Ala proxy would not be necessary and all amino acids could be rotated and checked for steric conflicts. In addition, side-chain dihedral angles could be rotated in smaller increments, with the Ramachandran "extreme" limit as the sole criterion when screening steric conflicts. Ideally, the backbone would also be allowed to move, and the evaluation would explicitly include Pro at any position, thereby eliminating the need for backbone paradigms.

Application to Proteins of Known Structure

A diverse set of 13 x-ray elucidated proteins was chosen for analysis by the above methods. The proteins and their parenthesized Brookhaven file names (Bernstein *et al.,* 1977) are: carboxypeptidase A (5CPA), parvalbumin (3CPV), cytochrome c (4CYT), dihydrofolate reductase (4DFR), flavodoxin (4FXN), human lysozyme (1LZ1), myoglobin (1MBO), plastocyanin (1PCY), avian pancreatic peptide (1PPT), pancreatic trypsin inhibitor (5PTI), ribonuclease (5RSA), scorpion neurotoxin (1SN3), and triose phosphate isomerase (1TIM).

Included were representatives from each of the four classes (Richardson, 1981; Levitt and Chothia, 1976): (i) predominantly α-helical, (ii) predominantly β sheet, (iii) mixed helix and sheet, and (iv) segregated domains of helix and sheet.

The 13 proteins include 54 helices. For consistency, "kinked" helices (such as residues 21 to 42 in MBO) are counted as two distinct helical segments. These helical segments can be examined for NTB's and CTB's (Fig. 3). Direct comparison between the structures and the histograms is instructive, although it does not allow for the existence of possible folding intermediates that are either modified or eliminated entirely in the final crystal structures. Comparison is further complicated by ambiguity in the precise location of helix boundaries in the x-ray structures. Our definition, described above, differs slightly from assignments listed in the header records of the protein database (Bernstein et al., 1977) or those given by Kabsch and Sander (Kabsch and Sander, 1983).

Most helices are bracketed by a conspicuous cluster of NTB's or CTB's. Of the 54 helices, 44 have an NTB that overlaps the N1 residue (or, on occasion, an NTB that approaches N1 to within a residue or two) or else a boundary within one helical turn of the protein NH_2-terminus, and 45 have either a corresponding CTB or terminate within one helical turn of a prolyl residue or the protein COOH-terminus. Alternatively, consecutive helices (for example, residues 4 to 40 in MBO), where a helical sequence is interrupted by four or fewer nonhelical residues, can be counted as single helical elements. In this case, 38 of 47 helix NH_2-termini are satisfied by an NTB or protein NH_2-terminus, and 40 of 47 helix COOH-termini are satisfied by a CTB or protein COOH-terminus or else terminated by a Pro residue.

The protein termini have considerable flexibility and are not well represented by our rigid six-residue paradigms. For this reason, the protein NH_2- or COOH-terminus is considered to be able to provide hydrogen-bond acceptors or donors, respectively, for a helix boundary that is no farther than three residues away. Nevertheless, many helices with boundaries near the protein termini have NTB's and CTB's.

Of the ten helices lacking NTB's, six have between one and three glycyl residues within the initial six-residue window: CPA[254], DFR[97], FXN[94], LZ1[25], TIM[138], and TIM[215]. (Numbers in brackets indicate the N1 residue of the helix.) Such cases would not be adequately represented by the backbone conformations in Tables 2 and 3 because Gly residues, lacking side chains, have unusual conformational flexibility. Moreover, of these six, LZ1[25] and FXN[94] do have NTB's if Met is considered to form hydrogen bonds (Baker and Hubbard, 1984; Srinivasan and Chacko, 1967), and TIM[138] could equally well be regarded as a "kink" in a longer helix beginning at residue 130.

Three other helices lacking NTB's — DFR[25], MBO[101], and TIM[46] — have Pro residues within the initial six-residue window, interposed between the ostensible helix boundary and an adjacent upstream helix or visible NTB. The tenth helix without an NTB, LZ1[110], has a "bridge" of 3_{10} turns to a nearby upstream NTB.

Fig. 3 (pages 37–39). Histogram of NTB's and CTB's for 13 x-ray–elucidated proteins. The proteins and their parenthesized Brookhaven file names (Bernstein et al., 1977) are: (A) carboxypeptidase A (5CPA), (B) parvalbumin (3CPV), (C) cytochrome c (4CYT), (D) plastocyanin (1PCY), (E) dihydrofolate reductase (4DFR), (F) flavodoxin (4FXN), (G) human lysozyme (1LZ1), (H) myoglobin (1MBO), (I) pancreatic trypsin inhibitor (5PTI), (J) avian pancreatic peptide (1PPT), (K) ribonuclease (5RSA), (L) scorpion neurotoxin (1SN3), and (M) triose phosphate isomerase (1TIM). For each protein, the sequence is shown in one-letter code (see footnote 1), with helical segments in boldface. Tic marks on the abscissa denote every tenth residue. The upper histogram indicates the results of searching the sequence for potential NH_2-terminal bounds (NTBs); each bar, positioned above window location N1, plots the number of backbone N–H to side-chain hydrogen-bond combinations found within a given six-residue window. The lower histogram indicates corresponding information for backbone $>C=O$ to side-chain hydrogen bonds at COOH-terminal bounds (CTBs), with bars positioned below window location C1. Dark bars in the histograms represent the number of combinations that satisfy all four consecutive N–H groups (N, N1, N2, N3) or all four consecutive $>C=O$ groups (C3, C2, C1, C), respectively. The superimposed light bars plot the number of combinations satisfying either the initial three (N1, N2, N3) or final three (C3, C2, C1) residues of the helix proper, that is, excluding residues N or C. Prolines, lacking an amide hydrogen, were considered to be satisfied automatically in an NTB. In an NTB, His was considered to be in the neutral form, with Nε protonated; in a CTB, His was considered to be in the neutral form with Nδ protonated. A small number of histogram bars that are isolated from neighboring bars by at least two residues on either side and that contain no combinations in which all four groups are satisfied have been omitted to enhance clarity.

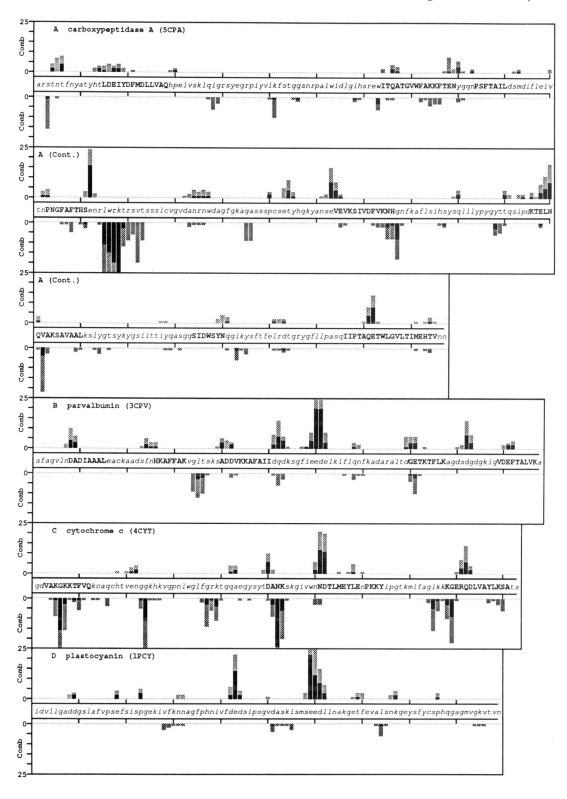

A   carboxypeptidase A (5CPA)

*arstntfnyatyht***LDEIYDFMDLLVAQ***hpelvsklqigrsyegrpiyvlkfstggsnrpaiwidlgihsrew***ITQATGVWFAKKFTEN***ygqn***PSFTAIL***dsmdifleiv*

A (Cont.)

*tn***PNGFAFTHS***enrlwrktrsvtssslcvgvdanrnwdagfgkagassspcset yhgkyanse***VEVKSIVDFVKNH***gnfkaflsihsysqllllypygyttqsipd***KTELN***

A (Cont.)

QVAKSAVAAL*kslygtsykygsiittiyqasgg***SIDWSYN***qgikysftfelrdtgrygfllpasq***IIPTAQETWLGVLTIMEHTV***nn*

B   parvalbumin (3CPV)

*afagvln***DADIAAAL***eackaadsfn***HKAFFAK***vgltsks***ADDVKKAFAII***dqdksgfieedelklflqnfkadaraltc***GETKTFLK***agdsdgdgkig***VDEFTALVK***a*

C   cytochrome c (4CYT)

*gd***VAKGKKTFVQ***kcaqchtvenggkhkvgpnlwglfgrktgqaegysyt***DANK***skgivwn***NDTLMEYLE***n***PKKY***ipgtkmifagikk***KGERQDLVAYLKSA***ts*

D   plastocyanin (1PCY)

idvllgaddgslafvpsefsispgekivfknnagfphnivfdedsipsgvdaskismseedllnakgetfevalsnkgeysfycsphqgagmvgkvtvn

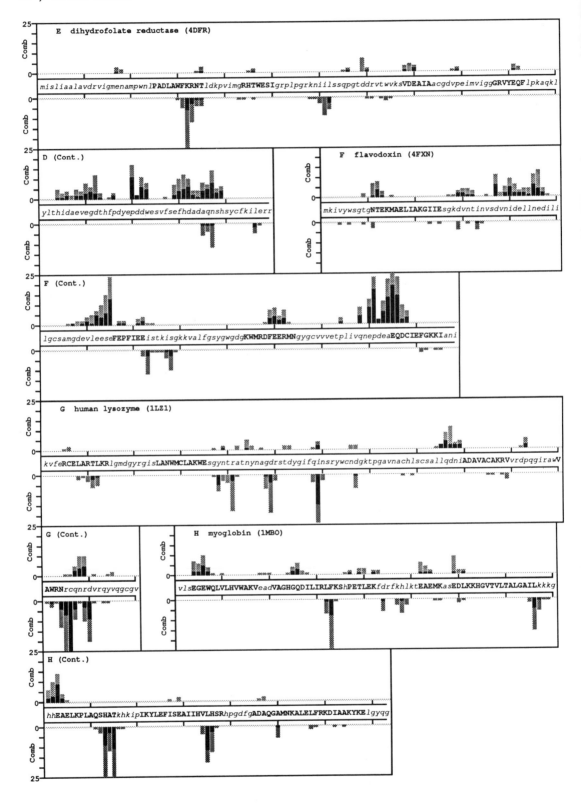

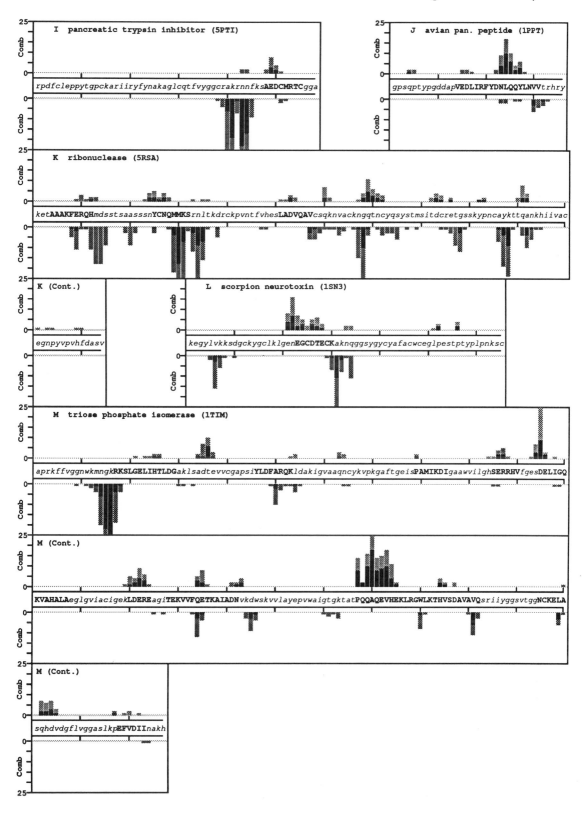

Similarly, of the nine helices lacking CTB's, five have either one or two Gly residues within the final six-residue window: CPV[87], FXN[104], TIM[85], TIM[100], and TIM[118]. (Numbers in brackets indicate the C1 residue of the helix.) A sixth helix, DFR[83], has both Pro and Gly within the final six-residue window. Moreover, TIM[100] can be regarded equally well as a "kink" in a longer helix that resumes after residue 104. A similar situation obtains for the seventh helix, MBO[17], that resumes after a disruption of three residues. The eighth helix, CPV[15], terminates in a series of near-helical turns. The ninth helix CPA[100], which lacks a CTB, does have hydrogen bonds stabilizing the C3, C2, and C1 residues, but all three hydrogens are contributed by donors distant in sequence. It is possible that helices lacking NTB's and CTB's can nevertheless be stabilized by tertiary interactions, although another explanation is also possible for CPA[100] (Kossiakoff, 1988).[2]

It is known that Gly (Schellman, 1980), like Pro (Chou and Fasman, 1978), can function as a helix breaker under suitable circumstances. If so, all but 1 of the 108 helix boundaries have an NTB or CTB or can be convincingly rationalized.

The 19 backbone paradigms used in our study represent only 60 percent of the observed distribution of turns at the NH_2-termini of helices and 50 percent at the COOH-termini. However, we confirmed that none of the preceding failures to find NTB's or CTB's would have been rescued by the inclusion of additional classes of turns. All failures were due instead to an insufficient number of polar residues.

According to the helix hypothesis, the presence of NTB's and CTB's is necessary for helix formation. The degree to which their presence is also sufficient is uncertain. An analysis of sufficiency is complicated by five factors:

(i) Conditions under which Gly or Pro (or both) will function as helix breakers must be made precise.

(ii) The assessment of sufficiency is not simply a matter of comparing those sequences bracketed by NTB's and CTB's against the location of known helices. When an NTB and CTB overlap (Fig. 3), those residues that can serve either as donors or acceptors (for example, Ser, Thr, Asn, and Gln) could contribute to either the NTB or the CTB, but not simultaneously to both. Either the CTB would be abolished when these pivotal residues contribute to the NTB, or, conversely, the CTB would be established at the expense of the NTB. An example of an overlapping, mutually exclusive NTB and CTB occurs near residue 60 in RSA. In this example, the residues Ser^{59}–Gln^{60}–Asn^{62} presumably contribute to the CTB of the observed helix, precluding the existence of an ostensible NTB at residue 60.

(iii) In our analysis, we have deliberately neglected any residues between the NTB and CTB, although these may contribute to helix stability as well.

(iv) Side chains of opposite charge can compete with side-chain to backbone hydrogen bonds and diminish the strength of some NTB's and CTB's. These competing interactions cannot be assessed at present because our hydrogen-bond library does not include side-chain to side-chain hydrogen bonds.

(v) NTB's and CTB's can often be augmented by main-chain to main-chain hydrogen bonds involving adjacent turns, but these interactions are also not included in the library at present.

After these factors are taken into account, some nonhelical sequences bracketed by NTB's and CTB's remain. Most often, examination of such sequences reveals variant or perturbed helical structures, such as CPV(61–68), which adopts a series of 3_{10} turns or LZ1(103 to 109), which adopts kinked 3_{10} turns.

---

2 Kossiakoff suggests that protein deamidation sites involve Asn-Ser sequences in which the Asn makes a hydrogen bond to the backbone at position $i + 2$ while the Ser hydroxyl makes a hydrogen bond to the Asn side chain. It is conceivable that the amino acid at CPA 101 was originally an Asn that became deamidated prior to sequence determination. If so, the one exceptional helix boundary lacking CTB, namely CPA[100], would then have a CTB.

Protein Folding and the Helix Hypothesis

A principal question raised by the helix hypothesis is whether segments bounded by NTB's and CTB's are helical in isolation. In studies of C peptide (residues 1 to 13 of ribonuclease A) and its analogs, Baldwin and co-workers (Bierzynski *et al.*, 1982; Kim and Baldwin, 1984; Jimenez *et al.*, 1987; Shoemaker *et al.*, 1987) showed the presence of stable helices in aqueous solution. In their work, helix stability can be attributed in large part to flanking residues that interact with the helix macrodipole. For example (Shoemaker *et al.*, 1987), four peptides that differ only at the NH_2-terminal residue were synthesized: the alteration being Lys^1, Ala^1, acetyl-Ala^1, and succinyl-Ala^1. Consistent with the helix dipole model (Shoemaker *et al.*, 1987; Wada, 1976; Hol, 1985), helix stability increases as the net charge at the NH_2-terminus becomes more negative in going from $Lys(+2)$ → $Ala(+1)$ → acetyl-$Ala(0)$ → succinyl-Ala (-1). Stability undergoes a small increase when there is a shift from Lys to Ala, with larger increases occurring from Ala → acetyl-Ala → succinyl Ala (Shoemaker *et al.*, 1987). The acetyl group not only removes the charge at the NH_2-terminus, but also strengthens the NTB by providing a hydrogen-bond acceptor for the >N–H of residue 4. Moreover, the succinyl group can provide two or possibly three additional acceptors that satisfy >N–H donors in residues 4, 3, and possibly 2 (Presta and Rose, unpublished data). The Baldwin and Stewart analogs (Shoemaker *et al.*, 1987) will be valuable compounds for assessing the helix hypothesis in isolated peptides.

While most helices in Fig. 3 are bracketed by NTB's and CTB's, all of the postulated main-chain to side-chain hydrogen bonds may not persist in the crystal structure, although many do (Baker and Hubbard, 1984; Richardson and Richardson, 1988). The crystal structures of the 13 proteins include 54 helices. Within these, 48 percent of the N–N1–N2–N3 residues and 35 percent of the C3–C2–C1–C residues are satisfied by side-chain or backbone hydrogen bond partners contributed by residues corresponding to the initial or final six-residue window of each helix. An additional 5 percent at the NH_2-termini and 9 percent at the COOH-termini are satisfied by sequentially distant side-chain or backbone intramolecular hydrogen-bond partners. Remaining groups are satisfied either by partners from neighboring protein molecules in the crystal lattice (Presta and Rose, unpublished data) or by solvent molecules.

We interpret these findings to mean that NTB's and CTB's, while required in the nascent helix, can often be liberated once the helix is "fixed" by the tertiary fold. During these postulated tertiary adjustments, the helix boundaries might be "peeled back" or extended by a few residues relative to the position of the NTB/CTB. Certainly the intermolecular hydrogen bonds that are apparent in the crystal structure (and possibly needed for successful crystallization) must, of necessity, involve a subsequent rearrangement of hydrogen bonds from the solution structure. A compilation of observed amino acid preferences at helix termini in 45 x-ray–elucidated proteins is presented by Richardson and Richardson (1988), who arrive at similar conclusions about hydrogen bonding.

Protein sequence comparisons often reveal surprising relationships and unanticipated homologies (Doolittle, 1987). Strategies for comparison implicitly are based on the assumption that conservative substitutions are synonymous with chemical similarity (for example, Glu for Asp). However, conservation of structure is also an important factor, and maintenance of NTB's and CTB's among homologous structures is expected. Indeed, these sites do appear to be conserved in the hemoglobins (Bashford *et al.*, 1987).

Many statistical approaches to helix prediction have been proposed (Chou and Fasman, 1978). For such procedures a database of known structures is used to derive an empirical probability that each residue type will be found in a helix. Most of the residues that participate in NTB's and CTB's are classified as helix breakers in statistical studies (Chou and Fasman, 1978). Exceptions include Glu, Lys, and Gln; and, although classified as helix formers, they have an observed tendency to be localized near the helix NH_2- or COOH-termini (Chou and Fasman, 1978). These empirical classifications are entirely consistent with our hypothesis that NTB's and CTB's comprise helix boundaries.

Initial results suggest that membrane-spanning helices do not require NTB's and CTB's, at least in the case of the photosynthetic reaction center (Deisenhofer et al., 1985). The extramembrane helices in this structure, which do have NTB's and CTB's, serve as a control. To pursue this observation further, we analyzed crambin, a hydrophobic molecule with two helices that crystallizes only in the presence of organic co-solvents (Hendrickson and Teeter, 1981). Such conditions are suggestive of a membrane-like environment, and crambin was chosen with this possibility in mind. Neither helix has NTB's, although one weak CTB is in evidence. In a membrane, a hydrophobic segment of a protein would favor a helix in order to satisfy backbone polar groups (Engleman et al., 1986). Such a segment, lacking an NTB and a CTB, may undergo conformational transition from nonhelix in a polar environment to helix in an apolar environment, and, in fact, the LamB signal sequence appears to function in this way (Briggs and Gierasch, 1986).

Some of the residues in NTB's and CTB's may also be involved in the binding of ligands or prosthetic groups. In such cases, changes in the structure of the apoprotein are expected. Examples include the binding of charged groups by peptide backbone (Quiocho et al., 1987) and the binding of heme by apomyoglobin (Harrison and Blout, 1965; Lecomte and LaMar, 1987).

The thermodynamics of helix formation remains to be assessed. Suitable models for cooperative hydrogen bonding in NTB's and CTB's could not be found. Presumably, such bonds are comparatively strong, especially those involving charged side chains. Our data also include the number of conformations for each combination shown in Fig. 3. Frequently these numbers are large, exceeding 10^6 in many instances. The corresponding decrease in conformational entropy needed to maintain

side-chain to main-chain hydrogen bonds in NTB's and CTB's may turn out to be surprisingly small.

The helix hypothesis leads to a number of testable predictions. For example:

(i) Transient side-chain to backbone hydrogen bonds at helix termini that do not persist in the x-ray–elucidated structure may be detectable by nuclear magnetic resonance during protein folding.

(ii) Sequences bracketed by NTB's and CTB's that contain no prolyl or glycyl residues should be helical in aqueous solution (provided that the complete peptide dissolves and does not aggregate). Further, sequential elimination of the residues involved in either the NTB or CTB should lead to an incremental reduction in helicity.

(iii) Site-directed mutagenesis can be used in a variety of ways. For example, removal of Pro or Gly helix terminators that are situated upstream from a nearby CTB should extend the helix. Similarly, nonhelical sequences bracketed by NTB's and CTB's but containing an intervening Gly or Pro sequence should become helical when these helix-breaking residues are removed. Introduction of a companion CTB downstream from an isolated NTB, or a companion NTB upstream from an isolated CTB, should induce formation of an additional helix. (These possibilities may be disrupted by tertiary interactions.)

(iv) Charged side chains that form a hydrogen bond with backbone >N–H or >C=O groups should exhibit both a shift in pK and protection against hydrogen exchange.

(v) Under suitable circumstances, neutral and protonated His should make pH-dependent contributions to an NTB and a CTB, respectively. Similarly, protonated Asp and Glu should participate in a pH-dependent CTB.

In addition to the specific tests mentioned here, the helix hypothesis should prove useful in protein engineering and design (Oxender and Fox, 1987).

The question of whether secondary structure is formed before tertiary structure has yet to be resolved in protein folding studies (Kim and Baldwin, 1982). The helix hypothesis implies that helical secondary structure need not depend on tertiary interactions. In particular, helices with a strong NTB and CTB together with an appropriately stable intervening sequence may function as independent "seeds for folding" (Baldwin, 1986).

Acknowledgments

We thank R. Baldwin, P. Kim, S. Taylor, and C. R. Matthews for many useful discussions; B. Zimm and J. Lecomte for their critical reading of the manuscript; an anonymous referee for helpful suggestions, and E. Lattman for insightful comments at every stage of this work. Thirteen years ago, Kensal Van Holde urged that the key question is not which sequences will be found in helices, but rather why all sequences are not found in helices. Good questions, like good teachers, leave a lasting imprint. Supported by NIH grants GM 29458 and AG 06084 and by a Dean's grant from John Burnside.

References

Baker, E. N., and R. E. Hubbard, *Prog. Biophys. Mol. Biol.* **44**, 97 (1984).

Bashford, D., C. Chothia, A. M. Lesk, *J. Mol. Biol.* **196**, 199 (1987).

Baldwin, R. L., *Trends Biochem. Sci.* **11**, 6 (1986).

Bernstein, F. C., *et al.*, *J. Mol. Biol.* **112**, 535 (1977).

Bierzynski, A., P. S. Kim, R. L. Baldwin, *Proc. Natl. Acad. Sci. U.S.A.* **79**, 2470 (1982).

Blagdon, D. E., and M. Goodman, *Biopolymers* **14**, 241 (1975).

Briggs, M. S., and L. M. Gierasch, *Adv. Prot. Chem.* **38**, 109 (1986).

Chothia, C., *J. Mol. Biol.* **105**, 1 (1976).

Chou, P. Y., and G. D. Fasman, *Biochemistry* **13**, 211 (1974).

_____, *Annu. Rev. Biochem.* **47**, 251 (1978).

DeGrado, W. F., F. J. Kezdy, E. T. Kaiser, *J. Am. Chem. Soc.* **103**, 679 (1981).

Deisenhofer, J., O. Epp, K. Miki, R. Huber, H. Michel, *Nature* **318**, 618 (1985).

Doolittle, R. F., *Of Urfs and Orfs* (University Science Books, Mill Valley, CA, 1987).

Eisenberg, D., R. M. Weiss, T. C. Terwilliger, *Nature* **299**, 371 (1982).

Engleman, D. M., T. A. Steitz, A. Goldman, *Annu.*

Rev. Biophys. Biophys. Chem. **15**, 321 (1986).

Harrison, S. C., and E. R. Blout, *J. Biol. Chem.* **240**, 299 (1965).

Hendrickson, W. A., and M. M. Teeter, *Nature* **290**, 107 (1981).

Hol, W. G. J., *Prog. Biophys. Mol. Biol.* **45**, 149 (1985).

Jimenez, M. A., J. L. Nieto, J. Herranz, M. Rico, J. Santoro, *FEBS Lett.* **221**, 320 (1987).

Kabsch, W., and C. Sander, *Biopolymers* **22**, 2577 (1983).

_____, *Proc. Natl. Acad. Sci. U.S.A.* **81**, 1075 (1984).

Kim, P. S., and R. L. Baldwin, *Annu. Rev. Biochem.* **51**, 459 (1982).

_____, *Nature* **307**, 329 (1984).

Kossiakoff, A. A., *Science* **240**, 191 (1988).

Lecomte, J. T. J., and G. N. LaMar, *J. Am. Chem. Soc.* **109**, 7219 (1987).

Lee, B. K., and F. M. Richards, *J. Mol. Biol.* **55**, 379 (1971).

Levitt, M., and C. Chothia, *Nature* **261**, 552 (1976).

Moult, J., and M. N. G. James, *Proteins* **1**, 146 (1986).

Oxender, D. L., and C. F. Fox, Eds., *Protein Engineering* (Liss, New York, 1987).

Pauling, L., R. B. Corey, H. R. Branson, *Proc. Natl. Acad. Sci. U.S.A.* **37**, 205 (1951).

Perutz, M. F., *Nature* **167**, 1053 (1951).

Presta, L. G., and G. D. Rose, unpublished results.

Quiocho, F. A., J. S. Sack, N. K. Vyas, *Nature* **329**, 561 (1987).

Ramachandran, G. N., and V. Sasisekharan, *Adv. Prot. Chem.* **23**, 283 (1968).

Richardson, J. S., *Adv. Protein Chem.* **34**, 167 (1981).

Richardson, J. S., and D. C. Richardson, *Science* **240**, 1648 (1988).

Schellman, J. E., *Compt. Rend. Trav. Lab. Carlsberg (Ser. Chim.)* **29**, 230 (1955).

Schellman, C., *Protein Folding*, R. Jaenicke, Ed. (Elsevier/North-Holland Biomedical Press, Amsterdam, 1980), p. 53.

Scheraga, H. A., Quantum Chemistry Program Exchange, Program No. 286, Indiana University Chemistry Department, Bloomington (1975).

Schulz, G. E., and R. H. Schirmer, *Principles of Protein Structure* (Springer, New York, 1979).

Shoemaker, K. R., P. S. Kim, E. J. York, J. M. Stewart, R. L. Baldwin, *Nature* **326**, 563 (1987).

Srinivasan, R., and K. K. Chacko, *Conformation of Biopolymers*, G. N. Ramachandran, Ed. (Academic Press, New York, 1967).

Taylor, R., and O. Kennard, *Acc. Chem. Res.* **17**, 320 (1984).

Vedani, A., and J. D. Dunitz, *J. Am. Chem. Soc.* **107**, 7653 (1985).

Wada, A., *Adv. Biophys.* **9**, 1 (1976).

4

The Water Structure Surrounding Proteins

Martha M. Teeter

Water is extremely important in all biological systems. Physiological systems have a high percentage of water, 80 percent in human beings. Water is the medium of biochemistry; it is the bath in which chemical reactions take place. In this chapter, I address the structural aspects of that water participation: how protein hydration stabilizes proteins and promotes reactions. Recently, the crystal structures of several enzyme mutants with altered activity have been determined. Remarkably, there was little change in the folding of the protein, but the water structure was slightly different. Hence, water may have a role in stability and activity which we are only beginning to understand.

In the first part of this chapter, I will discuss water in general. Then I will describe what we are learning about water from one protein crystal structure, and finally, we will see that some patterns in the role of hydration at the protein surface are beginning to emerge from this crystal structure.

Water is tetrahedrally coordinated. The angle between water molecules around the central water in ice I_h is within 0.2° of 109.5° (Savage, 1986). The exact oxygen-oxygen distances in this ice structure are well known from crystallography, namely 2.76 Å. In solution, water has a strong neighbor correlation at 2.8 Å, but the second neighbor distance peak is much broader. At longer distances there is little O–O correlation.

What do we know about the geometry of these linkages between water molecules? The things we know well about water come from crystallographic studies in the solid state. It is more difficult to be certain of the details of water connections from experimental or theoretical studies of solution. But from x-ray diffraction, we can determine atomic positions. Thus, for water, we know most about the structure of ice, which shows that ice forms hexagonal rings that adopt a chair conformation. This configuration permits hydrogen bonds to extend in all directions and fill space maximally.

Theoretical calculations can give us some idea about the short-lived linkages between water molecules in solution (Swaminathan *et al.*, 1978; Rahman and Stillinger, 1973). Here both five- and six-membered water rings are believed to form, and these two in equilibrium are the most abundant structures for water. Five-membered rings are primarily planar, as opposed to the nonplanar chair form of the hexagon in ice. The O–O–O angle in a planar pentagon is 108°, compared to the 109.5° tetrahedral angle. Both hexagons and pentagons would be expected to form in solution.

From crystallography, we find that the water pentagon commonly surrounds substrates that cannot readily hydrogen bond, such as $CHCl_3$ (Jeffrey and McMullan, 1961). The so-called clathrate hydrates have cages of water, based on planar pentagons of water molecules. This planar water array restricts the hydrogen bonds to equatorial positions close to the plane where they avoid the non-hydrogen bonding guest molecule. Clathrate hydrates form around xenon, which is an anesthetic. Pauling correlated the activity of xenon with its ability to form clathrates (Pauling, 1961). Many clathrate hydrates studied crystallographically are formed at high pressure and low temperature. Nonetheless one would expect to find these pentagonal water cages forming in solution.

Water is a critical factor in protein folding. It is the balance in protein-water interactions that distinguishes the folded and unfolded protein. A folded protein structure has many secondary structure hydrogen bonds. For a folded protein, protein-protein hydrogen bonds predominate. But for an unfolded protein, protein-water interactions predominate. So it is the dominance of the protein-water interactions that produces the unfolded protein or, in other words, it is the removal of water that induces a protein to form a three-dimensional structure. This tendency to remove water is usually attributed to hydrophobicity or to the avoidance by hydrophobic groups of the formation of clathrate hydrate structures, which would lower the entropy of the water significantly. If the hydrophobic groups remained on the outside in the folded protein, then there would be considerable ordering of the water. And this is viewed as the driving force for proteins to fold hydrophobic groups into the interior and to leave polar groups on the outside. However, despite this principle, a considerable amount (30 to 50 percent) of the accessible surface on the outside of proteins is hydrophobic (Lee and Richards, 1971).

The Role of Water in the Protein Crambin

Crambin is a small protein of only 46 residues. However, it has all fundamental types of secondary structure: β-sheet, α-helix, disulfide bonds, and β-turns (Fig. 1) (Teeter and Hendrickson, 1981). Crambin is isolated from the

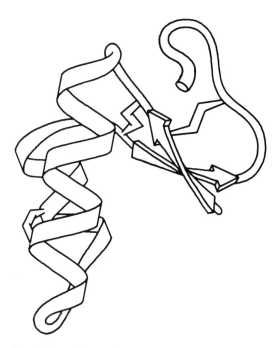

Fig. 1. Backbone ribbon diagram of crambin. The diagram is courtesy of Jane Richardson, with some modifications by Marc Whitlow. β sheets are represented by arrows and disulfides by lightning rods. The molecule is viewed down the crystallographic *b*-axis.

seeds of the plant *Crambe abyssinica*, an anhydrous environment. Although crambin is hydrophobic and water insoluble, it crystallizes extremely readily. In fact, water promotes its crystallization. Water induces crambin to aggregate and assume a crystal packing where the accessible hydrophobic surface area is minimized. So we can think of water as a driving force for its crystallization in a similar way to water as a driving force in protein folding.

Crystals of crambin diffract farther than any protein that has yet been crystallized—to at least 0.83 Å. Three diffraction data sets have been collected (Table 1). The resolution is better than one Å for the two x-ray data sets, one at room temperature and one at 130° K. Neutron diffraction data have been collected to 1.1 Å at room temperature. The 130° K structure refinement is nearly complete, and the neutron structure is currently being refined.

An important feature that emerges from

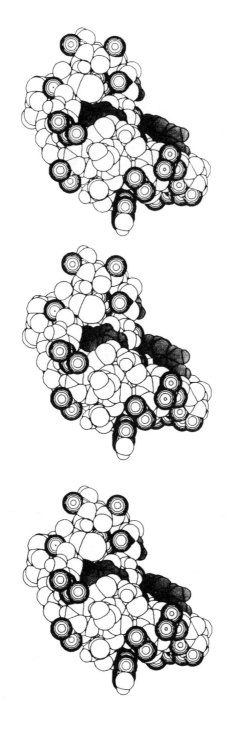

Fig. 2. Stereo van der Waals surface diagram of crambin showing its amphipathic character. The view is the same as Fig. 1. The charged groups are shaded. The hydrophobic side chains have solid circles. These surface diagrams have the following van der Waals radii: C = 1.7 Å, N = 1.7 Å, S = 2.1 Å, and H = 0.5 Å (only H's on O and N are shown). The left pair of molecules are for divergent stereo viewing and the right pair are for convergent (cross-eyed) viewing.

Table 1. Summary of crambin crystallographic data collected.

Radiation	Temperature (K)	No. of reflections	Resolution (Å)	R value (%)
X-ray	300	22,500	0.945[a]	11
X-ray	130	28,000	0.83[b]	14
Neutron	300	13,800	1.1[c]	14

[a]Collected with Wayne Hendrickson at the Lab for the Structure of Matter, Naval Research Laboratory, in 1980.
[b]Collected with Håkon Hope at the Department of Chemistry, University of California, Davis, in 1984. [c]Collected with Marc Whitlow and Bjarne Rasmussen at Brookhaven National Laboratory in 1984.

these results, perhaps because crambin is such a hydrophobic protein, is that nearly all of the water is ordered in the crystals. In fact, in the room temperature structures, 80 percent of the water is ordered, and in the low temperature structure nearly 100 percent of the water is ordered. Thus, there is much information about water available in these structures.

First, I will describe the overall structure of crambin, which is an amphiphathic protein (Fig. 2). The charged side chains are shaded, and the hydrophobic atoms have concentric circles. You can see that the charges lie on one surface of the protein, and the hydrophobic atoms are on the opposite side. In fact, crambin is a neutral protein with two positively and two negatively charged side chains. One arginine in crambin is central to the stabilization of the three-dimensional structure. Often, the amino and carboxy termini of proteins are close together. Arginine 10 forms two hydrogen bonds to residue 2 and a salt-bridge to

residue 46, the carboxyl terminus; it ties the two ends of the protein together. This residue is conserved in the 14 plant toxins that are homologous to this crambin (Teeter *et al.,* 1981), suggesting that they may have similar structures to it.

Bearing in mind crambin's amphipathic character (Fig. 2), we look at its packing in the crystal (Fig. 3). Here the five regions important for solvent are numbered. Note that the polar regions of the protein are adjacent to a fairly large channel of solvent (1), which is the largest free area for water in this protein. I have indicated with a 0 the hydrophobic surface which excludes water and forms a pseudodimer contact. In region 2, solvent bridges the protein molecules. Region 3 is near a mobile loop region (residues 38–42) in the structure, and region 4 is relatively isolated.

In Fig. 4, I have added the water molecules around the protein and connected them with hydrogen bonds. The protein is repre-

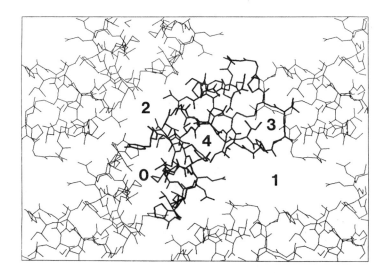

Fig. 3. Crystal packing of crambin in the crystal viewed along the *b*-axis. The central molecule is indicated by darker lines and symmetry- and translationally related molecules by lighter lines. Regions where water is absent [0] and present [1–4] are indicated.

Figure 4. Van der Waals surface diagram of cram-bin with surrounding waters at 300 K. The protein is viewed as in Fig. 1. The water molecules around the protein are indicated by 0 or by X (disordered alternative positions for water). Waters are considered to be hydrogen bonded (solid black lines) if the O–O distance is less than 3.3 Å.

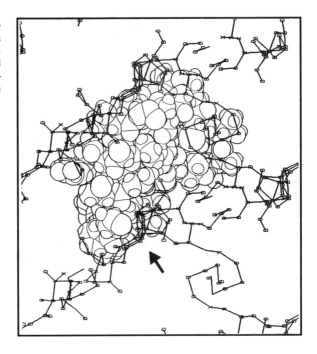

sented by a van der Waals surface. Region 0 (Fig. 3) is entirely devoid of solvent. We have known for a long time from x-ray diffraction (Blake, 1983) that water connects dipoles along the surface of a protein. It appears to have an amorphous and featureless arrangement. I will counter that hypothesis in the last part of this chapter.

In addition to the lines of waters on the surface, there is a tight cluster of water rings as indicated by the arrow in Fig. 2. Here the protein surface is quite hydrophobic. This water has more contacts to other waters than to protein and is perhaps similar in appearance to water solution on the surface.

The water cluster (Teeter, 1984) forms around one methyl of residue Leu 18 (Fig. 5a). The cluster, composed of five pentagonal rings (for clarity, only four are shown), lies at the end of the first helix and at the beginning of another related by a cell translation. Besides the "hydrophobic" contacts, there are numerous hydrogen bonds to these helices from the cluster. However, we do not understand all the forces that cause this structure to form. In a second view along the helix axis (Fig. 5b), the methyl of this leucine residue capped by the water cluster can be clearly

seen. One ring is nonplanar. The three others are planar and, thus, much like the clathrate hydrate structures. The fifth ring, which would extend to the right in this view, is also nonplanar (Fig. 5c). We would expect that nonplanar rings might not be as stable as the planar five-membered rings and, in fact, at 130 K, we find that the five-membered ring becomes a six-membered ring. I should mention that the vibrational factors of these water oxygens are smaller than the vibrations of other first shell waters (Teeter, 1984) and are close to the protein vibrational factors. Thus, they are an integral feature of the surface.

The third view of this cluster is more dramatic (Fig. 6). The leucine can be seen between the water rings, and the hydrophobic residues are stippled.

I should mention that one of these rings lies along the methylenes of Arg 17. We think ordinarily that arginine is very hydrophilic, but, in fact, it has a substantial nonpolar component to it. The charged portions of Arg 17, Glu 23, and Asp 43 bind the pentagonal clusters by a crystallographic translation, and these charged groups may induce the rings to form. Alternatively, the charges may disorganize the water-water structure and prevent

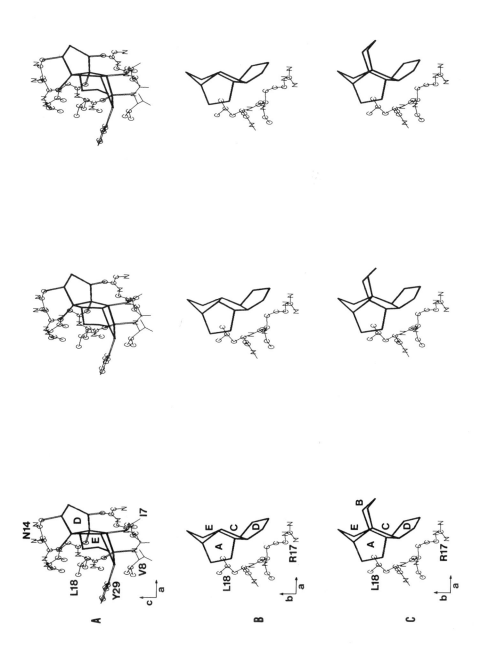

Fig. 5. Stereodiagram of the pentagon rings and crambin's side chains. View down the *b*-axis. **(A)** At the hydrophobic contact between symmetry-related crambin molecules, hydrogen bonds (open tubes) are formed between the water cluster and carbonyl groups at the carboxy terminal end of the long first helix and the amide groups of the amino terminal end of the same helix on a *c*-axis related molecule. Water hydrogen bonds are indicated by solid lines. **(B)** View along the helix axis (*c*-axis) showing the relationship of the water pentagon rings Leu18 and Arg17. Rings A, C, and E surround the Cδ2 of Leu18 and ring D lies above the hydrophobic methylenes of Arg17. **(C)** View along the *c*-axis showing the B ring which extends toward solvent. Figure 5A is viewed as in Fig. 1.

Figure 6. Van der Waals surface diagram of the water pentagon rings viewed along the *a*-axis. Rings A, C, and E form a cap around Leu18 methyl. Hydrophobic atoms have stippled circles, and water oxygens have dotted circles. The methyl group of Leu18 (shown in Figs. 5b and 5c) can be seen through the C ring. The B ring is omitted. The van der Waals radii used are the same as in Fig. 2; however, a radius of 1.8 Å is used for water oxygens. The larger radius compensates for the omission of water hydrogen atoms in this figure.

the pentagon clusters from being more extensive.

There is a close relationship between

these clusters and the small molecule clathrate hydrates. The pentagons here can be visualized as a fragment of the pentagonal dodecahedron-based clathrate hydrate (Fig. 7). Also, the geometry of the clathrate hydrate pentagonal rings and the planar water rings at the surface of this protein are very similar.

In packing region 4 (see Fig. 3), we can understand water structure disorder particularly well. Water is an extremely adaptable molecule that can fill space in many different ways. There are four different ways it can hydrogen bond. Figure 8 shows an electron density map of region 4 and the modeled water alternates that fit it. Protein hydrophilic atoms surround this elongated cavity. In the top right is a fully occupied ethanol position. The solvent cavity is too large for a single water molecule but not large enough for two. So water chains are hydrogen bonded, sometimes to one side (the dotted network) and sometimes to the other (the dashes), with equal probability. The electron density is clearly separated for these two alternatives. The positions are not simultaneously occupied in the crystal but represent the water in different unit cells in the crystal (static disorder) or possibly rapidly reorganizing water (dynamic disorder). We hope, when the neutron structure of crambin is analyzed, to find details not only of the water oxygen disorder but also of deuterium disorder, which may further clarify the nature of the phenomenon. In neutron diffraction, the solvent is D_2O, and deuterium scattering is as strong as oxygen. Thus, we can see details of the water structure

Fig. 7. Comparison of the pentagonal water cluster in crambin with a clathrate hydrate structure. **(A)** Four rings from crambin's structure viewed along the *a*-axis. The B ring has been omitted for clarity. **(B)** The polyhedral structure of the 17 Å gas hydrate cage, showing the pentagonal dodecahedra sharing faces three dimensionally (courtesy of G.A. Jeffrey, Department of Crystallography, University of Pittsburgh). The four-ring array comparable to crambin's has been outlined on the dodecahedra.

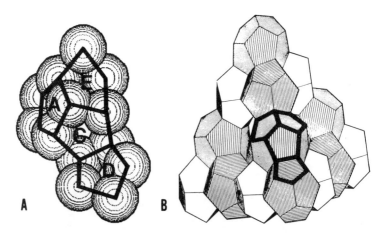

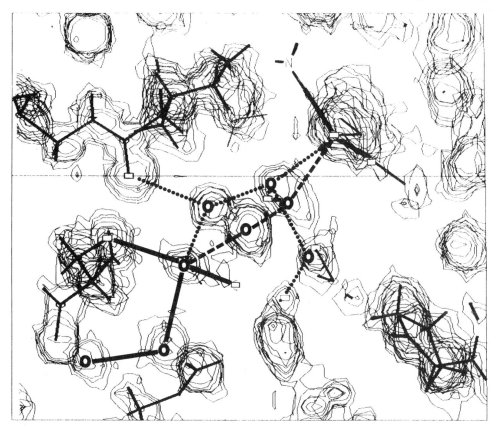

Fig. 8. X-ray electron density maps for disordered water networks in region 4 (see Fig. 3). One alternate water chain is indicated by a dotted line and the other by a dashed line. Water oxygen atoms are marked by heavy, rounded O's. Oxygen atoms in the protein and in the ethanol are rectangular and lighter. The map is viewed along the *b*-axis.

that are very complex when compared to the x-ray structure, which has hydrogen scattering that is 17 percent of oxygen's scattering.

Patterns in Hydration at the Protein Surface

Recently, I have attempted to find patterns in the water structure along the surface of the protein. There are two likely possibilities for ordering these waters. One is that all the surface residues will direct the positions of water on the surface. The other is that the positions of water will be directed only by certain residues, and others will have no influence on the position of the waters. This distinction is important because we would like to be able to predict the locations of waters on the surface of a protein in order to understand their role

in stability, and we would like to know which ones can be predicted. I have taken all of the residues that have more than one occurrence in the protein, of which I show a few representatives, and superimposed the amino acid side chains along with their hydrogen bonding environment (including waters). The patterns that emerge are extremely interesting.

First, let us consider the residue arginine. There are two arginines in crambin, one at residue 10 and one at 17. Arginine has a guanidinium group with nitrogens acting as proton donors. The environment of the Arg 10 (Fig. 9), which has dashed hydrogen bonds and has rectangular oxygen atoms, includes the carboxy terminus, the hydroxyl and the carbonyl of Thr 2. The hydrogen bonding network of Arg 17 has oval oxygen atoms. The fascinating thing is that the two hydrogen bonding networks are virtually superimpos-

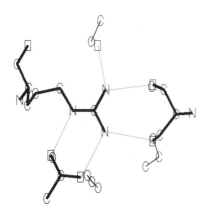

Fig. 9. Superposition of Arg 10 and Arg 17 with their hydrogen-bonding environments. The oxygens in the environment of Arg 10 are indicated by rectangular O's and include the carboxy terminus and Thr 2 carbonyl and hydroxyl. The oxygens in the Arg 17 environment are distinguished by their being oval O's. The latter includes three disordered waters which are connected by a line. Hydrogen bonds between the N's and the rectangular O environment are indicated. The view is perpendicular to the plane of the guanidinium group.

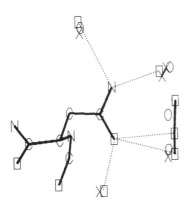

Fig. 10. Superposition of Asn 12, Asn 14, and Asn 46 with their hydrogen bonding environments. One environment has rectangular O's, one has oval O's, and the third has X's representing the oxygens. Disordered oxygens in the same environment are indicated by a line connecting them. Hydrogen bonds between the Asn side chain and the rectangular O environment are indicated. The view is perpendicular to the plane of the Asn side chain.

able. So arginine, to a very large extent, determines the pattern of hydrogen bonding around it. Both Arg 10 and Arg 17 are conserved in the 14 plant toxins that are homologous to crambin (Teeter *et al.,* 1981). Thus, these residues may be critical to folding as well as to stability because they have such

reproducible hydrophilic environments around them.

What happens if we look at a residue that has both NH's and oxygen? The residue I will describe is asparagine. There are three asparagines in crambin, and, when we superimpose those asparagines, we have three hydrogen-bonding networks (Fig. 10). There is very close agreement in position of waters around the nitrogens of asparagine. In fact, three waters are superimposable at one -NH and three or four at the other. The carbonyl oxygen has a much more variable environment around it. We will see that this variability also occurs for the oxygen atoms of negatively charged side chains: glutamic acid and aspartic acid.

Figure 11 shows the superposition of the one aspartic acid and the one glutamic acid in the structure. One of the side-chain oxygens binds to the backbone nitrogen, and there are two other atoms bound (the rectangular O's connected by the dotted lines). The latter are not disordered, but in this view they appear to be superimposed. The X's represent the second water environment. The second oxygen also binds to three waters. But you can see that the positions of the X's are quite different from the rectangular O positions.

So it seems that oxygen may be less determining of hydrogen bonding geometry than

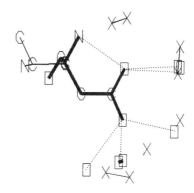

Fig. 11. Superposition of Glu 23 and Asp 43 with their hydrogen bonding environments. One environment has rectangular O's and the other has X's representing the oxygens. Hydrogen bonds between the side-chain O's and the rectangular O environment are indicated. The view is perpendicular to the plane of the carboxylate group.

nitrogen at the protein surface. And what might be the reason for this? Nitrogen is a proton donor, and those protons are well localized in space. Oxygen is a proton acceptor, and certainly with a charged species, there is a delocalized charge. The lone pairs of electrons on the oxygens are less localized than the hydrogens or nitrogen. In fact, in the case of aspartic acid and glutamic acid, there is primarily an electrostatic interaction, which would be less restraining in geometry and direction. This theoretical explanation is supported by experiment.

The final question is whether there are any patterns in the water structure in the nonpolar environments of the protein. I approach this cautiously, since it is indeed a complex issue. Theoretically, there should not be any regular order in the water around nonpolar

groups because they cannot hydrogen bond. But the answer I come up with is equivocal. There seems to be a pattern, but it is not nearly as extensive as we have seen in the previous cases or in the case of the clathrates.

Let us consider the distribution of water distances from the surface of crambin, including both hydrophilic and hydrophobic interactions (Fig. 12). We see the characteristic O–O peak at 2.8 Å. If we separate the hydrophobic contacts, the hydrophilic ones look very similar to water-water interactions. The hydrophobic interactions have a peak at a larger distance, at 3.8 Å, and a trough at 4 Å.

So, in Fig. 13, I considered all atoms within a 4 Å sphere of valine. We are viewing valine down one of its $C\gamma$–$C\beta$. Besides the waters, an ethanol molecule and a threonine are in the 4 Å shell. There seems to be very

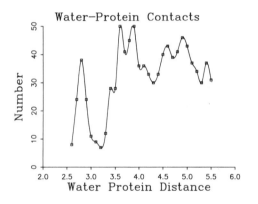

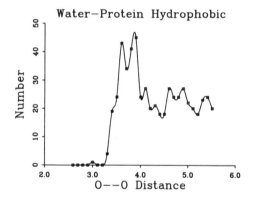

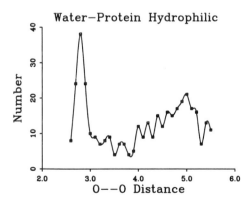

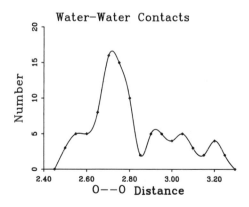

Fig. 12. Distribution of water oxygens in crambin crystals. The number versus water distance for all protein contacts, for hydrophobic contacts, for hydrophilic contacts, and for contacts between water oxygens is shown. The first three have 0.1 Å steps and the water-water contacts have steps of 0.05 Å.

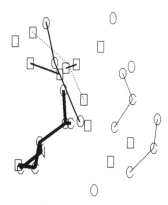

Fig. 13. Superposition of Val 8 and Val 15 with their hydrogen bonding environment. One environment has rectangular O's and the other has oval O's representing the oxygens. The two groups of three hydrogen bonding water oxygens that may constitute a pattern are connected by a dotted line and by a solid line, respectively. The view is down one of valine's $C\gamma$–$C\beta$ bonds.

little correspondence between the oval and rectangular oxygen-hydrogen bonding environments. If we compared the other end-branched residue (Leu18) in the same orientation, we would see the pentagonal water clusters discussed earlier. Clearly, we do not see that level of ordering for the valine side chain. However, we do see some patterns. Common to those two valines are three hydrogen bonded waters, which are connected in Fig. 13. We intend to analyze further this repeating array to understand the reason for its formation.

I leave you with this picture of water at a protein surface – both rings and residue patterns with specific geometries. The whole subject of water and water ordering is an open one and a very exciting one for protein folding.

Acknowledgments

The author wishes to acknowledge support from the National Science Foundation (DMB-8606636). Thanks is due to Marc Whitlow, now of Genex Corporation, who as a graduate student wrote programs to analyze the crambin structure. Also contributing to this work collaboratively were Wayne Hendrickson and Håkon Hope.

References

Blake, C. C .F., W. C. A. Pulford, P. J. Artymiuk, *J. Mol. Biol.* **167,** 693 (1983).

Jeffrey, G.A., and R. K. McMullan, *Prog. in Inorg. Chem.* **8,** 43 (1961).

Lee, B., and F. M. Richards, *J. Mol. Biol.* **55,** 379 (1971).

Pauling, L., *Science* **134,** 15 (1961).

Rahman, A., and F. H. Stillinger, *J. Phys. Chem.* **66,** 1773 (1973).

Savage, H., *Water Science Reviews* **2,** 1 (1986).

Swaminathan, S., S. W. Harrison, D. L. Beveridge, *J. Amer. Chem Soc.* **100,** 5705 (1978).

Teeter, M. M., *Proc. Nat. Acad. Sci. U.S.A.* **81,** 6014 (1984).

Teeter, M. M., and W. A. Hendrickson, *Nature* **290,** 107 (1981).

Teeter, M. M., J. A. Mazer, J. J. L'Italien, *Biochemistry* **20,** 5437 (1981).

5

Fibrous Proteins
Folding and Higher Order Structure

Barbara Brodsky

Before the molecular structure of proteins was understood, it seemed that fibrous proteins such as keratin, collagen, and silk were dramatically different from soluble proteins such as hemoglobin. With the current information on protein structure, it is clear that the molecular interactions are of the same basic nature in fibrous and globular proteins. Yet there are a number of distinguishing features. The building blocks of many fibrous proteins are helical polypeptide chains with a high stability. These molecules must first fold and then associate to form higher order structures. These requirements result in distinctive characteristics related to molecular folding, recognition of binding sites, and molecular association.

Fibrous or structural proteins can be classified in four categories. The first category includes rod-like helical molecules, which associate in a regular staggered manner to form structures such as keratin filaments or collagen fibrils.[1] A second category consists of helical aggregates of globular subunits and includes actin, microtubules, and sickle cell fibers. A third group contains structures formed from beta sheets such as feather keratin or silk. The last category includes the

increasing number of structural proteins whose molecular conformation or mode of association is either not regular, e.g., elastin, or not well characterized, e.g., laminin and fibronectin. A number of excellent reviews on fibrous proteins are available (Fraser and McRae, 1973; Fraser *et al.*, 1981; Squire and Vibert, 1987). I will focus on the first category, the highly ordered fibrous proteins which are staggered aggregates of rod-like helical molecules. Only two kinds of extended helical molecular structures form such staggered arrays: the coiled coil α-helix and the triple-helix (Fig. 1). My own research concerns triple-helices, but the similarities and contrasts between these two superhelical motifs will be presented.

Background: The Coiled Coil Alpha-Helix and the Triple-Helix

A coiled coil structure consists of two or, less commonly, three polypeptides in an α-helical conformation that are wound around each other at a small angle so that the hydrophobic side chains of one helix fit into the grooves of the second helix. Crick predicted that optimal

---

1   The terminology used to describe various fibrous proteins differs for different macromolecular assemblies. Collagen aggregates are termed fibrils, and fibrils may then associate to form larger fibers. For intracellular networks such as intermediate filaments, aggregates are usually called filaments, while muscle cells containing myofibrillar aggregates are called fibers.

TRIPLE-HELIX

COILED COIL α - HELICES

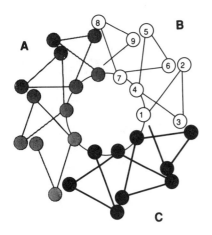

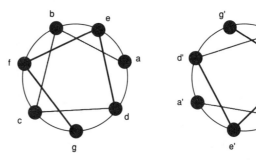

Fig. 1. Axial projections of the α-carbon backbone of (**left**) a triple-helical structure with three chains, A, B, and C; and (**right**) a two-stranded coiled coil α-helical structure.

packing of the two helices required that the amino acid sequence would have a heptad repeat with hydrophobic residues present at the second and sixth position of each seven-residue group (Crick, 1953). The coiled coil α-helix constitutes the rod-like region of a number of fibrous proteins: the muscle proteins — myosin, paramyosin, and tropomyosin; the intermediate filament proteins — keratin, desmin, vimentin, and neurofilaments; and fibrin. In all of these cases except tropomyosin, the rod-like portions associate with each other in a staggered manner to form filaments or fibers. Polypeptide regions with heptad repeats are also found in some membrane proteins, influenza hemagglutinin, and other nonfibrous proteins as set forth in an excellent review of coiled coil structures by Carolyn Cohen and David Parry (1986). In these cases, the packing of two alpha helices at angles close to 20° gives an elongated character to these molecules, but these regions do not aggregate further (Cohen and Parry, 1986).

The other molecular conformation that forms rod-like structures is the triple-helix. A triple-helix is formed from three polypeptide chains wound around a common axis to give a supercoiled structure. Each chain has a very extended helical structure, with the rise per residue for a single chain approximately twice that found in the compact α-helix (Table 1).

Every third residue of each chain must be a glycine, since only a hydrogen atom can be accommodated in this position near the central axis without distortion of the chains. The triple-helix is stabilized by close packing of atoms, hydrogen bonding between the three chains, and the high content of relatively rigid imino acids.

Extracellular matrix molecules that contain an extended region of triple-helix have been called collagens, and at least 12 distinct genetic types of collagens have been identified (Mayne and Burgeson, 1987; Miller, 1988). The most precisely characterized are the collagens found in fibrils with a characteristic axial repeat of 67 nm (the D repeat) in a wide variety of tissues such as tendon, skin, bone, and cartilage. This family includes five collagen types (I, II, III, V, XI), which can be reconstituted into D-periodic fibrils and which contain a central region of about 1000 amino acids in which every third residue is a glycine (Mayne and Burgeson, 1987; Miller, 1988). The gene structures of these five fibril-forming collagens are very similar, supporting their common origin and function (Weil *et al.*, 1987). Types I, II, and III collagen molecules are synthesized with a large C-terminal globular propeptide domain and an N-propeptide, which includes a short triple-helical region and sometimes another globular

Table 1. Comparison of the molecular features of coiled coil α-helices and triple-helices.

	Coiled coil	Triple-helix
Number of chains per molecule	2 (or 3[a])	3
Rise per residue	0.15 nm	0.29 nm
Residues per turn	3.5	3.3
Relative stagger of chains in molecule	No stagger (both chains in register)	1 residue
Repeating pattern	$(X-H-X-X-X-H-X)_n$	$(Gly-X-Y)_n$

[a]Fibrinogen contains three α-helices wound in a coiled coil structure [Weisel, J. W., *et al., Science* **230**, 1388 (1985)].

region. Before or during the formation of fibrils, the propeptides are enzymatically cleaved so that molecules with a large central triple helix and very short nonhelical ends are found in the tissue. The various fibril-forming collagens differ in terms of quantity and tissue localization. Types I and II are always major tissue components, while types V and XI are minor collagens. Bone and tendon contain over 95 percent type I collagen and a few percent of type V. Cartilage includes about 90 percent type II collagen and a small amount of type XI.

In addition to these fiber-forming collagens, there are extracellular matrix molecules that contain triple-helices but do not go on to form D-periodic fibrils. One example is basement membrane collagen (type IV), which contains a long triple-helical region with a C-terminal globular domain. In contrast to the fiber-forming collagens, there are more than 20 interruptions in the Gly-X-Y pattern in the triple-helical region (Brazel *et al.*, 1988; Timpl *et al.*, 1981). Examples of interruptions include the deletion of one glycine or the insertion of a stretch of 2−20 residues that do not have glycine as every third residue. Fibrillar collagen molecules associate with each other in an overlapping manner, while the type IV molecules associate in an end-to-end manner: the C-terminal globular domains of two molecules associate with each other and become disulfide linked; four N-terminal triple helical regions associate as tetramers and are covalently stabilized (Timpl *et al.*, 1981). Evidence of lateral association of type IV triple-helices has been reported as well (Yurchenco and Furthmayr, 1984; Barnard *et al.*, 1987).

X-ray patterns of lens capsule basement membrane indicate type IV molecules contain triple-helices with the same 0.29 nm rise per residue seen in fibril-forming collagens, but the even orders of the helical diffraction pattern are unusually strong compared with the odd orders, consistent with the presence of a two-fold axis of symmetry (personal observation). Recent electron microscopy studies of basement membranes suggest that two or more triple-helices may be wrapped around each other to form a superhelical structure (Yurchenco and Ruben, 1987), and such a structure could have a two-fold symmetry. Thus, both x-ray and electron microscopy data suggest that, in basement membranes, two or more triple-helices may be wound around each other in a manner reminiscent of a coiled coil structure, supporting a commonality in principles of construction of these two supercoiled structures.

The molecular structures for both the triple-helix and coiled coil structures were derived from model building to best fit the helical diffraction patterns, and thus are not accurate to atomic resolution. Crystallization of peptide fragments with these superhelical conformations could result in high-resolution structures and give details on molecular structure and stabilization.

Assembly of Fibrous Proteins

At least three distinct levels of assembly are required for this group of fibrous proteins: first, two or three polypeptide chains must associate to form a stable molecule, including a rod-like triple-helical or coiled coil region; second, these molecules associate with each other in a regular staggered manner to form fibrils; and third, in almost all cases these fibrils will interact with other components to form a muscle filament, cytoskeletal network, or the extracellular matrix of a tissue. The folding of molecules and their association into fibrils will be considered in some detail.

Folding of triple-helical and coiled coil molecules

To form a coiled coil or triple-helical structure, two or three polypeptide chains wrap around each other in a superhelical manner (Fig. 1). Supercoiling of several polypeptide chains gives these molecules a stability and mechanical strength required for fibrous protein function. In globular proteins, the presence of more than one polypeptide chain in a molecule is usually associated with regulatory functions, while it is likely that the multimeric nature of fibrous protein molecules fulfills mechanical requirements. In a multimeric globular protein such as hemoglobin, the individual α and β subunits can be seen as structurally separable units, while this is not true for those supercoiled molecules where each subunit traces a helical path around the molecule.

In a given coiled coil or triple-helical molecule, the polypeptide chains may all be identical, or there may be two or three distinct polypeptide chains. For example, type I collagen contains two distinct types of polypeptide chains, while type II collagen is a homotrimer (Miller, 1988). Tropomyosin molecules are found as heterodimers or as homodimers. The properties conferred by having homodimers or homotrimers versus mixed chains in a molecule could relate to the level of molecular folding and stability or to higher order association.

The overall appearance of an extended coiled coil or triple-helical region is a uniform rod-like structure. The amino acid sequence varies along the chains so there are distinguishing higher resolution side chain features appearing axially and laterally along the surface of these rods. Various studies suggest defined regions of such extended helices may have discrete functions or be recognition sites. For instance, tropomyosin has two exons that are specifically expressed in striated muscle, while two others are expressed in smooth muscle as a result of alternative splicing (Ruiz-Opazo and Nadal-Ginard, 1987). This suggests tissue-specific functions supported by the two particular exons. Since the coiled coil structure extends along the entire tropomyosin molecule, functionally identifiable regions must be distinguished by subtle structural features.

Another example is type I collagen with a continuous 300 nm triple-helical structure, which has one cleavage site in the triple helix for mammalian collagenase (Gross, 1976), one binding site for fibronectin (Kleinman et al., 1976), and one defined binding site for proteoglycans (Scott and Orford, 1981). In the case of fibrous proteins, the differences that create recognition sites or localized functional regions must be of a subtle nature involving side chain recognition and perhaps small modulations of the basic helical structure rather than structurally identifiable domains as seen in many globular proteins. In this respect, the fibrous protein molecule is reminiscent of the recognition of proteins by DNA, where specific interactions of bases with amino acids and perturbations of helical structure are involved (Wolberger et al., 1988).

Strict regularities in amino acid sequence are required to stabilize these two superhelical molecular structures. In the coiled coil helix, there is a repeating heptad pattern of hydrophobic residues, and for the triple-helix, every third residue is a glycine. Jonathan King and Lila Gierasch, in their preface to this volume, mentioned that if one looks at an amino acid sequence obtained from an unidentified piece of cloned DNA, one would not know the protein's three-dimensional structure. But this group of fibrous proteins is an exception. A triple-helical or coiled coil structure can be immediately predicted when its amino acid sequence follows the expected pattern for many repeats. The pattern for forming these two supercoiled structures must be stringently followed because of the regularity required for interactions between two or three helical chains over an extended length.

There are cases in which the regular sequence pattern is interrupted for triple-helices and coiled coil structures. What is the effect of such interruptions? Do they have any functional role? All five fibrillar collagens have glycine as every third residue along a thousand amino acid stretch for all species and chains that have been sequenced (Miller, 1988). As Peter Byers will discuss (see chapter 24, this volume), replacement of glycine by another amino acid is a lethal mutation. So the requirement in fibril-forming collagens is exact; there is no room for errors or substitutions. But, as mentioned, in basement membrane type IV collagen there are more than 20 interruptions of the Gly-X-Y pattern within the triple-helical region (Brazel *et al.*, 1988). Thus, for type IV collagen, the interruptions appear to be allowed and perhaps required for function. We do not know the structure of these nonregular regions or their function. They may serve as points of flexibility, as loops protruding from the helix, as kinks, or, in some cases, they may result in a perturbation of the helical structure.

A similar situation holds for coiled coil molecules. In tropomyosin, the heptad repeat is exact along the entire length of the molecule, except for small regions at the N- and C-terminus (Stone and Smillie, 1978). No breaks in the pattern are seen for all tropomyosins sequenced. But in myosin, there are four positions where one extra residue is inserted between heptads ("skip" residues) (McLachlan and Karn, 1983). These insertions occur at intervals that are multiples of 28 residues, and it is hypothesized that they modulate the basic coiled coil helical structure (McLachlan and Karn, 1983).

In all intermediate filament proteins, there is a central rod domain containing three highly conserved coiled coil regions with heptad repeats interrupted by two short spacers or linkers with no heptad repeat (Parry and Fraser, 1985). Interruption of the repeating sequence pattern may play a role in higher order structure or may constitute a recognizable break in the otherwise uniform helical structure.

In addition to rod-like helices, these fibrous protein molecules contain terminal domains that are not helical, usually globular regions or short irregular pieces, which may have independent functions. For fibrillar collagens, the C-terminal propeptide is involved in selection of the three chains which will form the molecule and serves as a nucleus for helix formation (Doege and Fessler, 1986). Myosin has an amino terminal globular region (head group, S-1 domain), which contains ATPase activity and binds to actin filaments (Knight and Trinick, 1987), while intermediate filament proteins have globular domains at both ends of the central coiled coil region (Parry and Fraser, 1985). In addition to their separate functions (e.g., enzymatic activity or chain selection), it is likely that the globular domains at the termini of these rod-like molecules are important determinants of fibril diameter and structure, as discussed below.

Some folding studies of molecules with triple-helical or large coiled coil regions have been reported. Molecular stabilization comes from the interaction between the chains, not just from the interactions involving one polypeptide chain itself, so the folding of a single chain and the folding of the molecule occur simultaneously (Crick, 1953; Veis, 1964). This contrasts with globular proteins containing more than one polypeptide chain where individual subunits may fold independently to a form close to their final structure and, in some cases, may be stable as monomers (Jaenicke, 1987). There is some evidence of folding and unfolding intermediates for these helical structures, suggesting some regions of coiled coil in tropomyosin may unfold before others (Woods, 1976); short triple-helices form first at the C-terminus and then elongate sequentially to the N-terminus (Doege and Fessler, 1986; Woods, 1976; Engel *et al.*, 1980).

Detailed studies have been done to investigate the folding of types I and III collagen molecules in several laboratories (Doege and Fessler, 1986; Engel *et al.*, 1980; Gerard *et al.*, 1981), and their results will be briefly summarized. The C-propeptides of three collagen polypeptide chains associate, resulting in selection of the three chains that will form the molecule. Disulfide bonding between the three C-propeptides occurs, and this disulfide-bonded C-terminus will act as a nucleus for triple-helix formation, which will proceed via a zipper mechanism from the C- to N-terminus. While the Gly-X-Y segments are unfolded, a series of posttranslational modifications occurs, including the hydroxylation of almost all prolines in the Y position, the hydroxylation of specific lysines in the Y position, and the attachment of galactose and then glucose to some hydroxylysines. The process of helix formation cannot begin until sufficient hydroxyproline has been enzymatically produced, since these hydroxyproline residues enhance the stability of the molecule. After triple-helix formation, no further posttranslational modifications can occur. The rate of folding is limited by proline isomerization, a factor that is particularly important in collagen because of its high imino acid content. The folding of collagen is a complex process involving many enzymes — prolyl hydroxylase, lysyl hydroxylase, glucosyl and galactosyl transferases, disulfide isomerase, and prolyl isomerase — all acting on the unfolded protein to ensure proper folding. It is a good candidate for being folded in a complex where these activities could be coordinated.

Association of molecules into fibrils

After proper folding, the molecules must associate to form fibrils. For some triple-helices and coiled coils, there is good evidence that the helical regions contain the information needed for the correct axial staggering of molecules. Experimentally, precipitation of triple-helices of type I or III collagen results in aggregates with an axial D period (Miyahara *et al.*, 1982; Lee and Piez, 1982; Wood and Keech, 1960). Similarly, isolated rods of myosin containing only the coiled coil region can form aggregates with a 14.3 nm and 43 nm axial repeat (Huzley, 1963; Koretz, 1979). A simple one-dimensional interaction analysis on the amino acid sequence of type I collagen, where molecules are translated past each other and the interactions at each relative stagger are summed, indicates that both hydrophobic and electrostatic interactions have a maximum when adjacent molecules are staggered by 67 nm (Hulmes *et al.*, 1973). A similar analysis for coiled coil regions of myosin (McLachlan and Karn, 1982) and keratin (Fraser *et al.*, 1985) indicates that the electrostatic interactions peak at the axial stagger seen in native filaments, but no clear maxima are seen for hydrophobic interactions. Thus, experimental results and theoretical analyses indicate that the axial staggering of molecules is determined by the rod-like helical regions for myosins and fibrillar collagens.

Much less is known about other aspects of fibril structure, such as the lateral packing of molecules in fibrils and the factors that influence the final diameter and length of fibrils. There are convincing models that give a good fit to fiber x-ray diffraction data for collagen (Fraser *et al.*, 1983) and myosin (Offer, 1987), but specific lateral interactions between a given molecule and its neighbors have not been defined yet for any fibrils. The unit cell of the crystalline three-dimensional fibril structure of collagen in rat tail tendon has been determined (Fraser *et al.*, 1983). The best positions for the five molecular segments within the unit cell were found, but the relative translations, rotations, and identification of the five helical segments are not known (Fraser *et al.*, 1983).

Fibrils reconstituted from purified type I collagen show the characteristic axial 67 nm repeat, but have larger intermolecular spacings than seen in native tissues and do not show crystalline packing (Eikenberry and Brodsky, 1980). Thus lateral packing may not be as straightforward a process of self assembly as seen for the axial packing. In our laboratory, we have investigated whether the presence of distinct genetic types of collagen in different tissues relates to three-dimensional molecular packing in fibrils with a 67 nm axial periodicity. The x-ray diffraction patterns of type II collagen in notochord indicate a crystalline molecular packing with a 67 nm axial repeat and with a significantly larger lateral intermolecular spacing than type I collagen, particularly along one direction (Eikenberry *et al.*, 1984).

At a higher level of structure, the determinants of the cylindrical form of fibrils (or fibers or filaments), their diameter, and their length are not well understood. Several lines of evidence suggest that the information determining these structural features is not totally present in the helical region of the molecules. Reconstitution of triple-helical regions of collagen (Miyahara, Njieha, Prockop, 1982; Lee and Piez, 1982) and of coiled-coil regions of myosin (Huxley, 1963; Koretz, 1979) and desmin (Weber and Geisler, 1985) results in sheets, tactoids, or ribbons, but not cylindrical fibrils. The wide range of fibril diameters seen in vivo for a given collagen type supports the concept that this is not a case of simple self assembly involving the triple-helical regions. For example, type I fibrils in the cornea are all about 40 nm in diameter, while type I fibrils in rat tail tendon show a broad distribution of diameters, ranging from 30 nm to 500 nm (Parry and Craig, 1984). Factors which may play a role in regulating fibril diameter include the processing of the propeptides of collagen, the presence of other minor collagens, the presence of noncollagenous components, e.g., specific proteoglycans, and cellular interactions (Brodsky and Eikenberry, 1985).

Summary

Structural molecules containing an extended region of coiled coil or triple-helical structure have a number of features of structure and folding which distinguish them from globular proteins: (i) the individual polypeptide chains are not structurally identifiable; (ii) molecules are stabilized by interchain interactions and individual chains are not stable; (iii) functions such as recognition and binding are not defined by domain-type features but may be distinguished by subtle side-chain features together with perturbations of the basic helical structure; (iv) strict sequence patterns are required to adopt these conformations, allowing identification of such structures from sequence data; (v) interruptions in the sequence patterns are found in some cases and may result in modulation of the helical structure, loops, kinks, or flexible regions; and (vi) folding and unfolding of triple-helices and coiled coils may progress through intermediates containing shorter segments of superhelix than the final structure, so the process may be less cooperative than seen for globular proteins. The long polymeric nature of these molecules results in structure and folding characteristics related to those of elongated polymers such as DNA rather than globular proteins.

The rod-like regions of these molecules associate in a staggered manner to form well-ordered fibrous proteins. The axial staggering appears to be determined by interactions between helical regions, while the lateral molecular packing is less well defined. The features that determine the cylindrical nature of the fibril and the fibril diameters may relate to the globular termini found on these structural molecules and to other tissue components.

In a complex system such as these fibrous proteins, errors and alterations can occur at many levels: protein folding, assembly of molecules into fibrils, or interactions with other molecules. Examples of genetic defects in collagen DNA that result in amino acid substitutions or deletions and defective collagen fibrils will be presented by Byers (see chapter 24, this volume). My laboratory has been working on alterations to collagen fibrils that occur as a result of decades of contact with serum glucose. The spontaneous reaction of ε-amino groups on collagen with glucose results in nonenzymatic glycosylation and cross linking, which in aging and diabetes alters the fibril structure and the mechanical properties of collagen (Tanaka *et al.*, 1988). Fibrous proteins present an opportunity for understanding how alterations at the molecular level and in higher order structures can alter macromolecular assemblies and their normal functions.

Acknowledgments

I thank Dr. Sarah Hitchcock-DeGregori for many helpful discussions and suggestions on this manuscript. This work was supported by Public Health Service Grant AR19626.

References

Barnard, K., L. J. Gathercole, A. J. Bailey, *FEBS Lett.* **212**, 49 (1987).

Brazel, D., R. Pollner, I. Oberbaumer, K. Kuhn, *Eur. J. Biochem.* **172**, 35(1988).

Brodsky, B., and E. F. Eikenberry, *Ann. N.Y. Acad. Sci.* **460**, 73 (1985).

Cohen, C., and D. A. D. Parry, *Trends Biochem. Sci.* **11**, 245 (1986).

Crick, F. H. C., *Acta Crystall.* **6**, 689 (1953).

Doege, K. J., and J. H. Fessler, *J. Biol. Chem.* **261**, 8924 (1986).

Eikenberry, E. F., and B. Brodsky, *J. Mol. Biol.* **144**, 397 (1980).

Eikenberry, E. F., *et al.*, *J. Mol. Biol.* **176**, 261 (1984).

Engel, J., H.-P. Bachinger, P. Bruckner, R. Timpl, in *Protein Folding*, R. Jaenicke, Ed. (Elsevier, Amsterdam, Netherlands, 1980), pp. 345–368.

Fraser, R. D. B., and T. P. MacRae, *Conformation in Fibrous Proteins* (Academic Press, New York, 1973).

Fraser, R. D. B., T. P. MacRae, A. Miller, E. Suzuki, *J. Mol. Biol.* **167**, 497 (1983).

Fraser, R. D. B., T. P. MacRae, E. Suzuki, D. A. D. Parry, *Int. J. Biol. Macromol.* **7**, 258 (1985).

Fraser, R. D. B., T. P. MacRae, E. Suzuki, P. A. Tulloch, in *Structural Aspects of Recognition and Assembly in Biological Macromolecules*, M. Balanban, J. L. Sussman, W. Traub, A. Yonath, Eds. (Balaban ISS, Rehovot-Philadelphia, 1981), pp. 327–340.

Gerard, S., D. Puett, W. M. Mitchell, *Biochemistry* **20**, 1857 (1981).

Gross, J., in *Biochemistry of Collagen*, G. N. Ramachandran and A. H. Reddi, Eds. (Plenum, New York, 1976), pp. 275–317.

Hulmes, D. J. S., A. Miller, D. A. D. Parry, K. A. Piez, J. Woodhead-Galloway, *J. Mol. Biol.* **79**, 137 (1973).

Huxley, H. E., *J. Mol. Biol.* **7**, 281 (1963).

Jaenicke, R., *Prog. Biophys. Mol. Biol.* **49**, 117 (1987).

Kleinman, H., E. B. McGoodwin, R. J. Klebe, *Biochem. Biophys. Res. Comm.* **72**, 426 (1976).

Knight, P., and J. Trinick, in *Fibrous Protein Structure*, J. M. Squire and P. J. Vibert, Eds. (Academic Press, London, 1987), pp. 247–281.

Koretz, J., *Biophys. J.* **27**, 423 (1979).

Lee, S. L., and K. A. Piez, *Collagen Relat. Res.* **3**, 89 (1982).

Mayne, R., and R. E. Burgeson, Eds., *Structure and Function of Collagen Types* (Academic Press, New York, 1987).

McLachlan, A. D., and J. Karn, *Nature* **299**, 226 (1982).

_____, *J. Mol. Biol.* **164**, 605 (1983).

Miller, E. J., in *Collagen: Biochemistry*, Vol. I, M. Nimni, Ed. (CRC Press, Boca Raton, FL, 1988), pp. 139–156.

Miyahara, M., F. K. Njieha, D. J. Prockop, *J. Biol. Chem.* **257**, 8442 (1982).

Offer, G., in *Fibrous Protein Structure*, J. M. Squire and P. J. Vibert, Eds. (Academic Press, New York, 1987), pp. 307–356.

Parry, D. A. D., and A. S. Craig, in *Ultrastructure of the Connective Tissue Matrix*, A. Ruggeri and P. M. Motta, Eds. (Martinus-Nijhoff Publishers, The Hague, 1984), pp. 34–64.

Parry, D. A. D., and R. D. B. Fraser, *Int. J. Biol. Macromol.* **7**, 203 (1985).

Ruiz-Opazo, N., and R. Nadal-Ginard, *J. Biol. Chem.* **262**, 4755 (1987).

Scott, J. E., and C. R. Orford, *Biochem. J.* **197**, 213 (1981).

Squire, J. M., and J. P. Vibert, Eds., *Fibrous Protein Structure* (Academic Press, London, 1987).

Stone, D., and L. B. Smillie, *J. Biol. Chem.* **253**, 1129 (1978).

Tanaka, S., G. Avigad, B. Brodsky, E. F. Eikenberry, *J. Mol. Biol.* **203**, 495 (1988).

Timpl, R., H. Wiedemann, V. van Delden, H. Furthmayr, K. Kuhn, *Eur. J. Biochem.* **120**, 203 (1981).

Veis, A., *The Macromolecular Chemistry of Gelatin* (Academic Press, New York, 1964).

Weber, K., and N. Geisler, *Ann. N.Y. Acad. Sci.* **455**, 126 (1985).

Weil, D., M. Bernard, S. Gargano, F. Ramirez, *Nucl. Acid Res.* **15**, 181 (1987).

Weisel, J. W., C. V. Stauffacher, E. Bullitt, C. Cohen, *Science* **230**, 1388 (1985).

Wolberger, C., Y. Dong, M. Ptashne, S. C. Harrison, *Nature* **335**, 789 (1988).

Woods, E. F., *Aust. J. Biol. Sci.* **29**, 405 (1976).

Wood, G. S., and M. K. Keech, *Biochem. J.* **75**, 588 (1960).

Yurchenco, P. D., and H. Furthmayr, *Biochemistry* **23**, 1839 (1984).

Yurchenco, P. D., and G. C. Ruben, *J. Cell. Biol.* **105**, 2559 (1987).

6

Protein Folding and Assembly

An Hydration-Mediated Free Energy Driving Force

Dan W. Urry

The hydrophobic effect and electrostatic interactions are two prominent considerations for protein folding and assembly in an aqueous medium. With the known crystal structures of globular proteins in an aqueous mother liquor, it is appreciated that hydrophobic side chains of residues such as Phe, Ile, Leu, and Val are generally buried within the interior of the protein. Additionally, there are examples where the change in a single charge can cause dramatic changes in the assembly of protein subunits. Such dramatic effects are cited as indicating the exquisite importance of electrostatic interactions in protein structure.

In this chapter, it is argued with experimental data that the existence of an interactive hydrophobic-electrostatic repulsive free energy in an aqueous environment is responsible for this exquisite modulation of protein structure. This has been called an aqueous-mediated, apolar-polar repulsion free energy. It is demonstrated here in terms of (i) the effect of changes in hydrophobicity on the pK_a of a weak acid, (ii) the effect of added charge on the endothermic heat of an inverse temperature transition, and (iii) the interconversion of mechanical and chemical work in elastic polypeptides that are capable of folding due to an inverse temperature transition (thermomechanical transduction) and which may also be designed to exhibit chemo-mechanical transduction by application of the apolar-polar free energy of interaction (Urry *et al.*, 1988b).

Assay System for Evaluating Apolar-Polar Interaction Free Energies

Sequential peptides in helical array

The aqueous polypeptide systems wherein the apolar-polar interaction free energies have been observed utilize elastomeric sequential polypeptides with repeating sequences that can become arranged in a dynamic, regular, helical array as the result of an inverse temperature transition, i.e., as the result of an increase in order within the polypeptide as the temperature is raised over the transition temperature range (Urry, 1988). The parent molecular system is poly(VPGVG) or (L-Val¹-L-Pro²-Gly³-L-Val⁴-Gly⁵)ₙ.

On raising the temperature of this sequential polypeptide in water, it orders into a helical array of pentamers in which there occur $Val^1C\text{-}O \cdots HN\text{-}Val^4$ hydrogen bonds in the formation of Type II β-turns (Fig. 1A) (Chang and Urry, 1989; Chang *et al.*, 1989). This helical array of β-turns is called a β-spiral, and there are approximately three pen-

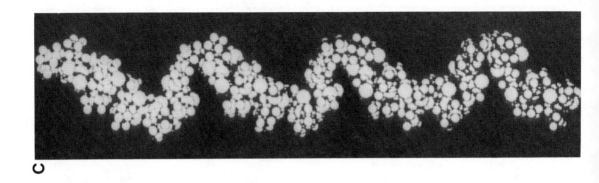

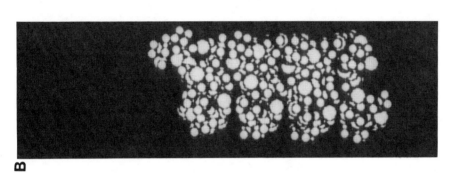

Fig. 1. (A) Stereo pair of the relaxed state of the poly(VPGVG) β-spiral with 2.9 pentamers/turn. (B) Space-filling model of the relaxed state of the poly(VPGVG) β-spiral with 2.9 pentamers/turn. The interturn hydrophobic contacts are apparent. (C) Space-filling model of the 130 percent extended state of the poly(VPGVG) β-spiral. Extension demonstrates the removal of the interturn hydrophobic contacts.

tamers per turn of spiral (helix) (Chang *et al.,* 1989). The β-turns function as hydrophobic spacers between turns on the spiral with the Pro β CH_2 hydrogens of one turn of the spiral in hydrophobic contact with the $Val^1\gamma$ CH_3 hydrogens of the adjacent turn. The interturn interactions are apparent in Fig. 1B, which is a space-filling model of the structure in Fig. 1A. Furthermore, these β-spirals associate by hydrophobic intermolecular interactions to form twisted filaments that may be seen by transmission electron microscopy using negative staining techniques (Urry, 1982).

Elastic matrices

On the source of elastomeric force: studies on natural elastin fibers and on γ-irradiation cross-linked matrices of poly(VPGVG), which determine the temperature dependence of force at constant length, have provided evidence for a dominantly entropic basis for the elastomeric force (see Urry, 1988; Chang and Urry, 1989; Chang *et al.,* 1989; and references therein). There have been three mechanisms put forward for the entropic elastomeric force. One derives from the classical theory of rubber elasticity and is based on a random chain network which is at odds with the above dynamic β-spiral structural description. A second mechanism utilizes the entropy change on solvation of hydrophobic side chains as they become exposed to solvent on extension. The third, which originated from studies on poly(VPGVG), is that of damping of internal chain dynamics on extension and is called the librational entropy mechanism of elasticity.

In particular, this derives from and is exemplified by the β-spiral structure described above and depicted in Fig. 1. In the relaxed state of this structure, there occur primarily in the Val^4-Gly^5-Val^1 segment, which is suspended between β-turns, large torsional oscillations involving the $\psi_4, \phi_5, \psi_5, \phi_1$ torsion angles which on extension become damped (Chang and Urry, 1989). This mechanism has been supported by synthetic analogs such as poly(VPGVA) where Gly^5 is replaced by Ala^5

in which there is total loss of elasticity, by dielectric relaxation studies that demonstrate the development of an intense Debye-like relaxation near 10 MHz assigned to the peptide backbone dipole moment that develops on raising the temperature through the inverse temperature transition with formation of the β-spiral structure of Fig. 1, and by molecular mechanics and dynamics computations that demonstrate the damping of the amplitude of torsional oscillations (called librations) on chain extension of the β-spiral structure of poly(VPGVG).

Thermomechanical transduction. When the aggregated state, which forms on raising the temperature above that of the inverse temperature transition, is γ-irradiation cross linked, the result is an elastomeric matrix without detectable change in carbon-13 and nitrogen-15 nuclear magnetic resonance (NMR) spectra (Urry, 1988). At temperatures below that of the inverse temperature transition, the elastomeric matrix swells and the polypeptide chains would become dispersed over the entire solution if it were not for the cross linking. With 20 Mrad cross linking, the increase in length due to swelling is approximately a factor of 2.2. On raising the temperature above that of the inverse temperature transition, the elastomeric matrix contracts and is capable of picking up weights that are several thousand times the dry weight of the matrix.

The temperature at which this thermomechanical transduction occurs depends on the hydrophobicity of the polypentapeptide. For poly(IPGVG) where I = Ile, the contraction—and, of course, the responsible inverse temperature transition—occurs at a lower temperature, near 10°C, rather than at 30°C as occurs for poly(VPGVG) (Urry, 1988). For poly(VPGAG) where A = Ala, the inverse temperature transition occurs near 70°C. (T. Parker, K. U. Prasad, D. W. Urry, unpublished data).

Chemomechanical transduction. When poly[4(VPGVG),(VPGEG)] where E = Glu is prepared and cross linked, the temperature for the inverse temperature transition and the contraction depends on the pH. In phosphate-buffered saline (0.15 N NaCl, 0.01M phosphate) at pH 2, the contraction occurs near 25°C, whereas at pH 7, the contraction occurs near 70°C (Urry *et al., 1988a*). Thus, it is possible to remain at 37°C and, by changing the pH, to bring about contraction and relaxation. This is chemomechanical transduction (mechanochemical coupling); it is a chemically induced folding and unfolding of the β-spiral. Determination of the chemical work, of lowering the pH (increasing proton concentration) required both to achieve the mechanical work and to drive the inverse temperature transition, provides a measure of the free energy changes involved. This is one means of demonstrating the presence of an interaction free energy, but there are more direct demonstrations of what is occurring at the molecular level, as will be discussed below.

Means of Directly Determining the Interaction Free Energy

Hydrophobicity-Induced p*K Shifts*

One of the advantages of a repeating sequence in a regular helical array is that an interaction free energy is amplified or multiplied by the number of repeats. This is particularly apparent when comparing the two sequential polypeptides: poly[4(VPGVG),(VPGEG)] and poly[4(IPGVG),(IPGEG)]. The conformations of these two molecular systems have been shown to be the same at low pH and to change to the same new conformation at high pH, as has been shown by two-dimensional (2D) NMR, particularly 2D nuclear Overhauser effect spectroscopy (NOESY) studies (Urry *et al.*, 1988a). This had also been shown by circular dichroism for poly(VPGVG) and poly(IPGVG) at temperatures below and then above their respective temperature ranges for their inverse temperature transitions (Urry *et al.*, 1986).

If, however, the polymers are titrated by acid or base to determine the pK_a of the carboxyl moiety in the Glu side chain, it is found that the pK_a is one pH unit higher for the more hydrophobic sequential polypeptide as shown

in Fig. 2. This pK_a shift is also apparent in the pH dependence of the temperatures of the inverse temperature transition and in the plots of the pH dependence of length at similar loads for the cross-linked elastomeric matrices (Urry *et al.*, 1988a). Thus, the addition of one CH_2 moiety per pentamer in a polypentapeptide that contains only four carboxyl functions in 100 residues is sufficient to make the occurrence of the COO^- moiety energetically less favorable.

An estimate of this repulsive free energy of interaction can be achieved from the change in chemical potential required to achieve 50 percent ionization, that is, $\Delta\mu = -2.3RT\,\Delta pK_a$. Since the ΔpK_a ($= 4.4 - 5.4$) is approximately -1 at 37°C, then $\Delta\mu$ is 1400 cal/mole. Interestingly, this is the difference in the hydrophobicities of Val and Ile on the Nozaki and Tanford (1971) hydrophobicity scale as listed by Bull and Breese (1974).

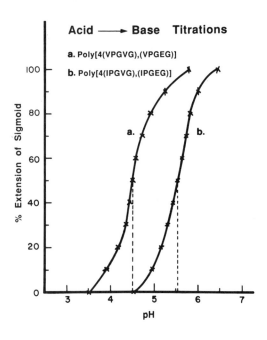

Fig. 2. Plots of percent ionization derived from the acid → base titrations of (A) poly[4(VPGVG),(VPGEG)] and of (B) poly [4(IPGVG),(IPGEG)]. The presence of one added CH_2 moiety in each pentamer achieved by replacing Val[1] by Ile[1] causes the pK_a of the Glu residues to be raised by one pH unit. This represents an increase in free energy of interaction for the carboxylate anion of 1400 cal / mole in the Ile[1] polypentapeptide.

Stretch-induced p*K* shifts and comparison of contractile mechanisms

As noted above, the contraction aspect of the thermomechanical transduction is the result of the polypeptide folding into a dynamic, regular, helical array of β-turns with formation of intramolecular as well as intermolecular hydrophobic contacts. Thus, on stretching of the elastomer by the application of a force, Δf, as shown in Fig. 1C, hydrophobic side chains become exposed to the water and clathrate-like water forms. Now it becomes of interest to know the direction of pK_a shift, if any, on increasing the force by stretching. On stretching, the pK_a of the carboxyl moiety is increased, that is, $\Delta \mu$ is negative. Thus, the $(\partial\mu/\partial f)_n < 0$. This is exactly the opposite of what is found for the polyelectrolyte mechanochemical system: polymethacrylic acid $[-(COOH)C(CH_3)-CH_2-]_n$ (Kuhn *et al.*, 1950). In this mechanochemical system, contraction also occurs on lowering the *p*H. But in this case, it is the relieving of electrostatic repulsion that causes the collapse of extended chains on lowering the degree of ionization from 50 percent or more to 0 or 10 percent. In this case, the $(\partial\mu/\partial f) > 0$, which means that the pK_a is lowered on stretching (Katchalsky *et al.*, 1960; Kuhn *et al.*, 1960).

Thus, for the same moiety, we have a clear distinction between the long appreciated electrostatic interaction mechanism, actually charge-charge repulsion, and the new mechanism referred to above, as an aqueous mediated, apolar-polar repulsion free energy. Since both the cross linked polymethacrylic acid and poly[4(VPGVG),(VPGEG)] systems contract to about one-half their extended length and since both can pick up weights that are several thousand times their dry weight, it is interesting to compare the amount of chemical work that is required to achieve the similar amount of mechanical work. For polymethacrylic acid, it takes the conversion of some 50 carboxylates to carboxyls to do the work, whereas for poly[4(VPGVG), (VPGEG)], it takes only the conversion of some four carboxylates to carboxyls in a matrix with more than an order of magnitude

lower density of carboxyl moieties. Thus, it would seem that the new mechanism is more efficient than electrostatic interactions by an order of magnitude. As will be shown below, a chemically elicited conformational change in a protein can be viewed as chemomechanical transduction. With the above considered efficiency, it is natural to expect that the mechanism of preference for the chemically elicited protein structural changes, which occur in the process of function in living organisms, would be that of an aqueous mediated, apolar-polar interaction free energy because much less food (chemical energy) would be required for the organism to function.

Effect of charge on the endothermic heat of the inverse temperature transition

The above shift in pK_a resulting from a change in hydrophobicity provides one means of evaluating the interaction free energy of charge hydration when proximal to hydrophobic hydration. As was seen from the increase in pK_a with increase in hydrophobicity, this is a repulsive interaction free energy; that is, on replacing Val by Ile, the increase in free energy of the carboxylate moiety is 1400 cal/mole. Thus, an interpretation of these data is that there exists an antagonism between the structure of water required for polar hydration and that required for apolar hydration when these disparate hydration processes are sufficiently proximal. This is the source of the proposed hydration-mediated, apolar-polar repulsive free energy of interaction. What is now desired is a means of observing the effect from the opposite perspective, i.e., to determine whether the addition of charge does indeed result in the destructuring of clathrate-like water surrounding hydrophobic groups.

At this stage it is useful to recall (i) that the solubility of a solute in water depends on the change in Gibbs free energy of dissolution $\Delta G = \Delta H - T\Delta S$, where ΔH and ΔS are the change of heat content or enthalpy and the change in entropy, respectively, on hydration;

(ii) that a negative ΔG is favorable for dissolution; (iii) that the dissolution of hydrophobic solutes in water is exothermic (i.e., ΔH is negative) (Franks and Evans, 1945; Kauzmann, 1959); but (iv) that solubility of hydrophobic solutes is low due to a substantially negative ΔS such that the quantity ($-T\Delta S$) is positive. Accordingly for hydrophobic solutes in water, ΔH and ($- T\Delta S$) are of similar magnitude but of opposite sign. The positive ΔS is considered to arise from an increase in the order of the water that is at the surface of the hydrophobic moiety (Franks and Evans, 1945; Kauzmann, 1959; Edsall and McKenzie, 1983). This more-ordered water abutting hydrophobic moieties has been referred to as clathrate water, and pentagonal dodecahedral water structure has been found surrounding methane gas molecules in crystals of gas hydrates (Stackelberg and Müller, 1951) and in Monte Carlo studies on the structure of a dilute aqueous solution of methane (Swaminathan et al., 1978).

Returning to our polypentapeptide of interest, poly [4(VPGVG),(VPGEG)], the dissolution in water below 25°C is considered to be an exothermic reaction dominated by the hydration of the Val and Pro side chains and resulting in the formation of clathrate-like water. On raising the temperature through the range of the inverse temperature transition, the more-ordered clathrate-like water is expected by an endothermic reaction to become less-ordered bulk water as the polypentapeptide folds into the β-spiral conformation. By means of differential scanning calorimetry, this inverse temperature transition is indeed seen to be an endothermic transition (Urry et al., 1990) which is, therefore, reasonably interpreted to be due to the destructuring of the clathrate-like water; that is, to be simply the inverse of the exothermic reaction of hydration of the hydrophobic side chains. The endothermic heat of the transition at pH 2.5, where essentially all of the Glu side chains are COOH, is 0.97 kcal/mole (Urry et al., 1990).

Now it is of interest to see the effect of converting carboxyls to carboxylate anions. At pH 4, one of the four carboxyl moieties per 100 residues has been converted to a carboxylate anion, and significantly the endothermic heat of the transition has been remarkably reduced to 0.27 kcal/mole (Urry et al., 1990). Since the endothermic heat of the inverse temperature transition is taken to cause the destructuring of the clathrate-like water, then the effect of converting one carboxyl moiety to a carboxylate anion per every 100 residues is to have destructured three-quarters of the clathrate-like water. Thus, hydration-mediated, apolar-polar repulsion free energy has been seen from both perspectives. From one perspective, when an increase in hydrophobicity is forced on the molecular system by replacing the Val residue with the more hydrophobic Ile residue, then the pK_a of the carboxyl moiety is increased, indicating the energetically less favorable situation for the carboxylate anion (Urry et al., 1988a). From the other perspective, if the carboxylate anion is forced on the molecular system by a change in pH, then the system responds by a destructuring of the clathrate-like water surrounding hydrophobic groups (Urry et al., 1990). It is this aspect of the capacity of a polar species to destructure clathrate-like water that is considered in the next section as a primary means of modulating protein folding and assembly.

Relevance of Apolar-Polar Interaction Free Energies to Protein Folding and Assembly

Protein folding: Analogy to a clam-shaped globular protein

By way of illustration, the effect of aqueous-mediated, apolar-polar interaction free energy can be demonstrated by consideration of a clam-shaped protein which is capable of existing in two conformations, open and closed (Fig. 3). Above the temperature of the inverse temperature transition for folding to form the closed state, the hydrophobic residues are buried within the fold. To the extent allowed by the Gibbs free-energy difference, there can be an occasional opening, in which case the formerly buried hydrophobic side chains become exposed to water with the formation of

Clam-shaped Globular Protein

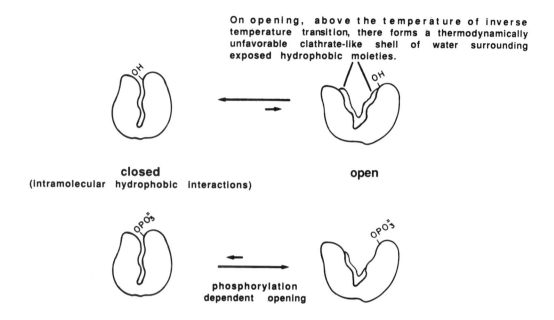

On opening, above the temperature of inverse temperature transition, there forms a thermodynamically unfavorable clathrate-like shell of water surrounding exposed hydrophobic moieties.

closed
(Intramolecular hydrophobic interactions)

open

phosphorylation dependent opening

On phosphorylation, there forms less thermodynamically measurable clathrate-like water on opening. Transition termperature is raised due to decrease in magnitude of ΔH and ΔS with $\delta\Delta H < \delta\Delta S$.

Fig. 3. Model of a clam-shaped globular protein capable of existing in two states, closed and open. (A) Above the temperature of the inverse temperature transition, the equilibrium favors the closed state, with hydrophobic side chains in intramolecular interaction. On opening, the hydrophobic surfaces become covered with a layer of clathrate-like water, which at this temperature is not thermodynamically favored. (B) On phosphorylation near the cleft, the effect of the added negatively charged phosphate is to destroy or to destructure, from the thermodynamically measurable point of view, the clathrate-like water in its vicinity such that now the open state is favored. This is chemomechanical transduction, which with the proper cross linking could be used to demonstrate mechanochemical coupling.

clathrate-like water at the contact surface. It is the formation of so much clathrate-like water that is unfavorable at the considered temperature. If, however, the polar phosphate species is added at the edge of the folding cleft, then this very polar species would destructure the clathrate-like water in its vicinity as shown in Fig. 3. Just as the formation of one carboxylate anion per 100 residues destructures three-fourths of the thermodynamically evidenced clathrate-like water in poly[4(VPGVG), (VPGEG)], phosphorylation is considered to remove a critical part of the thermodynamic driving force for closure, and the equilibrium is shifted toward the open state as indicated.

If it were possible to string together a series of clam-shaped globular proteins by means of fine bands attached near the mouth and connecting adjacent globular proteins, as shown in Fig. 4, it would be possible to measure the driving force for closure. While it is not possible to measure the driving force in this way for the conformational change of the clam-shaped globular protein, it is possible to do the equivalent with the polypentapeptide because of its β-spiral conformation. The continuous polypeptide backbone of the polypentapeptide β-spiral replaces the need for the band, and the interturn hydrophobic interactions (apparent when comparing Figs. 1B and

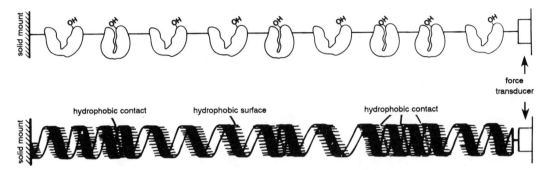

Analogy Between Conformational Change in Globular Proteins and
Contraction in Elastomeric Filaments

Fig. 4. Schematic drawing showing analogy between an aligned series of attached (cross-linked) clam-shaped globular proteins with about one-half opened and one-half closed and a partially extended β-spiral in which there are some interturn hydrophobic interactions and some turns of the β-spiral are too far apart to make hydrophobic contact. This demonstrates that a protein conformational change, as occurs in the opening and closing of a globular protein, can develop a mechanical force and that such forces can actually be measured in the polypentapeptide β-spiral system once interchain cross linking has occurred to form the macroscopic elastomeric matrix.

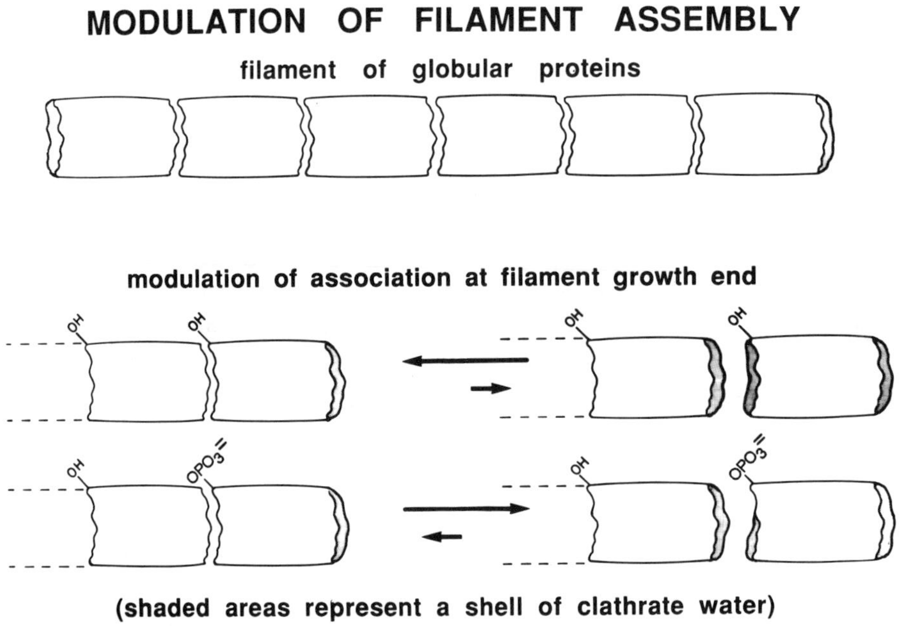

MODULATION OF FILAMENT ASSEMBLY

filament of globular proteins

modulation of association at filament growth end

(shaded areas represent a shell of clathrate water)

Fig. 5. Chemical modulation of filament assembly by means of hydration-mediated, apolar-polar interaction free energies. Demonstrated is a filament comprised of a globular protein subunit with two hydrophobic surfaces. Above the temperature of the inverse temperature transition for intermolecular hydrophobic association of subunits, on dissociation a thermodynamically unfavorable coat of clathrate-like water forms on the hydrophobic surfaces, shifting the equilibrium toward association. Once phosphorylated on dissociation, there is less thermodynamically measurable clathrate-like water formation and the equilibrium is shifted toward dissociation.

C) become equivalent to the hydrophobic interactions that occur on closure of the clam-shaped globular protein. It becomes possible, therefore, to measure the driving forces for the conformational change giving rise to contraction, and by chemical modulation (e.g., protonation or deprotonation), to demonstrate the existence of the apolar-polar interaction free energy. The simplicity of an experiment, wherein contraction and relaxation and the picking up and setting down of a weight occur, leaves little to the imagination as to whether or not work has been done and as to whether or not driving forces are turned on and off.

Protein assembly: Modulation of filament formation

By way of illustration for protein assembly, consider a filament comprised of globular proteins as shown in Fig. 5. The contact surfaces are hydrophobic such that at one end where the hydrophobic side chains are exposed to the aqueous milieu, there is a layer of clathrate-like water. At a temperature above that of the inverse temperature transition for association, the equilibrium favors filament formation. If, however, phosphorylation occurs near the contact surface, as shown, then the polar phosphate moiety will cause the destructuring of the clathrate-like water in its vicinity that would have otherwise formed. This shifts the equilibrium toward dissociation.

Acknowledgments

We would like to express appreciation to Larry Hayes for carrying out the titrations of Fig. 2 and to D. K. Chang for generating the molecular structure of Fig. 1. We would also like to acknowledge NIH grants GM26898, HL29785, and Department of the Navy Office of Naval Research contract N00014-86-K-0402.

References

Bull, H. B. and K. Breese, *Arch. Biochem. Biophys.* **161**, 665 (1974).

Chang, D. K., and D. W. Urry, *J. Comput. Chem.* **10**, 850 (1989).

Chang, D. K., C. M. Venkatachatam, D. W. Urry, *J. of Biomol. Struct. & Dyn.* **6**, 851 (1989).

Edsall, J. T., and H. A. McKenzie, *Adv. Biophys.* **16**, 53 (1983).

Franks, H. S., and M. W. Evans, *J. Chem. Phys.* **13**, 493 (1945).

Katchalsky, A., S. Lifson, I. Michaeli, H. Zwick, in *Size and Shape of Contractile Polymers: Conversion of Chemical into Mechanical Energy*, A. Wasserman, Ed. (Pergamon, New York, 1960), pp. 1–40.

Kauzmann, W., *Adv. Protein Chem.* **14**, 1 (1959).

Kuhn, W., B. Hargitay, A. Katchalsky, H. Eisenberg, *Nature* **165**, 514 (1950).

Kuhn, W., A. Ramel, D. H. Walters, in *Size and Shape of Contractile Polymers: Conversion of Chemical into Mechanical Energy*, A. Wasserman, Ed. (Pergamon, New York, 1960), pp. 41–77.

Nozaki, Y., and C. J. Tanford, *Biol. Chem.* **246**, 2211 (1971).

Stackelberg, M. V., and H. R. Müller, *Naturwissenschaften* **38**, 456 (1951).

Swaminathan, S., S. W. Harrison, D. Beveridge, *J. Amer. Chem. Soc.* **100**, 5705 (1978).

Urry, D. W., *J. Protein Chem.* **7**, 1 (1988).

———, in *Methods in Enzymology*, vol. 82, L. W. Cunningham and D. W. Frederiksen, Eds. (Academic Press, Inc., New York, 1982).

———, D. K. Chang, H. Zhang, K. U. Prasad, *Biochem. Biophys. Res. Commun.* **153**, 832 (1988a).

———, B. Haynes, H. Zhang, R. D. Harris, K. U. Prasad, *Proc. Natl. Acad. Sci. U.S.A.* **85**, 3407 (1988b).

———, M. M. Long, R. D. Harris, K. U. Prasad, *Biopolymers* **25**, 1939 (1986).

———, C. H. Luan, R. D. Harris, K. U. Prasad, *Polymer Preprints (Am. Chem. Soc. Div. Polym. Chem.)*, in press.

Part II

Interactions and Conformations of Amino Acids in Peptides

Lila M. Gierasch

Understanding protein folding must begin with an understanding of the behavior and conformational preferences of the various amino acids that form the polypeptide backbone. Many fundamental insights about amino acid building blocks have been achieved through the use of model peptides. The chapters presented in this section illustrate these approaches.

X-ray crystallography of peptides has yielded many precise images of possible conformations and modes of solvation of peptides. Karle and Balaram describe new observations on helical peptides and the factors that lead to preferences for 3_{10}- or α-helices. In protein crystals, it can generally be assumed that the structures observed are dominated by intramolecular forces and that the crystalline proteins are nearly completely bathed in solvent. By contrast, peptide crystals offer both the additional complexity and the added insights of crystal packing forces that can be as important as the intramolecular contributions. Extrapolation of these packing effects enables extension of peptide crystal results to the folding of longer chains. These aspects and examples of specific hydration of helices are also discussed.

In the widely accepted framework model of folding (Kim and Baldwin, 1982), formation of secondary structure by contiguous stretches of chain is followed by cooperative coalescence of complementary segments into the structural domains of the native protein. Thus, determining the factors that stabilize conformations of short peptides in water promises to enhance understanding of early steps in protein folding. Marqusee and Baldwin review several factors of importance in stability of α-helices in short peptides and then focus on contributions from charged side chains capable of forming intrachain salt-bridges. Interestingly, their efforts led them to the design of a monomeric, 17-residue, model peptide containing only Ala, Lys, and Glu that stably adopts an α-helical conformation in water at 1°C.

Wright *et al.* exploit the power of nuclear magnetic resonance (NMR) to study the conformations of linear peptides. In contrast to circular dichroism, NMR has the potential to reveal which residues of a sequence adopt particular conformations and thus may shed light on the residue "code" for structure. These authors find that both reverse turns and nascent α-helical structures can be characterized in small segments of native proteins in water. They suggest that such preferential visiting of specific conformational states may account for the ability of short peptide fragments to elicit an immune response with production of antibodies reactive to the native protein.

Peptide models can shed light on polypeptide chain behavior beyond the folding process, for example, the modes of interaction with other molecules such as lipids. Sparrow and Gotto have used synthetic model peptides to explore the nature of protein/lipid interactions in plasma lipoproteins. Central to the formation and function of these complex assemblies appears to be the ability of an amphipathic α-helix to interact favorably and stably with phospholipids. These authors also propose amphipathic β-structures as an alternate lipid-binding motif.

Reference

Kim, P.S., and R. L. Baldwin, *Ann. Rev. Biochem.* **51,** 7459 (1982).

7

Peptide Conformations in Crystals

Isabella L. Karle and Padmanabhan Balaram

Peptides occur naturally in animals, plants, and microorganisms. They are composed mainly of the same 20 residues that are the building blocks of proteins. Aside from their short length, 2 to ~ 30 residues, they can differ from proteins in several respects: natural peptides often contain D-residues as well as L-residues, the backbone of some peptides is cyclic, the amide bond is sometimes replaced by an ester bond (–O– instead of –NH–), and residues with rather unusual side chains are often incorporated. For the purpose of this chapter, mainly those peptides with linear backbones and the usual 20 residues with L-chirality will be used as examples, with one exception.

The Aib residue (α-aminoisobutyryl or α-methylalanyl) that occurs commonly in membrane-active antibiotic peptides such as emerimicin, zervamicin, and alamethicin is a very strong helix promoter in synthetic peptides. Many of the synthetic peptides discussed here are analogs or fragments of membrane-active peptides or sequences designed to generate model, stereochemically rigid helices as part of a modular approach to synthetic protein design.

The mode of investigation of the conformations of peptides is by single-crystal structure analysis using x-ray diffraction. The resolution attainable for crystals of peptides is generally 0.9 Å or better. This resolution compares favorably with the resolution attained with protein crystals, which is rarely better than 2.0 Å. Bond lengths, bond angles, and torsional angles are determined in peptides with standard deviations of the order of 0.01 Å, < 1.0°, and < 1.0°, respectively. Hence the geometry of a particular folding can be established with precision and small variations in conformation are readily detectable.

Conformational Stability

Peptides composed of a small number of residues can adopt a number of different conformations. The peptides are not long enough to have internal stabilizing forces such as intramolecular hydrogen bonds or hydrophobic attractions between side chains, e.g., Pro/Phe stacking. In small peptides, the attractions are external in the form of hydrogen bonding to other peptide molecules or to polar solvent molecules. Under those circumstances, the conformation of the peptide molecule is largely adjusted to the nature of the environment.

One example of multiple, stable conformations is shown by the Ac-Leu-Tyr-OMe molecule. There are three molecules co-crystallized side by side in an asymmetric unit of the unit cell of the crystal. Each molecule has a different folding for the backbone and for the side chains (Fig. 1). The maximum number of possible hydrogen bonds are formed, but only between adjacent peptide molecules

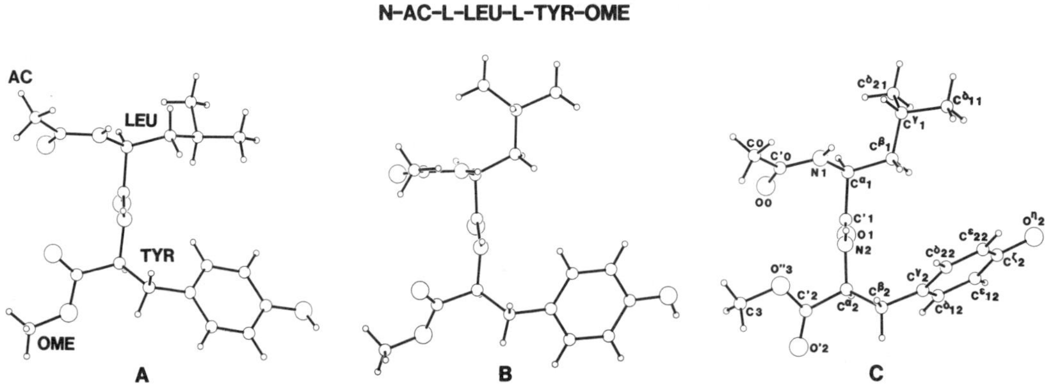

N–AC–L–LEU–L–TYR–OME

Fig. 1. Three different conformers of Ac-Leu-Tyr-OMe co-crystallized side by side in the same crystal.

(Karle and Flippen-Anderson, 1989).

Larger peptides, containing seven or eight residues or more, have conformations that are relatively unique and not easily perturbed. Crystal structure analyses of polymorphs, i.e., different crystal forms of a particular compound, have shown that cyclic peptides such as the 10-residue antamanide have a stable, unique conformation despite different space groups, different packing, different co-crystallized solvent ranging from H_2O to n-hexane, and even a number of different side chains obtained by replacements of some of the residues (Karle and Wieland, 1987). The only factor that has a large effect on the conformation of cyclic peptides is complexation with metal ions (Karle, 1986).

Helical Peptides

A general conservation of conformation has been found in helical peptides (e.g., 8–16 residues) in polymorphic crystals and with changes of polarity of solvent and co-crystallization of solvent, as has been found in cyclic peptides. However, some unwinding of the helix and a transition of helix type have been observed when a particular helical peptide is exposed to several different environments.

The Aib residue, which is present in the various linear apolar peptides investigated, is considered to be a helix former. A variety of calculations of conformational energy diagrams for the Aib residue shows an extremely restricted acceptable ϕ,ψ space (Marshall, 1971; Burgess and Leach, 1973) that allows only right- or left-handed helix conformation. A review of linear peptides containing 5 or fewer residues with at least one Aib residue showed a 3_{10}-helix or an incipient 3_{10}-helix formation in all but one (Toniolo *et al.*, 1983). Relatively few crystal structures of longer peptides are available, mainly those with 7 to 11 residues and containing a number of Aib residues. A few of these have a 3_{10}-helical conformation; most have a predominantly α-helix with one or two 3_{10}-type hydrogen bonds, and several are completely α-helical.

The question arises as to the number of Aib residues that are needed to promote helix formation. One Aib residue has been sufficient to promote a helix in Boc-Ala-Ala-Aib-Pro-Ala-Ala-Ala-OMe despite the presence of a Pro residue (Karle *et al.*, 1990a). On the other hand, one Aib residue is compatible also with an antiparallel β-sheet formation established for

Boc-Cys-Val-Aib-Ala-Leu-Cys-NHMe
S — — — — — — — — S

both in the crystal (Karle *et al.*, 1988b) and in solution (Kishore *et al.*, 1987).

Helix types and $3_{10}/\alpha$-transitions

Three types of helical formations passing from one to another in a continuous spiral are exhibited in the structure of Boc-Trp-Ile-Ala-

Aib-Ile[5]-Val-Aib-Leu-Aib-Pro[10]-Ala-Aib-Pro-Aib-Pro[15]-Phe-OMe, a synthetic apolar analog of the membrane-active fungal peptide antibiotic zervamicin IIA (Fig. 2). At the N terminus, the helix begins with two successive 4 → 1 type hydrogen bonds (3_{10}-helix), followed by four 5 → 1 type hydrogen bonds (α-helix), another 4 → 1 type, and then a β-bend ribbon wound into a spiral where each of the three β-bends contains a Pro residue. The entire structure can be described as a mixed 3_{10}/α-helix with the three Pro residues being incorporated into the helix with the loss of three hydrogen bonds. The curved helix can be approximated by two straight segments with a bend of ~30° in the vicinity of the first Pro residue (Karle *et al.*, 1987).

For the decapeptide composed of the first 10 residues of the peptide above, four different polymorphic crystals have been grown, either anhydrous or with water or alcohol solvent molecules. A superposition of the decapeptide molecule from a monoclinic cell with the same molecule in a triclinic cell (Fig. 3) shows the close fit between the two. A comparison with the first 9 residues of the 16-residue peptide in Fig. 2 also shows essentially the same conformation for the same sequence. A closer look at the superimposed diagrams in Fig. 3 shows that the helix in the molecule represented by the solid lines is somewhat elongated at both ends from that in the molecule represented by the dashed lines. This rather small difference corresponds to a change in hydrogen bonding from predominantly 4 → 1 hydrogen bonds (3_{10}-helix) in the longer helix to predominantly 5 → 1 hydrogen bonds (α-helix). Subtle changes in torsion angles ϕ and ψ, 3°–9°, cause sufficient distance or direction changes to switch hydrogen bonds from NH atoms to different O atoms (Karle *et al.*, 1988).

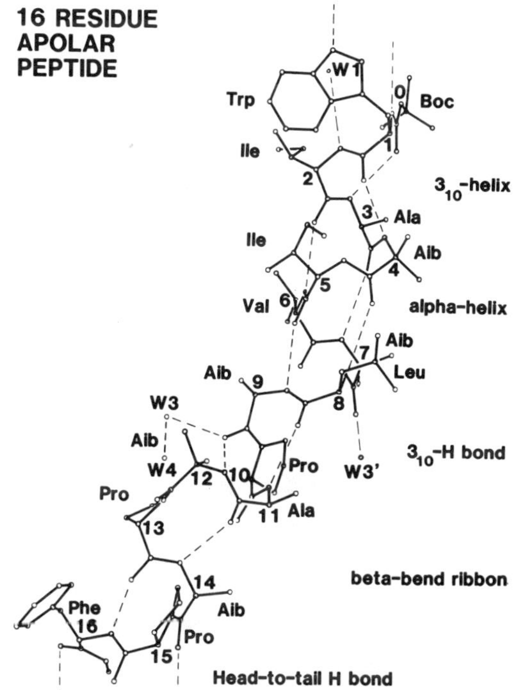

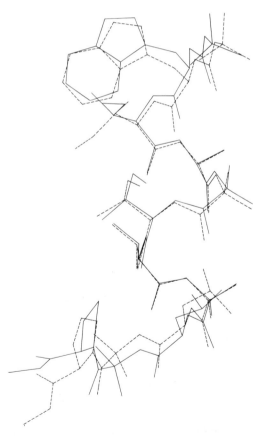

Fig. 2. A 16-residue apolar helical peptide. The C^{α} atoms are labeled 1–16. Hydrogen bonds are indicated by dashed lines. Water molecules are indicated by W (Karle *et al.*, 1987).

Fig. 3. A superposition of a decapeptide molecule in a monoclinic cell (solid lines) with the same molecule in a triclinic cell (dashed lines) (Karle *et al.*, 1988).

The above example compared the same decapeptide in two different crystal forms. The next example compares two molecules of another decapeptide co-crystallized in one crystal. The peptide in this case is Boc-Aib-Val-Aib-Aib-Val-Val-Val-Aib-Val-Aib-OMe (Karle *et al.*, 1989a).

The conformations of the two independent molecules are superimposed in Fig. 4. The molecule represented by solid lines is completely α-helical with seven 5 → 1 hydrogen bonds. In the molecule shown in dashed lines, the backbone at the Boc end has unwound from a helical form, the helix is longer at the OMe end, and the hydrogen bonding pattern has undergone a transition at both ends from 5 → 1 to 4 → 1 hydrogen bonds.

These examples show the elusive nature of 3_{10} /α-helix transitions. They are not sequence dependent, nor is it obvious from inspection of packing diagrams how crystal packing affects the conformation of helices. In actual molecules, there is no clear distinction between values for ϕ and ψ torsional angles for 3_{10}- or α-helical hydrogen bonds. The choice of hydrogen bond is based on N···O and H···O distances and the angular geometry about C=O···N and NH···O. Sometimes the N···O distances are as large as 3.2 Å. The H···O distances approach 2.4–2.5 Å at times. Hydrogen atoms bonded to N are often found in difference maps, and their coordinates are refined by least-squares along with the coordinates of the C, N, and O atoms. If the H atoms are not located experimentally, then they are placed in idealized positions on N atoms with planar geometry.

Table 1 shows the types of intramolecular hydrogen bonds observed in the helical peptides described herein. The N(1)H and N(2)H atoms are omitted, since these cannot be involved in intramolecular bonds. In the peptides shown, the helix usually, but not always, begins with a 4 → 1 hydrogen bond. The helix sometimes ends with a 4 → 1 bond. The central part of the helix always has only 5 → 1 hydrogen bonds. In almost every case, the NH between one involved in a 4 → 1 hydrogen bond and one involved in a 5 → 1 hydrogen bond is left unsatisfied, since there is no carbonyl oxygen in an appropriate position to act as an acceptor.

Head-to-Tail Hydrogen Bonding

Helical peptides have been found almost exclusively to form head-to-tail hydrogen bonds and, in this manner, to extend a column of helices throughout the length of the crystal. Even if the helix is curved due to the presence of a Pro residue, head-to-tail hydrogen bonding occurs. The presence of end groups, such as Ac (acetyl), Boc (t-butyloxycarbonyl), or OMe (methyl ester), does not interfere with the hydrogen bonding.

At the head of a helix of an individual

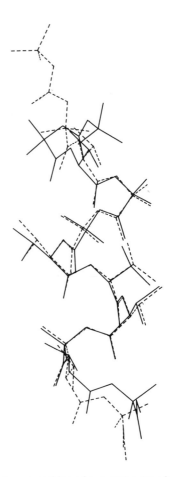

Fig. 4. A superposition of two molecules of Boc-Aib-Val-Aib-Aib-Val-Val-Val-Aib-Val-Aib-OMe co-crystallized side by side in the same cell.

Table 1. Intramolecular hydrogen bond type from NH(n) in apolar helical peptides.

	n	3	4	5	6	7	8	9	10	11	12	13	14	15	16
Co-crystallized	1a		A	A	A	A	A	A	A						
conformers	1b		T		A	A	A	A	T						
Polymorphs	2a	T		A	A	A	A	A	P						
	2b	T		A	A	A	A	A	P						
	2c	T	T		A	A	T	T	P						
	2d		A	A	A*	A	A	A	P						
Sequence 1–10 same as 2	3	T	T		A	A	A	A	P	T	T	P	T	P	T
Same repeat	4	T		A	A	A	A	T							
sequence	5	T	T		A	A	A	A	A	A	A	A			
	6	T	T	W	T	A	A	A	A						

T = 3_{10}-helix hydrogen bond (or 4 → 1 type); A = α-helix hydrogen bond (or 5 → 1 type); P = Pro residue; W = water insertion; A* = very long hydrogen bond.

1a,b = Boc-Aib-Val-Aib-Aib-Val-Val-Val-Aib-Val-Aib-OMe; 2a,b,c = Boc-Trp-Ile-Ala-Aib-Ile-Val-Aib-Leu-Aib-Pro-OMe; 2d = Ac-Trp-Ile-Ala-Aib-Ile-Val-Aib-Leu-Aib-Pro-OMe; 3 = Boc-Trp-Ile-Ala-Aib-Ile-Val-Aib-Leu-Aib-Pro-Ala-Aib-Pro-Aib-Pro-Phe-OMe; 4 = Boc-(Aib-Val-Ala-Leu-)$_2$-Aib-OMe; 5 = Boc-(Aib-Val-Ala-Leu-)$_3$-Aib-OMe; 6 = Boc-(Aib-Ala-Leu-)$_3$-Aib-OMe.

molecule, there are two or three NH moieties directed upwards (if the helix is viewed vertically) that cannot be involved in intramolecular 4 → 1 or 5 → 1 hydrogen bonds. Similarly at the tail of the helix, there are three or four carbonyl moieties directed downwards without hydrogen bonds.

Translation of a peptide molecule along the helix axis, or a translation and 180° rotation, places one helical molecule over another so that intermolecular hydrogen bonds may be made. In Fig. 5, the bottom end of one molecule fits neatly over the top end of the other so that three intermolecular hydrogen bonds, N(1)H···O(8), N(2)H···O(9), and N(3)H···O(10), are formed (indicated by heavy dashed lines). These bonds are in register with the intramolecular 5 → 1 bonds of the peptide Boc-Aib-Val-Aib-Aib-Val-Val-Val-Aib-Val-Aib-OMe (Karle *et al.*, 1989a).

Not all helical peptides can meet in good register for direct hydrogen bond formation because of the presence of very bulky side chains or a Pro residue near a terminus. An example for the peptide Boc-Trp-Ile-Ala-Aib-Ile-Val-Aib-Leu-Aib-Pro-OMe (Karle *et al.*, 1986, 1990b) is shown in Fig. 6. In this ex-ample, there are no direct NH···O hydrogen bonds between backbone atoms. The NH in the tryptophanyl side chain forms a bifurcated hydrogen bond to O(8) and O(9) in the molecule above. Furthermore, a solvent molecule, in this case isopropyl alcohol (IPA), mediates hydrogen bonding between the head and tail of the pair of peptide molecules by acting as an acceptor for N(1)H···O(IPA) as well as a donor for OH(IPA)···O(7). The N(2)H moiety does not participate in any hydrogen bonding. The N(2)–H bond is directed into a void where the nearest intermolecular approach to N(2) is 5.4 Å to the oxygen atom in IPA and 5.6 Å to an O(10) atom in a neighboring peptide molecule.

In other helical peptides, the head-to-tail region is characterized by a combination of hydrogen bond types, i.e., NH···O=C bonds, solvent-mediated hydrogen bonds (usually involving water molecules), and, at times, hydrogen bonds involving atoms in side chains. In several crystal structures of hydrophobic helical peptides, the N(2)H or N(3)H moieties remain unsatisfied in forming any hydrogen bonds, as shown in the example in Fig. 6.

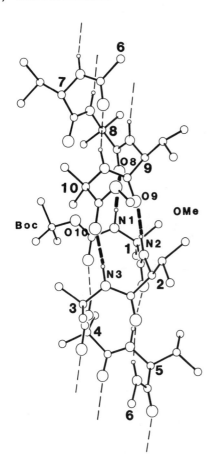

Fig. 5. Direct head-to-tail hydrogen bonds (middle of diagram, three heavy dashed lines) between two decapeptide molecules of the type shown in solid lines in Fig. 4. The light dashed lines represent 5 → 1 type hydrogen bonds in the helix.

Aggregation of Helices

One of the goals in our study of structures of apolar peptides is to gather information about the aggregation properties of helical peptides as a function of sequence and size of side chains. This type of information may be useful for gaining insights about the nature of transmembrane peptide channels. The initial surprise was the common occurrence of parallel packing of apolar helices. This is in contrast to antiparallel or oblique packing of neighboring helices generally observed in proteins (Richardson, 1981). Peptides 2a, 2b, and 3, listed in Table 1, crystallize in the triclinic space group P1 with one molecule per cell. As

a consequence, the only relationship between molecules is one of translation in the direction of the three crystal axes; hence the helices must necessarily be parallel to each other. Peptides 2c and 4 crystallize in the monoclinic space group $P2_1$ with their helix axes nearly parallel to the screw axis of the space group. Again, by the screw-axis operation, neighboring molecules have their helix axes directed in the same direction rather than in the antiparallel direction. The parallel packing motif of peptide 2c (Table 1) in space group $P2_1$ is illustrated in Fig. 7. The helical molecules in

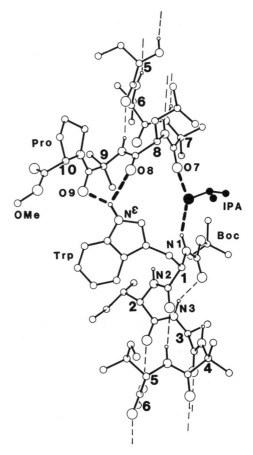

Fig. 6. Head-to-tail hydrogen bonds (middle of diagram, four heavy dashed lines) between two Boc-Trp-Ile-Ala-Aib-Ile-Val-Aib-Leu-Aib-Pro-OMe molecules. There are no direct hydrogen bonds between backbone NH and O=C groups. The hydrogen bonds between N(1) and O(7) are mediated by isopropanol (IPA). The N^ε atom in the Trp side chain provides the H atom for a bifurcated hydrogen bond to O(8) and O(9).

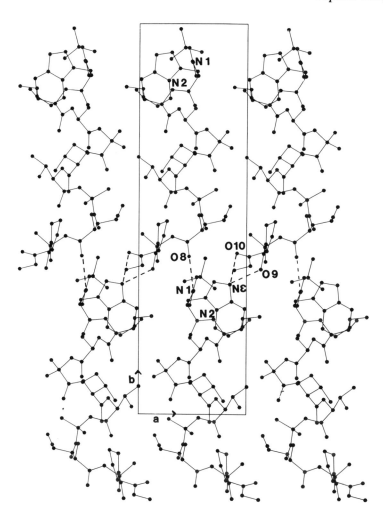

Fig. 7. Parallel packing of helices in monoclinic cell of anhydrous peptide with the same sequence as in Fig. 6 (Karle *et al.*, 1986).

the upper row are related by translation only, both in the plane of the page and perpendicular to the page. The upper molecules are related to the lower molecules by a two-fold screw operation. In the entire crystal all the helix axes are parallel and pointed in the same direction.

A primary stabilizing force for α-helices is the hydrophobic interaction of the side chains. The contacts between the side chains of neighboring molecules of the peptides listed in Table 1 are generally rather unselective. In fact, at times, the fit is inefficient, leaving voids of ~5 Å diameter. In peptide 2, there must be no special attractions or fit between particular types of side chains, since four different polymorphs were obtained easily in which the intermolecular contacts are quite different.

One exception is Boc-(Aib-Ala-Leu)$_3$-Aib-OMe (Karle *et al.*, 1988a), in which a Leu residue occurs in every third position. In the packing motif (Fig. 8), the Leu side chains of two neighboring, antiparallel molecules interdigitate very neatly.

Hydration of Apolar Helices

Apolar helices can acquire minipolar surface areas or even amphiphilicity by the action of water. Water molecules have been found to interact with the backbone atoms of an apolar helix in three different modes, as illustrated in the schematic diagram in Fig. 9. When a Pro residue is incorporated into an α-helix, the hydrogen atom normally occurring on the

Fig. 8. Packing in cell of Boc-(Aib-Ala-Leu-)₃-Aib-OMe. Three molecules of the peptide are shown. On the left, the leucyl side chains of two adjacent molecules interdigitate to form very efficient hydrophobic contacts. On the right, two adjacent molecules have hydrogen bonds (dashed lines) mediated by water molecules (indicated by W1 and W2) (Karle *et al.*, 1988a).

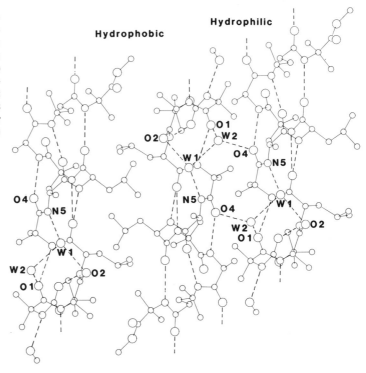

amide N is replaced by a pyrrolidine ring. The loss of the hydrogen atom interrupts the intrahelical hydrogen bonding and leaves a carbonyl oxygen free. In addition, the extra bulk of the pyrrolidine ring is accommodated by curving the helix by ~30°, thus exposing the carbonyl oxygen to the external environment, as shown in Fig. 9A. If there are no bulky side chains to shield the carbonyl oxygen, a water molecule can approach and form a OH···O hydrogen bond. Hydration of this type can be seen near the middle of the right side of the 16-residue peptide displayed in Fig. 2.

A second possibility for hydration of the backbone is shown schematically in Fig. 9B and observed on the left side of Fig. 2, in *4* of Table 1, as well as elsewhere (Karle *et al.*, 1988b; Satyshur *et al.*, 1988). In this case, the helix may be straight or bent, a normal NH···O=C bond is formed in the helix, and, in addition, the surrounding side chains are very small or directed away so that the carbonyl moiety is exposed to the outside environment. The opportunity is offered for the approach of a water molecule and the subsequent formation of an additional hydrogen bond with the water molecule.

The third event, shown in Fig. 9C, is the most fascinating. A water molecule actually intervenes between an NH and C=O pair expected to form a normal bond in a helix backbone. The N···O separation is increased to 5.0 Å from the normal 3.0 Å. The consequent curvature of the helix is due to rotations only about the bonds to the C^α atom following the

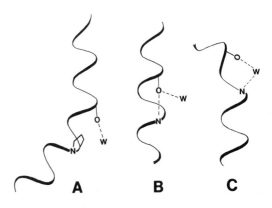

Fig. 9. Schematic diagram of three modes of hydrating the backbone in a helix.

C=O, where $\phi = -100°$ and $\psi = +15°$, instead of ϕ and ψ values near $-60°$ and $-40°$ that are normal for a 3_{10}- or α-helix. The water molecule accepts a hydrogen from the NH group and donates a hydrogen to the O=C group. In addition, the water molecule may attract other water molecules to increase the solvation effect, as shown in Fig. 10 (Karle *et al.*, 1988a). The result is the creation of an amphiphilic helix in a peptide containing only nonpolar residues. The packing of such a solvated helix is shown in Fig. 8 where, on one side of the helix, hydrophobic contacts are made by the interdigitating leucyl side chains

from two neighboring molecules, and, on the other side, the contacts between neighboring molecules are hydrogen bonds via water molecules.

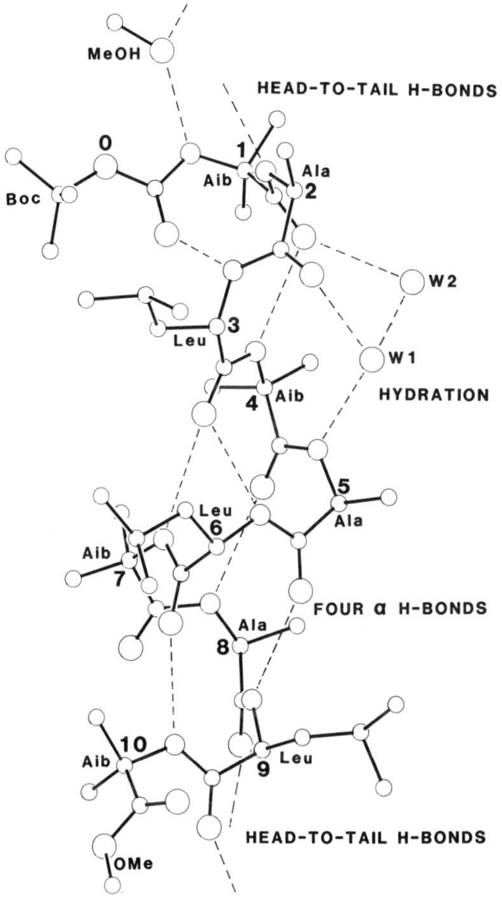

The insertion of water molecules into a helical backbone is not unique to the Boc-(Aib-Ala-Leu-)$_3$-Aib-OMe molecule shown in Figs. 8 and 10. It has also been demonstrated in Boc-(Ala-Leu-Aib)$_2$-OMe with identical geometry as in the decapeptide above (Karle *et al.*, 1989b) and in two sites in the protein Troponin C (Satyshur *et al.*, 1988).

Summary

The crystal structure analyses of peptides with well-resolved scattering data have provided detailed information on the conservation of unique conformations with different packing motifs and different solvent exposure, on transitions between 3_{10}- and α-helices in individual peptides, on conformational differences between two peptide molecules co-crystallized in the same cell, modes of head-to-tail hydrogen bonding in helical peptides, NH moieties not participating in hydrogen bonds, parallel packing of helices, interdigitation of side chains from neighboring helices, and the various modes of hydrating a nonpolar helix, including the insertion of a water molecule into the backbone between an NH and O=C group.

Acknowledgments

Research in the area of peptides has been supported in part by ONR and NIH grant #GM30902 and in part by a grant from the Department of Science and Technology, India.

Fig. 10. Conformation of Boc-(Aib-Ala-Leu-)$_3$-Aib-OMe with the intervention of a water molecule (W1) between N(5) and O(2). The N(5)···O(2) hydrogen bond has been broken and replaced by two hydrogen bonds, N(5)-W1 and W1-O(2). An additional water molecule (W2) is attracted to W1 and O(1). Hydrogen bonds are indicated by the dashed lines (Karle *et al.*, 1988a).

References

Burgess, A. W., and S. J. Leach, *Biopolymers* **12**, 2599 (1973).

Karle, I. L., in *Biomolecular Stereodynamics III. Proceedings of the Fourth Conversation in the*

Discipline Biomolecular Stereodynamics, R. H. Sarma and M. H. Sarma, Eds. (Adenine Press, Guilderland, New York, 1986), pp. 197–215.

Karle, I. L., and J. L. Flippen-Anderson, *Acta Cryst.* **C45**, 791 (1989).

Karle, I. L., J. L. Flippen-Anderson, K. Uma, H. Balaram, P. Balaram, *Proc. Natl. Acad. Sci. U.S.A.* **86**, 765 (1989a).

_____, *Biopolymers,* in press (1990a).

Karle, I. L., J. Flippen-Anderson, M. Sukumar, P. Balaram, *Proc. Natl. Acad. Sci. U.S.A.* **84**, 5087 (1987).

_____, *Int. J. Peptide Protein Res.* **31**, 567 (1988).

_____, *Int. J. Peptide Protein Res.,* in press (1990b).

Karle, I. L., J. Flippen-Anderson, K. Uma, P. Balaram, *Proc. Natl. Acad. Sci. U.S.A.* **85**, 299 (1988a).

_____, *Int. J. Peptide Protein Res.,* **32**, 536 (1988b).

_____, *Biopolymers,* **28**, 773 (1989b).

Karle, I. L., R. Kishore, S. Raghothama, P. Balaram, *J. Amer. Chem. Soc.* **110**, 1958 (1988b).

Karle, I. L., M. Sukumar, P. Balaram, *Proc. Natl. Acad. Sci. U.S.A.* **83**, 9284 (1986).

Karle, I. L., and T. Wieland, *Int. J. Peptide Protein Res.* **29**, 596 (1987).

Kishore, R., S. Raghothama, P. Balaram, *Biopolymers* **26**, 873 (1987).

Marshall, G. R., *Intra-Science Chem. Rep.* **5**, 305 (1971).

Richardson, J., in *Advances in Protein Chemistry,* vol. 34 (Academic Press, New York, 1981), pp. 167–339.

Satyshur, K. A., *et al., J. Biol. Chem.* **26**, 1628 (1988).

Toniolo, C., *et al., Biopolymers* **22**, 205 (1983).

α-Helix Formation by
Short Peptides in Water

Susan Marqusee and Robert L. Baldwin

Understanding helix formation by short peptides is an important step towards understanding protein folding and the control of protein stability. In many models of the protein-folding process, a common first step is the rapid acquisition of isolated units of secondary structure such as α-helices and β-turns (Kim and Baldwin, 1982; Dyson *et al.*, 1986). Using small peptides as model systems, we can determine if such isolated structural units are energetically feasible and, if they are, what the exact chemical basis of such local sequence information is. Specifically, we want to know what initiates and stabilizes an α-helix, and what localizes or terminates it.

Two types of short peptides have emerged that can serve as model systems for such studies. One is based on N-terminal fragments of ribonuclease A (C-peptide: residues 1–13, and S-peptide: residues 1–20) in which partial helix formation was first observed by Brown and Klee (1969, 1971) and has been characterized extensively subsequently by Baldwin and co-workers (Bierzynski *et al.*, 1982; Kim and Baldwin, 1984; Shoemaker *et al.*, 1985, 1987a, 1987b, and manuscripts in preparation) and by Rico and co-workers (Rico *et al.*, 1983, 1984, 1986). The second is a de novo designed system derived from a simple alanine-based

sequence (Marqusee and Baldwin, 1987).

Until recently, long synthetic polymers have been the dominant tools used in studies of helix formation (Poland and Scheraga, 1970). These studies led to a helix-coil transition theory pioneered by Zimm and Bragg (1959) and further developed by Lifson and Roig (1961). Host-guest experiments on random co-polymers of amino acids have provided numerical values for the Zimm-Bragg parameters 'σ' (nucleation) and 's' (propagation) for 18 of the 20 amino acids in the genetic code (Sueki *et al.*, 1984). Using these experimentally determined values, together with the Zimm-Bragg equation, all peptides containing fewer than 20 amino acids are predicted not to show observable helix formation in water at any temperature (see calculations for a 13-residue alanine peptide;[1] Shoemaker *et al.*, 1985). In addition, work on synthetic polymers has demonstrated that, once a stretch of amino acids overcomes the initial nucleation barrier to helix formation, the helix propagates on average about 100 residues before terminating. Nevertheless, the average helix length in proteins is only 11 amino acids (Schultz and Schirmer, 1979); the mechanism by which short helices are formed in globular proteins needs to be understood.

---

[1] The value of the nucleation parameter s is a key variable in determining the predicted stability of short peptides. The above statement is based on $\sigma \leq 10^{-3}$.

One important factor left out in the studies of long polymers is the contribution to helix stability from specific interactions between side chains. Such interactions are neglected in the Zimm-Bragg theory and are either missing or averaged out in host-guest studies. Specific interactions are proving to make important contributions both to helix stability and to the determination of specific helix endpoints in these small peptide models (Bierzynski *et al.*, 1982; Kim and Baldwin, 1984; Scheraga, 1985; Shoemaker *et al.*, 1985, 1987a, 1987b, 1989; Fairman *et al.*, submitted for publication; Marqusee and Baldwin, 1987). Recently, Vasquez and Scheraga (1987) developed a method to incorporate these effects into the existing theoretical formalism.

Intrahelical Side Chain Interactions Involving Charged Residues

Figure 1 shows two interactions involving charged groups that are postulated to be important in helix stability. Figure 1A depicts the macrodipole moment of the α-helix. A net dipole moment is intrinsic to the helical structure and arises from the alignment of the very polar carbonyl and amide groups along the helix axis (Creighton, 1983; Wada, 1976). The net partial charges result from the four amide and carbonyl groups at either end of the helix that do not participate in helical hydrogen bonding. The overall charge distribution is most simply represented as a line dipole with a net positive pole near the NH_2-terminus of the helix and a net negative pole near the COOH-terminus (Hol *et al.*, 1978; Sheridan *et al.*, 1982). This separation of charge is energetically costly to the helical conformation. Any electrostatic interaction which interacts favorably with it should increase helix stability. Interactions between a charged group and a nearby pole of the macrodipole will stabilize the helix if the two are of opposite sign and destabilize it if they are of like sign. For example, placing a negatively charged group like glutamic acid near the positive pole, or NH_2-

terminus of the helix, would probably favor the helical conformation. This type of charged group:dipole interaction implies that the formal charges present at the α-NH3$^+$ and α-COO$^-$ termini of a short peptide destabilize the helical structure. Therefore, in the design of a helical peptide, or in working with a protein fragment that might show helix formation, one wants to block these formal charges.

Shoemaker *et al.* (1987a) investigated this charged group:helix dipole interaction by studying a series of peptides in which the charge at the NH_2-terminal residue ranges from +2 (Lys 1) to −1 (succinyl-Ala 1). Peptides with Ala 1 (+1) and acetyl-Ala 1 (0) completed the series. These peptides showed a systematic increase in helix content as the NH_2-terminal charge varied from +2 to −1, consistent with the predicted effect of charge interaction with the helix macrodipole.

Figure 1B illustrates a second charged-group interaction involving intrahelical ion

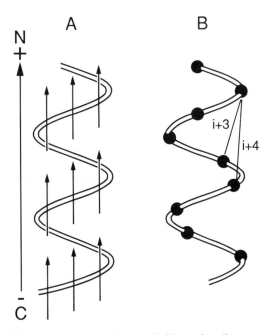

Fig. 1. (A) Diagram of an α-helix illustrating alignment of the individual dipoles to yield a net macrodipole. The positive pole of this macrodipole is at the N-terminus and the negative pole is at the C-terminus. (B) Diagram of an α-helix showing the juxtaposition of residues three and four amino acids apart. The side chains of these residues are close enough to interact.

pairs or salt bridges. We reserve the term salt bridge for explicit reference to hydrogen-bonded ion pairs (Marqusee and Baldwin, 1987) and use the general term ion pair to refer to any electrostatic interaction between oppositely charged residues. The α-helix has 3.6 amino acids per turn; therefore, residues three or four amino acids apart will lie along the same face of the α-helix. This geometry places the two side chains close enough to form a potentially favorable interaction. Such an interaction might stabilize or nucleate a single turn of the helix. Intrahelical ion pairs or salt bridges are postulated to be important

in a variety of systems (Maxfield and Scheraga, 1975; Sundaralingam *et al.*, 1985; Marqusee and Baldwin, 1987).

Intrahelical Interactions in the N-Terminal α-Helix of Ribonuclease A

Figure 2A is derived from the crystal structure of ribonuclease A and displays the backbone of the first 13 residues with the two prominent intrahelical interactions. One of these is a salt bridge between glutamic acid 2 (Glu 2) and

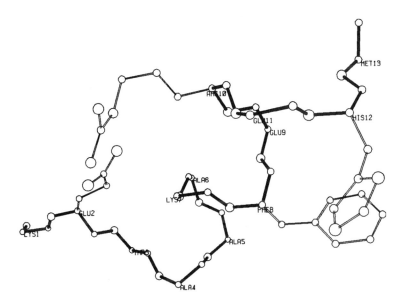

Fig. 2A. Diagram of residues 1–13 of RNase A illustrating two intrahelical side chain interactions: a salt bridge between Glu 2^- and Arg 10^+, and a possible aromatic interaction between Phe 8 and His 12. All other side chains have been omitted for simplicity.

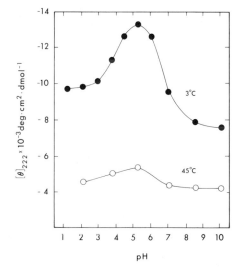

Fig. 2B. *p*H titration of helicity for the peptide Ac-AETAAAKFLRAHA-NH₂ (reference peptide III). A, alanine; E, glutamic acid; T, threonine; K, lysine; F, phenylalanine; L, leucine; R, arginine; H, histidine. Measurements were made at 0.1 *M* NaCl and 20 μM peptide; ●, 3°C; o, 45°C. Peptide synthesis and purification procedures are described in Shoemaker *et al.* (1985) and the peptide was acetylated with acetic anhydride. Circular dichroic (CD) data were recorded on an Aviv 60 DS spectropolarimeter.

arginine 10 (Arg 10) spanning two turns of the α-helix. The second is an interaction between two aromatic residues, phenylalanine 8 (Phe 8) and histidine 12 (His 12), which spans just one turn of the α-helix. The role of these four residues in the isolated peptide is examined by Shoemaker *et al.* (1985, 1987b, 1989), Fairman *et al.* (submitted for publication), and Rico *et al.* (1984, 1986). Shoemaker *et al.* have characterized the helix-forming properties of various synthetic analogs of C-peptide. Figure 2B shows the pH dependence of helix formation, measured by circular dichroism, of a reference peptide containing all four residues described above (reference peptide III). Helix stability shows a bell-shaped pH dependence. By mutating important residues one at a time (X → Ala), it was possible to assign the decrease in helix stability at alkaline pH to the titration of His 12. This pH-dependent titration of helicity depends on phenylalanine at position 8 (Shoemaker *et al.*, 1987b), as well as His 12, consistent with an interaction between these two residues. Similarly, the loss in helicity caused by titration to acidic pH has been assigned to Glu 2, which interacts with Arg 10. In conclusion, the interactions that exist within the isolated peptide are very similar to those seen within the native protein. Moreover, the pH dependence of helix stability indicates that these interactions are helix stabilizing.

Determinants of the Endpoints of a Helical Segment ("Helix Stop Signals")

The N-terminal α-helix of ribonuclease A extends from threonine 3 (Thr 3) to methionine 13 (Met 13). In order to form a salt bridge between Glu 2 and Arg 10, the backbone of Glu 2 is distorted out of an α-helical conformation. The α-carbons of Glu 2 and Lys 1 are thereby excluded from the α-helix. Since we know this Glu 2 ... Arg 10 interaction persists in the isolated peptide, this salt bridge provides a plausible N-terminal "helix stop signal" in the peptide fragment. In order to study helix termination on the C-terminal side,

it is preferable to use peptides that are longer than 13 amino acids. S-peptide is ideal since it contains the first 19 (or 20) amino acids of ribonuclease A (Fig. 3). In the intact protein, the amide proton of Asp 14 is hydrogen-bonded in a tertiary interaction with the carbonyl of Val 47 and cannot participate in helical hydrogen-bonding. No such interaction can occur in the isolated peptide. Using ^{1}H nuclear magnetic resonance (NMR), Rico *et al.* (1983) and Kim and Baldwin (1984)

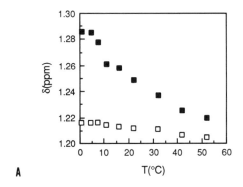

A

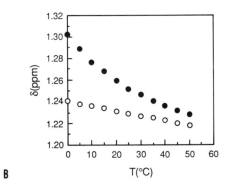

B

Fig. 3. (A) Temperature dependence of ^{1}H-NMR chemical shift for protons of Thr 3 (■) and Thr 17 (□) in S-peptide (sequence shown above). The average chemical shift for the γCH₃ doublets are shown. pH 3.8, 0.1M NaCl, D₂0. (B) Temperature dependence of ^{1}H-NMR chemical shift for the γ- CH₃ protons of an analog of S-peptide whose sequence is shown above. Thr 3, ●; Thr 17, o. Chemical shifts are reported relative to the internal standard, TSP. NMR methods used are those decribed by Kim and Baldwin (1984), and methods used for peptide synthesis and purification of the S-peptide analog are described by Marqusee and Baldwin (1987).

showed that the helical portion of S-peptide is nevertheless confined to approximately the same amino acids as in the intact protein. By using the chemical shifts of various side chain protons along the peptide sequence to monitor their participation in helix formation, Kim and Baldwin (1984) showed that the peptide helix stops somewhere around Met 13. Figure 3A summarizes results for the two threonines (Thr 3 and Thr 17) when temperature is used to cause unfolding. Thr 3, which is inside the α-helix, shows a striking nonlinear change in chemical shift as the helix is thermally unfolded. This behavior is expected for a cooperative helix-coil transition. The chemical shift of Thr 17, which is outside the α-helix in the intact protein, shows a very small and linear change in chemical shift. The residues between the approximate C-terminus of the helix, Met 13, and the proton probe, Thr 17, are Asp 14, Ser 15, and Ser 16. Most protein secondary-structure predictive schemes consider all three of these residues to be helix-destabilizing amino acids.

In order to investigate whether this cluster of helix breakers (Asp 14, Ser 15, Ser 16) causes the observed helix stop in the isolated peptide, an analog of S-peptide was synthesized in which all three amino acids were simultaneously replaced by alanine. Alanine is an amino acid which is observed to be helix favoring. The analysis of this S-peptide analog is shown in Fig. 3B and can be compared directly with the results found with S-peptide. Qualitatively, the results are similar and a nonlinear change in chemical shift is seen for Thr 3 but not for Thr 17. The C-terminal helix stop signal near Met 13 in S-peptide appears to remain intact in the absence of the three helix-breaking amino acids. We conclude that the information encoding the observed helix stop signal resides within the helical portion of the peptide. A two-dimensional NMR study of analogs of C-peptide (Osterhout *et al.*, 1989) shows that the peptide backbone conformation of His 12 is not that of an α-helix. Work is now under way to test whether the intrahelical side chain interaction between His 12 and Phe 8 is acting as a C-terminal helix stop signal in S-peptide.

Simple De Novo Designed Peptides Allow Characterization of Specific Side Chain Interactions

In order to characterize different possible side chain interactions, we decided to attempt the de novo design of a helix-forming peptide (Marqusee and Baldwin, 1987). Our goal was to use simple repetitive sequences in which we could systematically manipulate a side chain interaction of interest. Such simple peptides should provide a well-defined system for measuring the effects of specific side chain interactions on helix formation. We started with an alanine-based peptide and inserted the desired amino acids. Because oligo-L-alanine peptides are not soluble, the inserted amino acids must serve the dual purpose of solubilizing the resulting peptide.

To investigate intrahelical salt bridges, we designed peptides using the strategy shown in Fig. 4. Since side chains that are either three or four residues apart will be close enough to form ion pairs, two sets of peptides were dèsigned. In one set, (i+4), the residues of interest were positioned at alternating spacings of i+4 and i+1, while in the other set, (i+3), the spacing alternates between i+3 and i+2. Within each peptide there are three i+4 or i+3 pairs. Every positively charged residue has one negatively charged residue spaced three or four amino acids away; however, the oppositely charged residues spaced i+4 apart may also interact with nearby charged residues at an i+1 spacing. The pairs were positioned along the sequence so as to spiral around the face of an α-helix (see Fig. 4). This prevents the helix from being amphiphilic, and should avoid the presentation of a purely hydrophobic surface which could induce helix formation by association.

The formal charges at the ends of the designed peptides were blocked in order to avoid any complications caused by their charges. Blocking these charged groups should also enhance helix formation since the expected helix dipole interactions are destabilizing.

Interactions between charged groups on

Fig. 4. (upper) Sequences of the designed peptides. + refers to a positively charged residue: lysine (K) or histidine (H). − refers to a negatively charged residue: glutamic acid (E) or aspartic acid (D). Ac, Acetyl; A, alanine. **(lower)** Illustration of the potential helix-anchoring effect of salt bridges or ion pairs for the (i + 4) peptides. Note that the charges spiral around the surface of the helix. Methods for peptide synthesis and purification are described in Marqusee and Baldwin (1987).

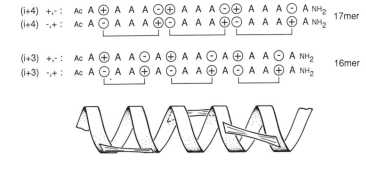

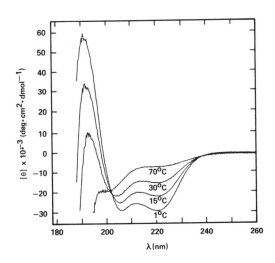

the side chains and the helix dipole can either stabilize or destabilize the helix (Shoemaker *et al.*, 1987a). To take account of this, two peptides were designed for each ion pair spacing (i + 3 or i + 4): the two peptides differ by interchanging the positive and negative charges. Thus, in a series of peptides with inserted pairs of glutamic acid and lysine residues, one set is termed E,K and the other K,E. E,K places a glutamic acid near the N-terminus or positive pole of the helix dipole and a lysine near the C-terminus or negative pole of the helix dipole. Any interactions with the helix dipole in this peptide should be helix-stabilizing. Conversely, in the K,E orientation, the charged lysine and glutamic acid residues should interact unfavorably with the helix dipole and be helix destabilizing. Ion pair or salt bridge formation in any of these peptides (E,K or K,E) should be helix stabilizing. There is no reason to expect that a salt bridge with the orientation E . . . K will have the same energetic properties as a K . . . E salt bridge. By studying all four peptides, however, information about salt bridges and helix dipole effects can be extracted.

Helix Formation in Designed Peptides

In order to obtain any information about helix stability from these peptides, the synthetic peptides must be soluble, and at least one of the peptides must show measurable helix formation. Fortunately, all the peptides were readily soluble in water, and all exhibited

some helicity. Figure 5 shows circular dichroism spectra at various temperatures for the peptide (i + 4)E,K. These spectra are characteristic of partial helix formation: they show the two characteristic helical minima (one at 222 nm and one near 208 nm) and the maximum near 193 nm. At 1°C, this peptide forms a remarkably stable helix. The mean residue ellipticity at 222 nm of −29,000 deg cm^2/dmol indicates > 80 percent helix formation. ($[\Theta]_{222}$ for 100 percent helix formation is estimated as −36,000, based on extrapolation with varying concentrations of trifluoroethanol (TFE) (Marqusee, unpublished results)). Helix formation appears to be a monomeric reaction. The circular dichroism

Fig. 5. CD spectra of peptide (i + 4)E,K (17 μM) at four temperatures in .01M KF (pH 7.0) (from Marqusee and Baldwin (1987)). Sample preparation and CD methods are described in Marqusee and Baldwin.

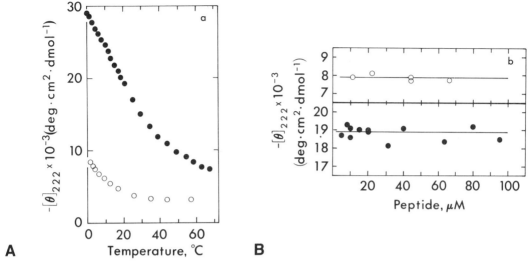

Fig. 6. (A) Thermal unfolding profiles for two peptides measured by −[Θ]222, the mean residue ellipticity at 222 nm (.01M NaCl). ●, (i+4)E,K (pH 7.3); o, (i+3)K,E (pH 7.0). (B) Dependence of helicity on peptide concentration (.01M NaCl). ●, (i+4)E,K (pH 7.1) at 20°C; o, (i+3)K,E (pH 7.3) at 1°C (from Marqusee and Baldwin (1987)).

(CD) spectra are independent of concentration in the measured range of 5–100 μM (see Fig. 6B). Gel filtration analysis, using a Sephadex G-25 sf column under optimal helix-forming conditions, is consistent with a monomeric species. Therefore, we have succeeded in designing a stable, short, isolated α-helix.

Helix formation in these peptides is strongly dependent on temperature (Fig. 6A). The helix is most stable at low temperature and unfolds with increasing temperature. The temperature unfolding curves are similar to those seen for C-peptide and its analogs. Since these peptides differ from C-peptide in composition and in the specific interactions that stabilize the helix, it is unlikely that the enthalpy driving helix formation arises from sequence-specific interactions. Most likely, it arises from some intrinsic property of α-helix formation. From work on polypeptides, Hermans (1966) determined the enthalpy of helix formation in water to be ∼−1 kcal/mole per residue. This value is consistent with the temperature-induced unfolding curves we observe for these short peptides. Calorimetric data will be needed to determine these parameters precisely.

Within the series of (Glu,Lys) peptides,

there is a wide range of helix-forming properties, with some of the peptides forming extremely stable helices. These differences cannot be attributed solely to changes in the helical propensity or s values of the component amino acids, since the peptides have similar amino acid compositions. The differences must arise from the specific sequences and side chain interactions.

Two approaches were taken to determine what side chain interactions stabilize these peptides: one approach is to compare helix stability between different peptides at pH 7 and the second is to determine the effects of side chain ionization on helix stability. Table 1 lists the extent of helix formation at neutral pH for the four (Glu,Lys) peptides. Comparison of two peptides that have the same charge orientation but differ in residue spacing, (i+3) versus (i+4), yields information about the effect of residue spacing. For instance, comparing (i+4)E,K to (i+3)E,K, the (i+4) peptide is seen to be significantly more stable. A similar effect is seen in comparing the K,E peptides: there is a net increase in helix stability going from (i+3)K,E to (i+4)K,E. Either some interaction in the (i+4) peptides not present in the (i+3) peptides is helix stabilizing, or else some interaction in the (i+3) peptides is helix destabilizing. The helix stabilizing interaction is assumed to be salt bridges or ion pairs that are either selectively formed or are more helix stabilizing in the (i+4) peptides.

Electrostatic stabilization is also observed in the pH dependence of helix formation. Figure 7 shows helix content as a function of pH for the four Glu,Lys peptides. The weakest helix, (i+3)K,E, is least stable at neutral pH where both the glutamic acid and lysine residues are charged. This is the pH where any effects from salt bridge stabilization would be the greatest. As charges on the glutamic acid or lysine residues are removed, helix stability increases. This inverted bell-shaped curve is inconsistent with helix stabilization by salt bridges. It is, however, exactly what is predicted for unfavorable interactions between charged groups and the helix macrodipole. It should be remembered that the s values of ionizable residues commonly decrease upon ionization, and this will also affect the pH dependence of helicity.

The pH dependence for (i+3)K,E can be compared directly to that for (i+4)K,E. At neutral pH, the (i+4)K,E peptide helix is more stable. Moreover, despite the potential destabilizing interactions with the helix dipole, this peptide shows a decrease in helicity when the charges are removed. Therefore, ion pairs or salt bridges apparently stabilize this peptide helix.

The data in Table 1 suggest that the i+4 peptides are stabilized more than the i+3 peptides by ion pairs. The pH dependence results indicate that, at least for (i+4)E,K, this stabilization may be caused by salt bridges rather than by nonhydrogen-bonded ion pairs. At the extremes of pH (pH 2 and pH 12), where only one member of the pair is charged, the difference in helix stability seen between (i+4)E,K and (i+3)E,K still exists. The simplest explanation for this effect is that a singly charged hydrogen bond is effective at stabilizing the helix. This interpretation suggests that salt bridges or hydrogen-bonded ion pairs stabilize the helix at neutral pH. Using site-directed mutagenesis of tyrosyl-tRNA synthetase, Fersht *et al.* (1985) find that singly charged hydrogen bonds are strong interactions. Model compound studies of bimolecular salt bridge formation by Springs and Haake (1977) indicate that hydrogen bonding is a measurable component of salt bridge formation.

Fig. 7. *pH* titration of helicity for the four (Glu,Lys) peptides in .01*M* NaCl at 1°C. (a) (i+4)E,K; (b) (i+4)K,E; (c) (i+3)E,K; (d) (i+3)K,E (from Marqusee and Baldwin (1987)).

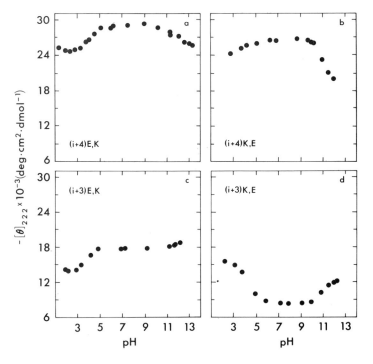

Table 1. Helix content (*p*H 7.0, 1.0°C).

Name	$-[\theta]_{222}$ (cm²degree/dmol)		Helix dipole interaction	Spacing
	.01*M* NaCl	1.0*M* NaCl		
(i+4)E,K	29,000	24,800	+	i+4
(i+4)K,E	25,300	25,700	−	i+4
(i+3)E,K	17,600	17,400	+	i+3
(i+3)K,E	8,500	12,000	−	i+3

Using the same basic design as a recipe for helix stabilization, additional pairs of interacting residues have been studied. The energetic importance of a salt bridge is seen quite clearly when studying two peptides containing aspartic acid and lysine. (These differ from the Glu,Lys peptides only by removal of three methylene groups from the three Glu residues.) As shown in Fig. 8, (i+3)K,D exhibits virtually no helix formation at neutral *p*H. When the residue spacing is changed to i+4, however, helix formation dramatically increases. The amount of helix formation in the (i+4) peptide is estimated to be > 60 percent. This dramatic difference in helix stability is caused solely by the change in residue spacing between the charged groups.

Selective salt bridge stabilization in the i+4 peptides is an unexpected result, since both i+3 and i+4 residues lie on the same face of the helix. The reasons for this behavior are not yet known. Helix stabilization may depend on a selective ability to form the ideal geometry for hydrogen-bonded ion pairs when the side chains are restricted to their energetically favored rotamer conformations (Janin *et al.*, 1978; Ponder and Richards, 1987; Rose, personal communication, 1987). Alternatively, helix stabilization may depend on the preferred geometries of side chain packing in relation to the ridges and grooves formed by the helix. Some of the observed differences in stability may arise from the different external spacing between the i+4 and i+3 pairs (i+1 versus i+2).

Relationship to Protein Structure and Folding

Both of these model peptide systems demonstrate at least two types of interactions that contribute to helix stability: interactions with the helix dipole and with intrahelical salt bridges. Both interactions can be correlated with what is observed in proteins. In the peptides of de novo design, helix stabilization results when charged groups lie in the opposite orientation to the helix macrodipole. In proteins, one frequently observes negative charges clustered around the N-termini of helices and positive charges clustered around the C-termini (Chou and Fasman, 1978). In isolated peptides, salt bridge formation increases helix stability when glutamic acid and lysine residues are separated four residues apart. In protein helices, a basic residue frequently occurs four residues away from a glutamic acid residue (Maxfield and Scheraga, 1975). No such correlation occurs, however, when a basic residue was only three amino acids away.

The framework model of protein folding

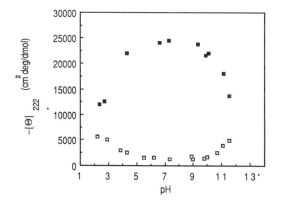

Fig. 8. *p*H titration of helicity for two (Asp,Lys) peptides in .01*M* NaCl at 1°C. ■ (i+4)K,D; □ (i+3)K,D.

considers the rapid acquisition of localized secondary structure to be the first step in the folding process. The fact that we are able to find measurable helix formation in isolated peptides, and that our results correlate with what is seen in protein helices, suggests that the framework model of protein folding is feasible. Our work on peptide helix formation suggests that such structures could form the basis for early intermediates in the protein folding process, and these results may lead to the discovery of new folding intermediates.

Acknowledgments

We thank all the members of the Baldwin Laboratory for stimulating discussion and advice, Virginia Robbins for technical assistance and Rob Fairman, Fred Hughson, and Alan Sachs for critical reading of this manuscript. This research was supported by National Science Foundation Grant DMB 85-18112 and National Institutes of Health GM 31475. S.M. is a predoctoral fellow of the Medical Scientists Training Program (GM 07365). Mass spectra were provided by the UC San Francisco Mass Spectrometry Resource (NIH Grant RR 01614).

References

Bierzynski, A., P. S. Kim, R. L. Baldwin, *Proc. Natl. Acad. Sci. U.S.A.* **79**, 2470 (1982).

Brown, J. E., and W. A. Klee, *Biochemistry* **8**, 2876 (1969).

_____, *Biochemistry* **10**, 470 (1971).

Chou, P., and G. D. Fasman, *Adv. Enzymol.* **47**, 45 (1978).

Creighton, T. E., *Proteins* (W. H. Freeman & Co., New York, 1983).

Dyson, J., *et al., Nature* **318**, 480 (1986).

Fairman, R., *et al.,* submitted for publication.

Fersht, A., *et al., Nature* **314**, 235 (1985).

Hermans, J., Jr., *J. Phys. Chem.* **70**, 510 (1966).

Hol, W., P. T. van Duijnen, H. J. C. Berendsen, *Nature* **273**, 443 (1978).

Janin, J., S. Wodak, M. Levitt, B. Maigret, *L. Mol. Biol.* **125**, 357 (1978).

Kim, P. S., and R. L. Baldwin, *Ann. Rev. Biochem.* **51**, 459 (1982).

Kim, P. S., and R. L. Baldwin, *Nature* **307**, 329 (1984).

Lifson, S., and A. Roig, *J. Chem. Phys.* **34**, 1963 (1961).

Marqusee, S., and R. L. Baldwin, *Proc. Natl. Acad. Sci. U.S.A.* **84**, 8898 (1987).

Maxfield, F., and H. A. Scheraga, *Macromolecules* **8**, 491 (1975).

Osterhout, J. J., *et al., Biochemistry,* **28** 7059 (1989).

Poland, D., and H. A. Scheraga, *Theory of Helix-Coil Transitions in Biopolymers* (Academic Press, New York, 1970).

Ponder, J. W., and F. M. Richards, *J. Mol. Biol.* **196**, 775 (1987).

Rico, M., *et al., FEBS Lett.* **162**, 314 (1983).

_____, *Biochem. Biophys. Res. Comm.* **123**, 757 (1984).

_____, *Biopolymers* **25**, 1031 (1986).

Schultz, G. E., and R. H. Schirmer, *Principles of Protein Structure* (Springer, New York, 1979).

Sheridan, R. M., R. M. Levy, F. R. Salemme, *Proc. Natl. Acad. Sci. U.S.A.* **79**, 4545 (1982).

Shoemaker, K. R., *et al., Proc. Natl. Acad. Sci. U.S.A.* **82**, 2349 (1985).

Shoemaker, K. R., P. S. Kim, E. J. York, J. M. Stewart, R. L. Baldwin, *Nature* **326**, 563 (1987a).

Shoemaker, K. R., *et al., Cold Spring Harbor Symposium on Quantitative Biology* **52**, 391 (1987b).

Shoemaker, K. R., R. Fairman, E. J. York, J. M. Stewart, R. L. Baldwin, *Biopolymers,* in press (1989).

Springs, R., and P. Haake, *Bioorganic Chemistry* **6**, 181 (1977).

Sueki, S., *et al., Macromolecules* **17**, 148 (1984).

Sundaralingam, M., W. Drendel, M. Greaser, *Proc. Natl. Acad. Sci. U.S.A.* **82**, 7944 (1985).

Vazquez, M., and H. A. Scheraga, *Biopolymers* **27**, 41 (1987).

Wada, A., *Adv. Biophys.* **9**, 1 (1976).

Zimm, B. H., and J. K. Bragg, *J. Chem. Phys.* **31**, 526 (1959).

9

Folding of Peptide Fragments of Proteins in Water Solution

Peter E. Wright, H. Jane Dyson
Jonathan P. Waltho, Richard A. Lerner

Protein folding is a highly cooperative process: the nascent polypeptide chain folds rapidly into a compact globular structure which slowly rearranges into the correctly folded native protein. The rate-determining step usually occurs towards the end of the folding pathway (Creighton, 1985, 1987, 1988; Brandts *et al.*, 1975) and can involve disulfide bridge rearrangement or cis-trans isomerization of proline. At present, little is known about the very early events that initiate protein folding because folding proceeds so rapidly and cooperatively to compact structures. A seemingly attractive approach to studying the initiation of folding is to search for structure in small peptide fragments of proteins in water solution for which the cooperative folding process cannot be completed. Early experiments (Epand and Scheraga, 1968; Taniuchi and Anfinsen, 1969; Hermans and Puett, 1971; Howard *et al.*, 1975) suggested that there is very little structure in peptide fragments of proteins. However, in recent years, it has become evident that linear peptide fragments of proteins are not the structureless entities in solution that were previously supposed. By using a combination of immunology to screen for likely folded sites of peptides and sophisticated nuclear magnetic resonance (NMR) measurements to determine structures that are formed, we have been able to identify several types of secondary structure in small linear peptides in water solution (reviewed in Wright *et al.*, 1988, and Dyson *et al.*, 1988a).

Anti-Peptide Antibodies Can Cross-React with Folded Proteins

Over the past few years, it has been recognized that short peptide fragments of proteins can induce antibodies that cross-react with the cognate sequence in the folded native protein (Niman *et al.*, 1983; Lerner, 1984). This phenomenon is difficult to understand unless the peptides themselves adopt preferred conformations in aqueous solution. Consider induction of an antipeptide antibody that recognizes, for example, a helical region within a folded protein (Fig. 1). If the peptide fragment against which the antibody is induced is totally disordered in solution, with a very large number of conformations of comparable population, it is extremely difficult to understand how the immune system can be stimulated to give rise to antibodies that can recognize the same sequence in a helical conformation in the folded protein. If, on the other hand, the peptide can adopt a helical conformation either free in solution or bound to the B cell receptor, then this process is

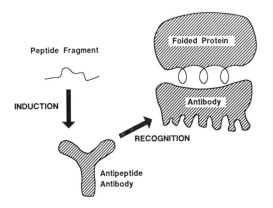

Peptide Fragment

INDUCTION

RECOGNITION

Folded Protein

Antibody

Antipeptide
Antibody

Fig. 1. Schematic diagram illustrating the induction of a hypothetical antipeptide antibody, which subsequently recognizes the same amino acid sequence in the folded protein.

Important Elements of Secondary Structure

There are several distances between backbone protons that become short when the peptide chain folds up into secondary structure. The distances are summarized in Fig. 2. For our purposes, the most important NOE connectivities are between the $C^{\alpha}H$ of residue i and the NH of residue i + 1 (the $d_{\alpha N}(i, i + 1)$ NOE), between the NH protons of adjacent residues (the $d_{NN}(i, i + 1)$ NOE) and the medium-range backbone NOE connectivities, $d_{\alpha N}(i, i + 2)$, $d_{\alpha\beta}(i, i + 3)$, and $d_{\alpha N}(i, i + 3)$. A conformational energy diagram may be used to predict the distances that will be shortest (and hence the NOEs to be expected) in different secondary structures (Wright et al., 1988). Thus, for example, if the peptide were in a helical conformation, we would expect a relatively short $d_{NN}(i, i + 1)$ distance and a relatively long $d_{\alpha N}(i, i + 1)$ distance. This would be reflected in the relative intensities of the NOE cross peaks in a nuclear Overhauser effect spectroscopy (NOESY) or rotating-frame NOESY (ROESY) spectrum.

readily understood. Peptide fragments of proteins that have a high propensity to adopt folded conformations in solution are likely to correspond to protein-folding initiation sites. Our strategy to screen for folding initiation sites is to begin with peptides that are very effective at inducing protein-reactive antibodies. We then use the powerful two-dimensional NMR techniques that have been developed in recent years for determining the structures of proteins in solution to identify the folded structures that are formed by peptides in water solution. For proteins, only a closely related family of structures is to be expected. In the case of peptides, interpretation of the NMR data is complicated by problems associated with conformational averaging. With proper care, however, secondary structure elements such as β-turns or helices can be readily identified by NMR methods (Wright et al., 1988).

The most important NMR parameter for our purposes is the nuclear Overhauser effect (NOE). This arises from a through space dipole-dipole interaction between nearby protons, and its magnitude is inversely proportional to the sixth power of the distance between the protons. The NOE between backbone protons is used as the primary indication of folded conformations in peptides (Dyson et al., 1988a, 1988b, 1988c; Wright et al., 1988).

β-strand $\qquad d_{\alpha N} = 2.2 \overset{\circ}{A}$

α-helix $\qquad d_{NN} = 2.8 \overset{\circ}{A}$
$\qquad\qquad d_{\alpha N}(i, i+3) = 3.4 \overset{\circ}{A}$
$\qquad\qquad d_{\alpha\beta}(i, i+3) = 2.5\text{-}4.4 \overset{\circ}{A}$

β-turn $\qquad d_{NN}(3,4) = 2.4 \overset{\circ}{A}$
$\qquad\qquad d_{\alpha N}(2,4) = 3.3 \overset{\circ}{A}$

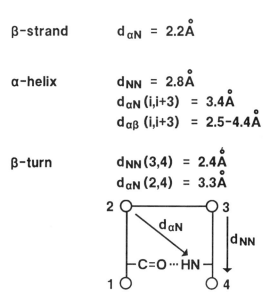

Fig. 2. Short interproton distances to be expected for various secondary structures. Values are taken from Wüthrich et al. (1984).

In addition, for a helical conformation, $d_{\alpha N}(i, i + 3)$ and $d_{\alpha\beta}(i, i + 3)$ NOE connectivities, which are diagnostic of a regular ordered helical structure, would be expected. We have observed these NOE connectivities in immunogenic peptide fragments of proteins.

Another important element of secondary structure is the β-turn. A schematic diagram of two common types of β-turn is shown in Fig. 3. The turn consists of four residues and often, but not always, has a hydrogen bond between the carbonyl of residue 1 and the backbone amide proton of residue 4. There are two major types of turns that occur for trans L-amino acid sequences, Types I and II. The NOE connectivities we would expect to see in β-turns would be between the amide protons of residues 3 and 4 ($d_{NN}(3,4)$) and between the $C^\alpha H$ of residue 2 and the amide proton of residue 4 ($d_{\alpha N}(i, i + 2)$). If the turn is hydrogen bonded, there may be a reduced temperature coefficient for the amide proton resonance of residue 4; if the amide proton is hydrogen bonded, then it is less sensitive to an increase in temperature than if it were exposed to solvent.

Formation of β-turns in Immunogenic Peptides

The first immunogenic peptide we studied was a 9-amino acid sequence from the HA1 chain of influenza virus hemagglutinin, which had been found to be the immunodominant region of a longer, 36-residue peptide immunogen (Wilson *et al.*, 1984). NMR experiments gave evidence for a reverse turn involving the first four residues, Tyr-Pro-Tyr-Asp (Dyson *et al.*, 1985). It was subsequently found that the peptide could be shortened to five residues, or even to four, and still form a β-turn in water solution. All of these experiments were done in water, because that is what is relevant to protein folding and to the induction of the immune response.

Once the presence of the turn in the original peptide sequence and the criteria for detection of the turn and quantitation of its population have been established, the se-

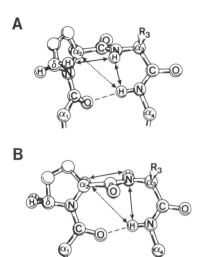

Fig. 3. Diagrammatic representation of **(A)** type I and **(B)** type II β-turns with proline at position 2. Short interproton distances are indicated, $d_{NN}(3,4)$ for both types, $d_{\delta N}(2,3)$ for type I, and $d_{\alpha N}(2,3)$ for type II. The longer $d_{\alpha N}(2,4)$ is indicated by a dotted arrow and the 4→1 hydrogen bond by a broken line (Dyson *et al.*, 1988a).

quence of the peptide can be varied to determine which factors stabilize it. We have studied three series of 5-residue peptides, placing all 20 amino acid residues at positions 3 and 4 of the turn and keeping proline at position 2. The series YPXDV and YPYXV have been most extensively studied, and the NMR evidence shows that the β-turn does indeed form in these short peptides. The extent of β-turn formation can be varied by changing the amino acid sequence (Dyson *et al.*, 1988b). The two-dimensional NOE spectrum (a ROESY spectrum) for the pentapeptide YPGDV is shown in Fig. 4. The spectrum shows a $d_{NN}(i, i + 1)$ NOE connectivity between the amide protons of Gly 3 and Asp 4, and a $d_{\alpha N}(i, i + 2)$ NOE connectivity between the $C^\alpha H$ of Pro 2 and the NH of Asp 4. In addition, there is a reduced temperature coefficient for the amide proton of Asp 4. All of the NMR parameters characteristic of a β-turn, which are not always observed even for a folded protein, are present in this small peptide in water solution at 5°C, pH 4.1.

The spectrum also shows that there are two forms of the peptide in solution under these conditions. This is caused by cis-trans

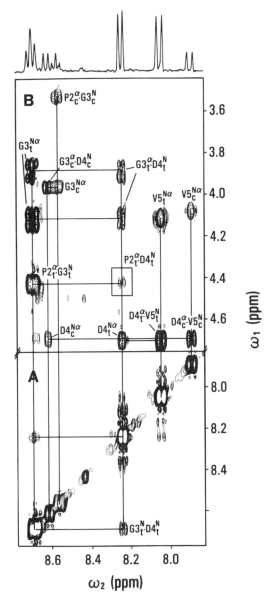

Fig. 4. Portion of a 300 MHz ROESY spectrum of the peptide YPGDV in 90 percent ^{1}H$_2$O/10 percent ^{2}H$_2$O at pH 4.1 and 5°C. (A) amide diagonal region. (B) C$^\alpha$H / NH cross peak region (Dyson *et al.*, 1988b).

range NOE connectivities characteristic of the turn, and there is a high temperature coefficient for Asp 4. The cis form provides an unfolded control. Likewise, YPIDV, which forms no detectable turn, has none of the characteristic β-turn NOE's, and the temperature coefficient for the Asp 4 amide proton is high. The NMR evidence for a turn conformation is confirmed by circular dichroism (CD) spectroscopy for YPGDV. CD spectroscopy of YPIDV shows no detectable population of β-turn conformations.

What factors stabilize the turn?

We are in the process of examining a number of possibilities. So far, several factors have emerged as influential, but no one factor is all important. First, aspartate at position 4 of the turn is important. It is not essential, but it certainly helps to stabilize the turn. When it is deprotonated, the turn is most stable; protonation or substitution with Asn at position 4 decreases but does not abolish the β-turn population.

We find that electrostatic interactions between the positively charged N-terminus and the negatively charged Asp or C-terminal carboxyl groups are relatively unimportant: blocking the N-terminus or adding another residue at this position does not greatly change the turn population in the trans form of the peptide. Similarly, blocking the C-ter-

isomerism about the Tyr-Pro bond. The NOE connectivities characteristic of the turn and the low temperature coefficient are present only in the trans form of the peptide. A summary of the NMR data for YPGDV and another peptide, YPIDV, is shown in Fig. 5. The cis form, which is present in about 25 percent of the peptide, has none of the long-

	trans Y P G D V		cis Y P G D V	
$d_{\alpha N}, d_{\alpha\delta}, d_{\alpha\alpha}$	▭		▭	
d_{NN}	▭▭		▭▭	
$d_{\alpha N}$ (i,i+2)	▭			
$\Delta\delta_{NH}/\Delta T$	10.8 3.3 7.4		6.3 6.2 5.6	

	trans Y P I D V		cis Y P I D V	
$d_{\alpha N}, d_{\alpha\delta}, d_{\alpha\alpha}$	▭		▭	
d_{NN}				
$d_{\alpha N}$ (i,i+2)				
$\Delta\delta_{NH}/\Delta T$	9.5 7.0 6.6		8.2 7.0 7.0	

Fig. 5. Summary of observed NOE's and temperature coefficients for the peptides YPGDV and YPIDV. Broken lines indicate weak NOE's.

minus does not appear to affect the turn population significantly.

The results obtained from the study in which all 20 amino acids were substituted at positions 3 and 4 are summarized in Fig. 6. The substitution at position 3 gave dramatic variations in turn population in water solution, and the population of the turn conformations could be estimated both from the types of NOE connectivities we observed and their relative intensities and also from the amide proton temperature coefficient for residue 4, which is indicative of the strength of the hydrogen-bonding interaction. The plot of temperature coefficient for the amide proton of residue 4 (which is proportional to the turn population) against the statistical probability of finding the same four residues in a turn conformation in a protein (by the statistics of Chou and Fasman, 1978) shows a linear correlation for the YPXDV peptides. For glycine

and the hydrophobic residues, there is a definite correlation between the likelihood of finding a β-turn in a given sequence in a linear peptide in water and the probability of finding a turn in the same sequence in the folded protein. There is a weaker, but still significant, correlation for the hydrophilic residues. This means that short-range local interactions specified by the amino acid sequence can determine β-turn conformation in the protein. That is, turns form in solution that are frequently retained in the folded protein; the local amino acid sequence codes sufficiently strongly for a β-turn conformation that the peptide forms a turn in aqueous solution. A turn initially formed in the earliest stages of protein folding may be eliminated in the fully folded protein, but very frequently it is stabilized and retained. No such correlation is seen for the peptides in which the residue at position 4 is substituted. Differences occur be-

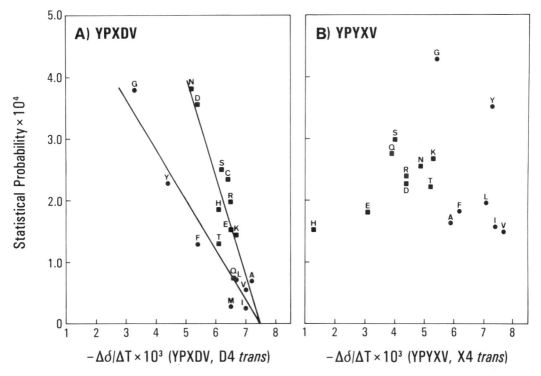

Fig. 6. Plot of temperature dependences for the Asp 4 amide proton resonances for the trans peptides of sequence (A) YPXDV and (B) YPYXV against turn probability calculated for each sequence by the method of Chou and Fasman (1978). Peptides for which residue X may be classified as hydrophobic (plus Gly) are represented by circular symbols; those for which residue X may by classified as hydrophilic are represented by square symbols. Straight lines were calculated by the method of least squares (Dyson *et al.*, 1988b).

tween different sequences, but there is no correlation with what happens in proteins. Further work is under way to investigate the influence of sequence changes at positions 1 and 2 of the turn.

What is the population of the β-turns in these peptides?

The peptide sequence YPGDV has the highest population of the type II turn: CD and NMR estimates indicate that there is between 30 and 50 percent of the type II turn in the trans isomer. Another system, where an additional residue has been placed at the amino terminus of the peptide, contains a highly populated turn in the cis form of the peptide. This is shown by characteristic NOE connectivities and coupling constants. For the peptides AYPYDV and SYPYDV, the diagnostic $d_{\alpha N}(i, i + 2)$ NOE connectivity for β-turn is present between the $C^{\alpha}H$ of Tyr 2 and the NH of Tyr 4 in the cis form of the peptide, placing the cis-proline at position 3 of the turn. In addition, the $^3J_{HN\alpha}$ coupling constant for Tyr 2 is significantly reduced in the cis isomer, but not in the trans isomer. These observations are consistent with the presence of a type VI β-turn in the cis isomer (Richardson, 1981). The presence of a large population of highly structured forms in the cis peptide causes the population of the cis form to be dramatically increased, and from this population increase, we can estimate the population of the type VI turn. In this isomer, it is estimated to be about 70 percent. About 50 percent of the peptide is in the cis conformation, which means that a total of 35 percent of the peptide molecules are present in a type VI turn conformation at any instant of time.

Note that the NMR experiments do not imply that the peptide is locked into a single turn conformation. The peptide is apparently spending a great deal of its time in conformations where the dihedral angles approximate those of type II or type VI turns. However, substantial fluctuations of the dihedral angles around the optimal angles for a β-turn are to be expected, and unfolded and folded confor-

mations coexist in rapid dynamic equilibrium. It is apparent that turn conformations can and do form in short peptides in water. We propose that these turns are extremely important, both for the understanding of the induction of protein-reactive, antipeptide antibodies and also probably as initiation sites for protein folding. Turns can be present in quite high populations in peptide fragments of proteins, but they are still transient structures that could be rearranged into other secondary structures as folding proceeds. Their formation depends on sequentially short-range interactions, i.e., depends only on the local amino acid sequence. As longer range interactions come into play as the protein folds, they may be stabilized or eliminated. Turns could function as folding initiation sites by restricting the conformational space available to the polypeptide chain as it folds and possibly by directing subsequent folding events and folding pathways (Wright et al., 1988). Turns have also been suggested by previous workers (Lewis et al., 1971; Zimmerman and Scheraga, 1977) to be important in the initiation of protein folding; we now have experimental evidence for the first time that this is probably true.

Helix Peptides

Another type of secondary structure with which we have been concerned is the helix, once again in water solution and once again using the results of an immunological study to select peptide candidates for study. A great deal is known about antibodies raised against peptides from myohemerythrin (MHr), a four-helix bundle protein from marine worms (Getzoff et al., 1987). In particular, antipeptide antibodies to the constituent helix peptides will cross-react with the native protein, suggesting that these peptides may have residual helical structure in solution. One of the peptides we have studied in detail is the C-helix peptide (Dyson et al., 1988c), with sequence given in Fig. 7. We find evidence by NMR for what we term a nascent helix, in the region of the peptide indicated. In addition,

A

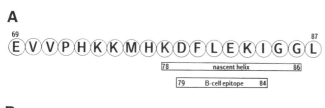

B

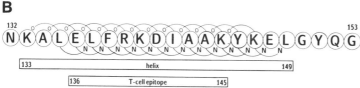

Fig. 7. (A) Amino acid sequence of the myohemerythrin C-helix peptide showing the position of the antigenic determinant (Fieser et al., 1987) and of the nascent helix in water solution (Dyson et al., 1988c). (B) Amino acid sequence of the C-terminal cyanogen bromide cleavage fragment of sperm whale myoglobin showing the location of the T cell epitope (Berkower et al., 1986) and of the helical region (Wright et al., 1988).

the nascent helix encompasses the antigenic determinant of this peptide (Fieser *et al.*, 1987). In other words, protein-reactive antipeptide antibodies raised against the C-helix peptide recognize the same region of the peptide that we have identified as being structured.

What is meant by a nascent helix? The NMR connectivities for the C-helix peptide in water solution indicate that the conformation consists of a number of turns, encompassing just the C-terminal half of the protein, with extended-chain conformations only in the N-terminal portion. This region fluctuates between extended-chain and turn conformations. There is no regular helix evident from either circular dichroism spectra or $(i, i + 3)$ NOE connectivities in the NMR spectra, but NMR clearly shows the $d_{\alpha N}(i, i + 2)$ connectivities characteristic of turns. The nascent helix then consists of a conformational ensemble in which turns at various positions in the peptide chain flicker in and out of extended conformations. Helix is beginning to initiate, but is not sufficiently stable to propagate into several successive turns. The addition of small amounts of trifluoroethanol (a solvent known to stabilize helix) causes the appearance of NMR and CD evidence for regular helix, but, again, only in the C-terminal half of the protein. From the NMR experiments, the N-terminal half remains extended chain, even in the presence of trifluoroethanol. In the folded protein, the entire sequence of the C-helix peptide is helical; presumably, long-range interactions in the folding of the protein and the incorporation of

the iron atoms (MHr contains 2 Fe atoms of the O_2-binding active site) have stabilized the helix at this end of the peptide. We propose that nascent helical structures, such as that observed for the C-helix peptide of myohemerythrin, are likely to play an important role in initiation of protein folding.

The final example is of an ordered helix, the C-terminal cyanogen bromide fragment (residues 132–153, part of the H-helix) of sperm whale myoglobin (Waltho *et al.*, 1989). This is one of the peptides studied earlier by Scheraga and Hermans and their co-workers (Epand and Scheraga, 1968; Hermans and Puett, 1971), and was one of the examples that led to the belief that peptides do not fold to an appreciable extent in water. NMR experiments show the presence of helix from residues 135–149 in water solution (Fig. 7). This is demonstrated by the presence of $d_{\alpha N}(i, i + 3)$ and $d_{\alpha \beta}(i, i + 3)$ NOE connectivities. This peptide is also a T cell-stimulating peptide. Of great significance, the T cell epitope lies between residues 136–145; that is, within the helical region detected in the NMR experiments. The stabilization of this helix is apparently by way of medium-range side-chain side-chain interactions, especially between hydrophobic groups. These studies were performed at concentrations where the peptide is monomeric in aqueous solution.

Conclusions

In summary, the combined use of immunological screening and two-dimensional NMR approach for studies of folding of peptide fragments of proteins in aqueous solution. Much of the power of this approach is that it is sensitive to relatively small populations of structured forms. In contrast to circular dichroism spectroscopy, the NMR methods indicate precisely where in the peptides those structures reside. By synthesizing "mutant" peptides in which certain amino acids are substituted, it is possible to probe the nature of the interactions that stabilize or destabilize secondary structures in short linear peptides in water solution. We suggest that, for the first time, the combined NMR and immunological approach provides an experimental method for detailed investigations of the amino acid sequence code for protein folding. Clearly, this is an enormous problem and only the first steps have so far been taken.

Acknowledgments

We thank Ms. L. Tennant and Ms. V. Feher for expert technical assistance, Ms. L. Harvey for assistance in preparation of the manuscript, and Dr. R. Houghten for helpful discussions and for providing peptides. This work was supported by grants CA27489 and GM38794 from the National Institutes of Health.

References

Berkower, I., G. K. Buckenmeyer, J. A. Berzofsky, *J. Immunol.* **136**, 2498 (1986).

Brandts, J. F., H. R. Halvorson, M. Brennan, *Biochemistry* **14**, 4953 (1975).

Chou, P. Y., and G.D. Fasman, *Adv. Enzymol.* **47**, 45 (1978).

Creighton, T. E., *Science* **240**, 267 (1988).

———, *Nature* **318**, 480 (1987).

———, *J. Phys. Chem.* **89**, 2452 (1985).

Dyson, H. J., R. A. Lerner, P. E. Wright, *Ann. Rev. Biophys. Chem.* **17**, 305 (1988a).

Dyson, H. J., M. Rance, R. A. Houghten, R. A. Lerner, P. E. Wright, *J. Mol. Biol.* **201**, 161 (1988b).

Dyson, H. J., M. Rance, R. A. Houghten, P. E. Wright, R. A. Lerner, *J. Mol. Biol.* **201**, 201 (1988c).

Dyson, H. J., *et al., Nature* **318**, 480 (1985).

Epand, R. M., and H. A. Scheraga, *Biochemistry* **7**, 2864 (1968).

Fieser, T. M., J. A. Tainer, H. M. Geysen, R. A. Houghten, R. A. Lerner, *Proc. Natl. Acad. Sci. U.S.A.* **84**, 8568 (1987).

Getzoff, E. D., *et al., Science* **235**, 1191 (1987).

Hermans, J., and D. Puett, *Biopolymers* **10**, 895 (1971).

Howard, J. C., A. Ali, H. A. Scheraga, F. A. Momany, *Macromolecules* **8**, 607 (1975).

Lerner, R. A., *Adv. Immunol.* **36**, 1 (1984).

Lewis, P. N., F. A. Momany, H. A. Scheraga, *Proc. Natl. Acad. Sci. U.S.A.* **68**, 2293 (1971).

Niman, H. L., *et al., Proc. Natl. Acad. Sci. U.S.A.* **80**, 4949 (1983).

Richardson, J. S., *Adv. Prot. Chem.* **34**, 167 (1981).

Taniuchi, H., and C.B. Anfinsen, *J. Biol. Chem.* **244**, 3864 (1969).

Waltho, J. P., V. A. Feher, R. A. Lerner, P. E. Wright, *FEBS Lett.* **250**, 400 (1989).

Wilson, I. A., *et al., Cell* **37**, 767 (1984).

Wright, P. E., H. J. Dyson, R. A. Lerner, *Biochemistry* **27**, 7167 (1988).

Wüthrich, K., M. Billeter, W. Braun, *J. Mol. Biol.* **180**, 715 (1984).

Zimmerman, S. S., and H. A. Scheraga, *Proc. Nat. Acad. Sci. U.S.A.* **74**, 4126 (1977).

10

Lipid-Protein Interactions
Structure-Function Relationships

James T. Sparrow and Antonio M. Gotto, Jr.

The plasma lipoproteins are complexes of lipids and proteins that transport cholesterol, cholesteryl esters, triglycerides, and phospholipids for bodily functions (see Segrest and Albers, 1988a, 1988b for a complete review). The apolipoproteins, i.e., the lipid-free proteins, will reassociate with phospholipids or phospholipid/cholesterol dispersions. The apolipoproteins usually display large increases in helical structure when they recombine with phospholipids; they also become helical when they self-associate. Since 1971, we have been studying synthetic fragments of these proteins in order to understand how they bind, transport, and deposit cholesterol in the arterial wall. We believe an understanding of these processes will allow us to develop protocols for regressing atherosclerosis.

The lipoproteins can be separated by their hydrated density in the ultracentrifuge into chylomicrons, very-low-density lipoproteins (VLDL), low-density lipoproteins (LDL), and high-density lipoproteins (HDL_2, HDL_3); Table 1 shows the compositions of the lipoprotein subclasses. Chylomicrons primarily transport exogenous triglycerides from the diet; the VLDL transport triglycerides synthesized in the liver. LDL carry cholesterol and cholesteryl esters; these lipoproteins interact with a cellular receptor to control cholesterol synthesis (Goldstein and Brown,

1977). Brown and Goldstein received the Nobel Prize in Medicine for their investigations of the interaction of LDL with this receptor (1986). HDL contain phospholipid and cholesteryl esters and are thought to be important for the reverse transport of cholesterol to the liver for excretion.

Structure and Function

The lipoproteins are believed to have on their surface a monolayer of phospholipid and the various apolipoproteins, e.g., VLDL contain apoA-I, apoA-II, apoB, apoE, and the apoC's; the apoA and apoC proteins are transferred to HDL during lipolysis. The apolipoproteins serve primarily as detergents to solubilize lipids, but some also serve other metabolic functions. For example, apoC-II activates lipoprotein lipase (LPL) for the hydrolysis of the triglycerides in chylomicrons and VLDL (LaRosa *et al.*, 1970); apoC-III is thought to have feedback control of apoC-II activation of lipase; apoA-I activates lecithin:cholesterol acyltransferase (LCAT) for the conversion of cholesterol to cholesteryl esters (Fielding *et al.*, 1972); and apoB and apoE are both important in controlling cholesterol synthesis by their interaction with the LDL receptor on cells (Brown and Goldstein, 1986; La Rosa *et al.*, 1970; Mahley, 1978).

Table 1. Composition of human serum lipoproteins.

	Chylomicrons	VLDL	LDL	HDL
Density range (g/ml)	< 0.95	0.95–1.006	1.006–1.063	1.063–1.210
Major lipids	Exogenous triglycerides	Endogenous triglycerides	Cholesterol	Phospholipids
			Cholesteryl esters	Cholesteryl esters
Protein (%)	2	10	25	50
Major apolipoproteins	ApoA-I[a]	ApoB	ApoB	ApoA-I[a]
	ApoB	ApoC-I[a]		ApoA-II
	ApoC	ApoC-II[b]		
		ApoC-III		
		ApoE		
Minor apolipoproteins	ApoA-II	ApoA-I[a]	ApoC	ApoC-I[a]
	ApoE	ApoA-II		ApoC-II[b]
	ApoD	ApoD		ApoC-III
				ApoD
				ApoE

[a]Activator of lecithin:cholesterol acyltransferase.   [b]Co-factor for lipoprotein lipase.

The structural properties of some of the apolipoproteins, as determined by circular dichroism (CD), are given in Table 2. The smaller proteins, apoC-I, C-II, and C-III, are fairly helical and contain very little beta-sheet structure. In general, they do not have a high average hydrophobicity. However, apoB, which contains 4536 residues (Chen et al., 1986), is very hydrophobic and contains a relatively large proportion of beta-sheet (Gotto et al., 1968).

Lipid-Apolipoprotein Interaction

After studying both native and synthetic fragments of the apolipoproteins in the presence and absence of phospholipids, Segrest et al. (1974) proposed the amphipathic- or amphiphilic-helical hypothesis to explain the interaction of the apolipoproteins with lipids. Since its publication, many investigators—including some of the authors of this monograph as well as Richard Epand, Bob Schwyzer, and the late Tom Kaiser—have used the amphipathic

hypothesis to explain a number of important biological functions of proteins.

The features of the hydrophobic amphipathic helix of apoC-III are illustrated in Fig. 1. The amino acid sequence of this protein is such that when it becomes helical, there are two distinct faces formed: one polar

Table 2. Structural properties of the apolipoproteins.

Protein	% α-helix	% β-sheet	Hydro-phobicity (cal/residue)
ApoA-I	75	9	−806
ApoA-II	64	26	−863
ApoA-IV	52	11	−772
ApoC-I	73	4	−825
ApoC-II	59	18	−838
ApoC-III	70	9	−752
ApoE	62	9	−772
ApoB	33	23	−916
ApoB3701–4536	33	24	−967

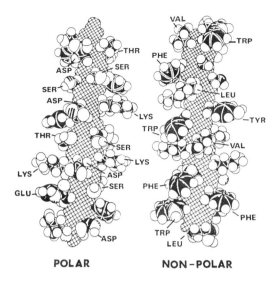

Fig. 1. The amphipathic helix in apoC-III between residues 40 and 67 showing the polar and nonpolar faces. In the polar face, there are pairs of acidic and basic residues separated by serine and threonine residues. In the nonpolar face beneath these ion pairs are hydrophobic amino acids as well as pairs of aromatic residues.

and the other nonpolar. One feature of the polar face is the preponderance of $i, i + 1$ and $i, i + 3$ ion pairs. There are glutamic and aspartic acids at the center of the helix paired with lysines and arginines at the edge separating the polar and apolar faces; beneath the ion pairs are hydrophobic residues. In addition, there are serines and threonines interspersed between the ion pairs. On the apolar face, pairs of aromatic residues such as tyrosine and tryptophan or phenylalanine and tryptophan or tyrosine are frequently found. With this type of structure, the polar face can orient toward an aqueous environment such as plasma while the apolar face can penetrate into the fatty acyl chain region of the phospholipids to form a complex between the protein and the phospholipid, which is stabilized by hydrophobic interactions. Initially, it was believed that the ion pairs might form salt bridges between the protein and the polar head group of the phospholipid. To date, there is no evidence that there is any ionic interaction between these molecules. We now believe that the ion pairs stabilize the amphiphatic helix. The ion pair density of the

polar face may also be important in the exchange of the apolipoproteins between various lipoproteins as the particles are being degraded by enzymes.

Peptide-Lipid Complex Formation

The criteria used to identify complex formation between synthetic peptides or native proteins and phospholipids include observing the blue shift in the intrinsic tryptophan fluorescence spectrum indicative of the Trp being placed into a more hydrophobic environment and measuring the ellipticity changes at 208 and 222 nm in the circular dichroic (CD) spectra that would indicate the formation of an alpha-helix.

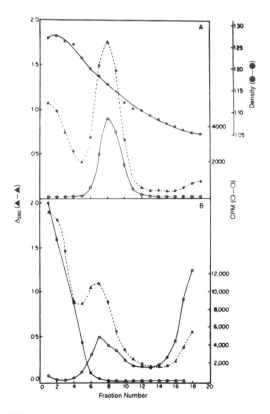

Fig. 2. The density gradient profiles of apoC-III(41–79) with **(A)** DMPC and **(B)** POPC. There is free peptide at the bottom of the gradient with the peptide-lipid complex at a density of 1.16 g/ml. In panel B, there is another complex at the top of the gradient which is unstable.

With complex formation, there is also clarification of phospholipid dispersions indicating that large vesicles have been converted to smaller soluble complexes. The final criterion is isolating any complexes by density gradient ultracentrifugation or column chromatography. The isolation of stable complexes is a very important part of our studies since we are interested in the mechanisms of complex formation and not just peptide-lipid association.

In Fig. 2 are the density gradient profiles of the amphipathic segment of apoC-III contained in residues 41 to 79 mixed with two different phospholipid dispersions. In the top panel is dimyristoylphosphatidylcholine (DMPC) and in the bottom panel is palmitoyl-oleoylphosphatidylcholine (POPC). The gradients are fractionated with a Densiflow and each fraction analyzed for peptide and phospholipid. A complex with DMPC is formed, containing about 12 lipid molecules per peptide molecule. However, with POPC, there appear to be two complexes; one at the top of the tube and the other lower in the gradient. In each case, there is also free peptide observed near the bottom of the tube.

We believe that with POPC there is peptide-vesicle association at the top of the tube and that the true complex is at the intermediate density. The complexes that enter the gradient are stable to column chromatography or re-centrifugation. When the complexes are examined by fluorescence and CD spectros-

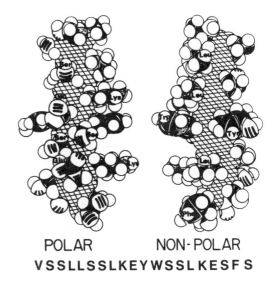

POLAR   NON-POLAR

V S S L L S S L K E Y W S S L K E S F S

Fig. 3. The amino acid sequence and the two distinct faces of the model lipid-associating peptide, LAP-20. In the polar face are two ion pairs separated by serine residues; the apolar face contains the hydrophobic amino acids.

copy, a 12 nm shift in the fluorescence spectra and 38 percent alpha-helicity are observed in the peptide bound to the lipid (Sparrow *et al.*, 1977).

Testing the Amphipathic Hypothesis

In order to test the amphipathic hypothesis, we designed and synthesized peptides to be

Table 3. Fluorescence and circular dichroic properties of lipid-associating peptides.

Peptide	Fluorescence		Circular dichroism	
	λ_{max}	λ_{max}	$[\theta]_{222}$	% α-helicity
LAP-16	350 nm	0	Nil	Nil
LAP-16 + DMPC	350 nm	0	Nil	Nil
LAP-16 + DMCP + 2M NaCl	336 nm	14	−16400	50
LAP-20	350 nm	0	Nil	Nil
LAP-20 + DMPC	334 nm	16	−16500	50
LAP-24	350 nm	0	Nil	Nil
LAP-24 + DMPC	338 nm	12	−28700	82

used as model compounds (Pownall *et al.*, 1980); Segrest and Kaiser have separately published studies on similar model peptides (Anantharamaiah *et al.*, 1985; Yokoyama *et al.*, 1980). In Fig. 3 are shown the sequence and amphipathic structure of one peptide, LAP-20, that we have used extensively to study the various features of the amphipathic helix. The sequence of this 20-residue peptide is such that, when it becomes helical, it forms polar and apolar faces. There are two i, i + 1 glutamic and lysine residues for ion pair formation; the apolar face contains valine, phenylalanine, and leucines with a pairing of tyrosine and trytophan. Many analogs of this peptide have been synthesized, including shorter and longer peptides derived by the subtraction or addition of Ser-Ser-Leu-Leu after the amino terminal Val. The Eisenberg helical hydrophobic moment of LAP-20 is such that it would be classified as a surface-seeking peptide as opposed to a membrane-spanning or water-soluble peptide.

The ellipticity and fluorescence maximum of three of these model peptides in the presence of DMPC are given in Table 3. The peptides free in solution are random coils. In the presence of DMPC, there is little change in the ellipticity of LAP-16 until NaCl is added; there is also a blue shift in the fluorescence spectrum. The fact that salt is needed to induce these changes is indicative of the hydrophobic nature of the binding process. The longer peptides, LAP-20 and LAP-24, spontaneously associate with DMPC with an increase to 50 percent and 82 percent alpha-helicity, respectively, and there is a 12 to 16 nm blue shift in their fluorescence spectra.

The results of a temperature study (Pownall *et al.*, 1980) on the interaction of LAP-20 with phospholipid are given in Fig. 4. The fluorescence intensity at 330 nm is monitored as a function of temperature. As the temperature is increased, the fluorescence intensity (curve A) decreases, indicating that the complexes dissociate above the DMPC lipid transition temperature of 24°C. The increase in intensity that occurs upon cooling indicates that the complexes reform in a re-

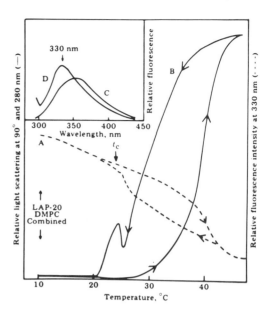

Fig. 4. The results of a temperature study of the stability of LAP-20/DMPC complexes. As the temperature is raised above the phase transition temperature (t_C) the fluorescence intensity at 330 nm decreases (curve A); when the sample is cooled, the intensity increases as the complex reforms near t_C. At the same time, the relative light scattering at 280 cm (curve B) increases above t_C and decreases upon cooling. The inset shows the fluorescence spectrum above (curve C) and below (curve D) the transition temperature.

versible process. The inset shows the fluorescence spectrum above (curve C) and below (curve D) the transition temperature. When the scattering of light at 90° (curve B) is monitored at 280 nm as the temperature is increased, the complexes are seen to dissociate near the transition temperature as

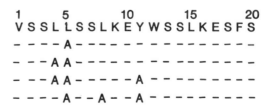

Fig. 5. The amino acid sequence of LAP-20 peptides with alanine substitutions synthesized for a study on the effects of hydrophobicity on complex formation.

Table 4. Fluorescence properties of Ala-LAP-20 peptides.

Peptide	Fluorescence maximum		L/P ratio	Hydrophobicity (cal/residue)
	Buffer	Peptide + DMPC		
5-Ala	350 nm	332 nm	52	−1007
4,5-Ala2	351 nm	348 nm	No complex	− 894
4,5,11-Ala3	351 nm	351 nm	No complex	− 792
5,8,11-Ala3	350 nm	350 nm	No complex	− 792

evidenced by the greater light scatter of the large lipid particles but reform upon cooling to give a nearly transparent solution of smaller peptide-lipid complexes.

To study the effects of hydrophobicity of the apolar face, alanines are substituted for hydrophobic residues as indicated in Fig. 5. The decrease in average hydrophobicity and the changes that occur in the fluorescence spectra of these peptides in the presence of DMPC are shown in Table 4. The 5-Ala LAP-20 displays an 18 nm shift, whereas the 4,5-Ala has a shift of 4 nm. The remaining peptides do not display shifts in their fluorescence spectra. In the CD spectra, alpha-helical structure is observed in 5- and 4,5-Ala LAP-20; the remaining peptides are random coils. The alanine replacement of the 8,15-leucines changes a critical hydrophobic region near the center of the peptide and beneath the ion pairs and has a more detrimental effect on binding than the replacement of the 4,5-leucines near the amino terminus.

To determine the importance of alpha-helix formation on phospholipid binding, the peptides in Fig. 6 were synthesized with the helix breaker, proline, substituted for various hydrophobic residues (Ponsin *et al.*, 1986); the hydrophobicity of these peptides changes very little, since proline is a moderately hydrophobic amino acid. The computer-generated Chou-Fasman structural analysis of these peptides, shown in Fig. 7, indicates that the length of the alpha-helix decreases as the Pro is moved toward the center of the peptide. As the Pro is moved to the carboxyl terminus, the helical length again increases.

The helical content of these peptides in phosphate buffer is shown in Table 5. Analysis of the spectrum by the method of Chang and Wu (Chang *et al.*, 1978) indicates that the peptides in solution either contain beta structure or are random coils. However, in the presence of hexafluoropropanol, a helix-forming solvent, 64 percent helix is observed in 1-Pro-

Table 5. Structural properties of Pro-LAP-20 peptides.

Peptide	% α-helicity		% β-sheet	
	Buffer	HFP	Buffer	HFP
1-Pro	7	64	46	13
5-Pro	5	40	44	29
8-Pro	0	37	50	25
11-Pro	0	29	48	31
15-Pro	0	38	50	30
19-Pro	8	44	47	24

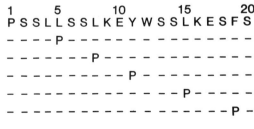

Fig. 6. The amino acid sequence of a series of proline-containing LAP-20 peptides used to investigate the importance of helix potential to complex formation and stability.

LAP-20, which is similar to the value of 68 percent observed for LAP-20. As the Pro is moved to the center of the peptide, the amount of alpha-helicity decreases as expected from the Chou-Fasman predictions; it increases again when the Pro is moved toward the carboxyl terminus.

The results of our fluorescence and CD studies on these peptides are summarized in Table 6. With the 1-, 5-, and 19-Pro LAP-20, there is a large blue shift in the fluorescence spectrum and a large corresponding increase in the alpha-helicity of the peptide in the isolated complexes. With the 8- and 11-Pro LAP-20, there is no complex formed; therefore, no changes occur in the fluorescence or CD properties. The complex with the 15-Pro LAP-20 appears to be unstable; there are small changes in the fluorescence and CD spectra in the peptide-lipid mixtures, but no complex is isolated. Since this peptide is very hydrophobic, we believe that peptide-lipid association is occurring but stable complex formation does not result because the helical length of the peptide is too short.

The density gradients in Fig. 8 indicate that stable complexes can be isolated from the mixtures of 1-, 5-, and 19-Pro LAP-20 near the middle of the gradient with lipid to peptide ratios of 40 to 53 to 1. With the 8- and 11-Pro LAP-20, the peptide is in the bottom of the tube, and the lipid is at the top. The 15-Pro LAP-20 forms an unstable complex that cannot be re-isolated by density gradient ultracentrifugation.

Using equilibrium dialysis of the

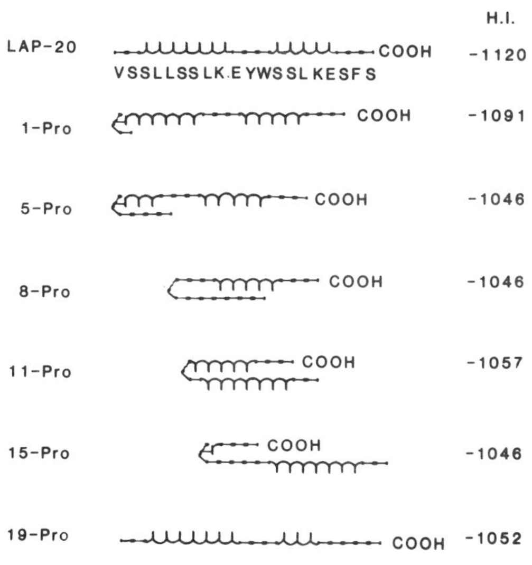

Fig. 7. The computer-generated Chou-Fasman structures for the Pro-LAP-20 peptides in Fig. 6. There are only minor changes in the average hydrophobicity (H.I.) of these peptides.

iodinated LAP-20s, we have been able to determine the equilibrium constants for dissociation (Ponsin *et al.*, 1986); these are shown in Table 6. The equilibrium constant decreases as the Pro is moved toward the center of the peptide and increases again as it is moved toward the carboxyl terminus, indicating that the more helical peptides form more stable complexes.

We have demonstrated that the following features are necessary for the amphipathic helix to interact with phospholipids: the amino acid sequence must have a high helix prob-

Table 6. Spectral properties of Pro-LAP-20 in the presence of DMPC.

Peptide	% α-helicity in complex	Fluorescence shift	L/P	K_{eq}
1-Pro	62	16 nm	40	3.6×10^4
5-Pro	54	16 nm	53	8.3×10^3
8-Pro	No complex	0	0	0.5×10^3
11-Pro	No complex	0	0	N.d.
15-Pro	Unstable	8 nm	0	4.2×10^3
19-Pro	47	10 nm	42	N.d.

Fig. 8. The density gradient profiles for the Pro-LAP-20 peptides mixed with DMPC. (A) 1-Pro; (B) 5-Pro; (C) 8-Pro; (D) 11-Pro; (E) 15-Pro; and (F) 19-Pro. There are stable complexes formed in A, B, and F; the complex in E is unstable and cannot be re-isolated. No complex is formed in C and D.

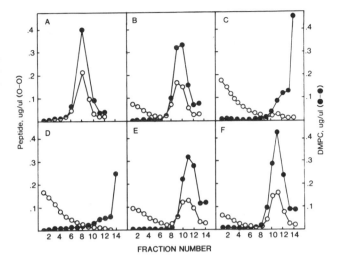

ability; the sequence must be such that two faces form, one polar and one apolar; the apolar face must have a high hydrophobicity; and the peptide length must be at least 15 to 20 residues for stable complex formation.

An illustration of the importance of the amphipathic helix to other biological functions is the interaction of apoE and apoB with the LDL receptor. In Fig. 9 are the amino acid sequences of the regions of apoE and apoB, which are believed to be responsible for their interaction with the LDL receptor; there is high homology between the two regions. It has been postulated by Mahley and co-workers (Innerarity *et al.*, 1983) that the positive charges on apoE are responsible for the interaction with the negative charges on the LDL receptor as the first step in receptor binding. They have also shown from studies with the apoprotein that phospholipid is important for the interaction of the protein with the receptor.

In Fig. 10 are the curves for the binding of

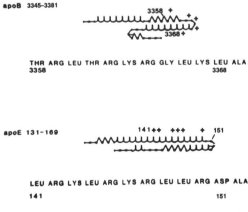

Fig. 9. The amino acid sequences and structural predictions for the putative receptor-binding regions of apoB and apoE; there is high homology between these amino acid sequences. When an amphipathic helix forms in these peptides as they bind lipid, a ridge of positive charges forms which has been hypothesized to interact with the negative charges on the LDL receptor.

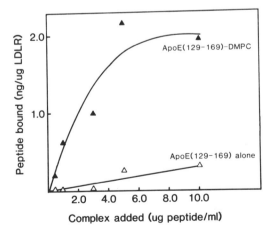

Fig. 10. The binding curves for apoE(129–69) to a partially purified LDL receptor preparation showing the dependence on lipid for binding to the receptor.

apoE(129–169) in the presence and absence of DMPC with the partially purified LDL receptor. In the absence of DMPC, there is little, if any, binding with the receptor, whereas in the presence of DMPC there is saturable binding. These results support those of Mahley and co-workers and show that one of the important functions of amphipathic

helices is to hold proteins in the correct conformation for interaction with receptors.

The importance of beta structures to the interaction of apolipoproteins with lipid has been addressed since the sequence of apolipoprotein B has become available (Chen *et al.*, 1986). As indicated in Table 2, apolipoprotein B contains significant beta-sheet structure. In some very early work on apoA-II, amino acid substitutions in apoA-II(50–77) were made to determine the importance of acid-base pairs and hydrophobicity to lipid

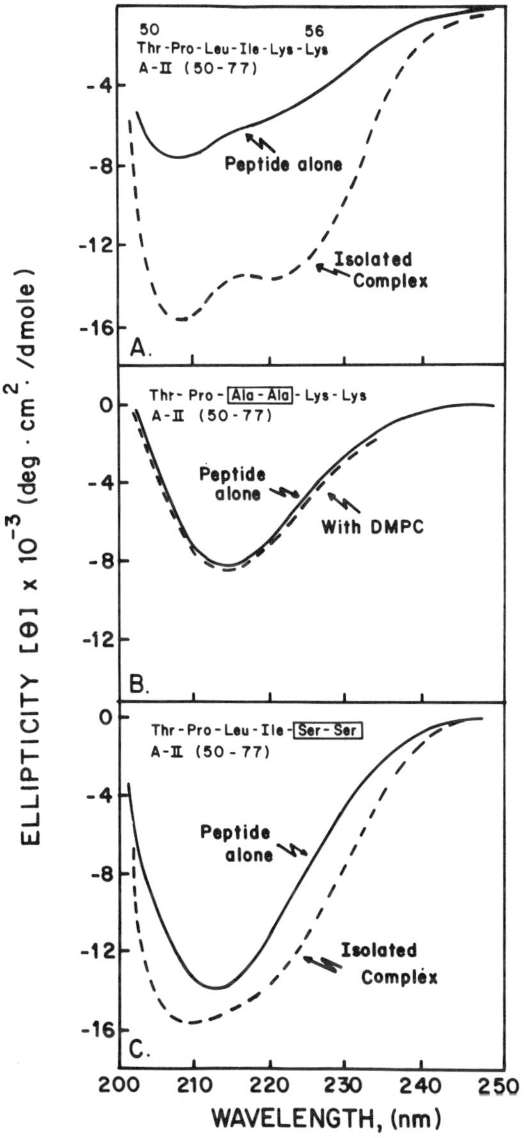

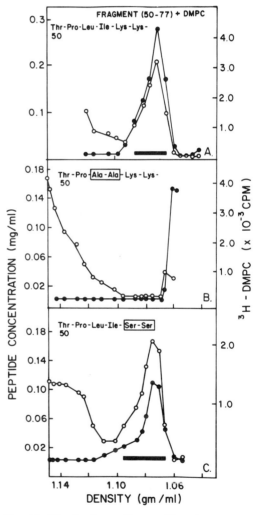

Fig. 11. The circular dichroic spectra of substituted apoA-II peptides in the presence and absence of phospholipid. The spectra of the substituted peptides indicate they contain significant beta-structure.

Fig. 12. The density gradient profiles of substituted apoA-II peptides. Complexes are isolated from the native sequence and the serine-substituted peptide but not with the alanine peptide.

binding (Mao *et al.*, 1981). In Fig. 11 are the CD results from the interaction of these peptides with DMPC. There is a change in alphahelicity of the native sequence, whereas the peptides with substitutions of Ala-Ala for Ile-Leu or Ser-Ser for Lys-Lys bring about changes that are more indicative of beta structure. Complexes could be isolated with the native sequence and the peptide with the Ser-Ser substitutions (Fig. 12); the CD spectra of the complexes indicated that the latter peptide had significant beta structure.

Peptides from two regions of apoB have been synthesized; one region is at the carboxyl terminus between residues 4507 and 4536 and contains both significant beta structure as well as a short amphipathic helical segment, while the region between residues 4154 and 4189 contains only an amphipathic helix. These peptides were synthesized by solid-phase techniques and studied for their lipid-binding properties. In hexafluoropropanol, there are changes in the ellipticity of apoB(4507–36) that are indicative of beta-structure, whereas apoB(4154–89) has a spectrum indicative of alpha-helix formation (Table 7); DMPC complexes can be isolated with apoB(4507–89) or apoB(4154–89) but not with apoB(4517–36) or apoB(4165–89) (Fig. 13). The CD spectrum of apoB(4507–89) confirms the beta-structure in the complex, whereas with apoB(4154–89),

Table 7. Circular dichroic properties of synthetic apoB peptides.

Peptide	% α-helicity			L/P
	Buffer	HFP	Complex	
B4517–36	13	17	No complex	—
B4507–36	17	42	β-sheet	80
B4165–89	11	27	No complex	—
B4154–89	23	29	39	100

the peptide appears to be alpha-helical. The polarized IR reflectance spectra of these peptides in the presence of DMPC has been obtained by Maryevonne Rosseneau. The Amide I band for apoB(4507–36) is characterized by a maximum at 1627 cm^{-1}, suggesting a beta-sheet structure, while that of apoB(4154–89) was near 1653 cm^{-1}, indicative of alpha-helix formation.

A proposed model for the interaction of the predominantly beta-sheet peptide with dipalmitoylphosphotidylcholine (DPPC) is shown in Fig. 14. The beta-sheet inserts into a phospholipid bilayer, with the hydrophobic residues on the beta-sheet lying parallel to the fatty acyl chains of the DPPC. The last three residues can penetrate into the lipid phase past the DPPC acyl chains and might interact

Fig. 13. The density gradient profiles for apoB synthetic peptides containing beta-structure (upper and lower left panels) and amphipathic alpha-helix (upper and lower right panels). Complexes are isolated with the two longer peptides (lower panels).

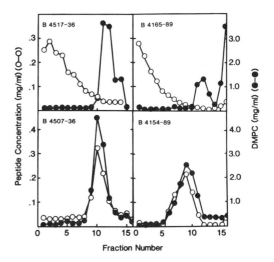

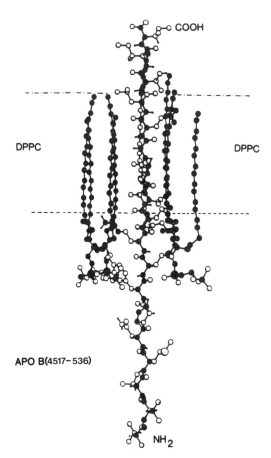

DPPC

DPPC

APO B(4517-536)

Fig. 14. A proposed model for the interaction of apoB(4517–36) with DPPC. The hydrophobic residues of the beta-sheet penetrate the phospholipid bilayer and interact with the fatty acyl chains.

with lipids in the LDL core. Residues 4527–33 could interact with the DPPC acyl chains; the remaining residues could be located at the lipid-water interface with those between 4507 and 4517 in a short amphipathic helix.

Conclusions

In conclusion, we believe that the amphipathic or amphiphilic alpha-helix is an important structural feature for lipid-protein interactions. The amphipathic helix can also stabilize the interaction of peptides with receptors for delivery of messages; Bob Schwyzer's studies (Sargent and Schwyzer, 1986) of peptide hormones indicates that there is good evidence for this mechanism. Other authors in this monograph have shown the importance of the amphipathic helix in the interaction of peptides with the T cell receptor. We now know that both amphipathic and hydrophobic beta-sheet structures are important for the lipid-protein interactions of apoB in LDL.

Acknowledgments

We would like to thank our many collaborating investigators whose work has been presented in this chapter. They are Doris Sparrow, Henry Pownall, Gabriel Ponsin, Simon Mao, Pradip Bhatnagar, Maryevonne Rosseneau, Bill Mantulin, Bill Bradley, and Sandra Gianturco. This research has been funded by HL30064 and a Specialized Center of Research in Atherosclerosis NIH Grant No. 27341.

References

Anantharamaiah, G. M., *et al., J. Biol. Chem.* **260,** 10248 (1985).

Brown, M. S., and J. L. Goldstein, *Science* **232,** 34 (1986).

Chang, C. T., C.-S.C. Wu, J. T. Yang, *Anal. Biochem.* **91,** 13 (1978).

Chen, S.-H., *et al., J. Biol. Chem.* **261,** 12918 (1986).

Fielding, C. J., V. G. Shore, P. E. Fielding, *Biochem. Biophys. Res. Commun.* **46,** 1493 (1972).

Goldstein, J. L., and M. S. Brown, *Annu. Rev. Biochem.* **41,** 897 (1977).

Gotto, A. M., Jr., R. I. Levy, D. S. Frederickson, *Proc. Natl. Acad. Sci. U.S.A.* **60,** 1436 (1968).

Innerarity, T. L., E. J. Friedlander, S. C. Rall, Jr., K. H. Weisgraber, R. W. Mahley, *J. Biol. Chem.* **258,** 12341 (1983).

LaRosa, J. C., R. I. Levy, P. Herbert, *Biochem. Biophys. Res. Commun.* **41,** 57 (1970).

Mahley, R. W., in *Disturbances in Lipid and Lipoprotein Metabolism,* J. M. Dietschy, A. M. Gotto, Jr., J. A. Onko, Eds. (American Physiology Society, Bethesda, 1978) pp. 181 – 197.

Mao, S. J. T., R. L. Jackson, A. M. Gotto, Jr., J. T. Sparrow, *Biochemistry* 20, 1676 (1981).

Ponsin, G., L. Hester, A. M. Gotto, Jr., H. P. Pownall, J. T. Sparrow, *J. Biol. Chem.* 261, 9202 (1986).

Pownall, H. J., A. Hu, A. M. Gotto, Jr., J. J. Albers, J. T. Sparrow, *Proc. Natl. Acad. Sci. U.S.A.* 77, 3154 (1980).

Sargent, D. F., and R. Schwyzer, *Proc. Natl. Acad. Sci. U.S.A.* 83, 5774 (1986).

Segrest, J. P., R. L. Jackson, J. D. Morrisett, A. M. Gotto, Jr., *FEBS Lett.* 38, 247 (1974).

Segrest, J. P., and J. J. Albers, Eds., *Plasma Lipoproteins,* vol. 128, *Methods in Enzymology* (Academic Press, New York, 1988a).

_____, *Plasma Lipoproteins,* vol. 129, *Methods in Enzymology* (Academic Press, New York, 1988b).

Sparrow, J. T., *et al.*, *Biochemistry* 16, 5427 (1977).

Yokoyama, S., D. Fukushima, J. P. Kupferberg, F. J. Kezdy, E. T. Kaiser, *J. Biol. Chem.* 155, 7333 (1980).

Part III

Recovering Active Proteins

David N. Brems

The advent of heterologous gene expression has given new impetus to the field of protein folding. Not only is protein folding of fundamental interest, but it now has great practical importance. Whether from the perspective of a 1 liter shake-flask or a 100,000 liter fermentor, both academic researchers and industrial scientists must concern themselves with protein folding. At the present time, *Escherichia coli* is the most common host, and the overexpressed foreign proteins frequently precipitate within the cytoplasm to form inclusion bodies. It was first thought, by analogy to work on covalently damaged proteins, that the protein in these inclusion bodies represented incorrectly transcribed or translated proteins (Prouty and Goldberg, 1972). However, it was soon discovered that active protein could be regenerated from such materials by, first, solubilizing the aggregated protein with strong denaturants and, second, by removing the denaturant under controlled conditions to induce proper refolding (Marston, 1986). This established that the problem was one of conformation and not of sequence.

Experience has shown that obtaining the conditions for proper refolding is not trivial. Many valuable studies have been precluded or resulted in poor recovery yields from difficulties encountered with the refolding step. A common problem experienced with the refolding step is the reoccurrence of precipitation. The chapters in this section will document examples in which the source of precipitation can be traced to the tendency of folding intermediates to agglomerate. (This is also addressed in chapter 23 by Jonathan King *et al.* in Part V, "Protein Folding Within the Cell.") The agglomerated folding intermediates are often end products of "off-pathway" or "abortive" reactions. Knowledge of protein folding pathways and mechanisms can provide clues to limit these undesirable reactions.

It may be expected that the difficulties encountered with recovering active proteins from inclusion bodies could be circumvented by exporting the overexpressed protein out of the cell. However, it is becoming evident that protein secretion and folding are integrally related (Gierasch, 1989; Randall *et al.*, 1987). For example, too-rapid folding can inhibit secretion. Presented in this section will be preliminary evidence from an *E. coli* secretion-based expression system, demonstrating that too-rapid folding initiates a mechanism for its preferential degradation.

In addition to the problem of recovering active proteins, there would be great utility in deciphering the code for folding so that a three-dimensional structure could be reliably predicted from the amino acid sequence. The project to sequence the human genome will yield the sequences of thousands of genes whose protein products are of unknown function. Without the ability to deduce the structure that these sequences fold into, much of the information in the sequences will be uninterpretable (see Gierasch and King, preface to this volume). The long-term potential of protein engineering will require a better understanding of the folding code. The amino acid sequence not only specifies the final three-dimensional structure but also specifies the route to that structure. The route or pathway of protein folding is specified by the intermediate structures that are populated. Thus, identification and characterization of folding intermediates are key to solving the protein folding problem (Kim and Baldwin, 1982). The chapters in this section will address techniques that have been successfully used to identify and characterize protein folding intermediates and folding pathways. It will be evident from these chapters that much has been discovered regarding protein folding in the past, but even more yet remains to be uncovered.

References

Gierasch, L. M., *Biochemistry* **28**, 923 (1989).

Kim, P. S., and R. L. Baldwin, *Annu. Rev. Biochem.* **51**, 459 (1982).

Marston, F. A. O., *Biochem. J.* **240**, 1 (1986).

Prouty, W. F., and A. L. Goldberg, *Nature (London)* **240**, 147 (1972).

Randall, L. L., S. J. S. Hardy, J. A. Thom, *Ann. Rev. Microbiol.* **41**, 507 (1987).

11

Expression and Stabilization
Bovine Pancreatic Trypsin Inhibitor Folding Mutants *in* Escherichia coli

Björn Nilsson, Irwin D. Kuntz, Stephen Anderson

Bovine pancreatic trypsin inhibitor (BPTI) has been called the "hydrogen ion of proteins." This refers to the fact that BPTI is arguably the best understood protein in the world. It is one of the smallest polypeptides that still has the attributes of a globular protein: a compact shape, a clearly defined exterior and interior, and alpha-helix and beta-sheet secondary structure. Because of its simplicity and because it has other attractive features such as high stability and solubility, BPTI has been intensively studied by a variety of biophysical, structural, and theoretical techniques. It has also been the subject of some of the most complete in vitro folding studies (Creighton, 1978, 1985).

For all of these reasons, we decided a number of years ago to focus on BPTI as the basic model system in a recombinant DNA-based (protein engineering) approach to the problem of protein folding. Accordingly, the BPTI gene was cloned (Anderson and Kingston, 1983) and expression systems were developed that allowed us to produce native, correctly folded BPTI in *Escherichia coli* (Marks *et al.*, 1986). These systems allowed us to produce in high yield and characterize mutants of BPTI that had altered folding properties (Marks *et al.*, 1987a, 1987b).

The problem of protein folding, namely how the one-dimensional amino acid se-quence of a protein determines its three-dimensional structure, can be thought of in terms of an analog computation (Fig. 1). The protein, via specific self-interactions involving its amino acid residues and intermolecular interactions with the environmental milieu, searches conformation space until it ends up in one of a number of closely related tertiary structures; this family of final-stage conformations is called "the native structure." Our understanding of the search process is rather crude, but the native structure seems to represent a thermodynamic minimum, with closely packed, nonpolar residues in the interior, with charged and otherwise hydrophilic residues generally on the surface, and with the hydrogen-bonding potential of the backbone amides as often as not neatly satisfied by the formation of helices or sheets of secondary structure. We also know that, at least in vitro, the protein proceeds from the unfolded to the folded state in a highly cooperative fashion, with few of the many possible intermediate states being populated.

Traditionally, if they wished to study protein folding experimentally, researchers could modify natural proteins with chemical reagents or with enzymes, and they could freely adjust the environmental influences (e.g., pH, ionic strength, temperature), but opportunities to study closely related proteins of

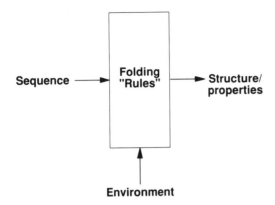

Fig. 1. The protein folding problem. Chemical information from the one-dimensional amino acid sequence and the environment (e.g., solvent composition, temperature) determine the three-dimensional structure of a protein.

similar but nonidentical amino acid sequence were rare. With the advent of recombinant DNA technology coupled with site-directed mutagenesis, however, protein folding investigations have literally been given a whole new dimension.

In principle, a very large number of mutant proteins, differing from the wild-type sequence in specific ways, can be systematically produced and their structures and properties characterized. In this way, a database for a particular protein can be assembled where the perturbing effects of specific amino acid substitutions upon folding are known. Since the rules that nature uses to "calculate" the folded structure remain constant, a study of this database should almost inevitably lead us to insights regarding the underlying principles of folding (Fig. 2). This approach is analogous to the medical science of pathology, in which the effects of abnormal disease states on the body are studied in order to deduce how the normal healthy organism functions.

Mutant Protein Instability

A significant problem with the "folding pathology" approach is that, in general, nature has evolved mechanisms to deal with misfolded, unstable, and otherwise abnormal proteins: they are rapidly degraded. Therefore, one of the major challenges in studying

protein folding mutants is the actual production of each mutant protein. In our own studies on disulfide mutants of BPTI, we have found that thermal stability in vitro is correlated with expression yields, presumably because sensitivity to proteolytic degradation in vivo increases as thermal stability decreases (Table 1).

This effect is so severe that we were unable, using our standard *Escherichia coli* expression systems (Marks *et al.,* 1987a, 1987b), to produce any detectable [Ala5, Ala55]BPTI, a representative of the class of mutants that lack the 5–55 disulfide bond. No combination of physiological conditions that we could devise, including doing fermentations at 15°C in the psychrophilic host *Erwinia herbicola* (S. Anderson, unpublished), was found that was permissive. The destabilizing effects of mutations were also found to be surprisingly pronounced in vivo. For example, the [Ala14, Ala38]BPTI mutant, which lacks the 14–38 disulfide bond (Marks *et al.,* 1987a), has a T_m at neutral pH of 70–75°C, yet this mutant is profoundly less stable in vivo at 37°C compared to 28°C (Tables 1 and 2).

Before we could solve the instability problem, we needed a way to monitor it. Absence of produced protein was *not* a suitable assay for instability because unrelated factors (e.g., transcription/translation efficiency, message stability) could also contribute to this result. Thus, we turned to fusion vectors based on the

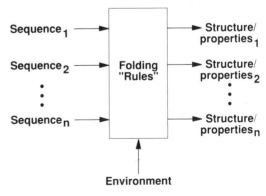

Fig. 2. An iterative approach to the elucidation of protein folding phenomena. By studying the structure and properties of a large number of related mutants, all of which have perturbed folding, some of the rules that govern the process of folding should begin to emerge.

Table 1. Recovery of BPTI disulfide mutants as a function of thermal stability.

BPTI variant	Thermal stability	Recovery of active material	
		30 °C	37 °C
Wild type	> 95°C[a]	High	High
Ala14, Ala38	70–75°C[a,b]	High	Low
Ala30, Ala51	60–62°C[b]	High	Low
Ala5, Ala55	< 37°C[c]	None	None

The results shown are for BPTI mutants expressed in *E. coli* in a secretion-coupled system using a heterologous signal peptide (Marks *et al.*, 1986, 1987a). Each mutant represents substitution of alanines for half cystines of one native disulfide.
[a]Vincent *et al.*, 1971. [b]M. Hurle *et al.*, in preparation. [c]Creighton *et al.*, 1978.

Staphylococcus aureus protein A gene. This system, developed at the Royal Institute of Technology in Stockholm (reviewed by Nilsson and Abrahmsén, 1990), involves the fusion of the signal peptide and two or more of the five IgG binding domains of protein A to the polypeptide of interest. The fusion protein can thus be isolated by affinity chromatography on immobilized IgG (Nilsson *et al.*, 1985b). By this strategy we hoped to be able to purify mutant fusion proteins based on their IgG-binding "tail," independent of the disposition of the BPTI moiety. Proteolytic instability in vivo, if it occurred, would be manifested by a truncated fusion protein. In IgG-purified preparations, we would thus be able to observe breakdown of the mutant BPTI domain directly, independent of other gene expression factors that might also be affecting the yield.

The actual expression construct that we employed consisted of the *S. aureus* protein A promoter, ribosome binding site, and coding sequences for the protein A signal peptide and two synthetic IgG-binding domains (Nilsson *et al.*, 1987) joined to that portion of the BPTI gene that codes for the mature 58 amino acid polypeptide (Anderson and Kingston, 1983; Marks *et al.*, 1986) (Fig. 3). In addition, codons for the Asn-Gly dipeptide were inserted between the protein A and BPTI domains to allow cleavage of fusion product at this junction by hydroxylamine (Bornstein and Balian, 1977). Such a cleavage allows purification of the domain of interest away from the protein A IgG-binding domains subsequent to the affinity chromatography step (Nilsson *et al.*, 1985a).

Serendipitously, and happily for us, we found that unstable BPTI mutants such as [Ala5, Ala55]BPTI, when expressed as such fusions in *E. coli*, not only became purifiable but also appeared to be endowed with greater stability (Table 3). The reason for this enhanced stability is unknown, but a similar phenomenon has been observed for other unstable mammalian proteins when they have been expressed as protein A fusions (Nilsson *et al.*, 1985a; Moks *et al.*, 1987; Hammarberg *et al.*, 1989). This effect is also not mutant specific because we have used the protein A fusion system to express other BPTI mutants

Table 2. Stability of wild type and [Ala14, Ala38]BPTI in the periplasm.

BPTI variant	Expression level (mg/l)					
	12 hours		24 hours		31 hours	
	28°C	37°C	28°C	37°C	28°C	37°C
Wild type	0.3	0.9	1.7	1.6	2.9	2.0
Ala14, Ala38	2.5	12.2	11.1	5.7	10.7	3.6

Shown are the expression yields in the *E. coli* periplasm of wild type and [Ala14, Ala38]BPTI at 28 or 37°C after 12, 24, and 31 hours of culture. The stationary phase was reached at approximately 12 hours for the cultures grown at 37°C and at approximately 24 hours for the cultures grown at 28°C.

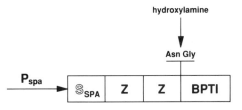

Fig. 3. Structure of the protein A-BPTI fusion vector. The coding sequence for BPTI was fused to two engineered IgG binding ("Z") domains of *S. aureus* protein A (Nilsson *et al.,* 1987), secretion was mediated by the protein A signal sequence (S$_{SPA}$), and expression via the protein A promoter (P$_{SPA}$) and ribosome-binding site. An asparagine-glycine dipeptide coding sequence was inserted in the linker region upstream of the BPTI coding sequence in order to provide a hydroxylamine cleavage site in the fusion protein.

that have reduced stabilities (e.g., mutants having Asn43 replaced with other residues) and which were difficult or impossible to produce in quantity as unfused polypeptides (B. Nilsson, unpublished).

Hydroxylamine cleaves between asparagine and glycine, hence BPTI from the hydroxylamine-cleaved fusion protein, unlike mature natural BPTI, has an extra glycyl group attached to the N-terminus. The α-amino group of the N-terminal arginine in native BPTI participates in a salt bridge with the C-terminal carboxyl group (Brown *et al.,* 1978). Therefore, we were concerned that the

Table 3. Qualitative comparison of fusion versus non-fusion expression systems for the recovery of unstable BPTI mutants.

BPTI variant	Thermal stability	Recovery of active material	
		"Direct" hookup	Protein A fusion
Wild type	Very high	+	+
Ala14, Ala38	High	+	+ + +
Ala30, Ala51	Moderate	+	+
Ala5, Ala55	Low	−	+

Approximate thermal stabilities are shown in Table 1. The "direct" hookup refers to BPTI expressed with the heterologous signal peptides discussed in Marks *et al.* (1987a, 1987b). The protein A fusion construction is shown in Fig. 3. All data are for growth at 30°C.

extra glycyl group introduced by hydroxylamine cleavage of the protein A fusion might disrupt this salt bridge and result in aberrant folding. However, control experiments with both N-glycyl wild-type BPTI and N-glycyl [Ala14, Ala38]BPTI showed that these behaved identically in folding experiments with their nonglycylated counterparts (data not shown). It does not appear, therefore, that the addition of the extra glycine significantly affects BPTI folding. Indeed, a minor natural variant of BPTI has been isolated that has an extra pyroglutamic acid residue attached to the N-terminus, and this protein appears to be correctly folded and active (Siekmann *et al.,* 1986).

Protein A–BPTI Fusions

Several surprising observations were made when the protein A fusions with wild-type

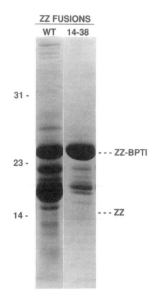

Fig. 4. BPTI fusion protein products exported from *E. coli.* The fusion proteins for wild-type and [Ala14, Ala38]BPTI were expressed in *E. coli* using the vector described in Fig. 3. Exported fusion proteins were purified by IgG-Sepharose immunoaffinity chromatography and analyzed by SDS-polyacrylamide gel electrophoresis. Sizes of protein molecular weight markers (in kD) are shown in the left margin. The location of the full-length protein A-BPTI fusion protein ("ZZ-BPTI") as well as the mobility of an unfused pair of IgG binding domains ("ZZ") is indicated in the right margin.

BPTI and [Ala14, Ala38]BPTI were compared. First, the fusion to wild-type BPTI appeared to be degraded, whereas the fusion to the *less stable* mutant, [Ala14, Ala38]BPTI, was produced predominantly intact (Fig. 4). Second, N-terminal sequencing and gel electrophoretic analyses of hydroxylamine-cleaved products indicated that the degradation was occurring in the BPTI portion of the fusion product (Fig. 5). Third, the extent of degradation did not increase with the time of fermentation, and spiking experiments indicated that exogenously added protein A-[wt]BPTI fusion was absolutely stable in the growth medium, suggesting that the degradation did not occur subsequent to export of the fusion protein from the cell (B. Nilsson, unpublished). Finally, the absolute amounts of the [Ala14, Ala38]BPTI fusion produced were several-fold greater than the amounts of the wild-type fusion. A similar enhancement of [Ala14, Ala38]BPTI yields relative to yields of wild-type BPTI, especially at reduced fermentation temperatures, was also observed upon expressing and secreting BPTI in the non-fused state by use of a "direct" hook-up to a heterologous signal sequence (Marks *et al.*, 1987a, 1987b) (Table 2 and Fig. 6).

The normal pathways of protein turnover in the cell are believed to involve the preferential degradation of damaged, misfolded, or otherwise unstable molecules. The results with the protein A-BPTI fusions, however, suggested that we were dealing with a novel and distinct pathway of protein degradation,

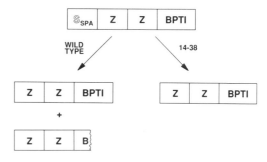

Fig. 5. Schematic illustration of exported fusion protein products. N-terminal amino acid sequencing and hydroxlamine cleavage analyses indicated that virtually all of the purified material shown in Fig. 4 that migrated with a mobility equal to or less than the mobility of the full-length fusion protein contained an intact set of Z domains. Hence, we concluded that the observed degradation was due to C-terminal proteolysis or truncation of the fusion proteins in the BPTI moiety. The [Ala14, Ala38]BPTI fusion is produced predominantly as the full-length molecule, whereas the wild-type fusion is produced as a heterogeneous mixture of full-length and degraded forms.

one that was *inversely* correlated with folding and stability.

The exact nature of this second pathway is unclear at present, but we are investigating the possibility that it represents an "unclogging" function that clears the secretion apparatus of molecules that have undergone secretion arrest due to premature folding. The inverse correlation between a folded protein structure and competency for secretion has been demonstrated for the *E. coli* maltose binding protein (Randall and Hardy, 1986; Randall *et*

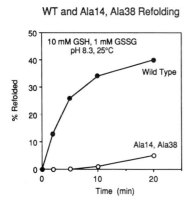

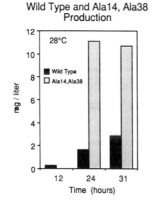

Fig. 6. The inverse correlation of folding and expression yield. Shown in the first panel is a comparison of the in vitro folding rates of wild-type and [Ala14, Ala38]BPTI in the presence of a thiol/disulfide exchange buffer consisting of oxidized and reduced glutathione (Marks *et al.*, 1987a). Shown in the second panel is a comparison of the in vivo expression yields of wild-type and [Ala14, Ala38]BPTI at 28°C (based on the data of Table 2).

al., 1987). Moreover, Creighton and his co-workers have argued persuasively that BPTI should be able to fold and form disulfides intracellularly, even though the redox potential inside the cell is highly reducing (Creighton and Goldenberg, 1984). Our working hypothesis, therefore, is that in a fraction of the fusion proteins, the BPTI portion of the molecule undergoes an intracellular folding reaction prior to secretion. The N-terminal protein A moiety of such molecules would initiate secretion, including partial extrusion and signal peptide cleavage, but the stable, folded, disulfide-bonded, C-terminal BPTI domain would block further translocation across the membrane (Maher and Singer, 1986). Proteolytic attack of the intracellular folded domain in the secretion-arrested molecules, possibly by a membrane-bound proteinase, would then be required for resumption of secretion. This model accounts for the fact that the [Ala14, Ala38]BPTI mutant, which folds much more slowly than wild-type BPTI (Marks *et al.,* 1987a), is secreted more efficiently and with less degradation (Fig. 6). Further biochemical and genetic characterization of this proposed protein degradation pathway will be necessary, however, before any firm conclusions can be drawn.

Summary

Because protein folding is such a complex, ill-understood phenomenon, we have chosen as a model system the extremely simple and well-characterized globular protein, BPTI. Our approach is to make specific BPTI mutants that have perturbed folding behavior, then study the properties of these variant polypeptides by structural and biophysical means. All of our mutants are produced by secretion-based expression systems in *E. coli.* We have noted that, for secreted mutant proteins, thermal stability in vitro is correlated with in vivo yields. However, relatively unstable BPTI mutants can be successfully recovered as fusions to the IgG binding domains of *S. aureus* protein A. The study of folding mutants with the protein A fusion ap-proach has also uncovered what may be a new pathway of protein turnover in *E. coli,* in which rapidly folding domains in secreted molecules appear not only to inhibit secretion but also to be preferentially degraded.

Acknowledgments

B. Nilsson was supported in part by a grant from the National Science Foundation (DMB86-06901) and in part by the National Swedish Board for Technical Development.

References

Anderson, S., and I. B. Kingston, *Proc. Natl. Acad. Sci. U.S.A.* **80**, 6838 (1983).
Bornstein, P., and G. Balian, *Meth. Enzymol.* **47**, 132 (1977).
Brown, L. R., A. DeMarco, R. Richarz, G. Wagner, K. Wüthrich, *Eur. J. Biochem.* **88**, 87 (1978).
Creighton, T. E., *J. Phys. Chem.* **89**, 2452 (1985).
_____, *Prog. Biophys. Molec. Biol.* **33**, 231 (1978).
Creighton, T. E., and D. P. Goldenberg, *J. Mol. Biol.* **179**, 497 (1984).
Creighton, T. E., E. Kalef, R. Arnon, *J. Mol. Biol.* **123**, 129 (1978).
Hammarberg, B., *et al., J. Biotechnol.,* in press
Maher, P. A., and S. J. Singer, *Proc. Natl. Acad. Sci. U.S.A.* **83**, 9001 (1986).
Marks, C. B., H. Naderi, P. A. Kosen, I. D. Kuntz, S. Anderson, *Science* **235**, 1370 (1987a).
_____, in *Protein Structure and Design 2,* D. Oxender, Ed. (Alan R. Liss, Inc., New York, 1987b), p. 335.
Marks, C. B., M. Vasser, P. Ng, W. Henzel, S. Anderson, *J. Biol. Chem.* **261**, 7115 (1986).
Moks, T., *et al., Biochemistry* **26**, 5239 (1987).
Nilsson, B., and L. Abrahmsén, *Methods in Enzymol.* **185**, 144 (1990).
Nilsson, B., *et al., Protein Engineering* **1**, 107 (1987).
Nilsson, B., L. Abrahmsén, M. Uhlén, *EMBO J.* **4**, 1075 (1985a).
Nilsson, B., E. Holmgren, S. Josephson, S. Gatenbeck, M. Uhlén, *Nucl. Acids Res.* **13**, 1151 (1985b).
Randall, L. L., and S. J. S. Hardy, *Cell* **46**, 921 (1986).
Randall, L. L., S. J. S. Hardy, J. R. Thom, *Ann. Rev. Microbiol.* **41**, 507 (1987).
Siekmann, J., *et al., Biol. Chem. Hoppe-Seyler* **367**, 92 (1986).
Vincent, J.-P., R. Chicheportiche, M. Lazdunski, *Eur. J. Biochem.* **23**, 401 (1971).

12

A Protein Folding Intermediate Analog

Design, Synthesis, and Characterization

Terrence G. Oas and Peter S. Kim

A major difficulty in the study of protein folding is that most proteins fold very cooperatively. This makes it hard to study structural details of folding because intermediates between the folded and unfolded states are often short-lived and not highly populated. One solution to this problem is to trap kinetic intermediates. Creighton took this approach in studying the oxidative refolding of bovine pancreatic trypsin inhibitor (BPTI) using chemical trapping of partially disulfide-bonded intermediates (1977, 1978; Creighton and Goldenberg, 1984). A simplified version of this pathway is shown in Fig. 1.

We are interested in the formation, structure, and stability of the early folding intermediates of BPTI, specifically those containing a single disulfide bond. Of the 15 possible ways to form a single disulfide bond in BPTI, only two species are populated significantly in refolding experiments (Creighton, 1977). Only one of these, involving a disulfide bond between cysteines 30 and 51, ([30,51]) has a native disulfide.

Representing 60 percent of the single-disulfide intermediates, [30,51] contains the only disulfide bond found in all subsequent intermediates in the folding pathway. Since disulfide bond formation and protein folding are thermodynamically linked functions, the predominance of [30,51] suggests that favorable interactions stabilize the structure of the intermediate (Creighton, 1977).

Figure 2 shows a Richardson drawing (Richardson, 1985) of BPTI, depicting the 30–51 disulfide and the β-sheet and α-helix in which cysteines 30 and 51 are located, respectively. Previously, one-dimensional nuclear magnetic resonance (NMR) spectra of [30,51] suggested that this intermediate contains a significant amount of native-like structure and that the structure is relatively stable, with a T_m of ~40°C (States *et al.*, 1987). These results suggest that specific native-like interactions between the α-helix and β-sheet may stabilize [30,51] and perhaps direct formation of the disulfide.

Possible mechanisms for forming this early intermediate are (i) formation of secondary structure, followed by tertiary structure, as predicted by the framework model (Kim and Baldwin, 1982) leading to the formation of the disulfide; (ii) collapse of hydrophobic side chains (Rose and Roy, 1980) directing formation of the disulfide, followed by folding of secondary and tertiary structure; or (iii) nonspecific formation of all possible one-disulfide intermediates, followed by rapid disulfide reshuffling leading to the thermodynamically most stable species — primari-

Fig. 1. Schematic diagram of the folding pathway of BPTI (25°C, 0.1*M* Tris-HCl, 0.2*M* KCl, 1m*M* EDTA, *p*H 8.7) as determined by Creighton (1977). Only the most populated intermediates are depicted in this diagram, which indicates the disulfide bonds formed at various stages of folding. The nonproductive intermediate, N(30SH, 51SH), is not shown. The one-disulfide intermediates are grouped together because they are in rapid equilibrium; the

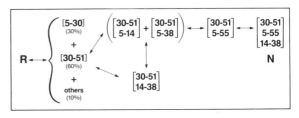

two most populated intermediates are indicated along with their relative proportions. The " + " between intermediates [30–51, 5–14] and [30–51, 5–38] indicates that they are both formed directly from the one-disulfide intermediates, that they are both converted directly to [30–51, 5–55], and that both are intermediates in the rearrangement of [30–51, 14–38] to [30–51, 5–55]. [Reprinted from *Nature* **336**, 42 (1988) with permission. Copyright 1988, Macmillan Magazines Limited.]

ly [30,51] (Creighton, 1975). Of course, other mechanisms, including mixtures of these, are feasible.

Research Methods

Our approach to studying the formation and stability of [30,51] is to use synthetic peptides with sequences corresponding to that of BPTI in the vicinity of the α-helix and the β-sheet. Since these two units of secondary structure are not contiguous in primary structure, this requires the synthesis of two short peptides, Pα and Pβ (Fig. 2). Their sequences are

Pα = Asn-Asn-Phe-Lys-Ser-Ala-Glu-Asn-
Cys-Met-Arg-Thr-Ala-Gly-Gly-Ala   (43–58)

Pβ = Arg-Tyr-Phe-Asn-Ala-Lys-Ala-
Gly-Leu-Cys-Gln-Thr-Phe   (20–33)

Pα corresponds in sequence to the C-terminal 16 residues of BPTI, which includes the α-helix, except that cysteine 55 has been replaced with alanine. Pβ corresponds in sequence to 14 residues found within the central β-sheet of BPTI. To mimic [30,51], these peptides are joined via their cysteines to form a disulfide bond between them. The desired heterodimer, called PαPβ, is then isolated using reverse-phase high-performance liquid chromotography (HPLC) (Fig. 3).

Selection of the sequences shown above was based on the following assumptions: (i) that the structure found in [30,51] is localized to the vicinity of the disulfide bond, and (ii) that structure of the folded peptide complex would be native-like. On the basis of

these assumptions, residues near the disulfide that are involved in close van der Waals or hydrogen-bonded contacts between the α-helical and β-sheet regions of BPTI (Wlodawer *et al.*, 1984) were included. The peptides chosen are short and readily synthesized in high yield and purity.

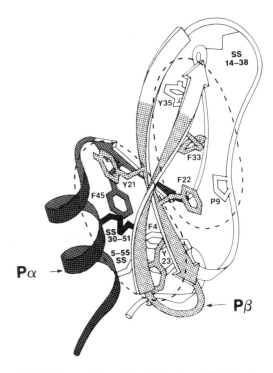

Fig. 2. Schematic drawing by Richardson (1985) showing the regions of BPTI corresponding to the peptides Pα and Pβ. Most of one of the hydrophobic cores in BPTI (indicated with dotted lines) is contained in the region corresponding to PαPβ. [Reprinted by permission from *Nature* **336**, 42 (1988), copyright © 1988, Macmillan Magazines Limited]

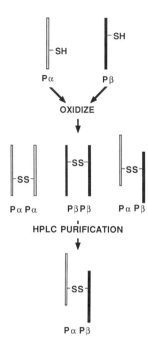

Fig. 3. Method used to synthesize and purify PαPβ starting from the single thiol-containing peptides, Pα and Pβ. The peptides were synthesized on an Applied Biosystems Model 430A peptide synthesizer using standard reaction cycles, modified to include acetic anhydride capping. PAM resins were used. The peptides were cleaved from the resin using TFMSA and desalted on a Sephadex G-10 column in 5 percent acetic acid. The peptide complex (PαPβ) was formed by air oxidation in 5M GuHCl, 0.2M Tris-HCl, pH 8, 25°C for 20 hours (GuHCl was present to prevent precipitation of the Pβ homodimer). PαPβ was purified from other products by HPLC on a Vydac C18 semipreparative column using a water/acetonitrile gradient in the presence of 0.1 percent TFA. The peptide complex was lyophilized from 5 percent acetic acid and stored in a desiccator. PαPβ synthesized by this procedure was indistinguishable, by analytical HPLC, from the product obtained under argon using glutathione as an oxidant. The identity of PαPβ was confirmed by analysis at the MIT Mass Spectrometry Facility (supported by the NIH), which gave the expected MH$^+$ molecular weight of 3353.

Results

Circular dichroism (CD) spectra of PαPβ in a standard buffer of 0.2M sodium sulfate, 10 mM sodium phosphate, pH 6 are shown in Fig. 4. At 0°C, the spectrum has features characteristic of a structured peptide, including a double minimum near 200 and 220 nm and a maximum at ~195 nm. At 60°C, the spectrum is typical of a random-coil peptide with a single minimum near 210 nm. Upon reduction

of the disulfide with dithioreitol (DTT), the spectrum at 0°C is that of random coil. This confirms the linkage of structure and disulfide formation in PαPβ. The temperature dependence of the CD signal at 218 nm for PαPβ, shown in Fig. 5, indicates a very broad unfolding transition. The first derivative of this data gives a T$_m$ of ~25°C (Fig. 5, inset). The transition is completely reversible up to 80°C, provided that the sample is degassed before use and can be eliminated by adding the denaturant, guanidine hydrochloride. The CD

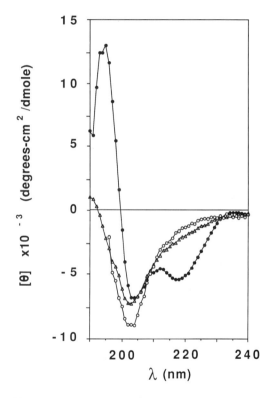

Fig. 4. CD spectra of PαPβ (disulfide-bonded peptide pair) at 0°C ($-\bullet-$) or 60°C ($-\triangle-$); and the reduced complex (Pα + Pβ) at 0°C ($-\bigcirc-$). All spectra were obtained in standard buffer (0.2M Na$_2$SO$_4$, 10 mM Na$_2$HPO$_4$, pH 6.0) on an Aviv Model 60DS CD spectrometer using a 1 mm pathlength cell at a sample concentration of 0.06 mM (as determined by tyrosine and cystine absorbance at 275.5 nm in 6M GuHCl (Edelhoch, 1967). PαPβ was reduced in 2 percent mercaptoethanol, 0.5 percent NH$_4$HCO$_3$ and then lyophilized to form reduced Pα + Pβ, as determined by HPLC. The CD spectrum of reduced Pα + Pβ was obtained in the presence of 0.5 mM reduced DTT and 1mM EDTA. [Reprinted from *Nature* **336**, 42 (1988) with permission. Copyright 1988, Macmillan Magazines Limited.]

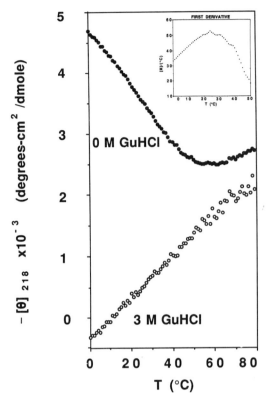

Fig. 5. Temperature dependence of the CD signal at 218 nm for PαPβ, in the presence or absence of guanidine hydrochloride (GuHCl). The inset shows the first derivative of the temperature dependence in the absence of GuHCl. For these studies, a 10 mm pathlength cell was used and the sample concentration was 0.02 mM. Temperature was maintained with a HP Model 89100A Peltier temperature control unit. All samples were degassed under vacuum prior to data collection. [Reprinted by permission from *Nature* **336**, 42 (1988), copyright © 1988, Macmillan Magazines Limited]

signal of PαPβ is not concentration dependent over a range of 15–300 μM, and PαPβ elutes as a monomer under these conditions on Sephadex G-25.

The ^{1}H NMR spectra of aromatic protons in PαPβ at various temperatures are shown in Fig. 6. These spectra contain several resonances with strongly temperature-dependent chemical shifts. They also show only one resonance for each proton at all temperatures. This indicates that the folded and unfolded states of PαPβ are in fast exchange on the NMR time scale (τ ~10^3 sec^{-1}). Thus, the chemical shift observed for each proton is the population-weighted average of the chemical

shifts in the folded and unfolded states. This allows the degree of folding in the vicinity of a proton to be determined conveniently by measuring chemical shift. Figure 7 shows such analysis for several assigned protons in PαPβ. These data confirm that the folding transition

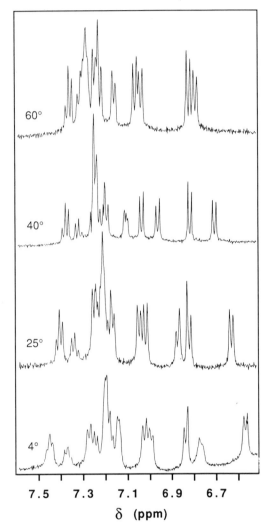

Fig. 6. Aromatic region of ^{1}H-NMR spectra for PαPβ at various temperatures. The sample concentration was 5 mM in standard buffer made with D$_2$O. The chemical shift standard was TMSP, whose chemical shift at pH 6.0 was assumed to be −0.017 ppm. The data were collected on a 500 MHz spectrometer at the MIT Francis Bitter National Magnet Laboratory (supported by the NIH), using presaturation of residual HOD for 2.0 seconds. A shifted sinebell apodization was used to enhance resolution. [Reprinted from *Nature* **336**, 42 (1988) with permission. Copyright 1988, Macmillan Magazines Limited.]

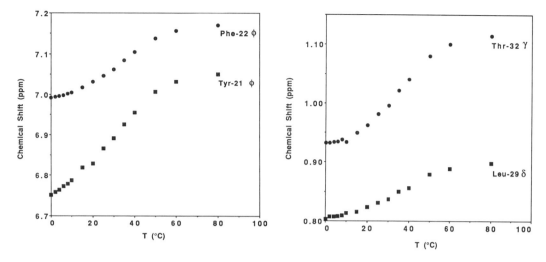

Fig. 7. Temperature dependence of chemical shift changes for selected resonances of PαPβ. Resonances are indicated using nomenclature for the corresponding residue in intact BPTI. [Reprinted from *Nature* **336**, 42 (1988) with permission. Copyright 1988, Macmillan Magazines Limited.]

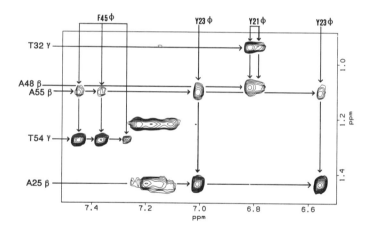

Fig. 8. Expanded region of the NOESY spectrum PαPβ showing several NOE's that result from native-like structure in the peptide model. The spectrum was collected in 90 percent H_2O, 10 percent D_2O, standard buffer, 4°C. Mixing time was 350 msec. The data were obtained on a Bruker AM-500 at the Fox Chase Cancer Center, Philadelphia, Pennsylvania.

is broad and indicate that the molecule is almost completely folded at 0°C. Different protons display qualitatively different melting curves. This may be the result of a non-cooperative folding transition, although more work must be done to establish the temperature dependence of chemical shifts in the fully folded and unfolded states.

Two-dimensional NMR data described in detail elsewhere (Oas and Kim, 1988) indicate that most, if not all, of the structure of PαPβ at 4°C is similar to the same region in BPTI. Unambiguously assigned nuclear Overhauser effect spectroscopy (NOESY) connectivities demonstrate the presence of the α-helix, the

β-sheet, and many of the tertiary interactions seen in BPTI. Figure 8 displays a selected region of the NOESY spectrum of PαPβ that contains such cross peaks between aromatic protons and upfield aliphatic resonances. These NOE's indicate that the distance between the correlated protons is less than ~5Å in the folded structure.

These data show that synthetic peptide fragments of BPTI, corresponding to regions near the 30–51 disulfide bond, fold into a native-like structure in aqueous solution and that this structure depends on the presence of the disulfide bond. The NMR spectrum of folded PαPβ (Oas and Kim, 1988) is qualitatively similar to that of [30,51] (States *et al.,* 1987). On the basis of these observations, we conclude that PαPβ is a good model of the [30,51] intermediate of BPTI. The fact that PαPβ does not contain regions of BPTI outside the vicinity of the disulfide bond makes it a de facto intermediate because it can not fold further. Peptide models of folding intermediates may, for the first time, permit one to obtain detailed structural information about the early events in protein folding.

Acknowledgments

We thank R. Rutkowski for expert assistance with synthesis and purification, E. Goodman and E. O'Shea for help with NMR analysis, T. Lin and J. Staley for help with disulfide chemistry. T. G. O. is an American Cancer Society Postdoctoral Fellow. This research was supported in part by grants from the National Science Foundation (DMB-8605617) and the Lucille P. Markey Charitable Trust.

References

Creighton, T. E., *J. Mol. Biol.* **87,** 603 (1974).

_____, *J. Mol. Biol.* **96,** 777 (1975).

_____, *J. Mol. Biol.* **113,** 275 (1977).

_____, *Prog. Biophys. Molec. Biol.* **33,** 231 (1978).

Creighton, T. E., and D. P. Goldenberg, *J. Mol. Biol.* **179,** 497 (1984).

Edelhoch, H., *Biochemistry* **6,** 1948 (1967).

Karplus, M., *J. Mol. Biol.* **195,** 731 (1967).

Kim, P. S., and R. L. Baldwin, *Ann. Rev. Biochem.* **51,** 459 (1982).

Oas, T. G., and P. S. Kim, *Nature,* **336,** 42 (1988).

Richardson, J. S., *Meth. Enzmo.* **115,** 359 (1985).

Rose, G. D., and S. Roy, *Proc. Natl. Acad. Sci. U.S.A.* **77,** 4643 (1980).

States, D. J., *et al., J. Mol. Biol.* **174,** 411 (1984).

Wlodawer, A., *et al., J. Mol. Biol.* **180,** 301 (1984).

13

Folding of
Bovine Growth Hormone

David N. Brems

The folding of bovine growth hormone (bGH) has been shown to be consistent with the following scheme (Brems, 1988):

$$N \longleftrightarrow I \longleftrightarrow U$$
$$\updownarrow$$
$$I_{assoc} \rightarrow precipitate$$

Scheme 1: N = native;
I = monomeric intermediate;
U = unfolded; and
I_{assoc} = associated intermediate.

In this chapter, the characteristics of the intermediates I and I_{assoc} will be described. Particular emphasis will be placed on I_{assoc} because it plays an important role in recovery of N from a refolding experiment.

The protein bGH is secreted from the pituitary gland, and it modulates a variety of metabolic processes, including growth-promoting activity, lactogenic activity, diabetogenic activity, and insulin-like activity (Daughaday, 1974). bGH consists of 191 amino acids and is a single-domain protein. The three-dimensional structure of porcine growth hormone has been solved and it is characterized as a four-helical bundle with the helices arranged in an antiparallel fashion (Abdel-Meguid, 1987). Several of these helices are amphipathic or dual-sided with hydrophobic and hydrophilic surfaces. From sequence homology and spectroscopic similarities, the architecture of the bovine

species must be very similar. The folding studies described here were on oxidized bGH that contains two native-like disulfide bonds. The third helix, spanning residues 107–128, is amphipathic (Brems *et al.*, 1987a) and is a region that will be the focus of much of the data presented.

The equilibrium denaturation of bGH has been studied and has the unusual property of having well-populated intermediates (Burger *et al.*, 1966; Holladay *et al.*, 1974; Brems *et al.*, 1985, 1986, 1987b, 1988; Havel *et al.*, 1986; Brems, 1988). Most proteins demonstrate a cooperative unfolding that is explainable by a simple N ↔ U two-state mechanism (Creighton, 1984). The intermediate structures of bGH have conformational stability simliar to the native state since they are stable in solvent conditions that disrupt the native state. Intermediates that are stable at equilibrium are easier to characterize than transient kinetic intermediates, and, as a result, bGH folding intermediates are relatively well characterized. All the relevant data relating to these intermediates cannot be reproduced here, but data relating to recovery of the native state from refolding will be reviewed.

Monomeric Intermediate I

Monomeric intermediate I has been described as a molten globule (Brems and Havel, 1989).

It is compact like the native state, is highly flexible in that the aromatic amino acids are not packed in the native environment as determined by a denatured-like absorbance spectrum, has a high content of alpha-helix, and has hydrophobic faces of the amphipathic helices that are relatively more exposed than in the native state. Some of these characteristics are illustrated in Fig. 1 where the equilibrium denaturation was monitored by UV absorbance, circular dichroism (CD), and high-performance liquid chromatography (HPLC) size-exclusion (at very low protein concentrations to avoid aggregation).

The noncoincidence of the denaturation transitions in Fig. 1 is due to the presence of I. According to Fig. 1, the aromatic absorbance of bGH is most labile to denaturation, and at higher concentrations of denaturant, the secondary structure (as detected by CD and the compactness (as detected by HPLC size-exclusion) denature somewhat simultaneously. In the intermediate state I, the hydrophobic face of the amphipathic helix 107–128 is not completely buried as it is in the native state, and it readily interacts with a similar hydrophobic surface from another bGH molecule at higher protein concentrations. This intermolecular hydrophobic bonding between helices is critical to the stabilization of I_{assoc} (Brems et al., 1988).

Associated Intermediate I_{assoc}

I_{assoc} has a mean average radius of ~4.5 nm (compared to ~1 nm for the native state and ~3.5 nm for the unfolded state) (Havel et al., 1986) and probably represents a family of aggregates of varying molecular weight. I_{assoc} is populated at equilibrium under conditions that induce partial denaturation and transiently populated during kinetic refolding as long as the protein concentration is greater than 0.2 mg/ml (Brems, 1988).

The presence of I_{assoc} has been identified by multiple methods: classical light scattering, photon correlation spectroscopy, size exclusion HPLC, second-derivative absorption spectra, fluorescence, and CD at 300 nm

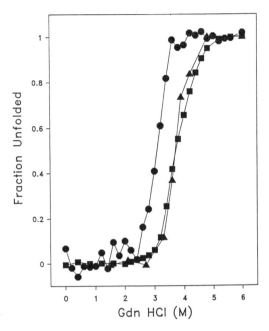

Fig. 1. Equilibrium unfolding curves for bGH in GdnHCl monitored by absorbance (●), circular dichroism (■), and molecular size (size-exclusion HPLC, ▲). Absorbance results are independent of protein concentration and were obtained with 23 μM bGH solutions. CD and HPLC results were obtained at dilute protein concentrations where association is minimized: 1.8 and 4.5 μM bGH solutions, respectively.

(Havel et al., 1986). Some of these methods are intrinsic measures of molecular size, while others are due to spectral changes of the tryptophan moiety as a result of association. In addition, the presence of I_{assoc} alters the shape of the equilibrium denaturation transition as detected by CD at 222 nm (Brems et al. 1986), retards the rate of kinetic refolding (Brems et al., 1987b), and because I_{assoc} is less soluble than all other conformations, it precipitates in refolding conditions that contain less than $2M$ GdnHCl (it is soluble in solutions of $>2M$ GdnHCl) (Brems, 1988). The precipitation of I_{assoc} that occurs as a result of refolding causes difficulties in recovering native bGH in high yields from heterologous expression in Escherichia coli.

The remainder of this chapter will focus on the "off-pathway" intermediate I_{assoc} and its relationship to overall solubility and recovery of native bGH from a refolding experiment. It will be shown that particular excipients or alterations in the amino acid sequence can greatly alter the stability of I_{assoc} and the resulting recovery of the native state from refolding.

Relative Insolubility of Iassoc

The relative insolubility of I_{assoc} compared to other bGH conformations was first implied from the precipitation that resulted in refolding experiments (Brems *et al.*, 1985). The equilibrium denaturation transitions were completely reversible within the zone of 2–6M GdnHCl. The denaturation transition region occurs between 2.8–5M GdnHCl; 2–2.8M GdnHCl concentrations are nondenaturing and are solubilizing for all bGH conformers. Reversible refolding of bGH can be studied, providing the refolding buffer contains > 2M GdnHCl. However, denatured bGH samples that were diluted to less than 2M GdnHCl resulted in significant precipitation. If refolding samples were allowed to fold to completion at 2M GdnHCl prior to dilution to lower denaturant, then precipitation did not appear. Thus, either the denatured state or some intermediate state was insoluble in solutions of less than 2M GdnHCl.

In order to investigate this phenomenon further, a two-step procedure for identifying the insoluble species was developed (Brems, 1988). The first step of the procedure is used to populate different bGH conformers. This was accomplished by varying the GdnHCl or protein concentration or by interrupting a kinetic folding experiment. In the second step of the procedure, the various conformers were introduced by a simple dilution into solvent conditions that induce precipitation. After 30–60 minutes following the second step, the amount of precipitate was quantitated in either of two ways. In one way, the turbidity at 450 nm was measured in a spectrophotometer. In the other way, the precipitate was sedimented by centrifugation, the soluble fraction was filtered through a 0.45 μm filter, and the remaining soluble protein content was determined by ultraviolet absorbance at 278 nm. The amount of precipitate was deduced by

subtracting the remaining soluble protein from the total expected protein.

Figure 2 demonstrates the results of such an experiment at two different temperatures. The results show that the native and denatured forms of bGH are soluble or gave rise to products that were soluble. However, if bGH was diluted from partially denaturing conditions (3–5M GdnHCl), then precipitation resulted. It was concluded that only partially denatured forms are responsible for the precipitation. In addition, the extent of precipitation depends on temperature, with less precipitation occurring at lower temperatures. The formation of turbidity in the two-step procedure was linearly dependent on the initial protein concentration in the first step (data not shown). The concentration dependence in the first step of the procedure indicates that intermolecular interactions between folding intermediates are a prerequisite for precipitation. Thus, the observed insolubility depends on the presence of an associated folding intermediate(s), and its concentration is related to the extent of turbidity. At 2 mg/ml and 3.5M GdnHCl, it can be deduced from Fig. 2B that at 3°C, approximately 50 percent, and at room temperature, 75 percent of the population is involved in the reaction that leads to insolubility.

The presence of I_{assoc} as a transient intermediate during kinetic refolding under soluble conditions (< 2M GdnHCl) was established by a variety of methods (Brems, 1988). The CD band at 300 nm that is uniquely related to I_{assoc} is absent in the initial unfolded bGH solution and the final refolded native solution but appeared transiently during the refolding. The transient appearance of the 300 nm CD band was dependent on the protein concentration. The rate of bGH refolding as monitored by absorbance at 290 nm was also found to be concentration dependent (Brems *et al.*, 1987b). Increasing the concentration of protein decreased the kinetic folding rate. Absorbance properties of I are identical to those of U, and the reaction of N↔I of Scheme 1 contains the total change in absorbance. Thus, for refolding at higher protein concentrations, dissociation of the off-pathway I_{assoc} is rate

Fig. 2. Precipitation following dilution from differing initial GdnHCl concentrations. The results were obtained by using the two-step procedure described in the text. In the first step, bGH (2 mg/ml) was incubated in varying concentrations of GdnHCl for at least 30 minutes. In the second step, the samples were diluted to 0.8M GdnHCl and 0.2 mg/ml bGH in order to induce precipitation. The amount of precipitate was determined by the absorbance at 450 nm (**A**) or by measurement of remaining soluble protein (**B**). The open symbols represent the results at 23°C, and the closed symbols represent results at 3°C.

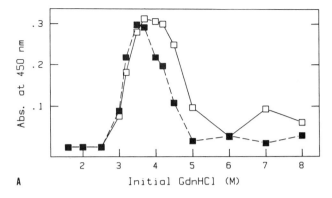

A

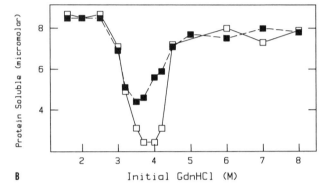

B

limiting, and the observed refolding kinetics as detected by absorbance are consequently affected.

As additional evidence for the transient existence of I_{assoc} during folding, the two-step procedure for selectively precipitating I_{assoc} was employed. Figure 3 represents data for which fully denatured bGH was diluted to 2.2M GdnHCl in the first step of a two-step procedure. In the second step, portions of the refolding solution were removed at varying times and diluted to the solution conditions that induce precipitation of I_{assoc}. As shown in Fig. 3, an intermediate that precipitated in the second step of the assay accumulated rapidly and disappeared with time. Two different protein concentrations in first step of the assay were explored. The amount of precipitated protein present during folding was dependent on the protein concentration. The presence of a transient species during folding that is protein concentration dependent and that precipitates as a result of the second step of the procedure demonstrates that an associated intermediate is populated during

kinetic refolding. From the amount of turbidity formed, it can be estimated that at the higher protein concentration, approximately 33 percent of the total protein was involved in the associated form at early times in the kinetic pathway.

Identification of a Site Critical to Association

We have studied a fragment from bGH (96–133 or 109–133) that contains considerable helical structure in aqueous solutions and corresponds to the third helix of the four-helix bundle (Brems et al., 1987a). Figure 4 shows that this helix is an example of an amphipathic helix. We demonstrated that the helical content of this fragment is strongly dependent on its concentration. It was concluded that the unusual helical stability of fragment 96–133 was due to the intermolecular packing between the hydrophobic faces of the amphipathic surfaces of the helices. Other data had shown that the helix-detected denatura-

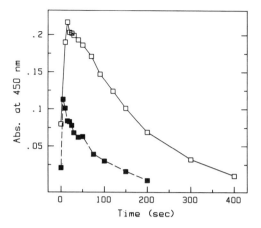

Fig. 3. Two-step procedure for the detection of precipitable species during refolding. In the first step, unfolded bGH in $6M$ GdnHCl was diluted to $2.2M$ GdnHCl and either 1.75 mg/ml (□) or 0.5 mg/ml (■) bGH. At varying times, samples were removed and diluted to the precipitating conditions of the second step of the procedure. After complete precipitation occurred, turbidity was measured by the absorbance at 450 nm. All solutions were maintained at 3°C.

tion transition of bGH was altered by the presence of I_{assoc}. It thus seemed possible that I_{assoc} formed from intermolecular interactions of the hydrophobic surfaces of its helices.

The next step was to determine if the fragment 96–133 could interfere with formation of

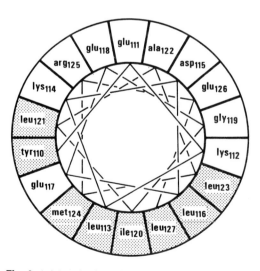

Fig. 4 Axial projection of the potential helical structure of residues 110–127. The top of the figure illustrates the hydrophilic surface; the bottom, the hydrophobic surface of the putative amphiphilic helix.

I_{assoc}. Under equilibrium conditions for the maximal population of I_{assoc}, addition of an excess of fragment 96–133 substantially decreased the intensity of the 300 nm CD band (Brems et al., 1986). Since the 300 nm band is diagnostic for the associated equilibrium intermediate, it was concluded that fragment 96–133 diminished the concentration of I_{assoc}. In addition, the extraneous fragments 96–133 or 109–133 could inhibit the formation of precipitate that occurred as a result of refolding (Brems, 1988).

Figure 5 shows the kinetics of precipitation following dilution from conditions for maximal population of I_{assoc} (3.5M GdnHCl) to the conditions of the second step of the two-step procedure. Preincubation of a 10-fold molar excess of the fragment 96–133 to bGH in 3.5M GdnHCl was effective in complete inhibition of precipitate. The truncated peptides 96–112 and 109–133 were also tested as inhibitors of precipitation. Fragment 109–133 was effective in preventing precipitation, but 96–112 was not. These results show that the C-terminal half of 96–133 (which corresponds to the third helical segment in bGH) is responsible for preventing precipitation and suggest that specific events are responsible for the formation of precipitate.

Peptide 96–133 was not as effective in preventing precipitation if it was only included in the final precipitation conditions. This indicates that the peptide inhibits precipitation by interacting with a species that is present in the initial conditions of the first step of the procedure. It was suggested that the helical fragment formed a complex with the intermediate I of Scheme 1, which prevented I from associating to form I_{assoc}. The complex is probably stabilized from interactions between the two hydrophobic surfaces of I and the peptide. If I had formed the amphipathic helix 107–133 with an exposed hydrophobic face, then in a complementary fashion, the corresponding hydrophobic face of the helix of the fragment might specifically interact and prevent further self-association. Other soluble fragments from bGH that did not overlap with 109–133 were tested for their ability to inhibit precipitation, but were ineffective.

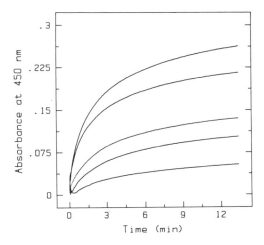

Fig. 5. Inhibition of precipitation that occurs during folding by peptide 96–133. Folding was initiated by diluting a solution of bGH at 1.75 mg/ml and 3.5*M* GdnHCl to refolding conditions that induce precipitation (0.8*M* GdnHCl and 0.18 mg/ml bGH). Formation of turbidity was continuously monitored by the absorbance at 450 nm. All solutions were maintained at 3°C. The top curve represents the time of turbidity formation in the absence of fragment 96–133. In descending order fom the top curve, the fragment was present at a 1-, 3-, 5-, and 7-fold molar excess to bGH, respectively. The fragment was preincubated with bGH in the initial 3.5*M* GdnHCl solution.

Stabilization of I$_{assoc}$ by Site-Directed Mutagenesis

With confidence that a region critical to the stabilization of I$_{assoc}$ had been identified, we set out to alter the stabilization of I$_{assoc}$ by site-directed mutagenesis (Brems *et al.*, 1988). Based on the amphipathicity of helix 107–128, the interface region between the hydrophobic and hydrophilic surfaces (Fig. 4) was altered. Modifications have been made to extend or decrease the hydrophobic surface. To date, only the modification that extends the hydrophobic surface by replacing lys-112 to leu has been thoroughly investigated. Other modifications have been constructed, and will be described at a later date.

Some dramatic folding results were observed with the lys-112 → leu mutant that are a result of stabilization of I$_{assoc}$. The increased stability of I$_{assoc}$ of the mutant protein is explainable by preferential intermolecular interactions between helices due to enhanced hydrophobic attraction of their amphipathic

surfaces. At low protein concentrations, the wild-type protein exhibits symmetrical equilibrium denaturation transitions, but the mutant protein exhibits biphasic or nonsymmetrical transitions. At higher protein concentrations, the wild-type protein demonstrates the biphasic or nonsymmetrical denaturation transitions that were observed for the mutant protein at low protein concentrations.

The mutant protein refolds slower (by a factor of 30) than the wild type, but they both unfold at similar rates. Stabilization of I$_{assoc}$ by mutation slows folding because this intermediate does not lie directly on the path to the native state (Scheme 1). Since the N ↔ I reaction of Scheme 1 accounts for the complete change in absorbance at 290 nm (Brems *et al.*, 1987b), the refolding as detected by UV absorbance at 290 nm is rate-limited by the dissociation, if I$_{assoc}$ is significantly populated. The effect of I$_{assoc}$ on the kinetics of refolding is manifested in a protein concentration dependence for wild-type bGH, with increasing concentration resulting in slower kinetics. The enhanced stability of I$_{assoc}$ resulting from the mutation causes the folding kinetics of the mutant bGH at low protein concentration to be similar to the wild type at higher protein concentration. The unfolding kinetics for the mutant or wild-type bGH are not altered by the increased stabilization of I$_{assoc}$ because association occurs subsequent to the unfolding that is detected by absorbance at 290 nm.

The two-step procedure was utilized to compare the solubility of I$_{assoc}$ from the mutant protein and wild-type protein. Figure 6 shows that the mutant protein precipitates more readily than the wild-type bGH. The abscissa in Fig. 6 represents the initial concentrations of protein in the first step of the procedure. Figure 6 demonstrates that the mutant protein precipitates to a greater extent than the wild-type protein. The greater precipitation of the mutant protein is attributed to an increased population of the associated intermediate. The results for the lysine-to-leucine mutation confirm our previous proposal regarding I$_{assoc}$.

For the future, we are working toward

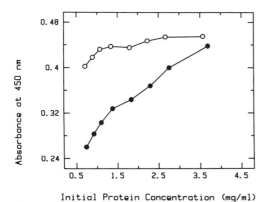

Fig. 6. Two-step procedure for selective precipitation of the associated intermediate. In the first step, various amounts of the associated intermediate were formed by equilibration in 3.7M GdnHCl and varying concentrations of protein. In the second step, the associated species were selectively precipitated by dilution to 0.8M GdnHCl and a constant final protein concentration of 0.18 mg/ml. After 30 minutes, the amount of precipitate was detected by absorbance at 450 nm. All solutions were at 23°C and 50 mM ammonium bicarbonate (pH 8.5). (○), mutant bGH; (●), wild-type bGH.

making modifications that will selectively decrease the stability of I_{assoc}. It is anticipated that such mutants will provide a better yield through the refolding step. Given the pharmaceutical implications for bGH, this would have considerable economic value. It is also hoped that by decreasing the tendency for formation of I_{assoc}, the general solution and solubility properties of bGH might improve.

Since aggregation accompanied by precipitation is one of the major solution state degradation pathways, decreasing the stability of the off-pathway intermediate I_{assoc} is expected to decrease the degradation rate of bGH.

Acknowledgments

I wish to thank H. A. Havel, S. R. Lehrman, T. F. Holzman, N. E. MacKenzie, C.-S. C. Tomich, and S. M. Plaisted whose invaluable collaborations have made this work possible.

References

Abdel-Meguid, S. S., *et al., Proc. Natl. Acad. Sci. U.S.A.* **84,** 6434 (1987).

Brems, D. N., *Biochemistry* **27,** 4541 (1988).

Brems, D. N., and H. A. Havel, *Proteins: Struct. Funct. Genet.* **5,** 93 (1989).

Brems, D. N., *et al. Biochemistry* **24,** 7662 (1985).

_____, *Biochemistry* **25,** 6539 (1986).

_____, *Biochemistry* **26,** 7774 (1987a).

_____, *J. Biol. Chem.* **262,** 2590 (1987b).

_____, *Proc. Natl. Acad. Sci. U.S.A.* **85,** 3367 (1988).

Burger, H. G., *et al., J. Biol. Chem.* **241,** 449 (1966).

Creighton, T. E., in *Proteins* (W.H. Freeman, New York, 1984), pp. 286–294.

Daughaday, W. H., in *Textbook of Endocrinology,* R. H. Williams, Ed. (W. B. Saunders Co., Philadelphia, 5th ed., 1974), pp. 31–79.

Havel, H. A., *et al., Biochemistry* **25,** 6533 (1986).

Holladay, L. A., *et al., Biochemistry* **13,** 1653 (1974).

14

Inclusion Bodies from Proteins Produced at High Levels in Escherichia coli

Joanna K. Krueger, Ann M. Stock
Clarence E. Schutt, Jeffry B. Stock

Foreign proteins produced at high levels in *Escherichia coli* from plasmid expression vectors frequently agglomerate to form approximately spherical particles with diameters of up to one micron. These inclusion bodies appear to be amorphous precipitates of the overproduced proteins. Proteins produced under the same conditions from *E. coli* genes tend to remain soluble. However, *E. coli* proteins containing point mutations frequently agglomerate into inclusion bodies as if they were foreign. Some mutant variants distribute both into native soluble structures and into inclusion bodies so that both forms are present in the same cells. The soluble and particulate forms are not in equilibrium; they appear to be stable products of distinct folding pathways. The protein in inclusion bodies can be purified, unfolded in guanidine-HCl, and refolded in vitro to form the native soluble structure. Apparently, subtle alterations in the kinetics of protein folding can favor intermolecular events that cause precipitation. Our results suggest that the advantage of efficient protein folding has provided a major selective factor in determining the primary structure of proteins.

Inclusion Bodies from Proteins Overproduced in *E. coli*

With the advent of modern recombinant DNA technology, it has become common practice to overproduce foreign proteins in *E. coli* (for a review, see Marston, 1986). These proteins frequently precipitate within the cytoplasm to form dense, finely granular inclusion bodies. They can be visualized in electron micrographs as large, dense structures without a surrounding membrane, often spanning the entire diameter of the cell. Inclusion bodies may be readily isolated from cell lysates by centrifugation at $10,000 \times g$. They appear to be comprised of essentially pure overproduced protein. Isolated inclusion bodies generally can be dissolved in denaturants such as sodium dodecyl sulfate, urea, or guanidine hydrochloride, but not in detergents such as Triton-X-100, high salt, and/or sulfhydryl reducing reagents. A survey of proteins that have been overproduced in *E. coli* indicates little correlation between formation of inclusion bodies with source of genetic material, type of expression vector, or molecular weight of the protein (Kane and Hartley, 1988). On the other hand, it is apparent that the strain of *E. coli* used for overproduction and the conditions of growth—as well as characteristics of the overproduced protein such as number of subunits, susceptibility to proteolysis, and presence of disulfide bonds—can all be important in affecting the extent of inclusion body formation.

There are a few examples of wild-type *E. coli* proteins that form inclusion bodies when they are overproduced in *E. coli*. These include β-galactosidase (Cheng, 1983), the sigma subunit of RNA polymerase (Gribskov and Burgess, 1983), and the protein kinase-osmoreceptor EnvZ (Masui *et al.*, 1984). These are exceptions, however; it generally has been possible to express *E. coli* proteins at very high levels in predominantly soluble form. For instance, each of the six cytoplasmic proteins that are required for the regulation of motility in *E. coli* and *Salmonella typhimurium* have been overproduced in soluble form from cloned genes in multicopy plasmids.

Point mutations in overproduced E. coli *proteins* can cause inclusion body formation

Techniques of site-directed mutagenesis allow new proteins to be engineered from those that currently exist in nature. Such variants can provide valuable insights concerning relationships of structure to function. We have used this approach to study the signal transduction proteins that control motility in *E. coli*. During the course of this investigation, we found that single amino acid substitutions in these proteins frequently caused them to form inclusion bodies.

CheB is a cytoplasmic protein with a central role in sensory adaptation. It functions to modulate the signaling activities of membrane chemoreceptors by catalyzing the hydrolysis of glutamyl methyl esters (Stock and Koshland, 1978). The protein has been purified as a 349 amino acid monomeric species comprised of two distinct domains, an N-terminal regulatory region of approximately 140 amino acids and a C-terminal esterase domain extending approximately 200 residues (Simms *et al.*, 1985). Deletions that remove the N-terminus do not adversely affect the activity of the catalytic domain; the truncated protein can be overproduced as a soluble species that actually exhibits enhanced esterase activity.

CheB has two cysteine residues, Cys-207 and Cys-309. Preliminary results with sulfhydryl inhibitors and cysteine mutants indicated that CheB was a sulfhydryl esterase (Snyder *et al.*, 1984; Simms *et al.*, 1987). The results with point mutations were complicated by the tendency of the mutant proteins to precipitate. A more detailed analysis showed

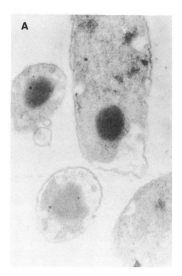
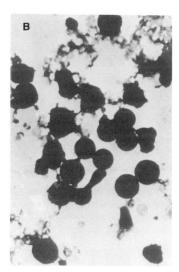

Fig. 1. (A) Electron micrograph of thin sections of inclusion bodies within *E. coli* JM109 containing the pUC12-derived expression vector for the cysteine 309 deletion CheB mutant, pME36. Cells were embedded and stained with uranyl acetate and Reynold's lead. (B) Electron micrograph of negatively stained cell extract containing inclusion bodies from pME36 in JM109 *E. coli* cells.

that the mutants tended to be produced as inclusion bodies within the cell (Fig. 1). This occured to some degree with every CheB point mutation that was examined, including several different substitutions at positions 207 and/or 309 as well as mutation of a glycine residue, Gly-284, within a putative nucleotide binding fold. In most cases there was a partition between soluble and included protein (Fig. 2). The soluble mutant proteins were generally active, while the protein in inclusion bodies completely lacked esterase activity. Since a Cys-207/Cys-309 double mutant retained esterase activity, CheB is not in fact a sulfhydryl esterase. As expected, sulfhydryl inhibitors such as 5,5'-dithiobis(2-nitrobenzoate), N-ethylmaleimide, and p-chloromercuriphenyl sulfonate had no effect on the activity of the double mutant.

CheY is a 128 amino acid cytoplasmic protein that functions in E. coli to regulate flagellar activity in response to signals from sensory receptors at the cell periphery. Its regulatory role involves a phosphoacceptor activity that may be assayed with the purified protein (Wylie et al., 1988; Hess et al., 1988). We recently solved the x-ray crystal structure of CheY to 2.7 angstroms resolution (Stock et al., 1989). This study was greatly facilitated by the use of site-directed mutagenesis to genetically engineer useful heavy-atom derivatives. The wild-type CheY protein is completely deficient in cysteine residues. Five mutant genes were constructed, each with a cysteine codon substituted at one of the five positions occupied by serine codons in the wild-type sequence. The behavior of these mutated CheY proteins was similar to that of the CheB mutants. When expressed at high levels, the mutant proteins aggregated to varying extents into inclusion bodies. Almost 90 percent of Ser-104-Cys CheY was found in the 10,000 × g pellet of the crude extracts; Ser-15-Cys and Ser-76-Cys CheY distributed as approximately 75 percent and 50 percent inclusion body, respectively. Ser-79-Cys and Ser-56-Cys were produced in predominantly soluble form.

Despite their tendency to aggregate, all of the mutant CheY proteins were active. When expressed at low levels in cheY mutant cells, they allowed essentially wild-type sensory motor regulation. Moreover, all of the purified mutant proteins were active in phosphotransfer assays. To obtain Ser-104-Cys in native form, it was necessary to dissolve the

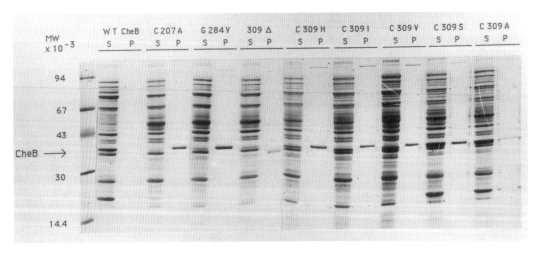

Fig. 2. Sodium dodecyl sulfate/polyacrylamide (12 percent) gel electrophoresis showing the partitioning of WT CheB and various CheB mutants into soluble, S, and precipitated, P, fractions. The pellet fractions were resuspended and homogenized in the same volume as the corresponding supernatant. CheB mutations are indicated by the amino acid that has been altered, its position in the CheB sequence, and the amino acid that has been substituted in its place. CheB 309Δ is a deletion extending from Cys 309 through the C-terminus.

inclusion bodies in guanidine hydrochloride and then allow the protein to refold by slowly removing denaturant under relatively dilute conditions. The other mutant CheY proteins were purified by conventional methods from soluble fractions. The soluble, active forms of the three mutant proteins that showed the greatest tendency to partition into inclusion bodies were distinct from other CheY variants in that they tended to precipitate during storage and upon perturbation of *p*H and ionic strength. Thus, there appeared to be a correlation between the stability of a pure CheY protein in vitro and its tendency to form inclusion bodies within the cell.

Mechanism of Inclusion Body Formation

The factors controlling the tendency of certain proteins to form inclusion bodies are not well understood. Our observations with the overproduced CheB and CheY proteins suggest that extremely small changes in structure can have profound effects on the tendency to precipitate in vivo. In most of the mutants we examined, protein solubility was dramatically altered by a conservative substitution of one out of over 5000 atoms, such as the exchange of an oxygen for a sulfur. Even more surprising was the finding that these effects appear to be the rule rather than the exception. It is as if almost any change in the primary sequence causes at least some degree of precipitation.

Another unexpected observation was the finding that most mutational variants partitioned between soluble and particulate fractions. We studied this in greater detail in the case of a CheB mutant, Cys-207-Ala, about half of which is produced as an active soluble protein and half as completely inactive material in inclusion bodies. Apparently these two forms of the enzyme are not in equilibrium. Protein in inclusion bodies does not become soluble unless it is unfolded by treatment with sodium dodecyl sulfate (SDS), urea, or guanidine HCl. For example, Cys-

207-Ala inclusion bodies suspended in 100 m*M* potassium phosphate buffer, *p*H 7.0, were incubated for several days with no release of nonsedimentable protein. Apparently, inclusion body formation is essentially an irreversible process.

One might expect that the soluble pool of Cys-207-Ala CheB is an intermediate in the precipitation process. This does not appear to be the case, however. The partition between soluble and insoluble CheB remains unchanged for more than an hour after inhibition of protein synthesis with chloramphenicol. Thus, it is apparent that the soluble and particulate pools of CheB can not exchange with one another. Once a CheB monomer aggregates, it remains aggregated, and once it folds into a native monomeric structure, it remains soluble. Moreover, this process can be duplicated in vitro. If Cys-207-Ala inclusion bodies are dissolved in 6*M* guanidine-HCl, and then the guanidine-HCl is removed by dialysis at 40°C against 100 m*M* potassium phosphate, *p*H 7.0, the CheB partitions between an active monomeric species and an inactive precipitate. Under these conditions, the active fraction varied from 15 to 40 percent of the total, as the concentration of CheB was reduced from 2.0 to 0.05 mg/ml.

These results can be understood in terms of a mechanism for inclusion body formation that involves the precipitation of partially folded intermediates. According to this idea, folding pathways involve intermediates with hydrophobic patches exposed to solvent. If sticky patches within a single polypeptide interact, the protein moves on toward a native structure; if sticky patches on different polypeptides interact, the folding intermediates are diverted into the aggregated denatured state that eventually produces an inclusion body. Thus, the partition between native and precipitate is controlled by the relative rates of intra- versus intermolecular folding. Overproduction favors precipitation because it increases the probability of intermolecular collisions. Mutations favor precipitation because they slow the kinetics of the native folding pathway, thereby allowing for the abnormal buildup of intermediate species.

Studies of temperature-sensitive mutants of the tail spike protein of phage p22 support the concept that mutations can cause a redirection in the folding pathway toward insoluble aggregates (Goldberg et al., 1985). In these studies, it was concluded that the defect was due to a temperature-sensitive folding defect rather than a problem with the stability of the folded mutant proteins. Interestingly, the improperly folded proteins produced at the restrictive temperature were found in insoluble aggregates. Studies of protein folding in vitro are also consistent with the production of sticky intermediates. This has been most clearly established in studies involving the folding of bovine growth hormone. When folding occurs in solutions that stabilize folding intermediates, most of the product ends up in an insoluble protein aggregate (Brems, 1988).

With knowledge of the three-dimensional structure of CheY, it is possible to begin to rationalize the effects of the mutations on folding. Four of the mutated serine residues — 15, 76, 79, and 104 — lie in surface loop regions rather than within regions of well-defined alpha or beta secondary structure (Fig. 3). Surprisingly, the Ser-56-Cys mutation, positioned within an internal beta strand of the

central sheet, produced a protein that was closest to wild-type CheY in terms of its stability and crystallizability. These results contrast with the notion that the rigid regions of proteins are most critical to the stability of the native structure (Alber et al., 1987; Matsumura et al., 1988). The three CheY mutants that most favored inclusion body formation were mutated in surface loop regions of the protein. One could imagine that if one step in the folding pathway involved the movement of a helix toward an adjacent beta-sheet by a bending within the connecting loop, a change in the amino acid sequence in that loop region might hinder the motion required to proceed along the folding pathway.

Conclusions: Evolutionary Considerations

Harrison and Durbin (1985) have argued that the existence of multiple folding pathways would be evolutionarily advantageous. In such a system, mutations in single amino acid residues would not affect the ability of proteins to fold into their native conformation; at worst, they might disable one of the folding pathways. This theory, however, runs counter to the generally accepted belief that proteins have a limited number of folding

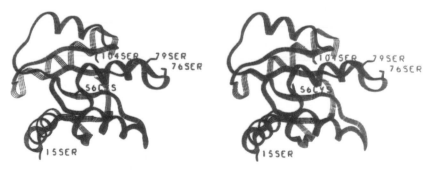

Fig. 3. Stereo view of the Ser-56-Cys CheY structure. The alpha carbon backbone is diagrammed as a flat ribbon; coiled regions represent the five alpha helices that flank the central five-stranded parallel beta sheet. The N-terminus of the protein lies just behind the 56Cys label and the C-terminus is at the upper right behind the 104Ser label. The side chains of the altered residues are indicated. Residue 56 is located within an internal beta strand. The other sites occur within loop regions connecting regions of alpha and beta structure. One atom substitutions at three of these sites — 15, 76, and 104 — resulted in formation of inclusion bodies.

pathways involving defined intermediates. Studies on bovine pancreatic trypsin inhibitor (BPTI) (Creighton, 1978), ribonuclease (Kim and Baldwin, 1982), collagen (Engle *et al.*, 1980), and bovine growth hormone (Brems *et al.*, 1988) in which kinetic folding intermediates have been isolated have lent strong support to the concept that proteins follow a limited number of folding pathways. It has been suggested that critical amino acid instructions directing these pathways appear to be dispersed throughout the sequence (King, 1986). Our results support this notion. Subtle changes in primary structure frequently cause a dramatic reduction in the efficiency of the folding process. Within the context of a cytoplasm essentially saturated with proteins, efficient folding would clearly be extremely advantageous since the likelihood of non-productive aggregation would be increased when there is a delay in the folding process.

The selective pressure for efficient folding may be one of the most important determinants of protein primary structure. There are only three conservative differences between the amino acid sequences of the *E. coli* and *S. typhimurium* CheY proteins (Matsumura *et al.*, 1984; Stock *et al.*, 1985), yet these two bacterial species diverged over 120 million years ago, and, with a generation time of under one hour, every possible point mutation in the *cheY* gene has occurred in both organisms (Ochman and Wilson, 1987). This is reflected in the nucleotide sequences of the two genes which, within the constraints of amino acid conservation and codon usage, have completely diverged. CheY is not unique in this respect. Similar results have been obtained with most genes that have been sequenced in these two closely related species (Yanofsky and vanCleemput, 1982). One must conclude that there is an enormous selective pressure that prevents the divergence of primary amino acid sequences. Our studies indicate that the requirement for efficiency in protein folding may be as important a constraint on the primary sequence as the need to correctly position residues involved in the active site.

Acknowledgments

We wish to thank Simon Simms for his generous donation of numerous cheB plasmids and Matt Kulke for his contributions to this work. This work was supported by grants from the NIH (AI-20980 to J. S. and AR-375590-03 to C. S.) and the American Heart Association (C. S.). A. S. was supported by a fellowship from the Damon Runyon-Walter Winchell Cancer Research Fund (DRG-933).

References

Alber, T., S. Dao-pin, J. A. Nye, D. C. Muchmore, B. W. Matthews, *Biochemistry* **26**, 3754 (1987).

Brems, B., *Biochemistry* **27**, 4541 (1988).

Brems, B. N., S. M. Plaisted, H. A. Havel, C.-S. C. Tomich, *Proc. Natl. Acad. Sci. U.S.A.* **85**, 3367 (1988).

Cheng, Y.-S. E., *J. Biochem. Biophys. Res. Comm.* **111**, 104 (1983).

Creighton, T. E., *Prog. Biophys. Mol. Biol.* **33**, 231 (1978).

Engel, J., H. P. Baechinger, P. Bruckner, R. Timpl, in *Protein Folding, Proceedings of the 28th Conference of the German Biochemical Society*, R. Jaenicke, Ed. (Elsevier/North Holland, Amsterdam, 1980), pp. 345-368.

Goldberg, D. P., D. H. Smith, J. King, *Proc. Natl. Acad. Sci. U.S.A.* **82**, 4028 (1985).

Gribskov, M., and R. R. Burgess, *Gene* **26**, 109 (1983).

Harrison, S. C., and R. Durbin, *Proc. Natl. Acad. Sci. U.S.A.* **82**, 4028 (1985).

Hess, J. G., K. Oosawa, N. Kaplan, M. I. Simon, *Cell* **53**, 79 (1988).

Kane, J. F., and D. L. Hartley, *Trends Biotechnol.* **6**, 95 (1988).

King, J., *Biotechnology* **4**, 297 (1986).

Kim, P. S., and R. L. Baldwin, *Annu. Rev. Biochem.* **51**, 459 (1982).

Marston, F. A. O., *Biochem. J.* **240**, 1 (1986).

Masui, Y., R. Mizuno, M. Inouye, *Biotechnology* **2**, no. 1, 81 (1984).

Matsumura, M., W. J. Becktel, B. W. Matthews, *Nature* **334**, 406 (1988).

Matsumura, P., J. J. Rydel, R. Linzmeier, D. Vacante, *J. Bacteriol.* **160**, 310 (1984).

Ochman, H., and A. C. Wilson, in Escherichia coli *and* Salmonella typhimurium, *Cellular and Molecular Biology,* F. C. Neidhart *et. al.*, Eds.

(American Society for Microbiology, Washington, DC, 1987), vol. 2, p. 1649.

Simms, S. A., M. G. Keane, J. B. Stock, *J. Biol. Chem.* **260,** 10161 (1985).

Simms, S. A., E. W. Cornman, J. M. Mottonen, J. B. Stock, *J. Biol. Chem.* **262,** 29 (1987).

Stock, A. M., D. E. Koshland, J. B. Stock, *Proc. Natl. Acad. Sci. U.S.A.* **82,** 7989 (1985).

Stock, A. M., J. Mottonen, J. Stock, C. Schutt, *Nature* **337,** 745 (1989).

Stock, J. B., and D. E. Koshland, Jr., *Proc. Natl. Acad. Sci. U.S.A.* **75,** 3659 (1978).

Snyder, M. A., J. B. Stock, D. E. Koshland, Jr., *Methods Enzymol.* **106,** 321 (1984).

Wylie, D. C., A. M. Stock, C.-Y. Wong, J. B. Stock, *J. Biochem. Biophys. Res. Comm.* **151,** 891 (1988).

Yanofsky, C., and M. vanCleemput, *J. Mol. Biol.* **154,** 235 (1982).

15

Folding of a Multidomain Oligomeric Protein
The Beta2 Subunit of Escherichia coli Tryptophan Synthase

Michel E. Goldberg

Twenty Years of Protein Folding

Since 1968, my research group has been actively involved in studies on protein folding, trying to answer some basic and originally very simple and naive questions about its mechanisms, using an essentially experimental approach. During these 20 years, we have studied a variety of proteins, each chosen because it appeared to be the best adapted for a given set of experiments. Thus, we have used as model systems several bacterial enzymes (beta-D-galactosidase, tryptophanase, and tryptophan synthase from *Escherichia coli*), bovine proteins (ribonuclease A and chymotrypsinogen), and rabbit enzymes (aldolase and phosphorylase).

Our main contributions to the understanding of protein folding have been as follows:

(i) At a time when it was commonly accepted that proteins fold in a one-step process into their thermodynamically preferred state, we proposed that the folding of galactosidase proceeds through the folding of independent regions of the polypeptide chain, which we called "globules" (now referred to as domains), which then get assembled through stereospecific, quaternary-like interactions (Goldberg, 1969).

(ii) We showed that the last detectable step in the folding of tryptophanase is a conformational change of each protomer occurring after the assembly of the subunits and induced by the quaternary interactions (Raibaud and Goldberg, 1976).

(iii) We showed that the inactive insoluble aggregates formed during the refolding of a protein are due to interchain interactions which, though illegitimate, are yet specific (London *et al.*, 1974).

(iv) We demonstrated in the case of chymotrypsinogen that such abortive interchain interactions which prevent the correct refolding can be minimized by performing the renaturation in the presence of intermediate concentrations of denaturing agents such as guanidine or urea. This enabled us to perform the first successful renaturation of reduced chymotrypsinogen in solution (Orsini and Goldberg, 1978).

These findings were made in the framework of basic research aimed only at understanding the molecular mechanisms of protein folding. Very few scientists expressed their interest in that work for over a decade, and most of these results remained unnoticed. Suddenly, with the advent of genetic engineering and the production of proteins by recombinant microorganisms, the knowledge that had been accumulated by "protein folders" became of some use. We were led to apply that knowledge to new systems, either in basic or in applied research. Thus, together with Y. Milner (University of Jerusalem), we succeeded in refolding and reassembling the 36 polypeptide chains (12 times 3 different subunits) of the alpha-ketoglutarate-dehydrogenase complex from *Acetobacter xylinum*. Similarly, we helped GENETICA (a branch of the French company Rhône-Poulenc) in setting up the procedures for the recovery of recombinant human serum albumin and tissue-specific plasminogen activator from the insoluble inclusion bodies obtained in the bacteria which overproduce them.

This, in my opinion, is a typical example of how a neglected, obscure field of basic research suddenly and unexpectedly finds itself on center stage and proves to be of considerable impact on practical problems.

The Folding Pathway of a Complex Protein

This chapter describes studies on the renaturation of a complex oligomeric protein, a process which involves the folding of "large" polypeptide chains as well as the formation of subunit interactions. I shall focus on two distinct aspects: the use of new experimental approaches to study protein folding (i.e., intramolecular fluorescence energy transfer and monoclonal antibodies), and the presentation of a concept (i.e., the conformational feedback).

Let me first very briefly describe the beta-2-subunit of *E. coli* tryptophan synthase on which these studies have been done. This protein catalyzes the condensation of indole and L-serine to produce L-tryptophan and water. It requires pyridoxal-5'-phosphate (pyridoxal-P) as a co-enzyme and is activated about 30 fold when it associates to the alpha-subunit. Thus, four specific ligands can be

used to probe the conformation of beta2: alpha, indole, serine, and pyridoxal-P. The latter is particularly convenient because it gives rise to optical signals, particularly fluorescence spectra, which make it easy to follow the binding of the various ligands to native beta2.

The native protein is a dimer made of two identical polypeptide chains of 397 residues each (Mr = 44,000), the sequence of which is known. The three-dimensional structure of the alpha2-beta2 complex from the *Salmonella* enzyme has very recently been solved (Hyde et al., 1988); this will render structural interpretations much more significant. Each polypeptide chain within the native protein can be cleaved by limited proteolysis into two autonomously folding domains (Högberg-Raibaud and Goldberg, 1977), the N-terminal (F1; Mr = 29,000) and C-terminal (F2; Mr = 12,000) peptides. F1 contains the sole tryptophan residue per beta chain (tryp 177), and lysine 87 with which pyridoxal-P forms a Schiff base. In the "nicked" protein (i.e., beta2 cleaved by trypsin), the four fragments (two F1 and two F2) remain assembled noncovalently. F1 and F2 can be separated on a molecular sieve column after denaturation with urea or guanidine.

After removal of the denaturing agent, the fragments refold into native-like conformations which could not be distinguished from their native conformations by a variety of physical-chemical criteria: far UV circular dichroism, fluorescence spectra (Högberg-Raibaud and Goldberg, 1977) and side-chain reactivity (Goldberg and Högberg-Raibaud, 1979). The refolded fragments reassemble spontaneously upon mixing, to restore the initial nicked protein. The kinetics of the assembly of F1 and F2 and of reactivation of nicked-beta2 will now be discussed.

Mechanism of formation of nicked-beta2 from the isolated domains

F1 labeled with IAEDANS (a fluorescent reagent comprising the dansyl fluorochrome) on cystein 170 and F2 labelled with FITC (fluorescein isothiocyanate) on its N-terminal aminogroup have been prepared. When the two labelled, folded fragments are mixed, they also reassemble into the nicked protein, in which the two fluorochromes are close enough to give rise to a fluorescence transfer. Thus, by observing the increase in the light emitted at 512 nm by the fluorescein moiety of F2 when the dansyl of F1 is excited at 350 nm, it becomes possible to follow the association of the F1 and F2 fragments. This showed that the assembly reaction obeys classical second-order kinetics (first order in each of F1 and F2) with a rate constant $k = 400$ $M^{-1} s^{-1}$ at 12°C (Zetina and Goldberg, 1982). The fluorescence transfer signal was shown to correspond to the association of F1 and F2 within the monomeric subunit; two such monomers then very rapidly associate into a dimer.

This dimer, however, is not yet functional: an isomerization must occur, after domain assembly, to generate the proper conformation of the active site, as judged by the ability of the molecule to give the fluorescent signal of the "aqua-complex" (a ternary complex formed between the native protein, pyridoxal-P and L-serine). The rate constant of this isomerization at 12°C was determined to be: $k = 0.0015$ s^{-1}. This study clearly showed that the assembly of the already folded (native-like) domains is followed by a change in the structure, occurring within the oligomer (Zetina and Goldberg, 1982).

The question could then be asked as to what is, in nicked-beta2, this postassembly isomerization? Does it correspond to an interdomain or an intradomain rearrangement? Is it confined in a limited region near the active site, or is it spread out in the whole molecule? Is the amplitude of this change minute or very large? As mentioned earlier, none of the classical spectroscopic signals investigated allowed us to distinguish the conformation of the isolated and refolded domains from that of the assembled domains. In order to study the postassembly change in structure of the molecule, we undertook a program aimed at using monoclonal antibodies as probes of the protein conformation. The idea behind this program was simple: if one prepares monoclonal antibodies specific to the native

conformation of the protein, recognizing epitopes (antigenic sites) distributed on several regions of the surface of the molecule, one should detect a change in conformation involving a region carrying a given epitope by a loss of the interaction between this modified epitope and the corresponding monoclonal antibody. This turned out to be a somehow naive view. Indeed, monoclonal antibodies are very sensitive to changes in conformations, but rarely behave in an all-or-none manner.

To follow changes in conformation of the antigen, one has to quantify its interaction with the antibody by determining the affinity constant of the antibody for the antigen. Thus, after having prepared and characterized a panel of monoclonal antibodies (Djavadi-Ohaniance *et al.*, 1984) and selected those that were more specific to the native state (Friguet *et al.*, 1984), we developed a powerful and reliable method, based on an enzyme-linked immunosorbent assay (ELISA), for measuring the true affinity constant in solution of the antigen/antibody complex (Friguet *et al.*, 1985). Using this method, we could determine the equilibrium-binding constants of six distinct monoclonal antibodies, recognizing six epitopes distant from each other on the surface of the native protein, for the isolated folded domains and compare them with the binding constants determined for the native protein (Friguet *et al.*, 1986).

The results were that, for all six monoclonal antibodies, the affinity for the native protein was higher by a factor ranging from 3 to 50 than for the isolated F1 or F2 domain recognized by the corresponding antibody. These results confirmed that isolated domains are not identical to assembled domains; thus an intradomain isomerization follows domain assembly. That the isolated domains, though having had plenty of time to refold before they were mixed, failed to reach their native conformations led us to the following conclusion: *Interdomain interactions impose a conformational feedback on the tertiary structure of the domains.*

In addition, the fact that the six distant epitopes are all modified indicates that this conformational change is reflected throughout a large area of the protein structure and involves both the F1 and F2 domains. But the amplitude of this postassembly isomerization appears very small, since the affinities are changed by factors no larger than 50 for F2 and from 3 to 10 for F1. Such relatively small changes of affinity reflect differences in the binding energy of the order of 1 to 2 kcalories per mole of complex, which in turn indicates a difference of perhaps one elementary interaction (e.g., hydrogen bond, van der Waals contact) per binding site. The quantitative analysis of the interaction between monoclonal antibodies and the isolated and assembled domains thus turned out to provide precise answers to the questions initially raised on the nature of the postassembly conformational change that takes place as the last step in the renaturation of nicked-beta2.

The pathway of folding of the beta2-subunit

The folding pathway of the intact, uncleaved beta2 protein has been investigated by following the evolution of a variety of fluorescence signals during the renaturation of the guanidine- or acid-denatured protein. Some experimental hints are given below. The signals observed were related to fluorescent markers very precisely localized in the molecule. These markers were as follows:

The tryptophan residue (177) present in each beta chain or F1 fragment. This is the single tryptophan residue per chain. Its fluorescence emission spectrum undergoes a 25 nm red shift, and the fluorescence intensity (quantum yield) is much reduced when this residue is exposed to the solvent upon denaturation. When one observes the fluorescence intensity at 325 nm (the emission maximum in the native state), one can therefore follow the increase in fluorescence that accompanies the burying of this residue in an hydrophobic environment during the refolding process.

The AEDANS moiety linked to cysteine 170. In the native state, this residue is located close enough to tryptophan 177 to permit a strong fluorescence energy transfer from the

tryptophan to the AEDANS. Thus, when one excites the tryptophan residue of native beta2 at about 280 nm (where AEDANS is barely excited), one observes light emitted around 460 nm, the emission maximum of AEDANS. This energy transfer signal is, however, very sensitive to the distance between the tryptophan and AEDANS fluorochromes: in the unfolded polypeptide chain, their average distance is too large to give rise to an efficient transfer. Following the transfer signal thus permits one to monitor the process by which the residues 170 and 177 come close together. Also, one can measure the fluorescence polarization of the AEDANS marker. This shows how mobile the marker is. We found that, in guanidine-denatured beta chains, the polarization of AEDANS is very low (i.e., the marker is very mobile), while it is higher in folded F1 and still higher in native beta2 where the marker seems to be immobilized on the surface of the molecule.

The reduced Schiff base between pyridoxal-P and lysine 87. The natural coenzyme of tryptophan synthase, pyridoxal-P, is linked to the protein through a Schiff base which is formed between its aldehyde group and the amino group of lysine 87. The double bond of the Schiff base can easily be reduced by a mild treatment with sodium borohydride. The reduced protein is inactivated. However, its structure is very close to that of the native protein and it is even more heat stable than native beta2.

In the reduced protein, the pyridoxine group is irreversibly bound to the protein and constitutes a convenient fluorescent marker. Indeed, when excited at around 330 nm (the fluorescence excitation maximum of the reduced Schiff base), it emits light at around 390 nm. Furthermore, in the native state of beta2, tryptophan 177 and lysine 87 are close enough to one another to give rise to a fluorescence energy transfer, while in denatured beta2, these two fluorochromes are too remote to interact with one another.

Monitoring this energy transfer (by exciting tryptophan 177 at 280 nm and observing the emission of the reduced Schiff base at 390 nm) thus permits us to follow the coming together of residues 87 and 177 during the folding of beta chains. Two facts are worth pointing out: first, it has been shown (Blond and Goldberg, 1986) that this energy transfer occurs between two fluorochromes carried by the same polypeptide chain and not during the association of two beta chains within the dimer; second, the tryptophan residue and the lysine residue involved in the Schiff base are very distant from one another in the sequence of the polypeptide chain. Their coming together, and therefore, the corresponding energy transfer thus characterizes a folding event that involves the formation of a tertiary structure requiring long-range interactions.

Let us consider the types of information that fluorescence energy transfer signals are likely to provide. Unfortunately, they can not give detailed indications on the precise conformation of the protein. However, they can be quite sensitive to two factors: the absolute distance and the relative orientation of the two interacting fluorescent molecules. For instance, in the case of beta2, tryptophan 177 and cystein 170 are located at two opposite ends of a regular alpha-helix, just two helix turns from one another. The distance between their alpha-carbons, onto which the side chains are hooked, is thus close to 10 angstroms (Fig. 1). Furthermore, the side chain of the tryptophan residue is immobilized by a variety of hydrophobic contacts, and the sulfhydryl group of cysteine 170 lies at the bottom of a cleft in which the AEDANS group will obviously be tightly surrounded and rigidly oriented. Thus, the final efficiency of the fluorescence transfer between tryptophan 177 and AEDANS linked to cysteine 170 will reflect both the formation of the alpha-helix they flank and the interactions that this helix forms with its neighbors.

Similarly, as we shall see below, when AEDANS-labeled beta2 associates with some monoclonal antibodies, some tryptophan residues of these antibodies are close enough and properly oriented relative to the AEDANS marker so that a fluorescence energy transfer between them can be observed. Again, no precise indication is given as to how the antigen and the antibody are hooked

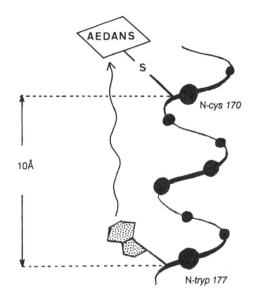

Fig. 1. Fluorescence energy transfer between tryp 177 and a reporter on cys 170.

together, but the transfer signal permits one to quantitatively follow their association.

Results

Using the markers described above, we could investigate for each signal the rate at which it regains the value characteristic of the native state during the refolding of the guanidine unfolded polypeptide chains. This enabled us to reach a rather precise description of some of the steps on the folding pathway of beta2. These steps will now be described, in the order in which they occur under the folding conditions used throughout this study, i.e., at 12°C in potassium phosphate buffer ($pH =$ 7.8). This somewhat low temperature was chosen in order to slow down the folding process and render it observable by conventional methods.

The first intermediate we could detect (species A in Fig. 2) is characterized by three distinct signals, reflecting three distinct conformational properties of the polypeptide chain that appear simultaneously with the same rate constant, $k = 0.02 \text{ s}^{-1}$. The following characteristics can be assigned to this intermediate: it has a hydrophobic core in which

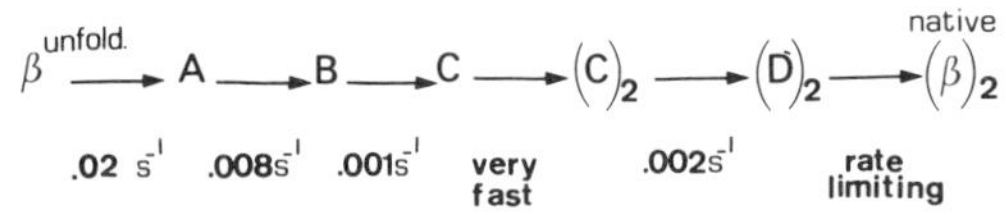

$$\beta \xrightarrow{\text{unfold.}} A \longrightarrow B \longrightarrow C \longrightarrow (C)_2 \longrightarrow (D)_2 \longrightarrow (\beta)_2^{\text{native}}$$

$$.02 \text{ s}^{-1} \quad .008\text{s}^{-1} \quad .001\text{s}^{-1} \quad \begin{array}{c}\text{very}\\\text{fast}\end{array} \quad .002\text{s}^{-1} \quad \begin{array}{c}\text{rate}\\\text{limiting}\end{array}$$

Fig. 2. Sequential intermediates and conversion rates in the pathway of the refolding of the beta polypeptide chain of tryptophan synthase into the native β_2-structure.

tryptophan 177 is buried, as seen from the blue shift in its fluorescence emission. It already has some tertiary structure, since lysine 87 and tryptophan 177 are close together, at the proper distance and in the right orientation to give rise to the native-like fluorescence transfer between the tryptophan and the reduced Schiff base. Finally, its overall shape must be that of a folded globular structure which resembles that of the folded F1 domain since the fluorescence polarization of AEDANS linked to cysteine 170 is high (.25) and the same as that of the folded isolated F1 fragment.

The second intermediate (B in Fig. 2) appears slightly later. The rate constant of its formation is $k = 0.008 \text{ s}^{-1}$. It was determined by following the appearance of the fluorescence transfer from tryptophan 177 to AEDANS on cysteine 170. Thus, in this intermediate, the indole ring of tryptophan 177 and the AEDANS marker are already at the proper distance and in the correct relative orientation as compared to the native state. As mentioned earlier, the distance between these two residues is determined, in the native protein, by their being in an alpha-helix. Because alpha-helices form very rapidly and are believed to be among the very first structures to appear during protein folding, the proper distance between the tryptophan and cysteine residues is probably reached very early in the folding of beta chains. It is therefore likely that the fluorescence transfer signal in fact comes with the orientation of the two fluorochromes (indole and AEDANS) as imposed by their environment.

The third intermediate (C in Figure 2) has been identified as the rate-limiting step for the association of two beta chains into a dimer. Indeed, when one follows the fluorescence polarization of the AEDANS marker during the folding of beta chains, one can see two phases. A rapid one corresponds to the appearance of the first intermediate and has been described above. A slower phase ($k = 0.001 \text{ s}^{-1}$) corresponds to an increase of the fluorescence polarization from .25 (the value found for intermediate A) to .35 (the value observed for the native dimer). Because the fluorescence polarization necessarily increases upon dimer formation, this phase is related to dimer formation. However, since the apparent rate constant of this phase was found to be independent of the concentration of beta chains, it was concluded that the slower phase of change in fluorescence polarization corresponds to an isomerization that must take place before the dimerization can occur. The dimerization would then very rapidly follow this isomerization.

The fourth intermediate (C2 in Fig. 2) would then be a dimeric form of the protein, formed very rapidly after the third intermediate C. Indeed, we could estimate indirectly the rate constant of association of two monomers at 25°C, and we found that the association is very rapid ($k = 180,000 \text{ M}^{-1}\text{s}^{-1}$) in the protein concentration range where all these studies were performed (Chaffotte and Goldberg, 1987).

The fifth intermediate (D2 in Fig. 2) results from an isomerization of the C2 dimer, which is induced by interdomain interactions. This isomerization could, in fact, be observed directly only when we investigated the reassembly of folded F1 and F2 fragments to give nicked-beta2. The isolated fragments were given all the time required to reach their folded state. They were then mixed together, and the appearance of the fluorescence of the "aqua-complex," formed between the native protein, pyridoxal-P and L-serine, was followed. As mentioned above for the refolding of nicked-beta2, it was observed that an isomerization of the domains, induced by interdomain interactions, occurs after the association steps. Its rate constant was found to be $k = 0.0015 \text{ s}^{-1}$. When nicked-beta2 is reconstituted from already folded fragments, this isomerization directly leads to the native protein.

When the renaturation of nicked-beta2 is initiated by diluting a mixture of unfolded F1 and F2 fragments in guanidine-free buffer, another slow isomerization must take place before the native state is reached. This last isomerization is also the rate-limiting step in the renaturation of beta2 and corresponds to the last step we could detect on the folding pathway of beta2. It corresponds to the appearance of the functional properties of the enzyme, since this step is required for the protein to bind its co-enzyme, give rise to the aqua complex, and become active.

This overview of the observations made on the renaturation of this protein is summarized in Fig. 2. It definitely demonstrates that the folding does not proceed through a unique concerted event. Intermediates do exist, and they appear along a favored pathway. This so-called "pathway" is, however, nothing more than a *kinetic sequence of events.* It should by no means be considered as an obligatory sequence of steps, which necessarily occur in a precise order. Thus, we have seen that the last rate-limiting step in the folding of beta2 can very well take place in the isolated F1 fragment before the assembly of the domains, the dimerization, and the postassembly isomerization.

Similarly, we have recently noted (Murry-Brelier and Goldberg, 1989) that when one observes the renaturation of acid-denatured beta2, one fails to see the slow phase of fluorescence polarization increase reported (see above) for the renaturation of guanidine-unfolded beta2. This is easily explained by the fact that acid-denatured beta2, though much denatured, is not a random coil, as it exhibits significant amounts of secondary structure. The residual structure present in the acid-denatured protein probably contains the "native-like" elements created by the third of the folding steps described above for guanidine unfolded chains. Therefore, the assembly of two chains can readily occur, as soon as the first folding step has taken place. This accounts for the fact that the fluorescence polarization reaches .35 (the native value) at the end of the first step ($k = 0.02 \text{ s}^{-1}$) of folding of acid-denatured beta2. Yet, all the sub-

sequent steps occur at identical rates for the acid-denatured and guanidine-denatured protein. These two examples clearly demonstrate that *the order in which the folding steps occur is not necessarily always the same and may depend on the conformation of the protein in the denatured state.*

Are folding intermediates immunoreactive?

Studies reported above have shown that the refolded isolated domains, which can be considered as folding intermediates at least for the nicked protein, are well recognized by antibodies specific for the native protein. Indeed, it has been shown that, though their affinity for monoclonal antibodies is slightly smaller than that of native beta2, their rate constants of association with these monoclonal antibodies are similar to those of the native protein. It therefore seemed to us of interest to ask where on the folding pathway of beta2 the polypeptide chain starts being immunoreactive. In other words, among the intermediates on the pathway described above, which one is the first to be immunoreactive? We tried to answer this question according to the experimental approach schematized in Fig. 3.

The principle is as follows. When one dilutes guanidine-unfolded beta chains into a guanidine-free buffer containing a given monoclonal antibody, the protein will start refolding. The first immunoreactive intermediate will appear at a certain stage along the folding pathway with a given rate constant, k_1. The antibody will then bind to this intermediate. This binding reaction, being a second-order reaction, will be rendered very fast if the antibody concentration is high enough. Thus, provided enough antibody is present, the rate-limiting reaction will be the formation of the first immunoreactive species and not the association reaction itself. Consequently, if one can monitor the formation of the antigenantibody complex, one will obtain the rate of appearance k_1 of the first immunoreactive intermediate. Then, by comparing k_1 with the rate constants of appearance of

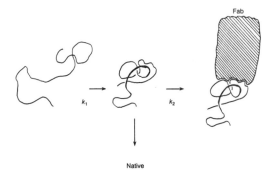

Fig. 3. At what stage in the refolding pathway do TS beta chains become immunoreactive? At high Fab concentrations, k_1 is rate limiting.

the various intermediates on the folding pathway, one should be able to state which of these intermediates is the first to be immunoreactive.

Such experiments were performed (Blond and Goldberg, 1987) using a monoclonal antibody that, when bound to native AEDANS-labeled beta2, gives rise to an important fluorescence energy transfer from the tryptophans of the antibody toward the AEDANS probe linked to cysteine 170 in beta2. In fact, to avoid complications that might arise from the bivalence of both the IgG molecule and beta2, we used the specific monovalent, Fab fragment from that monoclonal antibody. Because the antibody we used was named mAb19, we shall call Fab19 the corresponding Fab.

First, we studied the kinetics of association of Fab19 with native AEDANS-labeled beta2. We found the association reaction to obey second-order kinetics, with an association rate constant of 300,000 $M^{-1}s^{-1}$. Then, the renaturation of guanidine-unfolded, AEDANS-labeled beta chains was initiated by dilution into a buffer containing Fab19, and the fluorescence transfer from tryptophan to AEDANS was observed. The kinetics of appearance of the transfer signal were biphasic. A detailed analysis of these kinetics and of their variations with the concentration of Fab19 showed that the slow phase, independent of the concentration (and even of the mere presence) of the Fab, corresponds to the intrachain transfer from tryptophan 177 to

AEDANS already observed (see above) during the refolding of beta2 alone. The rapid phase, on the contrary, depended on the Fab concentration and was shown to be the association of Fab19 with a folding intermediate.

To our surprise, we found the following: (i) The immunoreactive species appears well before the first intermediate observed hitherto. Indeed, the rate constant of its formation seemed to be at least 0.07 s^{-1}, as compared to 0.02 s^{-1} for the first intermediate detected by the optical methods described in the previous section. (ii) The rate constant of association of this early intermediate with Fab19 is very close to that of the native protein. Thus, though still far from being in its native conformation, the polypeptide chain already carries an *epitope that binds Fab19 as rapidly as the native protein does.*

The rate constant of formation of this first immunoreactive species has since been determined by use of a stopped-flow instrument. Because of the technical difficulties involved in rapidly achieving, in a conventional stopped flow, the large dilutions required for reducing the guanidine concentration from 4M or 6M to less than 0.1M (so as to avoid interference of residual guanidine with the folding process), we first investigated the kinetics of appearance of the immunoreactive intermediate by submitting acid-denatured, AEDANS-labeled beta chains to a pH jump.

This jump was done by mixing the acid-denatured protein with concentrated buffer at neutral pH containing Fab19 in large excess. Again, the appearance of the fluorescence transfer from tryptophans to AEDANS was recorded, and again, two phases were observed. The slow one clearly corresponded to the intrachain transfer from tryptophan 177 to the AEDANS and had the same rate constant as the corresponding phase in the renaturation of guanidine-unfolded beta chains. The rapid phase corresponded to a second-order association reaction, provided the Fab concentration was not too high. But at high Fab concentration, the rate of the association became limited by an isomerization of the beta chain with a rate constant of about 0.06 s^{-1}. By performing a double mixing experiment, we could demonstrate that this isomerization reaction must take place before Fab19 can recognize it and bind to it. This illustrated that the unfolded protein is not recognized efficiently by the antibody and that *the appearance of the early immunoreactive species requires a folding step* (Murry-Brelier and Goldberg, 1988).

However, as mentioned earlier, acid-denatured beta chains exhibit some ordered structure. It could be claimed that, if the region of the molecule normally containing the epitope recognized by Fab19 is ordered in a "wrong" conformation (relative to the native state), then unfolding of this region would be a prerequisite for the epitope to appear. The isomerization just described would then reflect an unfolding rather than a folding step. This interpretation was ruled out by stopped-flow studies on the refolding of guanidine-unfolded beta2.

The technical difficulties, due to the large dilution factor needed, have been overcome by performing two successive seven-fold dilutions in a double-mixer, three-syringe stopped flow. The mixing and convection artifacts due to the large density difference between the concentrated guanidine and the renaturation buffer have been eliminated by preparing the renaturation buffer with deuterated water so that the density of the buffer was equal to that of the guanidine solution. This enabled us to observe the appearance of the early immunoreactive intermediate during the refolding of beta chains, fully unfolded with guanidine. We found that it follows first-order kinetics with a rate constant of 0.06–0.07 s^{-1} (Blond and Goldberg, unpublished results).

This confirms that the appearance of the immunoreactivity to Fab19 indeed corresponds to a real folding step, the first one that has been detected on the folding pathway of beta2.

Fab19 recognizes an epitope carried by the F1 domain in native beta2. It is worth pointing out that similar results have been obtained with another monoclonal antibody, recognizing an epitope on F2. But for that antibody, the rate of appearance of the epitope is so fast that, even at the highest an-

tibody concentration we could reach, the association step was too slow to permit unveiling the isomerization leading to the immunoreactivity of F2.

Let us now dwell on the significance of these observations. We shall start from the point of view of the protein folding problem. Our finding that folding intermediates that appear very early in the process and are incompletely folded can interact rapidly and strongly with a monoclonal antibody demonstrates that such intermediates are able to establish noncovalent intermolecular, specific, quaternary interactions with complementary structures. This occurs well before the native state is reached. This is of utmost importance in understanding the nature of abortive aggregation, which so often precludes the natural folding or the renaturation of concentrated protein solutions. Indeed, we showed for tryptophanase that such abortive aggregation results from illegitimate, yet specific, interchain interactions, and we proposed that they take place between partly folded intermediates (London *et al.*, 1974).

We suggested a similar mechanism for explaining the formation of aggregates upon incubation of the tryptophan synthase beta2 subunit at guanidine concentrations close to the midpoint of the unfolding-refolding transition: specific interdomain interactions, normally occurring between two domains of the same polypeptide chain, might form (at high protein concentration) between domains of different chains, thus leading to large aggregates that become insoluble upon removal of the guanidine (Goldberg and Zetina, 1980). It seems very likely that such interactions between folding intermediates may be a common phenomenon, which might well be one of the *major causes of the formation of "inclusion bodies,"* as found in genetically manipulated cells that overexpress a given protein.

Antibody-induced conformation of some proteins

For many years, immunologists have described the fit between the structures of an antibody and its specific antigen as "perfect," illustrating it by the "key and lock" image. Indeed, the first representation, obtained by x-ray crystallography, of the complex between the Fab fragment of a monoclonal antibody with its antigen, lysozyme, confirmed this image.

Our finding that folding intermediates of beta2, though far from having reached the native conformation, are already able to readily interact with a so-called "anti-native state" monoclonal antibody led us to question the key and lock model. We therefore investigated in more detail the molecular events occurring when the isolated F1 fragment interacts with Fab19, the anti-native beta2 probe already used for investigating the folding of beta2.

For that purpose, F1 labeled with AEDANS on cysteine 170 was prepared, unfolded with guanidine, and its renaturation was initiated by dilution in guanine-free buffer containing an excess of Fab19. Results identical to those reported above for the refolding of complete beta chains were obtained: a rapid association between the antigen and the antibody, with a second-order rate constant very similar to that of native beta2, precedes a slower first-order reaction revealed by the intra-F1 fluorescence transfer between tryptophan 177 and AEDANS. With both isolated F1 and complete beta chains, we could directly demonstrate by a quenching experiment that the latter reaction, corresponding to the slow phase, takes place in the complex already formed between the refolding polypeptide chain and the Fab. Indeed, when unlabeled native beta2 was added in large excess over the Fab just at the end of the fast phase, the slow phase still could be detected with no modification in the rates and amplitudes of either the slow or the fast phase. This clearly showed that all the refolding labeled polypeptide chains were already associated within the Fab at the end of the fast phase before the slow phase had progressed significantly (Blond and Goldberg, 1987). This similarity in the behavior of F1 and complete beta chains was not surprising, since we already had collected several pieces of information suggesting that the F1 domain folds up in a similar

way either alone or within the entire protein.

The surprise came when, just as a control, we checked the rate of association of the isolated but already refolded F1 fragment with Fab19. We found biphasic kinetics very similar to those described above for unfolded F1. This drew our attention to the fact that, while the isolated F1 fragment is able to refold into a nearly native conformation, the conformation of the polypeptide chains is such that it does not yet permit an efficient energy transfer from tryptophan 177 to AEDANS, even when the isolated F1 fragment is given plenty of time to renature. As soon as Fab19 binds to the refolded F1 fragment, it forces the polypeptide chain into a conformation closer to that of the native state, thus giving rise to the fluorescence energy transfer from tryptophan to AEDANS (Blond and Goldberg, 1987). When the quenching experiment described above was repeated during the association of folded F1 with Fab19, the same result as with unfolded F1 was obtained. The isomerization takes place within the already formed complex.

This rules out a model according to which folded F1 would be in equilibrium between two forms: a nonimmunoreactive state with no fluorescence transfer and a form with transfer to which the Fab would bind, thus shifting the equilibrium. Our results are not compatible with such a selective model; rather, they support a model according to which, after an initial binding of the antibody to the imperfectly folded chain, the complementarity between the antigen and the antibody is improved by an "induced fit" mechanism.

Thus Fab19 *also imposes a conformational feedback onto the isolated F1 domain.* Studies are in progress in our laboratory to test whether this is a peculiarity of Fab19 or whether the other monoclonal antibodies we have isolated also impose a conformational adjustment of F1 when forming the antigen antibody complex.

We do not know at present what happens to the native protein when it interacts with the antibodies. We do feel, however, that some conformational changes are also involved because we noted a decrease in the affinity of the antibodies when the stability, and hence probably the rigidity, of beta2 is increased. Thus, apo-beta2 binds the various Fabs with a higher affinity than holo-beta2, which binds with a better affinity than borohydride-reduced holo-beta2 (Djavadi-Ohaniance *et al.*, 1986). It was also shown that reduced holo-beta2 is less flexible than holo-beta2, which, in turn, is less flexible than apo-beta2 (Chaffotte and Goldberg, 1983).

Such conformational adjustments of the antigen upon binding the antibody may suffice to account for drastic modifications of the functional properties of the antigen, as we noted for the beta2 subunit of tryptophan synthase. Indeed, all the monoclonal antibodies thus far isolated and characterized inhibit the enzymatic activity upon binding, and for several of them, the inactivation is practically complete. But it is well known that even minute changes in the conformation of a protein may drastically affect its function. Therefore, even if the antibody-induced conformational changes of an antigen may be of small amplitude and, consequently, remain unnoticed at some stages of an x-ray diffraction study, it may play a crucial role in the molecular mechanisms by which an antibody plays its role in the natural defenses of an organism.

Conclusions

This rather detailed summary of many years of research on a multidomain oligomeric protein will hopefully have convinced the reader that, though obviously complex, the folding mechanism of this protein can be understood to a certain degree:

(i) It is not an untouchable one-step process. (ii) It proceeds through a sequence of events, the folding pathway, which is a kinetically favored and not a compulsory succession of steps. (iii) It can be manipulated by changing the unfolding conditions as well as the refolding conditions. (iv) It proceeds through the formation of intermediates, which can be characterized by a variety of approaches: physical, genetic, enzymological, and im-

munological. (v) Immunoreactive intermediates appear very early on the folding pathway. (vi) Folding intermediates, or independently folding fragments (domains) isolated from a protein, exhibit, even locally, only an approximation of the final structure of the polypeptide chain: a conformational feedback keeps modulating the conformation until the native state of the entire protein is reached. (vii) The folding is never final; the conformation continues to be modulated by interactions with specific ligands, like the substrates of an enzyme or like antibodies that induce an adaptation of the antigen.

There is no doubt that much work is still needed to reach a full understanding of the folding mechanism, even for a protein as extensively studied as the beta2 subunit of tryptophan synthase. However, several of the conclusions we have already reached are important. They give precious hints for manipulating the folding pathway in order to improve the renaturation steps often needed in the industrial processing of proteins produced by genetic engineering. They also give essential clues in the use of monoclonal antibodies as conformational probes for comparing a renatured protein with the native one, another essential phase in the valorization of proteins produced by recombinant strains. This seems to me a good example of how the progress of basic research can unexpectedly become of immediate economic and social use. Indeed, some 10 years ago, very few people accepted the idea that the protein folding problem was worth spending any time or money. Today, everybody agrees that much effort has to be devoted for a better understanding of this problem.

References

Blond, S., and M. E. Goldberg, *Proteins: Struct. Funct. & Genet.* **1**, 247 (1986).

_____, *Proc. Natl. Acad. Sci. U.S.A.* **84**, 1147 (1987).

Chaffotte, A. F., and M. E. Goldberg, *Biochemistry* **22**, 2708 (1983).

_____, *J. Mol. Biol.* **197**, 131 (1987).

Djavadi-Ohaniance, L., B. Friguet, M. E. Goldberg, *Biochemistry* **23**, 97 (1984).

_____, *Biochemistry,* **25,** 2502 (1986).

Friguet, B., A. F. Chaffotte, L. Djavadi-Ohaniance, M. E. Goldberg, *J. Immunol. Methods* **77,** 305 (1985).

Friguet, B., L.. Djavadi-Ohaniance, M. E. Goldberg, *Mol. Immunol.* **21,** 673 (1984).

_____, *Eur. J. Biochem.* **160,** 593 (1986).

Goldberg, M. E., *J. Mol. Biol.* **46,** 441 (1969).

Goldberg, M. E., and A. Högberg-Raibaud, *J. Biol. Chem.* **255,** 7752 (1979).

Goldberg, M. E., and C. R. Zetina, in *Protein Folding,* R. Jaenicke, Ed. (Elsevier/North-Holland Biomedical Press, Amsterdam, 1980), pp. 469–484.

Högberg-Raibaud, A., and M. E. Goldberg, *Biochemistry* **16,** 4014 (1977).

Hyde, C.C., S. A. Ahmed, E. A. Padlan, E. W. Miles, D. R. Davies, *J. Biol. Chem.* **263,** 17857 (1988).

London, J., C. Skrzynia, M. E. Goldberg, *Eur. J. Biochem.* **47,** 409 (1974).

Murry-Brelier, A., and M. E. Goldberg, *Biochemistry* **27,** 7633 (1988).

_____, *Proteins Struct. Funct. & Genet.* **6,** 395 (1989).

Orsini, G., and M. E. Goldberg, *J. Biol. Chem.* **253,** 3453 (1978).

Raibaud, O., and M. E. Goldberg, *J. Biol. Chem.* **256,** 2820 (1976).

Zetina, C. R., and M. E. Goldberg, *J. Mol. Biol.* **157,** 133 (1982).

Part IV

Intermediates in Protein Folding

C. Robert Matthews

Recent advances in genetic engineering and peptide synthesis have provided hitherto unavailable opportunities to probe the mechanism of protein folding and to design polypeptides that spontaneously fold to stable structures. Along with these technical advancements, new applications of statistical mechanics to the folding problem show promise in the interpretation of complex unfolding processes. The combination of theory and experiment presented in this volume demonstrates state-of-the-art approaches to the solution of the protein folding problem.

Thomas Creighton sets the stage for Part IV, "Intermediates in Protein Folding," with a cogent analysis of existing data on the thermodynamic and kinetic properties of folding reactions. Drawing on examples from a number of laboratories, Creighton argues that folding involves the rapid formation of marginally stable intermediates that serve to limit the search of conformational space. Since detailed structural information on such intermediates is generally lacking, Creighton then introduces the folding reaction with which his name is widely associated, the reformation of the three disulfide bonds in bovine pancreatic trypsin inhibitor. This system has proven to be a paradigm for protein folding, providing insights into early, intermediate, and late events in the process. The establishment of a similar data base for folding intermediates that are stabilized by noncovalent interactions is a current challenge for biophysicists who hope to solve the folding problem.

C. Robert Matthews and his colleagues have examined the effect of single amino acid replacements on the folding of the alpha-subunit of tryptophan synthase. They reason that, if sequence determines structure, amino acids that play key roles in folding should have discernable effects on the stability and kinetics of folding. The alpha-subunit is a particularly intriguing candidate for such studies, since it unfolds and refolds by means of a stable intermediate. One of the rate-limiting steps in folding is the conversion of this intermediate to the native conformation. Matthews *et al.* have found that some positions play a special role in the transition state, while others help stabilize the native conformation. It appears that detailed information on the order of events in folding, i.e., the folding pathway, can be obtained by mutagenesis.

Barry T. Nall and his colleagues have used single amino acid replacements to probe the structural basis for one of the rate-limiting steps in the folding of cytochrome c from yeast. Biophysical studies suggested that isomerization of the peptide bond at one X-Pro linkage in the unfolded protein was responsible. Nall *et al.* proved the hypothesis and identified the specific residue by replacement of the conserved prolines. They found that the state of isomerization of proline 76 plays a critical role in the formation of certain aspects of tertiary structure (burying tyrosines) but not others (positioning of the tryptophan side chain near the heme). The assignment of kinetic phases in folding to specific molecular events is a mandatory part of determining the folding mechanism.

Building on the availability of large quantities of pure peptides, a new-found understanding of the propensity of relatively short peptides to form alpha-helices in solution, and an appreciation of the role of hydrophobic effects in stabilizing folded proteins, William DeGrado, Lynne Regan, and their colleagues have made spectacular advances in the construction of the four-helix bundle. Beginning with a single helical peptide that spontaneously associates to form a tetramer, this chapter describes the rationale that has made possible the creation of a single polypeptide chain that can fold to the desired four-helix bundle. The stability of this structure is such that one can easily imagine it serving as a template for the incorporation of specific recognition and/or catalytic groups. The success of these efforts would have been difficult to predict even five years ago and emphatically demonstrates the progress being made in the protein folding field.

Tropomyosin, a two-chain, coiled coil protein, has long been known to unfold through a virtual continuum of partially folded intermediates. The challenge has been to develop an analysis that allows one to gain some insight into their structures. Alfred Holtzer, Marilyn Holtzer, and Jeffrey Skolnick have extended previous statistical mechanical approaches with the introduction of an interhelix interaction parameter and loop entropy to describe the thermal melting reaction. The impressive agreement between prediction and experiment shows that the complex folding reaction can, in favorable cases, be reduced to simple elements that interact in a statistical fashion. This is a reminder that one must not forget the forest for all the fascinating trees that new technologies make accessible.

16

Understanding Protein Folding Pathways and Mechanisms

Thomas E. Creighton

The "protein folding problem" can be formulated very simply: How do the primary structures of proteins determine their secondary, tertiary, and quaternary structures? In a native, biologically active protein, the linear polypeptide chain is folded into a complex, close-packed, three-dimensional structure. Yet, the genetic information for the structure of a protein specifies only the one-dimensional order of the amino acids, and the protein is synthesized as a linear polypeptide chain. The information for the three-dimensional structure must be contained within the amino acid sequence, for, under physiological conditions, the native conformation is adopted spontaneously (Anfinsen, 1973).

The protein folding problem can be divided into two parts. The first is to determine what particular three-dimensional structure is specified by a given amino acid sequence. The goal is to construct a three-dimensional model of a protein given just its amino acid sequence. At the present time, this is not possible unless the folded conformation or a protein with an homologous primary structure is known; homologous proteins invariably have essentially the same folded conformation within the core of the structure, differing most at the surface. The inverse problem of designing an amino acid sequence to adopt a desired three-dimensional structure has been solved recently for one case;

Regan and DeGrado (1988) have designed and synthesized a novel protein that folds into a remarkably stable bundle of four alpha-helices.

The second part of the folding problem is the sequence of events (i.e., the pathway) by which a protein actually folds to its native conformation. It is now recognized that folding to the correct conformation could not occur on the observed time scale simply by random fluctuations (Levinthal, 1968).

The two parts of the problem are not independent. If the rules governing protein conformation were understood sufficiently, the most favorable pathway for protein folding could be inferred and compared with experimental observations of folding. Conversely, the actual pathway by which a protein finds its native conformation might also be the best process by which the theoretician could find that conformation.

Both aspects of the folding problem are difficult to solve due to the size and complexity of proteins, the large number of amino acid residues that comprise a typical protein (about 300 on average), and the structural diversity of the 20 amino acids that can occur at each residue. Each amino acid residue in an unfolded polypeptide chain probably adopts, on average, eight different conformations (Privalov, 1979); therefore, up to 8^{100} different conformations are possible for a random coil polypeptide consisting of 100 amino acid residues. Clearly, this conformational space is too vast to be explored completely, either by theoreticians searching for the native conformation with computers or by means of protein molecules in solution (Levinthal, 1968). The obvious conclusion is that there must exist nonrandom pathways by which proteins actually fold and, perhaps, by which folded conformations might be predicted.

The central problem of protein folding is to determine the folding of a single structural domain. Many studies of large proteins, consisting of multiple domains and subunits, have demonstrated that the individual domains and subunits fold at least approximately to their final conformations and then associate (Privalov, 1982; Jaenicke, 1984), with some relatively small, but energetically difficult, conformational rearrangements. This limits the magnitude of the folding problem somewhat, and this discussion will focus upon relatively small, single-domain proteins.

Folding of a small protein from the fully unfolded state is usually found to occur within a second or a minute under optimal conditions in vitro. Although this time scale for folding is legitimately considered rapid when compared with the time required for a random search for the folded conformation (Levinthal, 1968), it is relatively slow for a unimolecular process in which there are no intrinsically high energy barriers limiting conformational transitions in the unfolded polypeptide chain. An unfolded protein molecule probably requires approximately 10^{-11} seconds to adopt a recognizably different conformation, so 10^{11} to 10^{13} conformational transitions can occur within the second or minute during which a protein is folding.

Clearly, it is not feasible, either experimentally or theoretically, to determine all of the transitions undergone while a single molecule is folding. This fundamental difficulty is compounded experimentally where populations of molecules (usually nmoles to fmoles, or 10^{15} to 10^{18} molecules) need to be observed. Consequently, it is probably practical to attempt to understand only the general aspects of protein folding pathways, such as the nature of the rate-limiting step(s) and the average conformations and their stabilities preceding the rate-limiting step in both unfolding and refolding.

Models for Protein Folding

Many models of how proteins might fold have been proposed, with varying degrees of detail and predictions that are capable of being tested. Most have stressed roles for secondary structure, since such regular local conformations seem most likely to be stable in isolation and at early stages of folding (Baldwin, 1986). At opposite extremes are models that predict a single pathway and one that predicts a vast number of pathways.

The nucleation rapid growth mechanism was initially considered one of the most likely explanations of how folding could occur rapidly. It envisaged the formation of a nucleation center by random conformational fluctuations of the unfolded protein that would serve as a template upon which folding could proceed rapidly to completion. The nucleation center would be sufficiently small that it could be encountered by random fluctuations on the appropriate time scale, and its formation would be the rate-limiting step in refolding (Wetlaufer, 1973). Either all molecules might encounter the same nucleation center and fold by the same pathway, or several different pathways could possibly be significant.

At the other extreme, folding has been compared with assembling a jigsaw puzzle (Harrison and Durbin, 1985); each time folding occurs, it uses a different pathway. Folding occurs on a finite time scale by limiting the protein to adopting only native-like local conformations. It requires a pathway that is essentially irreversible under folding conditions and predicts a wide variety of different folding times for different molecules. This mechanism has become the paradigm for protein folding in a recent popular textbook (Stryer, 1988), even though it will be shown here to be inconsistent with most experimental observations of protein folding.

The Folded and Unfolded States

The native conformation of a protein can be defined in exquisite detail by its crystal structure and usually can be considered to be a single conformation. Even this conformation has varying degrees of flexibility, but it can be defined as a macro-state made up of a finite number of micro-states. The unfolded state is much less well defined. One of its most important properties is its enormous conformational heterogeneity (this discussion assumes that all the molecules are homogeneous covalently). The number of micro-states is vastly greater than in the case of the folded state.

Ideally, the fully unfolded protein is a random coil, in which the rotation about every chemical bond of the polypeptide chain is independent of every other bond rotation and determined only by the local stereochemistry of the polypeptide backbone. This requires that there be no net interactions between non-neighboring atoms of the polypeptide chain (i.e., that such interactions be exactly balanced by interactions between the polypeptide and the solvent) other than the need to avoid too-close contact between atoms. Uncertainty about the latter factor means that the properties of such a random-coil polypeptide chain have not been described precisely. Nevertheless, there are an immense number of conformations possible, and the time required to find the native conformation by a random search of all such conformations is much longer than the age of the universe (Levinthal, 1968; Wetlaufer, 1973).

Unfolded proteins in a very good solvent, such as 6*M* guanidinium chloride or 8*M* urea, are believe to approximate ideal random coils (Tanford, 1968). Under other conditions, however, unfolded proteins are probably not truly random coils, for the physical properties of unfolded proteins can vary greatly (Griko *et al.*, 1988). Most short peptides in aqueous solution appear to be primarily disordered, but detailed studies (Shoemaker *et al.*, 1987; Wright *et al.*, 1988) have found varying amounts of marginally stable nonrandom conformation in some cases. Such local conformational preferences should be retained in unfolded proteins under the same conditions, and additional interactions between residues far apart in the sequence are also possible. Nevertheless, there are still a very large number of conformations that will be present in any unfolded protein.

Any interpretation of experimental observations of folding must take into account that the observations are of an initially heterogeneous population. The above considerations imply that within a typical experimental preparation of unfolded protein, containing some 10^{15} to 10^{18} molecules, each molecule will have a unique conformation at each instant of time. Consequently, each molecule must, at least initially, follow a different folding pathway. These individual folding pathways, however, must converge at some point. The point during folding at which this convergence actually occurs should be determined experimentally. Is it perhaps at the very beginning (as in the nucleation rapid growth model), not until the very end (as in the random pathway model), or at some intermediate step?

Heterogeneity of the unfolded state first became apparent experimentally when Garel and Baldwin (1973) found that unfolded ribonuclease A, with the disulfides intact, consisted of several populations of molecules with different rate constants for refolding. This phenomenon is now known to be due to the presence in the unfolded state of equilibrium mixtures of molecules with either the cis or trans isomer of each peptide bond preceding a proline residue (Brandts *et al.*, 1975). In the folded state, each such bond is either cis or trans in essentially all of the molecules, whereas, in the unfolded state, there is an equilibrium between the two isomers at each such peptide bond. At the time of refolding, some molecules happen to have all the isomers compatible with the folded state, and they can fold directly. Other molecules have one or more peptide bond isomers that prevent complete folding until isomerization takes place.

Cis-trans isomerization of peptide bonds is an intrinsically slow process, requiring seconds to minutes, depending on the temperature. It is slower than folding in the case of ribonuclease A, which occurs in less than a second, so the different populations of unfolded ribonuclease A refold at different rates. Although all the details of the effects of Pro peptide bond cis-trans isomerization on protein folding are not known, it is clear that this phenomenon complicates the folding kinetics of virtually all proteins. The remainder of this discussion will describe folding transitions that are not limited by cis-trans isomerization.

Equilibrium Unfolding Transitions

A native protein can be unfolded by changing the conditions to favor thermodynamically the unfolded state, either by altering the temperature or pressure or by changing the solvent. Additives such as guanidinium chloride or urea can induce unfolding or the pH can be adjusted. No covalent changes to the protein need or should occur. Proteins that require disulfide bonds for stability of the folded state can be unfolded simply by reducing the disulfide bonds, but such folding transitions are considered later.

Three types of experimental conditions can be classified: where the folded state is stable, where the unfolded state predominates, and the transition region between the two. Starting with folding conditions and the native protein, gradually changing the conditions to favor unfolding causes very little to happen initially to the structure of the native protein. The equilibrium constant between the folded and unfolded states ([N]/[U]) gradually decreases, but the N state still predominates (Fig. 1). Within the transition region, the equilibrium constant reaches values of approximately unity, so both folded and unfolded states coexist at equilibrium. With further changes, the equilibrium constant is decreased even further so that the unfolded state predominates.

Such unfolding transitions of small proteins are usually observed to be two-state (Fig. 2), in that the molecules present at equilibrium are either fully folded (N) or fully un-

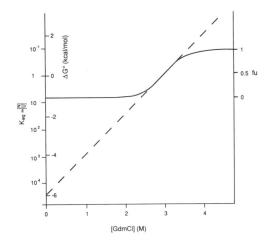

Fig. 1. Two-state unfolding transition of a protein induced by guanidinium chloride (GdmCl). The folded protein, N, is taken to be 6 kcal/mol more stable than U in the absence of denaturant and to unfold reversibly with a midpoint at 3.0M GdmCl. The solid curve demonstrates the fraction of unfolding (f_u, right scale, ranging from 0 to 1) that would be observed experimentally by any physical measurement of the average conformational properties. Within the transition region (2.8 to 3.2M GdmCl here), the free energy difference between N and U ($\Delta G°$) is usually observed to vary linearly with the denaturant concentration. Assuming that this linear relationship extends to other GdmCl concentrations, the dashed line gives the extrapolated values at other denaturant concentrations of $\Delta G°$ and the logarithm of the equilibrium constant, K_{eq} ($-RT \ln K_{eq} = \Delta G°$; R is the gas constant and T the temperature). The scales for f_u and $\Delta G°$ are co-linear at the midpoint of the transition region when the 0 and 1 values for f_u occur on the $\Delta G°$ scale at $-2\,RT$ and $+2\,RT$, respectively.

folded (U); partially folded intermediates with distinguishable physical or thermodynamic properties are not present at equilibrium to any substantial extent (less than 5 percent of the total) (Privalov, 1979). The values of the equilibrium constant for folding can be measured at points within the transition region to give the relative free energies of the two states (Fig. 1). Values under other conditions outside the transition region must be obtained by extrapolation. Although there is considerable uncertainty in such extrapolations, it seems clear that, even under optimal conditions, folded proteins are only 5 to 10 kcal/mol more stable than when fully unfolded, i.e., the equilibrium constant has a maximum value of between 10^4 and 10^7. Such

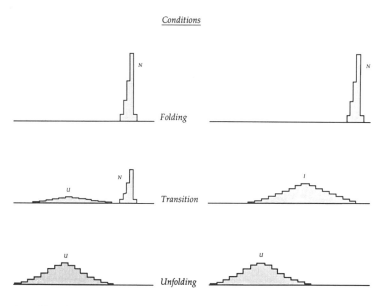

Conditions

Folding

Transition

Unfolding

Fig. 2. Illustration of the difference between a cooperative, two-state, first-order unfolding transition (**left**) and a noncooperative, multistate, second-order transition (**right**). Histograms of the distributions of molecules with different degrees of folding are illustrated for conditions favoring folding (**top**) or unfolding (**bottom**), and for the transition region (**middle**). Under folding conditions, the folded state, N, is represented as a narrow distribution of folded conformations. Under unfolding conditions, the unfolded state, U, is represented by a broad distribution of conformations. Within the transition region of a two-state transition, two distinct populations are present, similar to those at the two limiting conditions. Note that the distributions of the two states U and N may shift gradually as the conditions change, as is shown here for the unfolded state. In contrast, in a noncooperative transition, the distribution of the entire population shifts gradually as the conditions are varied, and, within the transition region, most molecules have intermediate (I) conformations.

numbers are relatively small differences between the free energies of the interactions stabilizing the two states.

The two-state nature of folding transitions implies that folding is a cooperative process. Stability of the folded state, N, requires the simultaneous presence of essentially all of the stabilizing interactions, and unfolding of one part of a folded conformation must produce destabilization of most other parts of the structure. In other words, the stabilizing effect of each interaction within N must depend upon the stabilities of the other interactions. When evaluating any theoretical model for protein folding or stability, it is worthwhile considering whether it incorporates cooperativity between the individual interactions.

All of the interactions within N are intrinsically weak, even under optimal conditions, because the unfolded protein makes the same type of interactions with the solvent. The folded conformation is stable only because of the simultaneous presence of many such interactions; the presence of one interaction increases the stabilities of adjacent interactions (Creighton, 1983). The magnitude of this cooperativity will vary, so the stabilities of dif-

ferent interactions of the same type, e.g., hydrogen bonds, can vary substantially, depending upon their positions within the folded conformation (Alber *et al.*, 1987).

The Kinetics of Protein Folding

The cooperativity of folding transitions and the instability of partially folded intermediates make it impossible to deduce the pathway or mechanism of folding from equilibrium measurements. It is necessary to study the kinetics of both unfolding and refolding in order to identify unstable kinetic intermediates and to characterize the transition state.

The kinetics of protein unfolding are remarkably simple. A single kinetic phase is usually observed, with a single rate constant, indicating that all the molecules have the same probability of unfolding and that no partially unfolded intermediates accumulate to substantial levels. The rate depends strongly upon the unfolding conditions; for thermal unfolding, for example, the activation energy is typically of the order of 50 to 100 kcal/mol.

The kinetics of refolding to the native

conformation are usually complicated by the effects of Pro peptide bond isomerization, which makes the unfolded protein kinetically heterogeneous. Nevertheless, for each population of molecules, a single rate constant is usually observed. Therefore, all molecules in each population have the same probability of folding, which implies that folding is governed by the same rate-limiting step. At least at this stage of folding, they will be following the same pathway, so all the initial unfolded conformations must have converged rapidly, prior to this rate-limiting step.

The fully folded protein generally appears without a lag period, so there is a single rate-limiting step, not two or more such slow steps with comparable rates. All steps preceding and following the rate-limiting step must be much more rapid.

The observed rate of folding depends only upon the final folding conditions, not upon the nature of the initial unfolded state. Whenever different unfolded states of a protein, with different physical properties, have been compared by folding them under the same final conditions, the rates have been indistinguishable (Kato et al., 1981; Denton et al., 1982; Lynn et al., 1984). This implies that there is a rapid conformational equilibration of all the molecules prior to the rate-limiting step, so that the same populations of unfolded molecules are obtained rapidly upon transfer to the same refolding conditions.

These observations indicate that individual protein molecules do not fold by totally independent, irreversible pathways, converging only at the same final native state, as envisaged in the jigsaw puzzle model (Harrison and Durbin, 1985). The conformationally heterogeneous population of unfolded molecules must initially follow different pathways, but these must converge relatively early in refolding. All the molecules appear to converge on a limited number of conformations, rapidly and reversibly, so that they are in a rapid pre-equilibrium. In this way, they can subsequently follow a limited number of those pathways to the fully folded conformations that are energetically most favorable (or least unfavorable energetically).

The Transition State for Folding

The absence of a lag period in appearance of N during refolding and of U during unfolding indicates that there is a single rate-limiting step in each direction, and it is pertinent to characterize this step and the transition state (assuming that the concept is valid for a large molecule). Does it occur early in folding or late? The transition state is generally defined as the intermediate species with the greatest free energy encountered during the folding process. Being also the most transient species, it is impossible to demonstrate its existence directly. It can be characterized only indirectly by studying the effect of changing the conditions or the protein on the rate constants for unfolding and refolding, which give the free energies of the transition state relative to N and to U, respectively.

The kinetics of unfolding have been widely characterized (Fig. 3) and usually demonstrate a large activation energy (50 to 100 kcal/mol) that is independent of temperature. This indicates that the transition state has considerably greater enthalpy than the N state, but the two have the same heat capacity (Lumry and Biltonen, 1969). The linearity of the Arrhenius plot also suggests that the nature of the transition state is not changing relative to N as the temperature is varied. Therefore, the same transition state will apply to both unfolding and refolding.

The most thoroughly characterized folding transition state is that of hen egg-white lysozyme (Segawa and Sugihara, 1984a, 1984b; Segawa and Kuma, 1986) because the rate of direct folding may be measured easily, due to the small population of slow-refolding molecules in this protein. It was found that the activation enthalpy for unfolding is independent of both temperature and the presence of a number of denaturants, indicating that the transition state is no more permeable to denaturants than the N state. A covalent cross link affected primarily the rate of refolding, whereas a substrate analog affected only the rate of unfolding. Taken together, these observations indicate that the transition state for folding is very similar to the fully folded

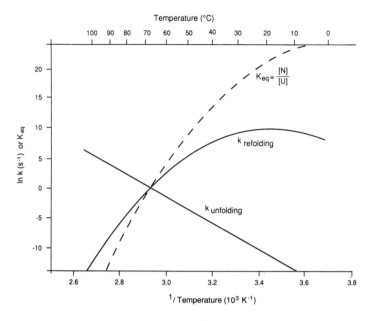

Fig. 3. Typical temperature dependence of the rates and equilibria of protein unfolding transitions. The natural logarithms of the rates of unfolding and refolding are plotted as a function of 1/temperature, in an Arrhenius plot. A similar plot of the equilibrium constant is a Van't Hoff plot. The curvature of the Van't Hoff plot is due to the greater apparent heat capacity of the unfolded state, U, than of N. The linear Arrhenius plot for the rate of unfolding indicates that the transition state has the same heat capacity as the folded state, N. The curvature of the Arrhenius plot for the rate of refolding results from the greater heat capacity of the U state, since $\ln K_{eq} = \ln k_{refolding} - \ln k_{unfolding}$. The data used to construct this diagram are for hen egg-white lysozyme at pH 3. The data for stability were from Pfeil and Privalov (1976); those for the rates of unfolding were from the data of Segawa and Sugihara (1984a), extrapolated to the absence of guanidinium chloride. The rates of refolding were calculated from the values of K_{eq} and $k_{unfolding}$. Although $k_{unfolding} = k_{refolding}$ at $K_{eq} = 1$, it is a coincidence that the rate constants had the value 1 second^{-1} at this temperature, so that all three curves intersect at a single point.

state, N, in being compact, having no additional nonpolar groups exposed to the solvent, and in having the cross linked groups in the same relative proximity. On the other hand, the transition state clearly is a perturbed form of N, in that it has higher free energy and enthalpy and does not bind ligands specifically.

That the transition state for folding is much closer to the native protein than the unfolded state was also suggested by the ample evidence that substantial partial refolding precedes the rate-limiting step in complete refolding, whereas there are few indications of partial unfolding preceding complete unfolding (Creighton, 1985). That the rate-limiting step in refolding occurs so late, very near N, demonstrates that folding does not occur by a rate-limiting nucleation event in the unfolded protein, followed by rapid completion of folding (Wetlaufer, 1973).

Arrhenius plots of the rate of unfolding are linear (Fig. 3), but those for refolding are very nonlinear; in particular, the rate of refolding first increases with increasing temperature, but then decreases at higher temperatures. This reflects the nonlinear effect of temperature on protein stability (as described by the analogous, nonlinear Van't Hoff plots, Fig. 3), since the equilibrium constant for folding is simply the ratio of the two rate constants. The rate of refolding reaches a maximum and then decreases with increasing temperature because the free energies of N and the transition state are changing in parallel, but differently from that of the unfolded state.

One explanation for such behavior would be that the unfolded state, U, is changing as the conditions are altered (Creighton, 1988b). The generally accepted explanation for such nonlinear plots, however, is that they reflect the substantial difference in the heat capacity, C_p, of the folded and unfolded states, which is commonly attributed to the hydrophobic effect. In this case, the temperature dependence of the rate of refolding merely reflects the difference in heat capacity of the unfolded and transition states.

Elucidating Protein Folding Pathways

A folding pathway would be defined in terms of the intermediate states that are encountered during the folding process. Ideally, one would like to describe the process of folding in a sequential manner:

$$U \rightarrow I_1 \rightarrow I_2 \rightarrow I_3 \rightarrow \ldots \ldots \rightarrow I_n \rightarrow N$$

where I_i are the various intermediate states. The observed kinetics of folding described above, however, indicate that it will be difficult to elucidate the process in this way. The initial intermediates are likely to be very heterogeneous, as each molecule of the original population of unfolded protein molecules initially will have a unique conformation. They will, however, converge rapidly to a limited number of partially folded conformations, which are in equilibrium with each other and the fully unfolded state, so all of these steps will be rapidly reversible and precede the rate-limiting step. Once this pre-equilibrium is attained, all the intermediate species will have indistinguishable kinetic behavior, and it will be difficult, if not impossible, to elucidate the kinetic role of each species, even to distinguish between intermediates on and off the folding pathway. Furthermore, many crucial intermediates are likely to be too unstable to be populated to significant extents.

It should be possible to characterize the equilibrium properties of the residual unfolded protein under refolding conditions, which might be described as the "refolding" state. Refolding protein has been observed to adopt, rapidly and reversibly, relatively compact conformations (Creighton, 1980), to be resistant to certain proteolytic cleavages (Schmid and Blaschek, 1984; Lang and Schmid, 1986), to have certain amide hydrogen atoms protected from exchange with solvent (Udgaonkar and Baldwin, 1988; Röder et al., 1988), and to have a variety of nonrandom conformations, such as elements of secondary structure (Kato et al., 1981; Kuwajima et al., 1987). With at least some proteins, the refolding state appears to be similar to the recently described "molten globule" conformational

state (Kuwajima, 1977; Ikeguchi et al., 1986; Ptitsyn, 1987). This conformational state is stable with some proteins under some conditions; it is only slightly greater in dimensions than the fully folded state and has similar amounts of secondary structure, but its side chains are not fixed in asymmetric environments, and it is thermodynamically indistinguishable from the fully unfolded state. Its conformational properties are one of the more interesting current questions about protein structure.

Pathways Determined Using Disulfide Bonds

The intermediates defining folding pathways are intrinsically unstable and are generally populated only marginally and transiently. They could be characterized much more readily if they could be trapped in some way and then fractionated on the basis of their degree of folding. For example, if it were possible to trap intramolecular hydrogen bonds, it would be feasible to isolate and to characterize the kinetic intermediates with various numbers of such bonds and to devise a folding pathway in terms of such species.

It is not possible to trap hydrogen bonds, but disulfide bonds can be trapped, due to the reduction-oxidation nature of the disulfide interaction between thiol groups, which requires electron transfer with other reagents in the solvent (Creighton, 1978, 1986, 1988a). Most useful is thiol-disulfide exchange between the protein and added thiol and disulfide reagents. Consequently, disulfide formation, breakage, and interchange can be quenched rapidly, usually by modifying irreversibly all free thiol groups. The protein species with different numbers of disulfide bonds can be separated and the disulfide bonds identified.

The kinetic roles of the intermediates can be determined relatively unambiguously, due to the ability to control the kinetics and thermodynamics of the disulfide interaction through variation of the concentration of the thiol and disulfide reagents. Under the appropriate conditions, the disulfide interaction can be very dynamic, with disulfides being formed, broken and rearranged on time scales as short as 10^{-5} seconds. The rates of the intramolecular steps reflect the protein conformational transitions involved.

Although only the disulfide bonds are trapped, the conformations that directed the disulfide bond formation are effectively trapped also, because it is a thermodynamic requirement that whatever conformation stabilized a particular disulfide bond must be stabilized to the very same extent by the presence of that disulfide. Therefore, the conformational basis of folding should be evident from the conformations of the trapped intermediates, unless the conformations are affected by the trapping procedure.

The approach is only useful with proteins that unfold when their disulfides are broken. Unfolding and refolding can be controlled by varying just the intrinsic disulfide stability. The strengths of all other types of interactions that stabilize proteins can be kept constant. There is no necessity to use denaturants, which affect protein stability in uncertain ways. Using the

appropriate methods, disulfide bond formation is rapidly reversible and not fundamentally different from other types of interactions, especially hydrogen bonds. On the other hand, a disulfide bond has no specific intrinsic stability relative to the two thiols, but this depends upon the redox potential of the environment. This also determines the stability of a folded protein, with disulfide bonds, relative to that unfolded, with the disulfides reduced.

Disulfide Folding Pathway of BPTI

The most detailed and informative folding pathway elucidated thus far is that of bovine pancreatic trypsin inhibitor (BPTI). This folding transition (Fig. 4) has all the properties observed for the folding of proteins not involving disulfides: it is nonrandom and cooperative, has rapid equilibration of early intermediates, and has a rate-limiting step that occurs late in refolding and is a distorted form

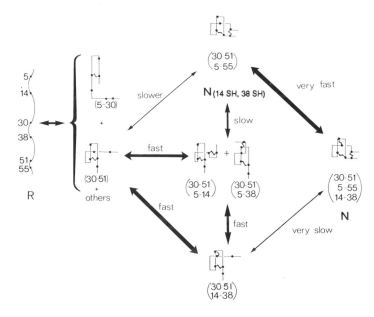

Fig. 4. The disulfide folding pathway of BPTI. The polypeptide backbone of the protein is depicted by the solid line, and the positions of the six Cys residues are depicted. The intermediates are designated by the disulfides they contain. The relative rates of the intramolecular steps are indicated only qualitatively, even though the actual values have been measured. The fully reduced protein, R, is unfolded and consequently makes initial disulfides nearly randomly; this is depicted with a single arrow and a bracket to encompass all the one-disulfide intermediates. They are in rapid equilibrium, and only the two predominant species are depicted. Three different second disulfides, 14–38, 5–14, and 5–38, are formed readily in intermediate (30–51), 10^5-fold more rapidly than is disulfide 5–55. These three second disulfides are rearranged intramolecularly to the stable native-like intermediate (30–51,5–55) [or, N(14SH,38SH)]; the + between (30–51,5–14) and (30–51,5–38) indicates that they have comparable kinetic roles. A quasi-native (5–55,14–38) intermediate that is formed directly from intermediate (5–55) is not included in this diagram, as it is not on the productive pathway. The native-like (30–51,5–55) readily forms the 14–38 disulfide bond to complete disulfide formation and refolding. Unfolding and disulfide reduction occur by the reverse of this process.

of the native conformation. Therefore, it will be described briefly to illustrate a prototype mechanism for protein folding.

The three disulfide bonds of native BPTI (between cysteines 5–55, 14–38, and 30–51) are required for stability of the folded conformation, and the reduced protein is unfolded, although not necessarily a random coil. It is at least sufficiently unfolded that formation of the first disulfide bond involves all six Cys residues in at least approximately random pairings. The rate is the same as that in the presence of 8M urea, where random, one-disulfide intermediates are generated, and is close to that expected for a random coil.

In contrast, the one-disulfide intermediates that actually accumulate under folding conditions are far from random. That with the native-like Cys 30–51 disulfide [designated as (30–51)] accounts normally for 60 percent of the one-disulfide molecules, the non-native (5–30) comprises another 30 percent, while the remaining 10 percent comprise the other 13 possible disulfides. The explanation for this apparent paradox is that whatever disulfide is formed initially is rapidly rearranged intramolecularly, and the accumulating intermediates reflect the equilibrium mixture of one-disulfide species. Those that accumulate to the greatest extent are those with the lowest free energies, as a result of their favorable conformational properties, and this depends upon the conditions and the sequence of the protein.

The preferential accumulation of intermediate (30–51) has important kinetic consequences, for the productive pathway for refolding leads from this intermediate, and all further intermediates retain the 30–51 disulfide bond. This demonstrates how the equilibrium stability of an intermediate can be important kinetically. Also, the rapid equilibration of the one-disulfide species demonstrates how unfolded proteins can equilibrate rapidly prior to refolding, how all unfolded molecules can follow the same pathway, and why the initial state of the unfolded protein is not important.

The conformational properties of intermediate (30–51) that account for its preferen-

tial stability and its role in further refolding are of utmost importance for understanding this folding mechanism. In native BPTI, the 30–51 disulfide links the major alpha-helix of the protein to the beta-sheet, raising the possibility that the stability of the (30–51) intermediate arises from an interaction between these two elements of secondary structure (Creighton, 1974). Relatively little evidence for the presence of the secondary structure was obtained (Hollecker et al., 1981), however, until nuclear magnetic resonance (NMR) analysis of the trapped intermediate detected the presence of the beta-sheet (States et al., 1987).

That both elements of secondary structure are undoubtedly present comes from the work of Oas and Kim (1988), who showed that two synthetic peptides of 16 and 14 residues, respectively spanning the sequence around Cys 30 and Cys 51, adopt these conformations when linked by the disulfide. This simple system appears to be a remarkably good model for the (30–51) intermediate. The presence of the helix and sheet suggest that the conformation stabilizing this crucial early intermediate in refolding arises from the interaction between the two major elements of secondary structure of the protein. This interaction also involves much of the hydrophobic interior of the protein.

The conformation present in (30–51) is not highly populated in reduced BPTI or in the individual model peptides, in the absence of the disulfide bond, and is probably present in reduced BPTI in approximately 0.1 percent of the molecules (Creighton, 1988c). The stability of (30–51) is not a result of the preexistence of the conformation in the reduced protein, but is due to the stabilization by the presence of the disulfide bond of the conformation that stabilized that disulfide. This linkage principle applies not only to disulfides, but to any interaction within folded proteins, and explains the cooperativity of individually weak interactions that stabilize folded conformations (Creighton, 1983).

Whatever other conformations are adopted by the bulk of the reduced BPTI molecules, whether random or not, do not lead to productive further folding. Consequently, nonrandom conformations present in unfolded proteins do not need to be highly populated to lead to productive folding. The ones that are important are those that interact with and stabilize each other and, consequently, lead to further productive folding. Nevertheless, the more stable the individual conformational elements in the unfolded protein, the more stable the interaction between them is expected to be.

No reason has been found for why intermediate (5–30), with a non-native disulfide, is the second most stable one-disulfide intermediate. The trapped intermediate appears to be nearly as unfolded as the reduced protein (States *et al.,* 1987), but the blocking groups on the free thiols may have disrupted its original nonrandom conformation. Clearly, whatever conformation is stabilizing this non-native disulfide bond must be different from the native conformation, although it may be significant that Cys 5 occurs in a short helical segment in the native protein (Wlodawer *et al.,* 1984).

Of the three disulfides in native BPTI, the only one well-populated at the single-disulfide stage is 30–51, even though 5–55 is more stable in the fully folded conformation (Creighton and Goldenberg, 1984). The corresponding one-disulfide intermediate, (5–55), is present as only about 3 percent of the one-disulfide intermediates. This could be due to it being formed kinetically at a slower rate, since this intermediate may be an exception to the rapid equilibration of the other one-disulfide species (Creighton, 1977). Alternatively, the thermodynamic stability of (5–55) might be correspondingly lower than that of (30–51). This could be due to the entropic effect of the greater number of residues between these two most-distant Cys residues in the primary structure.

The most likely explanation is that the high stability of the 5–55 disulfide in native BPTI results from simultaneous interactions between residues in three different regions of the polypeptide chain, around Cys 5 and Cys 55, plus the beta-sheet. The simultaneous presence of all three regions of the polypep-

tide chain would not be favorable at such an early stage of folding. The other native disulfide, 14–38, is less stable than 30–51 in native BPTI and is not present at a detectable level in the one-disulfide intermediates.

The example of the 5–55 disulfide demonstrates that the most stable parts of a fully folded protein are not necessarily those that are formed initially in folding. The most stable early intermediates will be those that have the greatest stabilizing interactions at the smallest cost in loss of conformational entropy of the unfolded protein. These are likely to involve only pairs of the most stable local conformations, weighted toward those closest in the sequence, which would provide an explanation as to why elements of secondary structure adjacent in the folded conformation tend to be those that are also adjacent in the primary structure (Levitt and Chothia, 1976).

The nonrandom conformation in intermediate (30–51) is clearly limited to only about half of the residues in the protein, and the amino-terminal half of the polypeptide chain appears to be largely disordered. Disulfides are formed randomly between Cys 5, 14, and 38 at a rate comparable to that observed in the fully reduced protein. These second disulfides contribute somewhat to the stability of the nonrandom conformation already present but do not produce significant amounts of additional folded conformation. The intermediate (30–51,14–38) has two native disulfides and can adopt a meta-stable, native-like conformation.

In contrast, Cys 55 of intermediate (30–51) does not readily form a disulfide with any of the other three Cys residues, even though its thiol group is accessible and normally reactive. The nonrandom conformation of (30–51) probably prevents Cys 55 from encountering Cys 14 and 38, but formation of a disulfide with Cys 5 would produce the two-disulfide species (30–51,5–55), which adopts a stable, native-like conformation. The reason this step is so slow is that it involves traversing the high-energy barrier that separates the more unfolded species from the native conformation (Fig. 5), which means going through a high-

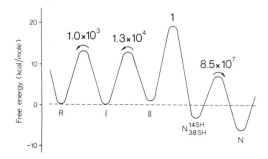

Fig. 5. Free energy profile of the disulfide rearrangement folding transition of BPTI. The free energies of the intermediates were calculated from the measured equilibrium constants under redox conditions where the native protein is 5.4 kcal/mol more stable than the fully reduced protein. The free energies of the transition states were calculated from the rates of the intramolecular steps in disulfide formation, using classical transition state theory. All the one-disulfide intermediates were classed together as species I, and intermediates (30–51,14–38), (30–51,5–14), and (30–51,5–38) were classed together as II. The reaction coordinate was drawn arbitrarily, with the various intermediates evenly spaced.

energy distorted form of the native conformation. For the same reason, intermediate (30–51,14–38) does not readily complete refolding by forming directly the third disulfide.

The energetically most favorable pathway, on an intramolecular basis, into and out of the native conformation of BPTI is by intramolecular rearrangement of the non-native second disulfides of intermediates (30–51,5–14) and (30–51,5–38) to the native-like (30–51,5–55). This is believed to reflect the exceptionally high stability of the native conformation of BPTI, distortion of which is also exceptionally difficult.

The disulfide rearrangement pathway is not the most favorable energetically with less stable homologues of BPTI (Hollecker and Creighton, 1983). Although slow, formation of the 5–55 disulfide in intermediate (30–51) is the energetically preferred rate-limiting step into and out of these less stable native conformations. Consequently, the disulfides of these proteins are formed in a seemingly simple, sequential manner, first 30–51, then 5–55, finally 14–38, but the rate-limiting step still involves a distortion or rearrangement of the native-like conformation. In this case, there are no Cys

residues in appropriate positions to detect these rearrangements by disulfides.

The high free energy barrier of the rate-limiting step (Fig. 5) also means that these sequential steps do not take place in an irreversible progression. Instead, the initial one- and two-disulfide intermediates rapidly unfold and have their disulfides broken much more rapidly than they complete refolding. Under redox conditions where native BPTI has the usual stability relative to the reduced form, say 5 to 10 kcal/mol, there is a relatively rapid, reversible pre-equilibrium between the reduced protein and the initial one- and two-disulfide intermediates. This pre-equilibrium is probably typical of an unfolded protein under refolding conditions.

Similar energetics were observed with every other protein that has been examined in this way, especially ribonuclease T1 (Pace and Creighton, 1986) and ribonuclease A (Creighton, 1988b). The disulfide rearrangements of BPTI demonstrate vividly, if to a somewhat exaggerated extent, the importance of the high free energy barrier of the distorted native-like conformation, which undoubtedly reflects the cooperativity of the interactions stabilizing the folded conformation (Creighton, 1983). These observations are consistent with the other evidence that the transition state for folding is generally late in refolding, very close to the native conformation (Segawa and Sugihara, 1984a, 1984b).

The disulfide intermediates are less stable than either the fully reduced or fully folded states under all redox conditions (Fig. 5), and have less stable folded conformations than N, so the BPTI disulfide folding transition demonstrates the usual cooperativity of folding. The reason for this cooperativity is apparent from the stabilities of the three disulfides at varying stages of folding: the stability of a disulfide reflects the stability of the conformation stabilizing it, which is determined in part by the presence or absence, and the stability, of the other disulfide bonds. Such cooperativity is not unique to disulfides and should apply to any other type of interaction within a folded protein.

Summary

Ignoring complexities due to peptide bond isomerization, experimental observations of unfolding and refolding of a number of small, single-domain proteins give a coherent general description of what usually happens when an unfolded protein refolds. Upon initiation of refolding by altering the conditions, the conformationally heterogeneous unfolded protein molecules rapidly converge to a limited set of nonrandom, partially folded conformations that are rapidly interconverted with each other and with more unfolded conformations. Predominating within this pre-equilibrium are those conformations with the lowest free energies, which arise primarily because pairs of marginally stable, local, nonrandom conformations interact with and stabilize each other. The nature of these conformations will depend upon the local conformational tendencies of the polypeptide chain. Other less stable and more ordered conformations are also populated to smaller extents, and some of them approach the native-like conformation sufficiently to overcome the highest free energy barrier in refolding—a distorted form of the native conformation. Completion of refolding is then rapid, with only small conformational rearrangements, only slightly greater than the conformational flexibility normally exhibited by folded proteins under similar conditions.

References

Alber, T., S. Dao-pin, J. A. Nye, D. C. Muchmore, B. W. Matthews, *Biochemistry* **26**, 3754 (1987).

Anfinsen, C. B., *Science* **181**, 223 (1973).

Baldwin, R. L., *Trends Biochem. Sci.* **11**, 6 (1986).

Brandts, J. F., H. R. Halvorson, M. Brennan, *Biochemistry* **14**, 4953 (1975).

Creighton, T. E., *J. Mol. Biol.* **87**, 603 (1974).

———, *J. Mol. Biol.* **113**, 313 (1977).

———, *Prog. Biophys. Mol. Biol.* **33**, 231 (1978).

———, *J. Mol. Biol.* **137**, 61 (1980).

———, *Biopolymers* **22**, 49 (1983).

———, *J. Phys. Chem.* **89**, 2452 (1985).

———, *Methods Enzymol.* **131**, 83 (1986).

———, *BioEssays* **8**, 57 (1988a).

———, *Proc. Natl. Acad. Sci. U.S.A.* **85**, 5082 (1988b).

———, *Biophys. Chem.* **31**, 155 (1988c).

Creighton, T. E., and D. P. Goldenberg, *J. Mol. Biol.* **179**, 497 (1984).

Denton, J. B., Y. Konishi, H. A. Scheraga, *Biochemistry* **21**, 5155 (1982).

Garel, J.-R., and R. L. Baldwin, *Proc. Natl. Acad. Sci. U.S.A.* **70**, 3347 (1973).

Griko, Yu.V., P. L. Privalov, S. Yu, V. Venyaminov, P. Kutyshenko, *J. Mol. Biol.* **202**, 127 (1988).

Harrison, S. C., and R. Durbin, *Proc. Natl. Acad. Sci. U.S.A.* **82**, 4028 (1985).

Hollecker, M., and T. E. Creighton, *J. Mol. Biol.* **168**, 409 (1983).

Hollecker, M., T. E. Creighton, M. Gabriel, *Biochimie* **63**, 835 (1981).

Ikeguchi, M., K. Kuwajima, M. Mitani, S. Sugai, *Biochemistry* **25**, 6965 (1986).

Jaenicke, R., *Angew. Chem. Intl. Ed. Engl.* **23**, 295 (1984).

Kato, S., M. Okamura, N. Shimamoto, H. Utiyama, *Biochemistry* **20**, 1080 (1981).

Kuwajima, K., *J. Mol. Biol.* **114**, 241 (1977).

Kuwajima, K., H. Yamaya, S. Miwa, S. Sugai, T. Magamura, *FEBS Letters* **221**, 115 (1987).

Lang, K., and F. X. Schmid, *Eur. J. Biochem.* **159**, 275 (1986).

Levinthal, C., *J. Chim. Phys.* **65**, 44 (1968).

Levitt, M., and C. Chothia, *Nature* **261**, 552 (1976).

Lumry, R., and R. Biltonen, in *Structure and Stability of Biological Macromolecules*, S. N. Timasheff and G. D. Fasman, Eds. (Marcel Dekker, New York, 1969), pp. 62–212.

Lynn, R. M., Y. Konishi, H. A. Scheraga, *Biochemistry* **23**, 2470 (1984).

Oas, T. G., and P. Kim, *Nature* **336**, 42 (1988).

Pace, C. N., and T. E. Creighton, *J. Mol. Biol.* **188**, 477 (1986).

Pfeil, W., and P. L. Privalov, *Biophys. Chem.* **4**, 23 (1976).

Privalov, P. L., *Adv. Protein Chem.* **33**, 167 (1979).

———, *Adv. Protein Chem.* **35**, 1 (1982).

Ptitsyn, O. B., *J. Protein Chem.* **6**, 273 (1987).

Regan, L., and W. F. DeGrado, *Science* **241**, 976 (1988).

Röder, H., G. A. Elöve, S.W. Englander, *Nature* **335**, 700 (1988).

Schmid, F., and H. Blaschek, *Biochemistry* **23**, 2128 (1984).

Segawa, S.-I., and M. Sugihara, *Biopolymers* **23**, 2473 (1984a).

———, *Biopolymers* **23**, 2489 (1984b).

Segawa, S.-I., and K. Kuma, *Biopolymers* **25**, 1981 (1986).

Shoemaker, K. R., P. S. Kim, E. J. York, J. M. Stewart, R. L. Baldwin, *Nature* **326**, 563 (1987).

States, D. J., T. E. Creighton, C. M. Dobson, M. Karplus, *J. Mol. Biol.* **195,** 731 (1987).

Stryer, L., *Biochemistry* (W. H. Freeman, New York 1988).

Tanford, C., *Adv. Protein Chem.* **23,** 121 (1968).

Udgaonkar, J. B., and R. L. Baldwin, *Nature* **335,** 694 (1988).

Wetlaufer, D. B., *Proc. Natl. Acad. Sci. U.S.A.* **70,** 697 (1973).

Wlodawer, A., J. Walter, R. Huber, L. Sjölin, *J. Mol. Biol.* **180,** 301 (1984).

Wright, P. E., H. J. Dyson, R. A. Lerner, *Biochemistry* **27,** 7167 (1988).

17

Helical Proteins
De Novo Design

Lynne Regan, Siew Peng Ho
Zelda Wasserman, William F. DeGrado

How the amino acid sequence of a protein determines its final three-dimensional structure is an important question. Currently, one cannot take an amino acid sequence and, using only this information, predict the final three-dimensional structure of protein. However, we recently initiated a converse approach to this problem (Eisenberg *et al.,* 1986; Ho and DeGrado, 1987; Regan and DeGrado, 1988; DeGrado *et al.,* 1989): to try to design an amino acid sequence that will fold to give the three-dimensional structure we desire. As an initial target, we chose to design a four-helix bundle, a motif that was described in naturally occurring proteins by Weber and Salemme (1980). In this motif, four α-helices, inclined at an angle of about 20°, are connected by three loops. The motif is found in several naturally occurring proteins, such as myohemerythrin, cytochrome c', and growth hormone. In the naturally occurring proteins, the helices tend to be of different lengths and are connected by loops of varying lengths. In our idealized model, we initially have tried to design a protein that has identical helices connected by identical loops.

At the outset of the design process, it was not clear that it would be possible to design an entire sequence that will fold to give a novel protein. It was possible, however, to design elements of secondary structure, particularly α-helices, that will fold as monomeric units (Shoemaker *et al.,* 1987; DeGrado, 1988). Therefore, the approach we adopted was to design an α-helix that would associate with three other identical helices to give a four-helix bundle. Hence, in the initial stages, we had to design only one α-helix. An advantage of this approach was that it provided an experimental measure of how good the helical sequences are through measurement of the tetramer-monomer association-dissociation equilibrium. This information allowed us to make improvements in the model to optimize the helix sequence (see Fig. 1A). The next step, having optimized the helix, was to design loops that would connect to helices and then repeat the same process. The free energy of dimerization of the "helical hairpin" was measured, and this information used to optimize the loops connecting the helices (see Fig. 1B). Finally, having achieved this stage of the design, a third loop connecting the two hairpins was incorporated, creating an entire protein (see Fig. 1C).

Initial α-Helix Design

The initial α-helix was designed (Eisenberg *et al.*, 1986) with leucine residues on one face that form the hydrophobic core of the protein.

A

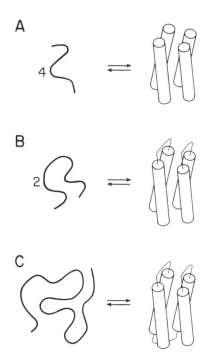

B

C

Fig. 1. A schematic illustration of the incremental approach to the design of a four-helix bundle protein.

On the other face, hydrophilic residues, lysine, and glutamic acid were positioned such that they could form salt bridges. To achieve maximum solvent exclusion from the hydrophobic core, it was necessary to pack four helices into the bundle structure. Trying to pack two or three helices gives insufficient shielding from solvent of the hydrophobic residues.

The sequences of the helical peptides α_{1a} and α_{1b} are shown in Fig. 2 (Ho and De-Grado, 1987). Their helicity was monitored by circular dichroism (CD) spectroscopy. The characteristic CD spectrum of an α-helix has double minima at 209 and 222 nm. Thus, it is possible to monitor α-helix formation by following the CD signal at 222 nm. For peptide α_{1a}, at low peptide concentration, one sees a CD spectrum indicating essentially random coil; however, at high concentration, one sees the characteristic double minimum indicative of α-helix. Measurements at intermediate points were made to determine the concentration dependence of association to form helical structure. If we fit the data points to calculated curves for a monomer-dimer, monomer-trimer, or monomer-tetramer equilibrium, the best fit is indeed that for a monomer-tetramer equilibrium. This result is supported by size-exclusion experiments, which indicate that α_{1a} is a tetramer at high concentration.

The CD experiments on α_{1a} were performed by varying the concentration of peptide; however, as the designs for the helix improved, it was no longer possible, simply by varying peptide concentration, to cause the bundle to dissociate. The bundles are so stable that it was necessary to include chaotropic agents (e.g., guanidine HCl, GuHCl) to actually see dissociation. Figure 3 illustrates a GuHCl denaturation curve for α_{1a} at a given, fixed peptide concentration. By repeating this experiment at various GuHCl concentrations, it is possible to obtain the free energy of tetramerization versus [GuHCl] (Fig. 3B). Extrapolation back to the value of ΔG at zero GuHCl concentration gives the free energy in the absence of chaotropes. The data are shown (in Fig. 3B) for peptide α_{1a}, the original helical peptide of 16 amino acids. With this peptide, the degree of tetramerization could be measured either directly by performing dilutions and measuring the α-helicity or, as I described, by measuring at different con-

Fig. 2. The amino acid sequences of the peptides. Peptide α_{1a} contains an N-terminal acetyl and a C-terminal carboxylate group. Peptide α_{1b}, α_{2a}, and α_{2b} contain N-terminal acetyl and C-terminal carboximide groups. Peptide α_4 has unmodified N and C termini.

α_{1a} Gly-Lys-Leu-Glu-Glu-Leu-Leu-Lys-Lys-Leu-Leu-Glu-Glu-Leu-Lys-Gly

α_{1b} Gly-Glu-Leu-Glu-Glu-Leu-Leu-Lys-Lys-Leu-Lys-Glu-Leu-Leu-Lys-Gly

α_{2a} α_{1b}-Pro-α_{1b}

α_{2b} α_{1b}-Pro-Arg-Arg-α_{1b}

α_4 Met-α_{1b}-Pro-Arg-Arg-α_{1b}-Pro-Arg-Arg-α_{1b}-Pro-Arg-Arg-α_{1b}

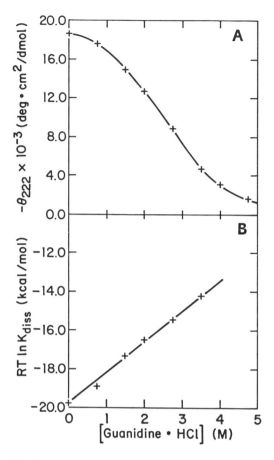

Fig. 3. (A) GuHCl denaturation curve and (B) a plot of free energy versus GuHCl concentration.

centrations of GuHCl and extrapolating back to zero GuHCl. In this case, the two values for the free energy of association are quite close, -18.6 kcal mol^{-1} and -19.7 kcal mol^{-1} respectively, which gives validity to the linear extrapolation. This is important as the next peptide, the improved version of α_{1a}, does not dissociate by dilution alone under our experimental conditions, and the extrapolation method must be used.

Improvements in α_{1b}

From the data presented to date, we see that α_{1a}, the original peptide sequence, does form the desired tetramers. However, the sequence was improved upon, and the changes that were made are illustrated in Fig. 4. Figure 4

shows helical net representations in which the back of the helix has been cut and opened out flat. The top panel shows peptide α_{1a} that was described, the initial 16-residue model for the α-helix, and the bottom panel shows α_{2b}, which is an improved version. The following changes were made: leucine 11, which on closer inspection would seem to fall on the hydrophilic face, was changed to lysine, and glutamic acid 13, whose carboxylate group was somewhat solvent shielded, was changed to leucine. Also, because of work from Baldwin and co-workers (Shoemaker *et al.*, 1987) concerning the potential interactions of the helix macro-dipole with charged amino acids, we changed lysine 2 at the N-terminus to a glutamic acid.

Let us now consider the properties of this improved version of the α-helix, peptide α_{1b}. One can do a similar experiment to the one described previously, measuring the concentration dependence of the tetramerization by monitoring α-helix formation at different concentrations of GuHCl, then extrapolating to zero GuHCl. In this case, compared to the value for the free energy of folding of peptide α_{1a} in the absence of denaturant, the stability is increased by about -2 kcal mol^{-1} due to the changes introduced. The concentration dependence curves show that the most likely equilibrium is the monomer-tetramer equilibrium, which was confirmed by size exclusion chromatography. Because of its stability, α_{1b} was used in the next stage of the design.

Forming the Four-Helix Bundle Protein

The next stage in the design was to link these helices to give two helix hairpins that would dimerize to give the four-helix-bundle protein. Two loop sequences were investigated. The first loop introduced a single proline making ends of the helices Gly-Pro-Gly. This loop seemed as if it would be able to form the necessary turn between the helices; however, gel-filtration experiments indicated that the peptide containing this loop was not forming a dimer of hairpins as expected. It was actually

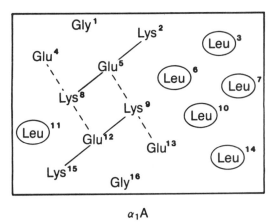

Fig. 4. Helical net diagrams of peptides α_{1a} and α_{1b}.

forming a trimer, which was not the desired structure. The next variant on the loop was an attempt to try to destabilize any trimer that might be forming by introducing two charged hydrophilic amino acids, two arginine residues, and this proved successful. The peptide with a Gly-Pro-Arg-Arg-Gly loop was shown by gel filtration to form the desired dimer of helical hairpins.

This illustrates the advantage of the stepwise approach, since we were easily able to identify the difficulty as a problem in the loop sequence and not in the helical portion of the molecule. By measuring the concentration dependence of the ellipticity at 222 nm at different concentrations of GuHCl, one can again extrapolate to zero GuHCl and estimate the stability of the peptide. It is a somewhat long extrapolation for the linked helices, as they are so very stable to GuHCl denaturation. A value of about -13 kcal mol^{-1} is obtained as the free energy of association of the helical hairpins. Such a molecule is somewhat destabilized compared to the unlinked helices, presumably because of the constraints involved in confining the loop geometry. However, this loop seemed at least stable enough to go on to subsequent stages of the design.

Up to this point, we have discussed the helices as if they are indeed aligned as shown in Fig. 1B, with the two loops close together at one end of the molecule. But this is just a model, and one can quite easily model the two

helical hairpins to be in exactly opposite orientations with the loops separated by the length of the molecule, or even something completely different. We therefore needed to test (Fig. 1B) that this was really an energetically reasonable orientation.

In our model, the loops come quite close together, suggesting that it should be possible to insert cysteine residues such that they would form interloop disulfide links. Such bonds would link the two dimers only if the orientation of the hairpins was as we proposed. The original loop sequence is Gly-Pro-Arg-Arg-Gly, and the loops with potential to form disulfide bonds between hairpins are Gly-Cys-Arg-Arg-Gly and Gly-Pro-Cys-Arg-Gly. These peptides were synthesized and had the following properties; first, the disulfides form readily in the folded peptides. If we allowed the cysteine-containing peptides to associate in native conditions, we could quite readily form disulfide bonds by incubating the peptides with oxidized dithiothreitol (DTT) or allowing air oxidation. We did not have to employ any extreme methods to achieve disulfide bond formation. Using size-exclusion chromatography, we found that the disulfide-linked peptides are compact and monomeric and have not assumed a higher aggregation state upon formation of the disulfide linkage. The CD spectra we observed were characteristic of α-helices, indicative of high helical content.

We also studied the stabilities of the differently positioned disulfides by incubating the peptides with different ratios of oxidized and reduced DTT, quenching the reaction with iodoacetamide, then analyzing the relative amounts of disulfide-linked versus monomeric forms of the peptides by sodium dodecyl sulfate (SDS) polyacrylamide gel electrophoresis. In this way, we were able to estimate the relative stabilities to reduction of the disulfide bonds in the two loop positions. The Gly-Cys-Arg-Arg-Gly disulfide was about three times more resistant to reduction than was the Gly-Pro-Cys-Arg-Gly disulfide. Although the structural basis for disulfide stability in proteins is not well understood, in this case, we can consider the relative strengths of these similar disulfides as an indication of the degree to which each is strained from the preferred dihedral angles.

We can also study the effect of disulfide linkages on the stability of the proteins to denaturation by GuHCl. If formation of the disulfide linkages greatly perturbed the protein structure, we would expect the disulfide-linked proteins to be destabilized relative to the unlinked species. We compared the GuHCl denaturation curves of nondisulfide-linked peptides (protecting the sulfhydryl by the acetamidomethyl group to prevent disulfide formation) with curves for the peptides linked by disulfide bonds. For both positions of the disulfide bond, the peptides were significantly stabilized to denaturation when the disulfide link was present. Also, the disulfide-bonded form of the peptide containing the Gly-Cys-Arg-Arg-Gly loop was more stable than the peptide with the Gly-Pro-Cys-Arg-Gly loop. This differential stability confirms results seen in the redox experiments, which suggest that the former disulfide is the stronger. To summarize, these data indicate that the orientation of the helix hairpins shown in Fig. 1B can be assumed quite readily, with the loops close enough together that they can be linked by a disulfide bridge. In further analyses of the differential stabilities of the different positions of the disulfide, more should be learned about the possible conformations available to the loop sequences.

These results gave us confidence in the design to go ahead and add the third loop that would connect the second and third helices, giving peptide α_4. Initially, this was accomplished by solid-phase peptide synthesis. Although the properties of the entire four-helix bundle were encouraging, we could never purify the protein to homogeneity.

It is difficult to overestimate the importance of protein purity if one wishes to make quantitative conclusions concerning the success of a design. Therefore, we decided to change our approach from peptide synthesis to gene manipulation in order to prepare the 73-residue protein (Reagan and DeGrado, 1988). A gene encoding the desired protein was synthesized and inserted into a plasmid that expressed the protein intracellularly from the *tac* promoter. The advantage of this technique is that we were able to incorporate many restriction sites scattered throughout the protein so that in subsequent manipulations, we will be able to change entire helical sequences or entire loops quite readily. Also, we will be able to break the symmetry that was imposed in the initial design.

In order to be able to detect expression of this protein in *Escherichia coli*, we raised antibodies against peptide α_{1b} as a method of identifying the protein. We were easily able to detect protein α_4 in crude *E. coli.* extracts by Western blot analysis and saw no indication of its degradation by cellular proteases. We were able to use these antibodies to follow the purification of α_4 from *E. coli* extracts. The protein was characterized by amino acid composition and N-terminal sequencing of the first 25 residues. The sequence corresponds to the desired sequence, with the initiator methionine retained.

As we might expect, the CD spectrum of this protein is again indicative of high helical content. Gel-filtration experiments reveal the protein to be monomeric, with no indication of aggregation into higher molecular weight structures. Figure 5 shows GuHCl denaturation curves for α_{1b}, α_{2b}, and α_4, performed at equal peptide concentration. It is evident that α_4 is significantly stabilized to denaturation by GuHCl. The mean residue ellipticity of pep-

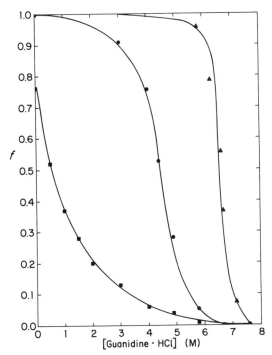

Fig. 5. GuHCl denaturation curves of the peptides α_{1b} (square), α_{2b} (circle), and α_4 (triangle) at equal peptide concentrations. To compare the curves, we plot f (the observed mean residue ellipticity at a given concentration of denaturant, normalized to the observed mean residue ellipticity in the absence of denaturant) versus the concentration of denaturant. In the case of α_{1b}, at the peptide concentration used, the tetramer is partially dissociated and hence does not reach $f = 1$ at zero GuHCl concentration.

tide α_4 is independent of protein concentration even at the midpoint of the GuHCl-induced denaturation curve, where any aggregation-induced stabilization of secondary structure would be expected to be most apparent.

The free energy associated with the transition from the unfolded, random coil state to the folded helical state for α_4, in the absence of denaturants, was estimated by linear extrapolation to zero GuHCl concentration. We estimate the stability of peptide α_4 to be approximately -20 kcal mol^{-1}. Although this value is approximate because of the assumptions invoked in the development of linear free energy models, it enables us to compare α_4 with other small natural proteins that have been analyzed in this way. For example, the free energies of folding of lysozyme and ribonuclease are estimated to be -8.9 kcal mol^{-1} and -7.5 kcal mol^{-1}, respectively. Thus, α_4 possesses considerable stability when compared with other small proteins and will provide a stable framework for the incorporation of other design modifications.

We are now in a position to introduce changes into the loops and helices to create proteins that will provide an ideal system for studies on protein folding and of factors influencing the stability of the four-helix bundle. We would also like to extend the design process to include binding sites for ligands and to perhaps eventually introduce catalytic sites into the protein.

References

DeGrado, W. F., *Adv. Prot. Chem.* **39**, 51 (1988).

DeGrado, W. F., Z. R. Wasserman, J. D. Lear, *Science* **243**, 622 (1989).

Eisenberg, D., *et al.*, *Proteins* **1**, 16 (1986).

Ho, S. P., and W. F. DeGrado, *J. Amer. Chem. Soc.* **109**, 6751 (1987).

Regan, L., and W. F. DeGrado, *Science* **241**, 976 (1988).

Shoemaker, K. R., *et al.*, *Cold Spring Harbor Symp. Quant. Biol.* **52**, 391 (1987).

Weber, P. C., and F. R. Salemme, *Nature* **287**, 82 (1980).

18

Does the Unfolding Transition of Two-Chain, Coiled-Coil Proteins Involve a Continuum of Intermediates?

Alfred Holtzer, Marilyn Emerson Holtzer, Jeffrey Skolnick

Overview

The thermal unfolding equilibria of globular proteins can often be described in terms of only two conformations: native and random coil. In contrast, unfolding equilibria in single-chain homopolypeptides involve essentially a continuum of partially helical molecules comprising all possible sequences of site conformations. For the latter, the very successful Zimm-Bragg theory assesses the conformational populations by statistical mechanics. Only two parameters are required: σ dictates the free energy of helix initiation; s determines the free energy of helix propagation. These are known from experiments for essentially all the amino acids in proteins.

Which model is appropriate for two-chain, coiled coil proteins, wherein we have two completely α-helical chains, in parallel and in register and slightly supertwisted? For these, the two-state model is inadequate, and interpretation of data has long been made in an ad hoc manner in terms of a series of putative, regional, two-state equilibria along the rod-like molecule. Each independent region is supposed to denature as does a globular protein. Recently, an alternative picture on the Zimm-Bragg model was developed for coiled coils. An additional parameter (w) dictates

the interhelix interaction, and loop entropy plays an important role. Experimental tests are described, including the use of various cross linked species and of isolated molecular segments.

We will deal entirely with tropomyosin, and the discussion will be confined to equilibrium states; if the word "intermediate" is used, it simply means intermediate in conformation and has no temporal connotations at all. Coiled coil proteins are very important in biochemistry. They exist in vivo in cell frameworks, muscle, and even in bacterial cell walls. However, our interest stems from the simplicity of their structure, which provides a model for testing general concepts of protein folding.

Models of Protein Unfolding Equilibria

The globular protein case is depicted in the left part of Fig. 1. There is a complex, folded structure involved in a relatively simple, two-species equilibrium; very often, the system is satisfactorily described by just the native state and the randomly coiled state (Privalov, 1979). About 35 years ago, a group of us in Paul Doty's lab started to look at some simple

Globular Proteins   Homopolypeptide Models

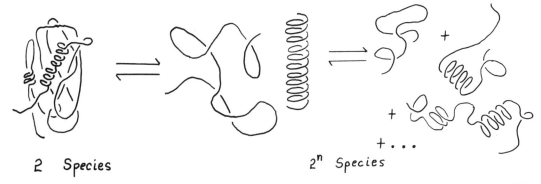

2 Species 2^n Species

Fig. 1. Heuristic representation of the unfolding equilibria in globular proteins (**left**) and model homopolypeptides (**right**).

models for this process and made synthetic homopolypeptides (right part of Fig. 1) for solution studies (Doty *et al.,* 1954, 1956). The structures, indeed, are related to protein secondary structure and are very simple. Those attributes qualified them as good models, but it turns out that the equilibrium is very complex.

In homopolypeptides, we have 2n species, where n is the degree of polymerization, because each of the residues in the chain can be either in the helix or coiled state. The result is a very large number of species. If one has a polymer where n is in the vicinity of 200 or so, which is true in the polymers we are talking about, then $\sim 10^{80}$ species are involved in this equilibrium. Nonetheless, this model system can be very beautifully handled by the Zimm-Bragg theory for homopolypeptides (Zimm and Bragg, 1959; Poland and Scheraga, 1970).

This theory adopts the following approach. If every residue in the chain is randomly coiled, then the free energy is defined as zero, i.e., the standard state is a random coil. Then, one can write down the free energy of any of the other species in a simple parametric fashion. For example, consider the following sequence, where the entire chain is random coil except for two separate sequences of helix of different length:

cc . . . cchhccccchhcc . . .

Zimm and Bragg argued that at the terminal points of a helical stretch, i.e., at the helix boundaries, there must be some loss of rotational freedom; to account for that, they assigned a free energy of $-kT \ln \sigma$ to the ends of such a stretch. Since there are two such stretches in this molecule, we get $-kT \ln \sigma^2$. For each of the helical residues there are also hydrogen bonds, so in this case with three in one stretch, two in the other, and assigning $-kT \ln s$ for each, we obtain an additional $-kT \ln s^5$ in free energy, a total of $-kT \ln (\sigma^2 s^5)$ for this species.

Thus, in these terms, the free energy of all of those 2n states can be documented and, through the magic of statistical mechanics, the populations of each of them and all the conformationally dependent properties can be calculated (Zimm and Bragg, 1959; Poland and Scheraga, 1970).

Others in the field have commented on the Zimm-Bragg theory, expressing skepticism concerning its application to small peptides. We quite concur with this opinion. We think that it is an inappropriate theory for small peptides. It is inherently polymeric in that it does not deal at all well with end effects. In a helix that is only 16 residues long, since the first four NH groups and the last of the CO groups cannot possibly hydrogen bond, 25 percent of the structure is already atypical. The Zimm-Bragg theory is essentially helpless in dealing with these end effects. Consequently, it is best applied to polymers, wherein end effects are immaterial. We only use it in that context.

In applying Zimm-Bragg theory to heteropolypeptides, one has an additional difficulty. The problem lies in determining the appropriate local σ and s in a heteropolymer. This can be seen in any arbitrary sequence of amino acids such as (in single-letter code): LEEKSTASTEFINE, in which, for example, a glutamate (E) residue, can exist in many different environments. Nevertheless, we have to use the same σ and s as evaluated from the data in which glutamate is a guest in a neutral host polymer (Scheraga, 1978). That is the best we can do at present. Nobody believes that helical wheel interactions, e.g., from one residue to another four residues ahead, are not important in many peptides. However, the long peptides to which we will be applying the Zimm-Bragg theory have no such regularities as have been observed in some specific-sequence, short peptides. We have looked for their statistical distribution in tropomyosin without success. There is a great diversity of examples in the 284-residue chain of tropomyosin, but such interactions do not seem to form a general pattern in the structure (Holtzer and Holtzer, 1987). We therefore think that in a long chain they may not materially alter properties such as overall helix content. Thus, we employ σ and s(T) as obtained from host-guest experiments.

The Coiled Coil and Its Unfolding Equilibrium

The actual system that we are working with is the coiled coil protein tropomyosin (Fraser and MacRae, 1973; Cohen and Szent-Györgyi, 1957; Holtzer et al., 1965; Woods, 1969; Caspar et al., 1969; Johnson and Smillie, 1975; Lehrer, 1975; Stewart, 1975). Figure 2 shows that, conformationally speaking, it is somewhere in between the simple model homopolypeptides and globular proteins. It has a somewhat higher order structure, since it is just a long, double α-helix. In tropomyosin itself, the helices have about five times as many turns as shown; it is 400 Å long and has 284 residues per chain. The helices are in register and in parallel. The parallelism is surprising in

view of the importance sometimes ascribed to the helical backbone dipole moment. This structure, in spite of the putatively large, unfavorable interaction of those dipoles, stays together very nicely.

The reason for dimer formation was first guessed by Crick (1953), first proved and improved in the laboratories of Hodges and of Smillie (Hodges et al., 1972; Mak et al., 1979, 1980). The sequence is based on a pseudo-repeating heptet of amino acids designated abcdefg, where residues a and d are hydrophobic—respectively, the black squares and the black triangles on the right part of Fig. 2. These form a very pronounced hydrophobic streak. The presenting face is hydrophobic, and, if the like structure alongside it is folded over like a book and closed on the first, the hydrophobes interleave very nicely by what Crick called knobs-into-holes packing.

Crick pointed out quite correctly, however, that this hydrophobic packing interaction works just as well with antiparallel helices. What Crick did not—and could not—know at the time was that the e residues are negatively charged, so that we get a line of negative charge alongside the hydrophobic streak. The g residues, in turn, are positively charged, so we get another line on the other side (Hodges et al., 1972; Mak et al., 1979, 1980). Closing the book thus allows the negative streak to form salt linkages with the positive streak. If the chains were antiparallel, electrostatic repulsion would result. It is therefore generally accepted that the discrimination for parallel packing comes from the charges and not from the hydrophobes. The total interaction comes, of course, from both. In fact, we believe that the hydrophobic interaction is much the larger of the two (see below).

The empirical basis of our studies is shown in Fig. 3, which gives fraction helix (from circular dichroism [CD]) versus temperature for $\alpha\alpha$ tropomyosin (Isom et al., 1984). Notice that it starts at very high helix content, almost 100 percent. It is a highly cooperative transition. It looks as though it is monophasic, but there is more to it than that. These are two extreme concentrations shown

Fig. 2. Schematic representation of the structure of two-chain, α-helical, coiled coil proteins. On the left, a picture of the coiled coil. Tropomyosin actually has ~5 times as many helical turns as shown. The small segment indicated on the left is opened like a book and expanded on the right to show the pseudo-repeating heptet of residues, abcdefg, in which a (filled squares) and d (filled triangles) residues are hydrophobic and e (negative) and g (positive) residues are oppositely charged. [Through an oversight, the supertwist is shown right handed. It should be left handed.]

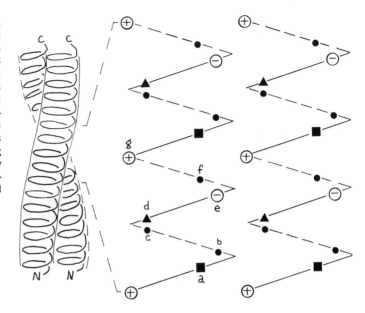

Fig. 3. Experimental percent helix (from CD) versus T for αα tropomyosin. Medium is NaCl$_{500}$NaPi$_{50}$DTT$_1$ (7.4). Filled points, 5.2 mg/cm³. Open points, 0.0044 mg/cm³. Full curves are spline curves through the data. [Reprinted from *Macromolecules* **17**, 2445 (1985) with permission. Copyright 1985, American Chemical Society.]

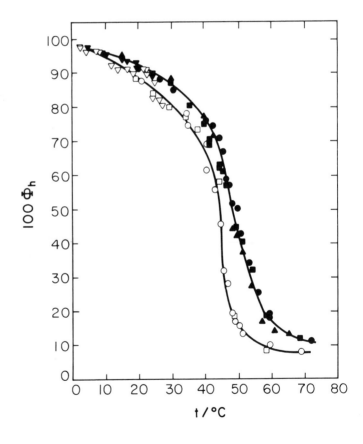

because the two chains, of course, disassociate when they unfold, and the transition is concentration dependent (Holtzer *et al.,* 1983a). The higher concentration is 1000 times the lower, so the dependence is, in this system, actually rather difficult to demonstrate, but it is there. To indicate some of the complexity, we simply note that calorimetric data, i.e., heat capacity versus temperature, show two peaks (Potekhin and Privalov, 1982), even though the CD curve appears monophasic.

Figure 4 shows the possible origin of this complexity. It was pointed out in work from Smillie's lab that, if you cut the tropomyosin rods approximately in half by either enzymatic or chemical (e.g., cyanogen bromide) means, the two halves have very different stabilities (Pato *et al.,* 1981). Figure 4 shows our CD data (Kumar *et al.,* 1988) as fraction helix versus temperature and shows how striking the effect is. The squares represent two different con-

centrations of the N-terminal half of the molecule. The circles represent two extreme concentrations of the C-terminal half, so the N-terminal half is much more stable than the C-terminal half. Notice that, if one did not carefully study the concentration dependence and looked at very different concentrations, one might conclude erroneously that the two halves have the same stability. Clearly, the nonuniformity in the molecule can introduce some complexity.

Models for Coiled Coil Unfolding Equilibria

Our key concern is what model to use for the unfolding equilibrium in two-chain coiled coils. The all-or-none (two-state) model is appropriate for globular proteins; the 2^n-states model, virtually a continuum of states, is appropriate for the synthetic polypeptides. What should we use for tropomyosin, which has a double-helical (coiled coil) structure? Most people use, sometimes tacitly, what we call the all-or-none segments model. It is assumed that the molecule can be divided into very-well-defined, independent segments, each of which denatures in the same manner as a globular protein, that is, in an all-or-none, two-state process.

This model is heuristically represented in Fig. 5. Let us suppose, for simplicity, that there are three such regions and that at some lower temperature, the first of them unfolds. The result is the kind of structure seen in the center of Fig. 5. At some higher temperature, we assume, again for simplicity, that both end segments unfold, producing two randomly coiled chains. The result, in this simplistic case, is that each of the three substantial segments can be in one of two possible conformations, leading to a very limited number of molecular species. While more regions can and have been postulated, the result is still a relatively small number of species (Potekhin and Privalov, 1982).

We question the validity of this model because it is rather nonphysical. The assumptions it makes about the independence of

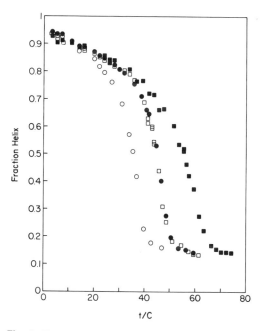

Fig. 4. Experimental fraction helix (from CD) versus T for N-terminal and C-terminal "halves" of the $\alpha\alpha$ tropomyosin molecule. Medium is NaCl$_{500}$NaPi$_{50}$DTT$_1$ (7.4). Squares are data for N-terminal segment (residues 11–127) at 0.0094 mg/cm^3 (open) and 9.4 mg/cm^3 (filled). Circles are data for C-terminal segment (residues 142–281) at 0.010 mg/cm^3 (open) and 4.0 mg/cm^3 (filled). [A preliminary report of these experiments is found in Kumar *et al.,* 1988]

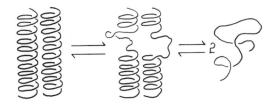

Fig. 5. Heuristic representation of unfolding equilibrium species in the all-or-none segments model.

different segments—indeed, about their very existence—are arbitrary. No one has been able to indicate specific amino acid positions in the structure that would provide the punctuation to lead a given region to unfold as a group without including any residues from a neighboring segment. There are other non-physical aspects that will be presented below.

For this reason, we decided to develop what we call a continuum-of-states model (Skolnick and Holtzer, 1982a, 1982b, 1983a, 1983b; Skolnick, 1983a, 1983b, 1984, 1985) because it is related to the Zimm-Bragg model for single-chain helices. Of course, it is not a continuum; there are discrete states, but when one gets to 2^{284} states and the process has only just begun, it may as well be called a continuum. So we count all the states just as in the Zimm-Bragg technique, but now we add something new because whenever there is a turn of a helix that is associated with another turn of a helix, as in a coiled coil, we add an additional free energy of $-kT \ln w$. Thus, we now have a parameter $w(T)$ that characterizes the helix-helix interaction separately from the short-range interactions that are embodied in

σ and $s(T)$.

Using a formalism developed by Skolnick (1983a, 1983b, 1984, 1985), we can evaluate all the conformational populations, some of which are represented in Fig. 6. It is important to understand certain features that are included in the theory. Consider the first two structures on the right side of the double arrow. Notice that every residue that is helical in the first is also helical in the second, and every residue that is random in one is also random in the other. Yet these two species have very different free energies for two reasons. The lower helical portion of the first species on the right is interactive; in the second species, it is not. Thus, a free energy of $-kT \ln w(T)$ for every turn of interacting helix in the first species gives it a more favorable free energy.

However, the residues in the randomly coiled region of the two species also have to be assigned different free energies. This is because the randomly coiled sections of the second species have all the degrees of freedom associated with linear random coils. On the other hand, the randomly coiled region of the first species is constrained to form a closed loop and, therefore, has much less freedom. The result is that these two randomly coiled regions have very different entropies. In fact, that difference, which is called loop entropy, can be very, very large—the more so the larger the unfolded internal segment.

This effect of loop entropy is so large that, in general, the population of species containing such internal random segments (as seen in

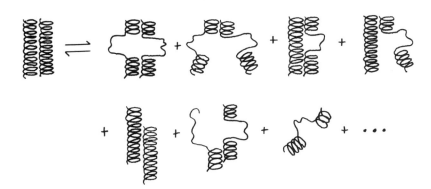

Fig. 6. Heuristic representation of unfolding equilibrium species in the continuum-of-states model.

the first and third species on the right-hand side of Fig. 6) may be discounted. We also count nonregistered structures such as the fifth species on the right-hand side because we don't see how we can logically exclude them. Statistical mechanics then allows conformational populations and conformationally dependent properties to be evaluated in terms of σ, $s(T)$, and $w(T)$ (Skolnick, 1983a, 1983b, 1984, 1985).

Noncross-linked Coiled Coils

How do we treat the data with the theory? This is shown in Fig. 7B, wherein appear smoothed data points for two extreme concentrations of tropomyosin (Holtzer *et al.,* 1983a; Skolnick and Holtzer, 1985). The first conclusion to be drawn from this theory employs the bottom (dashed) curve, which represents the single-chain curve from the Zimm-Bragg theory. This curve says that a single chain of tropomyosin would not be very helical if it were all by itself, about 25 percent helix at most. The tropomyosin coiled coil is almost 100 percent helix.

All we do next is to find, by trial, a value of the helix-helix interaction parameter $w(T)$ that, when inserted into the two-chain theory, provides a value of helix content in accord with the data. The resulting values of RT ln $w(T)$, a measure of the free energy of helix-helix interaction per mole of helical turn pairs, are shown in Fig. 7A. Notice that the interaction is approximately 500 calories per mole of turn pairs. Thus, this combination of theory and experiment allows us to extract from the data the contribution of the helix-helix interaction to the overall stability. We then are able to fit the data for helix content fairly well (Fig. 7B, solid lines).

We can also learn other things about the system that are rather difficult to measure. The uppermost (dashed) curve of Fig. 7B gives the helix content of the dimer molecules, the ones that are not dissociated. As can been seen, in this theory a great deal of the loss of helix is attributed to the separation of the chains. Neither chain would be very helical,

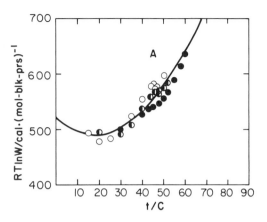

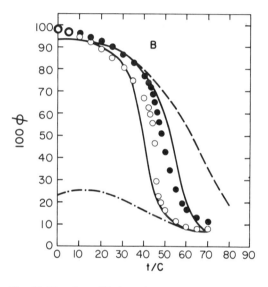

Fig. 7. Fit of equilibrium thermal unfolding of $\alpha\alpha$ tropomyosin in $NaCl_{500}NaPi_{50}DTT_1$ (7.4). **(A)** Values of the negative of the helix-helix interaction free energy versus T needed to fit data. Solid curve is best fit to the points. **(B)** Percent helix versus T. Circles are smoothed data for 0.0044 mg/cm³ (open) and 5.2 mg/cm³ (filled). Solid curves are theoretical at same two concentrations using interaction from A. Dashed curve is from theory for two-chain species. Dot-dashed curve is from theory for single-chain species. [Reprinted from *Macromolecules* **18,** 1549 (1985) with permission. Copyright 1985, American Chemical Society.]

according to this picture, if the chains were not associated.

Figure 8 shows another set of data, this set taken at *p*H 2 (Holtzer *et al.,* 1983b; Skolnick and Holtzer, 1985), the previous being taken near *p*H 7. It has been pointed out that, in some of the small, specific-sequence peptides,

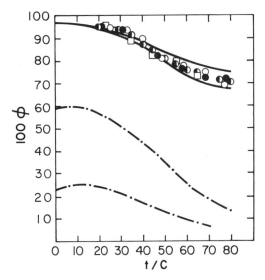

Fig. 8. Equilibrium thermal unfolding of $\alpha\alpha$ tropomyosin at acid pH, i.e., in NaCl$_{590}$HCl$_{10}$DTT$_{0.5}$ (2.0). Data points are for various protein concentrations. Solid curves are from theory for, respectively, the two extreme experimental concentrations. Upper dot-dashed curve is from theory for single chains at pH 2. Lower dot-dashed curve is from theory for single chains at near-neutral pH. [Redrawn from Skolnick and Holtzer, 1985]

the stability of the helix goes down as the pH decreases. Here is a counter example. It has been known — and puzzling — for 20 years that tropomyosin is much more strongly helical at low pH (Noelken, 1962; Noelken and Holtzer, 1964). Comparison of Figs. 7 and 8 shows this clearly. Why is that? First, when the net charge is higher (at pH 2), there should be more repulsion, which should make the helix *weaker*. Moreover, the carboxylates are discharged at pH 2, so the salt linkages that we described before must be gone. That also should weaken the helix. Why is it, instead, much more stable at pH 2?

We think that the answer can be seen at the bottom of Fig. 8 in the (dot-dashed) theoretical curves for single chains. The lower one is for pH 7, again showing only 25 percent helix at best. The upper one is the result for pH 2; it rises for single chains to something like 60 percent. The reason is clear: The experiments on host-guest polymers insist that discharged glutamic or aspartic residues have much higher σ and s(T), i.e., much greater

inherent tendency to form a helix in a single chain, than the corresponding charged residues (Scheraga, 1978; Holtzer et al., 1983b; Skolnick and Holtzer, 1985). Moreover, tropomyosin has a great many acidic residues, so it makes a big difference.

If we now fit these data for low pH, according to the theory, in order to obtain the helix-helix interaction, we find that they are not very different from what we get from the pH 7 data (Skolnick and Holtzer, 1985). In fact, they are a little bit smaller for the pH 2 data. What we think that is telling us is that, since the salt bridges are gone at pH 2, they probably contribute only a relatively small amount (perhaps 20 percent) to the helix-helix interaction. The bulk of it must come from the hydrophobic packing. That 20 percent, however, must be enough to dictate parallel chain packing rather than antiparallel chain packing. The theory thus gives us some insight into the importance of helix-helix interaction in maintaining the native structure and allows us both to estimate its magnitude and make the pH dependence of the stability intelligible.

As we have mentioned, the continuum-of-states model embodied in the theory indicates that chain dissociation and loss of helix are closely related. Notice that the two different concentrations of Fig. 3 seem to depart from one another near the beginning of the transition, which also implies that chain dissociation occurs at rather low temperatures. On the other hand, researchers who favor the all-or-none segments models ascribe dissociation to the last stage of the transition. We therefore tried to distinguish between these two models by measuring the molecular weight directly. We performed these experiments with our colleagues at Nagoya University, where they have outstanding light-scattering equipment. Figure 9 shows the weight average molar mass of tropomyosin as a function of temperature (Skolnick and Holtzer, 1985; Yukioka et al., 1985); the values have been divided by the chain molar mass, so at low T, the ordinate starts out at two chains and it goes to one chain at high T.

Unfortunately, experimental errors are

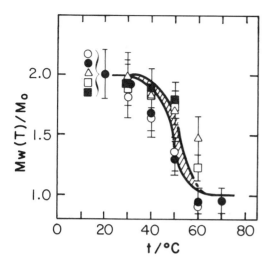

Fig. 9. Weight average number of chains per molecule from light scattering versus T by $\alpha\alpha$ tropomyosin at near-neutral pH. Medium is $NaCl_{500}NaPi_{50}$ (7.4). Data points are for various protein concentrations in the range 0.33–1.17 mg/cm³. Shaded band is from theory for same concentration range. [Reprinted from *Macromolecules* **18**, 1549 (1985) with permission. Copyright 1985, American Chemical Society.]

rather large, but there is no way to draw a curve through these data to indicate dissociation as the last step in the process (e.g., Fig. 5), as required by the all-or-none segments model. The shaded band shows our calculations from the continuum-of-states theory. The reason that it is a band and not a line is that the light-scattering experiments had to be done at various concentrations, and the band covers the full range of experimental concentrations (Yukioka *et al.*, 1985). We therefore believe that dissociation sets in essentially from the beginning of the transition, just as the continuum-of-states theory requires.

Nonuniformity in Noncross-linked Coiled Coils

We next return to a point mentioned earlier concerning nonuniformity within the coiled coil molecule, i.e., differences in stability between the N-terminal half and the C-terminal half. Figure 10 shows some of our theoretical fits (Skolnick and Holtzer, 1983) to data from Smillie's lab on the two segments (Pato *et al.*,

1981). Notice that the two lower theoretical curves, one for the C-terminal half peptide and the other for the N-terminal half, do not differ very much. Even though the amino acid sequences and composition are different in the two halves, the curves are very similar. Yet, at comparable concentrations, the N-terminal piece is much more highly helical than the C-terminal piece. When we apply the theory to this system, we find that the helix-helix interaction is responsible for the difference between the two ends of the tropomyosin molecule. There is an approximately 200-calorie difference between helix-helix interactions in the two segments.

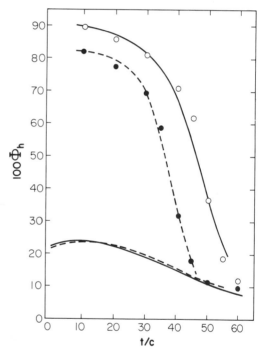

Fig. 10. Equilibrium thermal unfolding of segments of $\alpha\alpha$ tropomyosin at near-neutral pH, i.e., in KCl_{100} $KPi_{50}DTT_1$ (7.0). Data source is Pato *et al.*, 1981. Open circles, data for segment comprising residues 1–133 at 1.015 mg/cm³. Filled circles, data for segment comprising residues 134–284 at 0.723 mg/cm³. Upper solid curve, theoretical curve for N-terminal segment employing larger helix-helix interaction ($-RT \ln W_N$). Upper dashed curve, theoretical curve for C-terminal segment using smaller helix-helix interaction ($-RT \ln W_C$). Lower solid curve, theory for single chains of N-terminal segment. Lower dashed curve, theory for single chains of C-terminal segment. [Reprinted from *Macromolecules* **16**, 1548 (1983) with permission. Copyright 1983, American Chemical Society.]

The theory, once again, allows us to interpret stability differences in terms of long-range (i.e., tertiary and quaternary) interactions and short-range (secondary) interactions.

Cross-Linked Coiled Coils

We next turn to a somewhat different issue. In studies of the unfolding equilibria in globular proteins, much is made of the influence of disulfide bonds. The experiment summarized in Fig. 11 (Holtzer et al., 1986) investigates the effect of a disulfide bond on the unfolding of a coiled coil. The tropomyosin represented is $\alpha\alpha$ tropomyosin, which has two identical chains. Each has a single sulfhydryl in an interior position at position 190 (out of 284/chain); thus, it is about two-thirds of the way up from the amino terminus. These are our data, but this effect was first demonstrated by Lehrer (1978), who showed that a cross link placed at C190 results in a prominently biphasic denaturation curve, as shown in Fig. 11. Lehrer referred to the low-temperature phase as a "pretransition" because in that range the cross-linked material has less helix content than the noncross-linked. Since data for cross linked samples show a second phase in which they have greater helix content than noncross linked ones, we call the second phase a "posttransition." In other words, some of the molecule appears to be more stable and some of it less stable when the cross link is added. Lehrer thought about this physically, making molecular models, and found that one had to strain the model in order to link the sulfurs at the 190 positions. He proposed, therefore, that this local strain was causing the pretransition.

The all-or-none segments model thus led to the picture of the pretransition and posttransition shown in Fig. 12. The cross link strains the area near 190; therefore, at a relatively low temperature (i.e., in the pretransition), one gets an equilibrium between native coiled coils and a species with a randomly coiled bubble in the C190 region of the otherwise intact double helix. Then at higher temperature, one eventually gets a transfor-

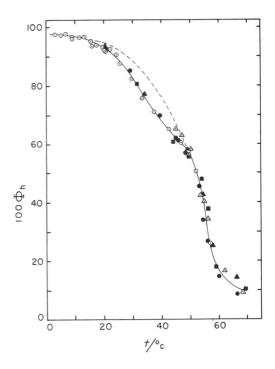

Fig. 11. Equilibrium thermal unfolding curve of C190-cross linked $\alpha\alpha$ tropomyosin at near-neutral pH, i.e., in NaCl$_{500}$ NaPi$_{50}$ (7.4). Data points are for concentrations in the range 0.0057–8.5 mg/cm^3. Solid curve is spline curve through the data. Dashed curve is hypothetical, monophasic continuation of the high-temperature transition (posttransition). [Reprinted from Biochemistry 25, 1688 (1986) with permission. Copyright 1986, American Chemical Society.]

mation to a cross-linked pair of random coils. Clearly, this is an ad hoc model, but it has some merit. We did not trust it completely, since interior randomly coiled bubbles are un-

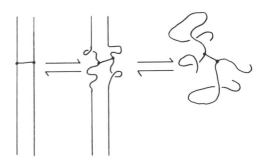

Fig. 12. Heuristic representation of unfolding equilibrium species in the all-or-none-segments model for C190-cross linked $\alpha\alpha$ tropomyosin.

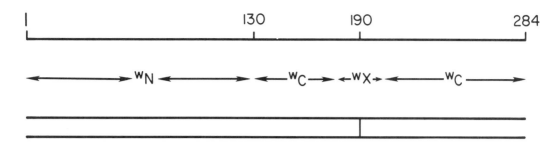

Fig. 13. Schematic representation of pattern of helix-helix interaction parameters used in simulating equilibrium unfolding curves for C190-cross linked $\alpha\alpha$ tropomyosin. The tropomyosin coiled coil is represented above as two parallel lines with the cross link joining them. Scale of residue number is at top. Middle of diagram shows regions in which indicated values of helix-helix interaction parameter were used. Strong interaction (W_N) characterizes residues 1–130. Weak interaction (W_C) characterizes residues 131–284, except for region very near the crosslink (residues 180–210) where an extremely unfavorable interaction (W_X) is used to characterize the strain at the crosslink.

stable because of loop entropy. We were concerned that this idea would not work out very well if we tried to mimic it by the theory.

The theory for cross linked molecules is rather long-winded, and the resulting calculations are complex, so we decided to model the system in prototypical fashion, rather than to perform a detailed fit (Skolnick and Holtzer, 1986). The prototypical model adopted is shown in Fig. 13. We know that the N-terminal piece has a larger helix-helix interaction; the left arrow marks a region (in round numbers, residues 1–130) where we can have strong interactions (w_N). The right part, the C-terminal half, has weaker interactions (w_C); in non-cross-linked molecules, this comprises residues 130–284. Values for $w_N(T)$ and $w_C(T)$ can be chosen to be in line with the values found from data on the individual segments; with these values, the theory mimics data for noncross linked tropomyosin. For cross linked molecules, we embodied Lehrer's assessment of the strain near C190 by inserting in the region near C190 a value for the interaction (w_X) that is highly unfavorable to helix formation, thus mimicking the alleged strain of the cross link. Figure 13 summarizes this description of the nonuniformity. Our goal was to see if the theory then produced a two-phase transition corresponding to the species pictured in Fig. 11.

What we found was that one has to put in both the nonuniformity and a strained section near the disulfide, or one cannot mimic the

shape of the experimental curve (Skolnick and Holtzer, 1986). But with both features, one can mimic the curve, as Fig. 14 shows. Here we see that the simulation gives a pretransition

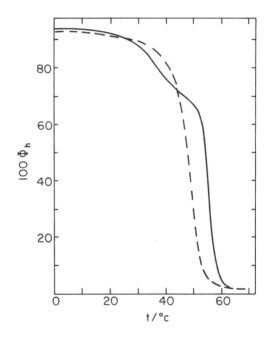

Fig. 14. Theoretical equilibrium thermal unfolding curves employing scheme of Fig. 13. Solid theoretical curve for cross-linked species simulates the biphasic experimental curve (see Fig. 11). Dashed curve is also from theory and simulates corresponding noncross-linked species (at 0.104 mg/cm^3) by employing W_N for residues 1–130 and W_C for residues 131–284. [Reprinted from *Biochemistry* **25**, 1688 (1986) with permission. Copyright 1986, American Chemical Society.]

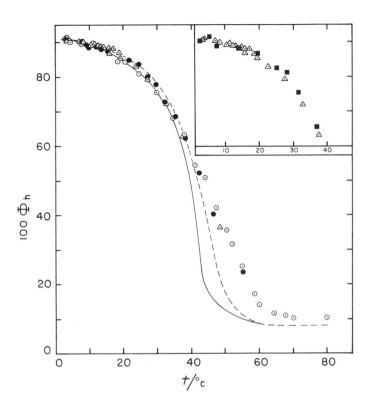

Fig. 15. Experimental equilibrium unfolding data for $\beta\beta$ tropomyosin in NaCl$_{500}$ NaPi$_{50}$ (7.4). Data points are in the range 0.74–1.15 mg/cm^3 for $\beta\beta$ species disulfide cross linked at both C36 and C190. Solid (dashed) curve is spline curve through data for non-cross linked $\beta\beta$ species at 0.100(4.72) mg/cm^3. Inset shows experiment to double check for absence of pretransition. Open triangles, same points as on main graph. Filled squares are data taken from same solutions after *in situ* reduction in the CD cell. [Reprinted from *Biochemistry* **25**, 1688 (1986) with permission. Copyright 1986, American Chemical Society.]

and a posttransition as in the experiment. We found that if one looks at the population in detail, one finds there are no internal randomly coiled species such as are seen in Fig. 12. Loop entropy renders such internal loops unstable enough to make their population negligible. Instead, the molecules predominantly unfold in from the weak (C-terminal) end in the pretransition. The reason for the posttransition also became clear. The region of residues 130–190 has only relatively weak helix-helix interaction (w_c or w_x). However, that region is caught between the cross link and the strongly interacting region (residues 1–130). Unfolding residues 130–190 at moderate temperatures can only produce a randomly coiled loop. The process is disfavored by loop entropy, and the coiled coil in the 130–190 region is thereby strongly stabilized in the 190-cross linked species.

Another experiment has bearing on this question (Holtzer *et al.*, 1986). We wanted very much to see whether loop entropy really was as important as the continuum-of-states theory avers. We chose a genetic variant of

tropomyosin that has two (β) chains, each with two cysteines, C36 and C190. Thus, one can have three different cross linked species: cross linked at C190 only, at C36 only, or at both. Since C36 and C190 are in the same "a" interior position within the heptet, we argued that if the cross link is destabilizing the helix at C190, then it must also do so at C36. Thus, in a doubly cross linked species, if nothing else were important, one would expect to see an enormous pretransition; indeed, one suspects that the whole structure might melt in the pretransition.

One experiment on doubly cross linked species is shown in Fig. 15 (Holtzer *et al.*, 1986) and obviously demonstrates no pretransition whatsoever. In fact, the doubly cross linked species is more stable than the non-cross linked ones at all temperatures. Clearly, the idea of a disulfide strain is inadequate as the sole basis for prediction. The reason for the remarkable stability of the doubly cross linked species, we think, is that if one has two cross links—one at C190 and one at C36— then unfolding the region between them

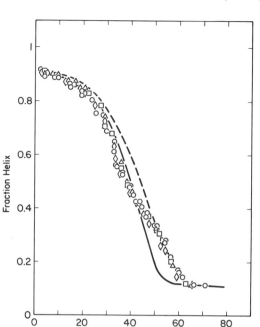

Fig. 16. Experimental equilibrium unfolding data for $\beta\beta$ species in NaCl₅₀₀ NaPi₅₀ (7.4). Data points are for species cross linked at C190 and sulfhydryl blocked at C36 in concentration range 1.18–3.48 mg/cm³. Solid curve is spline curve through data for noncross linked species at 2 mg/cm³. Dashed curve is spline curve through data for doubly cross linked species (Fig. 15). [Reprinted from *Biopolymers* **27**, 1223 (1988) with permission. Copyright 1988, John Wiley & Sons, Inc.]

necessarily forms a 308-residue randomly coiled loop, and that is enormously destabilized because of loop entropy.

Figure 16 shows a recent experiment (Bracken *et al.,* 1988) that closes a loophole in the argument made above concerning the doubly cross linked species. The argument assumes that a $\beta\beta$ species cross linked only at C190 would show a biphasic transition, i.e., a pretransition and a posttransition, similar to C190-cross linked $\alpha\alpha$ species. The absence of a pretransition in doubly cross linked $\beta\beta$ thus requires explanation. However, if $\beta\beta$ species cross linked only at C190 also do not show a pretransition, then the entire basis for interpreting the effect of a cross link is invalid.

Unfortunately, nobody had ever shown that there is a pretransition in C190-cross linked $\beta\beta$ species because such a demonstration requires a difficult selective cross linking

at C190 and not at C36. Nevertheless, we have recently produced the $\beta\beta$ species selectively cross linked at C190 only (Bracken *et al.,* 1988). As seen in Fig. 16, this species indeed displays a pretransition and a posttransition. Thus, the lack of a pretransition and the extraordinary stability of the doubly cross linked species must be due to loop entropy. We believe these experiments demonstrate that loop entropy must be an ingredient in any successful model of coiled coil folding equilibria.

Conclusion

We believe that these results show that the experimental findings on unfolding equilibria in coiled coils cannot be accommodated by the ad hoc physical ideas embodied in the all-or-none segments model. The continuum-of-states model, on the other hand, is not demonstrably at variance with experiment. Although many questions remain, the continuum-of-states model with the associated statistical mechanical theory fits data for the temperature dependence of helix content and molecular mass reasonably well, provides an estimate of the helix-helix interaction, makes the enhanced stability of coiled coils in acid intelligible, simulates the experiments on singly cross linked species, and explains the hyperstability of doubly cross linked species. We believe, therefore, that it better represents the physics underlying coiled coil unfolding equilibria.

Acknowledgment

This work has been supported by Grant No. GM-20064 from the Division of General Medical Sciences, United States Public Health Service and by a grant from the Muscular Dystrophy Association.

References

Bracken, W. C., J. Carey, M. E. Holtzer, A. Holtzer, *Biopolymers* **27**, 1223 (1988).

Caspar, D. L. D., C. Cohen, W. Longley, *J. Mol. Biol.* **41**, 87 (1969).

Cohen, C., and A. G. Szent-Györgyi, *J. Am. Chem. Soc.* **79**, 248 (1957).

Crick, F. H. C., *Acta Crystallographica* **6**, 689 (1953).

Doty, P., J. H. Bradbury, A. Holtzer, *J. Am. Chem. Soc.* **78**, 947 (1956).

Doty, P., A. Holtzer, J. H. Bradbury, E. Blout, *J. Am. Chem. Soc.* **76**, 4492 (1954).

Fraser, R. D. B., and T. P. MacRae, *Conformation in Fibrous Proteins* (Academic, New York, 1973), pp. 419–468.

Hodges, R. S., J. Slodek, L. B. Smillie, L. Jurasek, *Cold Spring Harbor Symp. Quant. Biol.* **37**, 299 (1972).

Holtzer, A., R. Clark, S. Lowey, *Biochemistry* **4**, 2401 (1965).

Holtzer, A., and M. E. Holtzer, *Macromolecules* **20**, 671 (1987).

Holtzer, M. E., K. Askins, A. Holtzer, *Biochemistry* **25**, 1688 (1986).

Holtzer, M. E., A. Holtzer, J. Skolnick, *Macromolecules* **16**, 173 (1983a).

_____, *Macromolecules* **16**, 462 (1983b).

Isom, L. L., M. E. Holtzer, A. Holtzer, *Macromolecules* **17**, 2445 (1984).

Johnson, P., and L. Smillie, *Biochem. Biophys. Res. Commun.* **64**, 1316 (1975).

Kumar, S., M. E. Holtzer, A. Holtzer, *Biophys. J.* **53**, 97a (1988).

Lehrer, S., *Proc. Natl. Acad. Sci., U.S.A.* **72**, 3377 (1975).

Lehrer, S., *J. Mol. Biol.* **118**, 209 (1978).

Mak, A., W. Lewis, L. B. Smillie, *FEBS Lett.* **105**, 232 (1979).

Mak, A., L. B. Smillie, G. Stewart, *J. Biol. Chem.* **255**, 3647 (1980).

Noelken, M., Ph.D. thesis, Washington University (1962).

Noelken, N., and A. Holtzer, in *Biochemistry of Muscle Contraction,* J. Gergely, Ed. (Little, Brown, Boston, 1964), pp. 374–378.

Pato, M., A. Mak, L. B. Smillie, *J. Biol. Chem.* **256**, 593 (1981).

Poland, D., and H. Scheraga, *Theory of Helix-Coil Transitions in Biopolymers* (Academic, New York, 1970) p. 188f.

Potekhin, S., and P. Privalov, *J. Mol. Biol.* **159**, 519 (1982).

Privalov, P., *Adv. Protein Chem.* **33**, 167 (1979).

Scheraga, H., *Pure Appl. Chem.* **50**, 315 (1978).

Skolnick, J., *Macromolecules* **16**, 1069 (1983a).

_____, *Macromolecules* **16**, 1763 (1983b).

_____, *Macromolecules* **17**, 645 (1984).

_____, *Biochem. Biophys. Res. Commun.* **129**, 848 (1985).

Skolnick, J., and A. Holtzer, *Macromolecules* **15**, 303 (1982a).

_____, *Macromolecules* **15**, 812 (1982b).

_____, *Macromolecules* **16**, 1548 (1983).

_____, *Macromolecules* **18**, 1549 (1985).

_____, *Biochemistry* **25**, 6192 (1986).

Stewart, M., *FEBS Lett.* **53**, 5 (1975).

Woods, E., *Biochemistry* **8**, 4336 (1969).

Yukioka, S., I. Noda, M. Nagasawa, M. E. Holtzer, A. Holtzer, *Macromolecules* **18**, 1083 (1985).

Zimm, B., and J. Bragg, *J. Chem. Phys.* **31**, 526 (1959).

19

The Alpha Subunit
of Tryptophan Synthase
Probing the Multistate Folding Mechanism
by Mutagenesis

C. Robert Matthews

The mechanism by which the amino acid sequence of a protein directs the rapid and efficient folding to the native conformation has been a subject of intense interest since Anfinsen and his colleagues first proposed this hypothesis in 1961. A decade of effort on a large number of proteins, using numerous spectroscopic and thermodynamic methods and a variety of ways of inducing reversible unfolding (e.g., changes in temperature, pH, chemical denaturants) provided support for the hypothesis but little insight into the molecular events that occur during folding.

The principal reason for this failure is the cooperative nature of the folding reaction. Only the native and unfolded forms appear at measurable concentrations under equilibrium conditions for most proteins. Stable, partially folded conformations that would provide data on the types of substructures that arise and the order of their appearance are generally not observed. Kinetic studies on folding reactions have demonstrated that intermediates do appear transiently during folding (Kim and Baldwin, 1982); however, the lifetimes of these transient intermediates are so short (10^{-3} to 1 second) that detailed structural studies have been impossible. Recent developments involv-

ing the combination of rapid-mixing technology and two-dimensional nuclear magnetic resonance (NMR) spectroscopy suggest that information may soon be available on the hydrogen bonding patterns in transient intermediates in cytochrome c (Roder *et al.*, 1988) and ribonuclease A (Udgaonkar and Baldwin, 1988).

The Alpha Subunit of
Trp Synthase

An interesting exception to the all-or-nothing folding observed for most proteins is the alpha subunit of tryptophan synthase. The tryptophan synthase holoenzyme is an $\alpha_2 \beta_2$ tetramer that is responsible for the synthesis of tryptophan (Yanofsky and Crawford, 1972). The separated alpha subunit retains partial enzymatic activity, as does the β_2 dimer, implying that the isolated subunits are folded in a very similar fashion as in the intact tetramer. Physical properties that make the alpha subunit an ideal candidate for folding studies include the fact that it is a single polypeptide chain (29 Kdalton), that it has no disulfide bonds, and that it contains no prosthetic groups. These properties mean that folding will be a unimolecular phenomenon and that there are no covalent cross links (disulfide bonds) in the unfolded form that would constrain the folding pathway.

A series of studies on the reversible unfolding of the alpha subunit have provided convincing evidence that folding proceeds through a stable, highly populated intermediate, as well as some ideas about the structure of this novel form. Optical experiments on the chemically induced unfolding reaction demonstrated that both the secondary structure (Yutani et al., 1979) and the tertiary structure (Matthews and Crisanti, 1981) are disrupted in stages. As an example, the transition curve obtained by monitoring the change in extinction coefficient at 287 nm as a function of urea concentration is shown in Fig. 1. The break in the transition curve at ~3M urea indicates that the exposure of buried tyrosine residues to solvent does not occur in a single, molecule-wide reaction. Rather, another conformation, intermediate between native and unfolded forms, must exist.

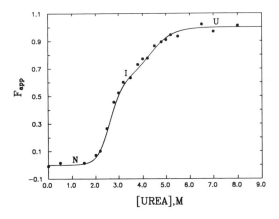

Fig. 1. The urea-induced equilibrium unfolding transition of the alpha subunit of tryptophan synthase at pH 7.8, 25°C. Changes in extinction coefficient at 287 nm were monitored as a function of the urea concentration and converted to apparent fraction unfolded, F_{app}, by $F_{app} = (\varepsilon_{OBS}-\varepsilon_{NAT})/(\varepsilon_{UNF}-\varepsilon_{NAT})$. ε_{OBS} is the observed extinction coefficient at a given urea concentration while ε_{NAT} and ε_{UNF} are the extinction coefficients for the native and unfolded forms, respectively, at the same urea concentration. These latter values were estimated in the transition zone by linear extrapolations of the appropriate baseline regions.

Evidence for Independent Folding Units

The first clues as to the conformation of this intermediate were provided by Higgins et al. (1979), who found that the alpha subunit could be cleaved at a single arginine residue by a limited tryptic digestion of the intact $\alpha_2\beta_2$ tetramer. Separation of the two alpha fragments and subsequent characterization showed that cleavage occurred at Arg 188. Guanidine hydrochloride-induced unfolding of the isolated fragments demonstrated that the larger amino fragment, residues 1–188, undergoes a cooperative unfolding reaction, while the smaller carboxyl fragment, residues 189–268, does not (Miles et al., 1982). Furthermore, the midpoint of the unfolding reaction for the amino fragment is very similar to that for the conversion of the intermediate to the unfolded form for the intact protein (Fig. 1). The conclusion was drawn that the folding intermediate has a folded amino folding unit and an unfolded carboxyl folding unit. This model is depicted in schematic form in Fig. 2.

A critical question that can be asked of this model is whether the intermediate that appears at equilibrium in several molar denaturant is relevant to the normal folding reaction, which takes place during or after synthesis in the cell and in the absence of denaturant. To answer this question, we (Beasty and Matthews, 1985) designed an experiment that probed the formation of stable hydrogen bonds in the early stage in folding, i.e., in the conversion of U to I. If I actually involves a folded amino fragment and an unfolded carboxyl fragment, then one would expect a significantly greater formation of secondary structure (stable hydrogen bonds) in the amino fragment than the carboxyl fragment. The success of this experiment depended upon prior observations in our laboratory (Matthews and Crisanti, 1981) that the U → I reaction occurs on the millisecond time scale, while the I → N reaction requires ~10^2 seconds. The 10^4 to 10^5 difference in rates can be used to trap tritium selectively in hydrogen bonds that form in the U → I reaction. This can be done by allowing folding from U to I to occur in tritiated water, remov-

Simplified Folding Model
for α Subunit of Trp Synthase

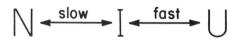

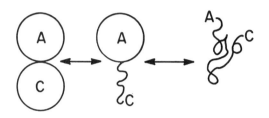

Fig. 2. Simplified folding model for the alpha subunit. The stable intermediate has been found to have a folded amino terminal region and an unfolded carboxyl terminal region. Relative values for the relaxation times for the two kinetic processes at 25°C, pH 7.8 are shown. Note that this simplified model does not include additional unfolded and intermediate forms, which are thought to reflect slow isomerization reactions (Hurle and Matthews, 1987).

ing tritium from the solvent by a rapid gel exclusion column, and then allowing folding from I to N to continue in water. The labeled protein is then digested under limiting conditions by trypsin and the fragments separated on a high-performance liquid chromatography (HPLC) column. The results are shown in Table 1.

Digestion of the isolated alpha subunit results in cleavage at both Arg 70 and Arg 188 and the production of three fragments: 1–70,

71–188, and 189–268. The first two fragments correspond to the amino fragment isolated by Higgins *et al.* (1979) and the third to the carboxyl fragment. As a control, the protein was allowed to fold completely in tritiated water to label all stable hydrogen bonds. As can be seen in Table 1, fragments 1–70 and 71–188 both form over 90 percent of their stable hydrogen bonds in the conversion of U to I. In contrast, the carboxyl fragment forms only ~43 percent of its stable hydrogen bonds in the same time frame. From these data, it is possible to conclude that the amino terminus of the protein folds independently and is indeed more stable than the carboxyl folding unit under conditions strongly favoring the native conformation. Therefore, the intermediate that appears at equilibrium in the chemically induced unfolding reaction also appears during the actual folding reaction.

The Alpha Subunit Is a Single Structural Domain

Given these results, we were extremely surprised to learn that the alpha subunit adopts an α/β barrel conformation (Hyde *et al.*, 1988). Eight parallel beta strands arranged in a barrel-like form comprise the structural core; alpha helices are arranged on the exterior (Fig. 3). Strands and helices alternate as the primary sequence is scanned. This basic structural pattern has been observed for over a dozen proteins (Chothia, 1988), making the alpha subunit a potential model for the folding of a whole class of proteins.

The structure was surprising because the

Table 1. Stable hydrogen bond formation in the folding of the alpha subunit of Trp synthase.

Labeling condition	³H/peptide[a]		
	Fragment 1–70	Fragment 71–188	Fragment 189–268
Intermediate labeled	19.0 ± 3.7	75.0 ± 4.0	10.5 ± 1.4
Fully labeled	20.8 ± 2.5	80.2 ± 7.5	24.1 ± 2.9
Ratio (A/B × 100)	91 ± 21	93 ± 10	43 ± 8

[a]From Beasty and Matthews, 1985.

Fig. 3. Simplified drawing of the alpha subunit of Trp synthase. The ribbons correspond to beta strands and the cylinders to alpha helices. The numbers on the strands and helices reflect the order of appearance of these elements of secondary structure, beginning at the amino terminus. The chemical moiety, represented by filled circles, is indole propanol phosphate, a competitive inhibitor of the enzyme. Approximate positions of single amino acid replacements are indicated. (Adapted from Hyde *et al.*, 1988.)

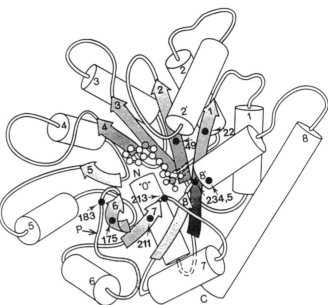

presence of a stable folding intermediate had led us to expect two structural domains. Fragments from single structural domain proteins, such as the alpha subunit, have generally been found to be devoid of organized structure (Epand and Scheraga, 1968; Taniuchi and Anfinsen, 1969), although some peptides have secondary structure under favorable conditions (Bierzynski *et al.*, 1982; Oas and Kim, 1988). The requirement for the complete sequence to achieve stability has led to the concept that the cooperative unit in folding corresponds to the entire structural domain. The multistate folding process of the alpha subunit shows that this connection is not absolute and provides an unparalleled opportunity to break down a complex folding reaction into simpler steps.

The amino folding unit, as defined by tryptic cleavage at Arg 188, consists of beta strands 1–6 and alpha-helices 0–5; the carboxyl folding unit consists of strands 7 and 8 and helices 6–8 (Fig. 3). Thus, the stable amino folding unit consists of a contiguous polypeptide that is very close to three-quarters of the α/β barrel. The implication is that the highly symmetric barrel motif is assembled from folding units that correspond to recognizable elements of secondary structure. It will be interesting to determine if this 6 + 2

process for the formation of the 8-stranded barrel is a general phenomenon in the folding of barrels or is specific to the alpha subunit.

Mutations as Probes of the Folding Mechanism

To probe the molecular details of the folding of the alpha subunit, we employed genetic engineering techniques to make single amino acid replacements. The earlier-described biophysical studies on the equilibrium and kinetic properties of the folding of the wild-type alpha subunit provide the framework within which the effects of such replacements can be understood. In particular, the effects of replacements on the rate-limiting step in folding, i.e., the interconversion of the native and intermediate forms, can be readily measured. In physical chemical terms, the information can be used to probe the nature of the transition state linking these two forms and the interactions that stabilize them.

The procedure that we have adopted to analyze the effects of amino acid replacements involves the use of reaction coordinate diagrams and has been described in detail elsewhere (Matthews, 1987). Previous studies had shown that the slow step in unfolding is the reverse of the rate-limiting step in refolding, i.e., the N ↔ I reaction is rate limiting in both directions (Hurle *et al.*, 1987). The ability to measure directly the unfolding, N → I, and refolding, I → N, relaxation times and the equilibrium constant, K = [I]/[N], provides all the data required to construct the corresponding reaction coordinate diagram.

Amino acid replacements that change the stability and either the unfolding or refolding relaxation time *but not both* report on side chains that selectively alter the energy of the native or intermediate state, respectively. Such replacements are instructive on the interactions that stabilize the native or intermediate conformations. This class of mutations has been designated as equilibrium mutants (Matthews, 1987). Kinetic mutations, which permit a mapping of the transition state, selectively alter the energy of the transition state relative to native and intermediate states. The experimental consequences would be to alter the relaxation times of both unfolding and refolding; the stability may or may not be affected.

Application of this approach to a series of single amino acid replacements in the alpha subunit from *Escherichia coli* generated by Yanofsky and his colleagues (1967) has led to

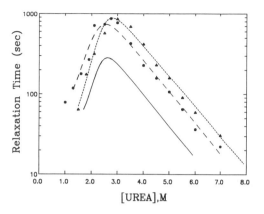

Fig. 5. Effects of the Phe 22 → Leu (●–●–●) and Gly 234 → Asp (▲–▲–▲) replacements on the relaxation times for the rate-limiting step in unfolding and refolding of the alpha subunit at *p*H 7.8, 25°C. The solid line represents the results for the wild-type alpha subunit (Phe 22). Only the data for the urea-dependent rate-limiting step in unfolding and refolding are shown.

the observation of both types of mutants and the beginnings of an understanding of the transition state linking N and I. For example, the replacement of Tyr 175 with Cys results in a selective increase in the unfolding relaxation time; the refolding relaxation time is not changed (Fig. 4). The simplest interpretation of this result is that the energy of the native conformation is decreased by a small amount, ~0.6 Kcal mol^{-1}, relative to the transition state and intermediate conformation. Thus, it appears that position 175 does not participate in the transition state but rather participates in interactions that form when the native conformation appears (i.e., after the transition state is passed). Kinetic mutations were observed at position 22 when Phe was replaced by Leu and at position 234 when Gly was replaced by Asp (Fig. 5). In both cases, unfolding *and* refolding relaxation times were increased when the results were compared to the wild-type alpha subunit.

Given these results and the x-ray structure for the alpha subunit from *Salmonella typhimurium* (Hyde *et al.*, 1988), one can now ask detailed questions about the structure of the transition state for the N ↔ I reaction. Note that the *E. coli* and *S. typhimurium* alpha subunits are 85 percent homologous and that the alpha subunit from *S. typhimurium* is

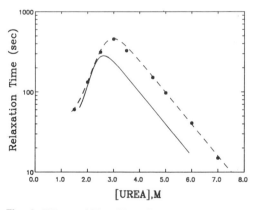

Fig. 4. Effects of Tyr 175 → Cys replacement on the relaxation times for the rate-limiting step in unfolding and refolding of the alpha subunit at pH 7.8, 25°C. The data points and dashed line represent the results for the Tyr 175 → Cys replacement; the solid line represents the results for wild-type alpha subunit (Tyr 175). Only the data for the urea-dependent rate-limiting step in unfolding and refolding are shown.

capable of forming a complex with and enhancing the activity of the β_2 subunit from *E. coli* (Schneider *et al.*, 1981). Therefore, it is reasonable to assume that the three-dimensional structures of these two proteins are very similar. The nine positions in which Yanofsky obtained mutations that decreased activity but left the secondary and tertiary structure intact all frame the active site (Fig. 3). Most of these positions are in or are just after several of the beta strands that comprise the staves in the barrel.

Two striking observations emerge. First, the sidechains at position 22 in strand 1 and at position 234 just after strand 8 are in proximity. Because replacements at both sites result in kinetic mutations, it appears that this region defines a part of the transition state for the N ↔ I reaction. Second, position 175, in strand 6, and position 211, in strand 7, are also in contact; however, these replacements appear to alter selectively the energy of the native conformation. The situation at position 211 is complex because Arg and Glu at 211 give kinetic effects; however, Val and Ser give results that are best interpreted as equilibrium effects. Long-range electrostatic interactions are a possible explanation for the dual nature of replacements at position 211 (Tweedy *et al.*, 1990).

Therefore, although the folding of the intermediate to the native conformation involves the docking of strands 1 and 8 and strands 6 and 7, only the first event appears to be involved in the transition state. The association of strands 6 and 7 appears to occur after the transition state is passed, in the folding reaction. Further replacements are required to test this hypothesis and to define more precisely the structure of the transition state and the preceding and succeeding events. However, at this time, it certainly appears that the folding unit association reaction follows a specific sequence of events.

Conclusions

The biophysical and mutagenic studies on the folding of the alpha subunit of Trp synthase, in conjunction with the x-ray structure, provide several insights into the folding mechanism: (i) The folding of a single structural domain can occur in stages. (ii) For the alpha subunit, the folding units correspond to recognizable elements of secondary structure. (iii) The rate-limiting step in folding is the association of the amino and carboxyl folding units.

These observations lead immediately to many new questions whose answers will require both biophysical and mutagenic studies of the sort described earlier. However, it seems quite feasible at this stage to identify the specific interactions that play key roles in the rate-limiting step in folding. Because the α/β barrel motif of the alpha subunit is representative of the structure of a large number of proteins, this information may well provide general understanding of the folding of a whole class of proteins.

Acknowledgments

This work was supported by the National Institutes of Health, General Medical Sciences grant GM23303.

References

Anfinsen, C. B., E. Haber, M. Sela, F. H. White Jr., *Proc. Natl. Acad. Sci. U.S.A.* **47**, 1309 (1961).

Beasty, A. M., and C. R. Matthews, *Biochemistry* **24**, 3547 (1985).

Bierzynski, A., P. S. Kim, R. L. Baldwin, *Proc. Natl. Acad. Sci. U.S.A.* **79**, 2470 (1982).

Chothia, C., *Nature* **333**, 598 (1988).

Epand, R. M., and H. A. Scheraga, *Biochemistry* **7**, 2864 (1968).

Higgins, W., T. Fairwell, E. W. Miles, *Biochemistry* **18**, 4827 (1979).

Hurle, M. R., G. A. Michelotti, M. M. Crisanti, C. R. Matthews, *Proteins* **2**, 54 (1987).

Hurle, M. R., and C. R. Matthews, *Biochim. Biophys. Acta* **913**, 179 (1987).

Hyde, C. C., S. A. Ahmed, E. A. Padlan, E. W. Miles, D. R. Davies, *J. Biol. Chem.* **263**, 17857 (1988).

Kim, P. S., and R. L. Baldwin, *Ann. Rev. Biochem.* **51**, 459 (1982).

Matthews, C. R., and M. M. Crisanti, *Biochemistry,* **20**, 784 (1981).

Matthews, C. R., *Methods in Enzymol.* **154**, 498 (1987).

Miles, E. W., K. Yutani, K. Ogasahara, *Biochemistry* **21**, 2586 (1982).

Oas, T. G., and P. S. Kim, *Nature* **336**, 42 (1988).

Roder, H., G. A. Elove, S. W. Englander, *Nature* **335**, 700 (1988).

Schneider, W. P., B. P. Nichols, C. Yanofsky, *Proc. Natl. Acad. Sci. U.S.A.* **78**, 2169 (1981).

Taniuchi, H., and C. B. Anfinsen, *J. Biol. Chem.* **244**, 3864 (1969).

Tweedy, N. B., M. R. Hurle, B. A. Chrunyk, C. R. Matthews, *Biochemistry* **29**, 1539 (1990).

Udgaonkar, J. B., and R. L. Baldwin, *Nature* **355**, 694 (1988).

Yanofsky, C., *The Harvey Lectures* **61**, 145 (1967).

Yanofsky, C., and I. P. Crawford, in *The Enzymes*, P.D. Boyer, Ed. (Academic Press, New York, 1972), vol. 7, p. 1.

Yutani, K., K. Ogasahara, M. Suzuki, Y. Sugino, *J. Biochem. (Tokyo)* **85**, 915 (1979).

20

Proline Isomerization and Folding of Yeast Cytochrome c

Barry T. Nall

How is the linear information in the amino acid sequence converted into three-dimensional structure? Since it is the process of protein folding that transforms one-dimensional information into three-dimensional structure, our primary interest is in how changes in information—that is, changes in amino acid sequence—affect protein folding reactions.

The model system selected for our investigations is cytochrome c. The cytochrome c protein family contains numerous members with different amino acid sequences, but all family members fold to essentially the same three-dimensional structure (Dickerson, 1972; Dickerson, 1980). Among mitochondrial cytochromes c there are a number of conserved sites, i.e., positions at which the same amino acid occurs in all of the known varieties. For example, the active site residues comprising the heme ligands are conserved while other residues at other locations are highly variable.

The fact that different sequences fold to essentially the same structure is informative. It tells us, for example, that the folding code is highly degenerate. It also suggests that experimental studies of how changes in sequence affect folding should concentrate on the conserved residues. Our hypothesis is that while conserved residues may be retained for a variety of reasons, they are conserved in part for their critical role in facilitating folding.

Yeast cytochrome c

Since conserved residues are the same within a protein family, to look at amino acid changes at conserved sites and how they affect folding, we must look at mutant proteins. Over a 25-year period, Fred Sherman and his colleagues at the University of Rochester School of Medicine and Dentistry have isolated and characterized a large number of mutant cytochromes c (Hampsey et al., 1986). Mutations have been obtained almost everywhere in the primary structure, including many replacements at or next to conserved sites. In many cases, multiple mutations at the same site provide some crosschecks with regard to whether observed changes in folding result from the location of the perturbation in the primary structure or from the nature of the perturbing residue.

Total in vivo activity of mutant cytochromes c can be estimated by growth of yeast on nonfermentable carbon sources and in vivo protein levels measured by low temperature visible spectrophotometry. By these criteria, some mutations entirely eliminate function while others generate altered proteins with specific activities less than or equal to that of the native protein. The genes for the two yeast iso-cytochromes c were among the first to be cloned (Montgomery et al., 1980), and iso-1-cytochrome c in particular has been developed into an important model system for the study of the effects of mutations on electron transfer reactions in biological systems (Pielak *et al.*, 1985).

Kinetic properties of folding of yeast cytochromes c: The multiple physical variable test

Consider the following experiment (Fig. 1). Start with completely unfolded protein at a high guanidine hydrochloride concentration and dilute out the denaturant in a rapid mixing device – a stopped flow. A 1:5 or 1:10 dilution is usually sufficient to insure complete refolding in the final conditions of the experiment. Refolding rates are monitored by three different physical properties: ultraviolet absorbance, absorbance at 695 nm, and tryptophan fluorescence.

Fluorescence at 350 nm reflects changes in the environment of the single tryptophan residue in cytochrome c. Fluorescence has a fairly simple interpretation for cytochrome c.

The heme, a strong fluorescence quencher, is covalently attached to the polypeptide chain. So the heme remains associated with the polypeptide in the unfolded state, and, as the protein refolds, the heme will move closer to the tryptophan residue, quenching the fluorescence. Roughly, changes in fluorescence as the protein refolds reflect changes in distance between the heme and the tryptophan.

Ultraviolet absorbance changes at 287 nm reflect changes in the polarity of the environment about the five tyrosine and single tryptophan side chains distributed throughout the protein. The 695 nanometer absorbance band for cytochrome c has been assigned to Met-80 ligation of the heme (Schechter and Saludjian, 1967). So visible absorbance changes at 695 nm monitor a unique step in folding, ligation of the heme by Met-80.

The refolding properties of yeast cytochromes c are readily summarized.[1] In a fast time range on a 0.1 second per division time scale, we have a kinetic event that has the

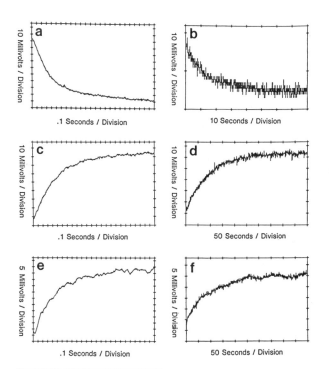

Fig. 1. Iso-2 refolding kinetics monitored by absorbance and fluorescence changes. In the initial conditions, the protein is fully unfolded in 2.0*M* Gdn.HCl. In a stopped-flow mixing experiment the Gdn.HCl is diluted to 0.4*M* to induce refolding. Both fast (A, C, E) and slow (B, D, F) phases are shown monitored by fluorescence at 350 nm with excitation at 287 nm (A, B), absorbance at 287 nm (C, D), and absorbance at 695 nm (E, F). Other conditions are 0.1*M* sodium phosphate, *p*H 7.2, 20°C. [Reprinted from *Biochemistry* **22**, 1423, 1983, with permission. Copyright 1983, American Chemical Society.]

---

1   Yeast contains two isozymes, iso-1 and iso-2. Despite minor differences in their amino acid sequence, to a first approximation, the folding behavior of the two related proteins is the same. The kinetics of folding of cytochromes c with large differences in amino acid sequence is very similar, suggesting that the qualitative features of protein folding reactions are conserved within a protein family (Nall and Landers, 1981).

same rate by all three physical probes of folding; all three physical properties change coordinately in the fast-folding kinetic phase. Following completion of the fast-folding phase, a slow kinetic phase is observed by fluorescence (but not absorbance) on a 10 seconds per division time scale. A second slow phase, on an even slower 50 seconds per division time scale, is detected by absorbance (but not fluorescence) at either 287 nm or 695 nm. So we have a division into fast- and slow-folding reactions.

It is important to note that, at a qualitative level, many kinetic features of folding appear to be universal properties shared by most small globular proteins. There are fast-folding reactions and slow-folding reactions, and sometimes additional fast- and slow-folding phases can be detected by monitoring different physical properties.

strongly favors the trans form. In folded proteins too, with a few rare exceptions, amide linkages are trans. Proline, however, is an iminoacid with a cyclic side chain formed by a carbon atom bonded to the amide nitrogen atom. The steric constraints introduced by the ring shift the equilibrium more towards the cis form. The exact point of the isomeric equilibrium depends on local amino acid sequence, but, in unstructured polypeptides containing proline, appreciable amounts of both cis and trans isomers occur. Moreover, the rate of the isomerization reaction from trans to cis or cis to trans is of the order of 10 to several hundred seconds, i.e., exactly the same time range as slow protein folding reactions! In addition, the activation enthalpy for isomerization is about 25 kcals per mole, the same as for slow protein folding reactions for several small globular proteins.

Proline isomerization and slow-folding reactions

What is the explanation for the similar kinetic behavior of protein folding reactions for different proteins? More than a decade ago, Brandts *et al.* (1975) suggested that isomerization of proline imide bonds generated the slow-refolding species. In polypeptides, most amino acids are linked by amide bonds (Fig. 2). Although, in principle, both cis and trans amide bonds are possible, the isomeric equilibrium (at least in unfolded polypeptides)

The double jump experiment and coupling of isomerization to folding

How can isomerization couple to folding to generate kinetic phases? The protocol for the "double jump" experiment (Fig. 3) describes how this occurs. The experiment was first performed by Brandts *et al.* (1975) in support of their hypothesis and depends on the fact that small proteins (e.g., ribonuclease A, lysozyme, cytochrome c) can be fully unfolded in 10 to 100 milliseconds, a short time compared to the 10–100 second time scale for isomerization.

Fig. 2. (A) Cis and trans forms of an amide bond. In unstructured polypeptides the trans form is much more highly favored than the largely undetectable cis form. (B) Cis and trans forms of a prolyl imide bond. Both isomers occur in unstructured polypeptides with a slight preference for one form or the other depending on local amino acid sequence. [Reprinted from *Comments on Molecular and Cellular Biophysics* **3**, no. 2, 123 (1985) with permission. Copyright 1985, Gordon and Breach Science Publishers, Inc.]

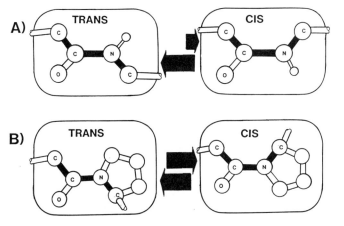

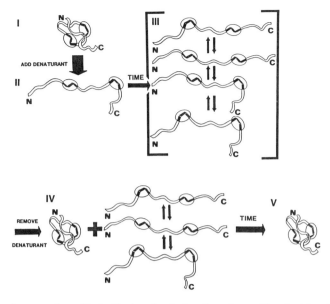

Fig. 3. The double jump experiment. I. In the folded protein, the proline residues are constrained to their native format, cis or trans, by the tertiary structure. II. Denaturant is added and the tertiary structure is disrupted releasing the constraints on the isomeric states of the proline residues. III. On incubation in the unfolded state, some prolines isomerize to non-native formats as the prolines approach an isomeric equilibrium in the structureless polypeptide. IV. When the denaturant is diluted out, the native structure is regained rapidly for that fraction of the protein with all prolines in the native format. V. With time, the remaining protein refolds in a slow kinetic phase. The double jump experiment uses the amplitude of the slow phase observed on diluting the denaturant (IV to V) as an assay for the extent of isomerization in the unfolded protein (II and III). For a short incubation time in the unfolded state (a few seconds), little isomerization occurs and the slow phase has a small amplitude. For long incubation times (several hundred to a few thousand seconds), isomeric equilibrium is attained and a full slow phase is observed. Incubation for intermediate times allows measurement of the rate at which isomeric equilibrium is attained in the unfolded protein. [Reprinted from *Comments on Molecular and Cellular Biophysics* **3**, no. 2, 123 (1985) with permission. Copyright 1985, Gordon and Breach Science Publishers, Inc.]

Let us start with a fully folded protein with, for example, one cis and one trans proline. If, *immediately* after unfolding, the denaturant is diluted out to induce refolding, then the entire population snaps back to the native form in a fast kinetic phase. Now try the same experiment a second way—unfold the protein and incubate it in the unfolded state for a time comparable to the time it takes for proline imide bonds to isomerize. Then dilute out the denaturant. The fraction of the unfolded polypeptide that retains both prolines in a native format will refold in a fast-refolding reaction, but polypeptide chains in which one or both prolines have isomerized to a nonnative format will be constrained to refold more slowly in a slow reaction involving proline imide bond isomerization. For incubation times comparable to the isomerization time scale, the fraction of slow-folding species will increase with increasing incubation times. If, however, the experiment is performed a third way, in which the incubation time is long compared to isomerization times, then isomeric equilibrium will be attained and equilibrium fractions of fast- and slow-refold-

ing species will be observed.

Iso-2-cytochrome c: The unfolded state contains both fluorescence-detected and absorbance-detected slow-folding species

Figure 4 shows the results of a double jump experiment with yeast iso-2 cytochrome c (Osterhout and Nall, 1985). The experiment starts without denaturant so that the protein is fully folded. Denaturant is added to unfold the protein, and the protein incubated in the unfolded state for an amount of time shown on the x-axes. After incubation, the denaturant is diluted out and the amplitude of the slow-folding reaction measured by absorbance or by fluorescence. As shown in Fig. 4, we get the predicted behavior: for increasing incubation time in the unfolded state, there is an increasing amount of slow-folding material. For long times, a plateau or equilibrium amount of slow-folding species is attained. The same kind of behavior is observed by both absorbance and fluorescence—but the fluores-

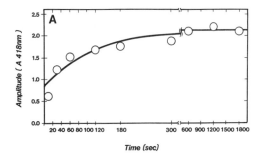

Fig. 4. Double jump experiments on iso-2 cytochrome c. The experiment starts with the protein in the absence of denaturant. At time zero, the protein is quickly unfolded by addition of 3.0*M* Gdn.HCl. After incubating for a time (t) in the unfolded state, refolding is initiated by diluting to 0.3*M* Gdn.HCl. The total kinetic changes associated with slow refolding are measured by changes in absorbance at (**A**) 418 nm or fluorescence at (**B**) 350 nm as an assay for the amount of slow-folding species generated in time t. Total amplitudes are plotted on the y-axis versus incubation times, t, on the x-axis. Other conditions are 0.1*M* sodium phosphate, *p*H 7.2, 20°C. [Reprinted from *Biochemistry* **24**, 7999 (1985), with permission. Copyright 1985, American Chemical Society.]

cence-detected slow phase builds up at a somewhat faster rate than the absorbance-detected slow phase, suggesting that different prolines generate the fluorescence-detected and absorbance-detected slow-folding reactions.

Another test of the imide isomerization model is to look at the activation enthalpies for refolding. The activation enthalpies for slow refolding detected by either fluorescence or absorbance fall in the expected range of about 25 kcals per mole (Osterhout and Nall, 1985).

Site-directed mutagenesis as a test of the isomerization model: Assignment of kinetic phases to specific prolines

So far, all the evidence in favor of the isomerization model is circumstantial. What is needed is a more direct test of the involvement of prolines in slow-folding reactions and the assignment of specific kinetic phases to particular prolines. To achieve this objective, we have used site-directed mutagenesis to replace each of the three conserved prolines with other amino acids (Fig. 5; also see White *et al.*, 1987; Wood *et al.*, 1988a). Two prolines that are not conserved among mitochondrial

cytochromes c are being replaced too, in work under way.

The conserved prolines play different roles in the cytochrome c tertiary structure. Pro-71 occurs between two short segments of alpha-helix, as if it breaks one long helical segment into two short segments. Pro-76 occurs in a classic type II reverse turn, a common location for prolines. Pro-30 is in the protein interior at a tight bend important in positioning the His-18 heme ligand.

We have replaced Pro-30 with a threonine residue, but we have not been able to obtain sufficient protein to characterize the in vitro folding of the Pro-30 mutant. The presence of the mutant protein in whole yeast cells in vivo is confirmed by low temperature spectrophotometry. We know too that the mutant protein provides some function, since the yeast containing this mutation grows slowly on media based on nonfermentable carbon sources.

Pro-71 to Thr-71 iso-2: Presence of the absorbance-detected slow phase depends on final folded conformation

We made a mutant protein in which threonine occurs at position 71. For slow folding

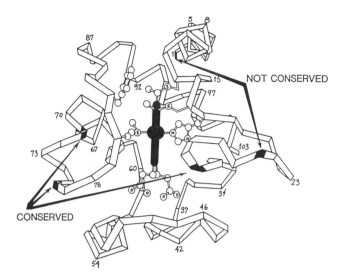

Fig. 5. Prolines in iso-2 cytochrome c. The positions in mitochondrial cytochromes c at which proline is always found are labeled "conserved." Of the two sites that are not conserved, both iso-1 and iso-2 contain proline at position 25. The ribbon schematic is after Almassy and Dickerson (1978) and is based on x-ray crystallographic structures for tuna cytochrome c (Swanson *et al.*, 1977; Takano *et al.*, 1977; Mandel *et al.*, 1977; Takano and Dickerson, 1981a, 1981b) and the two yeast iso-cytochromes c, iso-1 (Louie *et al.*, 1988) and iso-2 (Leung *et al.*, 1989; Murphy and Brayer, unpublished). [Reprinted from *Biochemistry* **27**, 8562 (1988), with permission. Copyright 1988, American Chemical Society.]

detected by fluorescence, this mutant behaves no differently than does the wild-type protein, in which proline occurs at position 71 (White *et al.*, 1987). The experimental conditions are such that the protein starts in a completely unfolded state and ends as a fully folded protein.

Now look at refolding of the same mutant, but this time by absorbance (Fig. 6). At pH 7.2 or at pH 5.5, the wild-type protein has a healthy slow phase as expected. The mutant protein has lost the slow phase at pH 7.2, but surprisingly, the phase returns for the mutant when refolding occurs at pH 5.5.

An explanation for the pH dependence of the amplitude for slow folding is provided in Fig. 7. Between pH 5.5 and pH 7.2, the folded conformation of the protein passes through a pH-dependent transition. The structural changes that occur in this transition are largely unknown, but one thing almost certainly involved is loss of Met-80 as a heme ligand. The presence of the 695 nm absorbance band in ferri-cytochrome c is correlated with heme ligation by Met-80 (Schechter and Saludjian, 1967), and this absorbance band, present at pII 5.5, is lost by pH 7.2 in the mutant protein. The pH dependence of absorbance-detected slow folding can be explained in the following way. Folding of the mutant protein and the normal protein to native-like conformations is very similar: both have an absorbance-

detected slow-folding phase. But folding of the mutant protein to the mutant conformation (i.e., no 695 nm absorbance band) occurs without the slow-folding phase. This provides an important lesson in using mutants to study the folding of normal proteins: mutant proteins sometimes have altered kinetic properties because they fold to very different (mutant) conformations.

Pro-76 to Gly-76 iso-2: Isomerization of Pro-76 generates the absorbance-detected slow phase

In another mutant protein, Pro-76 is replaced with a glycine residue (Wood *et al.*, 1988a). At pH 6 and pH 7.2, fluorescence-detected refolding of the mutant protein is the same as refolding of the normal protein (Wood *et al.*, 1988b). So Pro-76 is not involved in generating the fluorescence-detected slow-folding phase.

Absorbance-detected slow folding is a different story. The wild-type control shows presence of a slow phase for refolding at both pH 6 and pH 7.2. If we look at refolding of the mutant, however, there is no evidence of an absorbance-detected slow-folding phase. We do see a kinetic event at either pH 6 or pH 7.2, but one with the wrong sign to be a folding reaction (Fig. 8). Since there is no evidence of an absorbance-detected slow-folding phase,

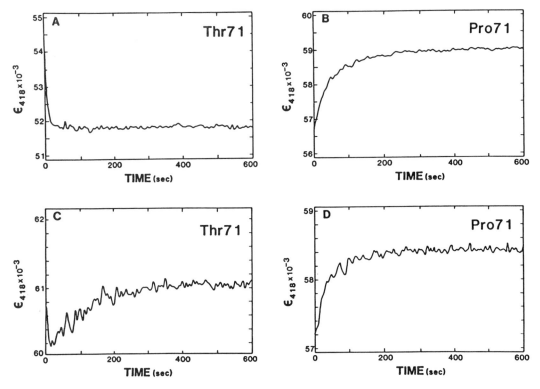

Fig. 6. Slow-folding phases for Pro-71 (wild-type) and Thr-71 (mutant) iso-2 measured by absorbance changes at 418 nm. Kinetic changes are shown for refolding of the mutant protein (**A**) and the normal protein (**B**) following a 3.0 to 0.3M Gdn.HCl concentration jump at pH 7.2 and 20°C in the presence of 0.1M sodium phosphate. Absorbance changes for refolding of the mutant and normal protein from 3.0M Gdn.HCl, pH 7.2 to 0.3M Gdn.HCl, pH 5.5 at 20°C are shown in (**C**) and (**D**), respectively. [Reprinted from *Biochemistry* **22**, 1423 (1983), with permission. Copyright 1983, American Chemical Society.]

we conclude that replacement of pro-76 with glycine *eliminates the absorbance-detected slow-folding phase*. Thus, according to the isomerization hypothesis, isomerization of Pro-76 generates the absorbance-detected slow-folding phase.

Gly-76 iso-2 folds to a mutant conformation via a native-like intermediate

If we examine the pH dependence of the conformation of the fully folded Gly-76 mutant protein, we find that there is a dramatic change in conformation — at least as judged by 695 nm absorbance — with pK 6.71 (Nall *et al.*, 1989). The kinetics of this conformational change can be examined without unfolding the protein by pH jumps across the (conformational) transition zone.[2] The results (Fig. 9) show that the rate and the pH dependence of the rate for the conformational reaction are the same as for the reaction observed in refolding. We conclude that the protein refolds to a native-like conformation without an absorbance-detected slow phase, but following folding, the native-like species equilibrate with a non-native mutant conformer resulting in the slow reaction of opposite sign.

---

2   A very similar reaction, termed the alkaline conformational change, occurs in the normal protein at very high pH (pH 8.5–9).

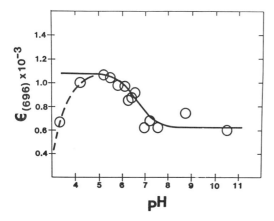

Fig. 7. *p*H dependence of the absorbance of Thr-71 iso-2. The solid line represents a titration curve with *p*K = 6.63. Conditions are 20°C with 0.1*M* sodium phosphate. [Reprinted from *Biochemistry* **26**, 4358 (1987), with permission. Copyright 1987, American Chemical Society.]

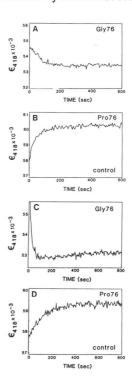

Fig. 8. Slow-refolding kinetics of Gly-76 iso-2 (mutant) and Pro-76 iso-2 (wild-type) measured by absorbance changes at 418 nm. Refolding is measured at (**A, B**) *p*H 6 and (**C, D**) *p*H 7.2. At *p*H 6.0, both the mutant and normal proteins fold to predominantly native-like conformations. At *p*H 7.2, the normal protein folds to a native conformation, but Gly-76 iso-2 folds to a mutant conformation. The protein is unfolded in 3.0*M* Gdn.HCl in the initial conditions and refolding initiated by dilution to 0.3*M* Gdn.HCl, 0.1*M* sodium phosphate, 20°C in the final conditions. [Reprinted from *Biochemistry* **27**, 8562 (1988), with permission. Copyright 1988, American Chemical Society.]

Proline replacements and slow-folding phases

A summary of our results to date is presented in Table 1. The two normal isozymes, iso-1 and iso-2, both have a fluorescence-detected slow-folding phase and an approximately 10-fold slower absorbance-detected slow-folding phase. A mutant protein in which Pro-30 is replaced by threonine has been constructed, but the protein is very unstable and it has not been possible to characterize the folding of that mutant. Three different replacements of Pro-71 in iso-1 cytochrome c and one in iso-2 have been studied.

All mutants with Pro-71 replacements have full amplitude fluorescence-detected slow phases and, as long as folding goes to a native-like conformation, have absorbance-detected slow phases as well. The absorbance-detected slow phase disappears for refolding to a mutant or alkaline conformation lacking the 695 nm absorbance band. For Pro-76 replacements, the fluorescence-detected phase is present, but the absorbance-detected phase is gone even for folding to the native-like conformation. We conclude that Pro-76 is directly involved in generating the absorbance-detected slow-folding reaction.

Mutations and fast-folding phases

Replacements of prolines also affect fast folding. Slow-folding phases are believed to involve prolines directly, so the entire phase should go away when the (right) proline is removed (e.g., the Pro-76 to Gly-76 mutant). It is not clear what is involved in fast folding. Fast folding does not involve imide isomerization, but not much else is known about it. Information on how mutations affect fast folding will tell us about new phenomena for which there are not even good hypotheses. The unusually large fast phase amplitude (70–80 percent of the total) makes cytochrome c an

Table 1. Summary: Replacement of prolines and slow-folding phases.

Protein/proline	Slow phase			
	Fluorescence-detected		Absorbance-detected	
	*p*H 7.2	*p*H 5–6	*p*H 7.2	*p*H 5–6
	Normal proteins			
(1) Iso-1-MS[a]	Yes	Yes	Yes	Yes
(2) Iso-2[b]	Yes	Yes	Yes	Yes
	Mutant proteins			
Proline 30:				
(1) Thr-30 Iso-2[c]	?	?	?	?
Proline 71:				
(1) Val-71 Iso-1-MS[d]		Yes	Small	Yes
(2) Ile-71 Iso-1-MS[d]		Yes	Small	Yes
(3) Thr-71 Iso-1-MS[d]		Yes	Small	Yes
(4) Thr-71 Iso-2[e]	Yes	Yes	No	Yes
Proline 76:				
(1) Gly-76 Iso-2[f]	Yes	Yes	No	No

[a]Zuniga and Nall, 1983; Ramdas and Nall, 1986; Ramdas, 1987. [b]Nall and Landers, 1981; Nall, 1983; Osterhout and Nall, 1985; Nall *et al.*, 1988. [c]Wood *et al.*, 1988a. [d]Ramdas and Nall, 1986; Ramdas, 1987; Ernst *et al.*, 1985. [e]White *et al.*, 1987. [f]Wood *et al.*, 1988b. [Reprinted from *Biochemistry*, vol. 27, pp. 8562–8568, 1988, with permission, copyright 1988, American Chemical Society]

excellent experimental system for investigating the effect of mutations on fast folding.

An example is the denaturant dependence for folding/unfolding of iso-2 and Gly-76 iso-2 (Wood *et al.*, 1988b). Skipping over some of the details, the overall result is quite simple: refolding of the mutant occurs at the same rate, but unfolding occurs at a faster rate than for the normal protein. For the refolding reaction, the qualitative interpretation is that the mutation affects folding at a point *following* the transition state. Conversely, if one looks at the situation from the point of view of the unfolding reaction, the mutation perturbs a step in unfolding *preceding* the transition state. This sort of mapping of mutational effects on fast folding should soon provide us with a clearer picture of the molecular events involved in fast folding/unfolding.

Acknowledgments

This chapter on the folding properties of yeast

cytochromes c is a review of work carried out by a number of individuals over the past nine years. Beto Zuniga studied refolding of yeast iso-1 cytochrome c, prepared most of the figures, and helped us all at various stages. Tony Mathews studied folding of iso-1/iso-2 composite proteins. Latha Ramdas performed the studies on refolding of yeast iso-1 mutants in which proline 71 was replaced. Ladonna Wood performed many of the molecular genetic experiments, including replacement of both Pro-30 and Pro-76 in iso-2 cytochrome c. Wood also performed the initial refolding experiments on the Gly-76 iso-2 mutant. Kamali Muthukrishnan performed NMR studies of normal and mutant yeast cytochromes c. John Osterhout characterized the slow-folding behavior of iso-2 cytochrome c. Terry White, in a collaborative project with Peter Berget's lab, set up the iso-2 site-directed mutagenesis system, constructed a Pro-71 to Thr-71 mutant, and characterized the folding properties of the mutant protein. Donna Montgomery provided plasmids containing the cloned gene

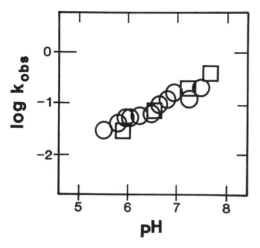

Fig. 9. Comparison of the *p*H dependence of the rate of a conformational change between two folded states and the *p*H dependence of the rate of a slow absorbance-detected reaction following refolding for Gly-76 iso-2. The rate of the *p*H-induced conformational change (circles) is measured by *p*H jumps in the presence of 0.3*M* Gdn.HCl, 0.1*M* sodium phosphate. The *p*H dependence of the rate of the slow phase that follows refolding (squares) is measured by jumps in both *p*H and Gdn.HCl concentration. Initial conditions for the unfolded protein are 3.0M Gdn.HCl, 0.1*M* sodium phosphate, *p*H 6. Refolding is induced by dilution to 0.3*M* Gdn.HCl, 0.1*M* sodium phosphate, and the indicated final *p*H. Rates are monitored by absorbance changes at 418 nm at 20°C. [Reprinted from *Biochemistry* **27**, 8562 (1988), with permission. Copyright 1988, American Chemical Society.]

for iso-2, and Peter Berget helped with the molecular genetics experiments. Fred Sherman and colleagues have supplied numerous yeast strains. In particular, I want to thank Robert L. Baldwin and Fred Sherman for providing encouragement and advice throughout the past several years.

This work was supported by grants from the National Institute of General Medical Sciences (GM 32980) and the Robert A. Welch Foundation (AQ-838) and was carried out during the tenure of an Established Investigatorship of the American Heart Association.

References

Almassy, R. J., and R. E. Dickerson, *Proc. Natl. Acad. Sci. U.S.A.* **75**, 2674 (1978).

Brandts, J. F., H. R. Halvorson, M. Brennan, *Biochemistry* **14**, 4953 (1975).

Dickerson, R. E., *Sci. Am.* **226**, 58 (1972).

———, *Sci. Am.* **242**, 136 (1980).

Ernst, J. F., *et al., J. Biol. Chem.* **260**, 13225 (1985).

Hampsey, D. M., G. Das, F. Sherman, *J. Biol. Chem.* **261**, 3259 (1986).

Leung, C. J., B. T. Nall, G. D. Brayer, *J. Mol. Biol.* **206**, 783 (1989).

Louie, G. V., W. L. B. Hutcheon, G. D. Brayer, *J. Mol. Biol.* **199**, 295 (1988).

Montgomery, D. L., *et al., Proc. Natl. Acad. Sci. U.S.A.* **77**, 541 (1980).

Mandel, N., *et al., J. Biol. Chem.* **252**, 4619 (1977).

Nall, B. T., J. J. Osterhout, Jr., L. Ramdas, *Biochemistry* **27**, 7310 (1988).

Nall, B. T., and T. A. Landers, *Biochemistry* **20**, 5403 (1981).

Nall, B. T., *Biochemistry* **22**, 1423 (1983).

———, *Comments Mol. Cell. Biophys.* **3**, 123 (1985).

Nall, B. T., E. H. Zuniga, T. B. White, L. C. Wood, L. Ramdas, *Biochemistry* **28**, 9834 (1989).

Osterhout, J. J., Jr., and B. T. Nall, *Biochemistry* **24**, 7999 (1985).

Pielak, G., A. G. Mauk, M. Smith, *Nature* **313**, 152 (1985).

Ramdas, L., and B. T. Nall, *Biochemistry* **25**, 6959 (1986).

Ramdas, L., Ph.D. thesis, University of Texas Health Science Center, Houston (1987).

Schechter, E., and P. Saludjian, *Biopolymers* **5**, 788 (1967).

Swanson, R., *et al., J. Biol. Chem.* **252**, 759 (1977).

Takano, T., *et al., J. Biol. Chem.* **252**, 776 (1977).

Takano, T., and R. E. Dickerson, *J. Mol. Biol.* **153**, 79 (1981a).

———, *J. Mol. Biol.* **153**, 95 (1981b).

White, T. B., P. B. Berget, B. T. Nall, *Biochemistry* **26**, 4358 (1987).

Wood, L. C., K. Muthukrishnan, T. B. White, L. Ramdas, B. T. Nall, *Biochemistry* **27**, 8554 (1988a).

Wood, L. C., T. B. White, L. Ramdas, B. T. Nall, *Biochemistry* **27**, 8562 (1988b).

Zuniga, E. H., and B. T. Nall, *Biochemistry* **22**, 1430 (1983).

Part V

Protein Folding Within the Cell

Jonathan King

Within cells, polypeptide chains fold up in much more concentrated and complex environments than occurs with the purified proteins refolded in vitro. The chain comes into existence sequentially, initially tethered to the ribosome synthesizing it, in the presence of other partially folded species. For proteins that need to be exported to a cellular compartment other than the cytoplasm in which they are synthesized, it may be necessary to prevent the folding of the protein until the correct compartment is reached. Signal sequences, signal recognition particles, export factors, molecular chaperonins, and other cellular factors are required to guide and regulate many intracellular folding processes.

The experience of those trying to recover proteins from cloned genes has revealed some of the pitfalls of intracellular folding processes (Mitraki and King, 1989). Polypeptide chains frequently fail to fold successfully in foreign cytoplasms, accumulating as aggregated states called "inclusion bodies," discussed in an earlier section of this volume.

Those newly synthesized chains which must be directed to a particular cellular or extracellular compartment before they reach the native state carry signal sequences that allow them to find the appropriate compartment. These sequences are removed from the protein by specific membrane-associated proteases during the maturation phase. Lila Gierasch describes a series of elegant biophysical experiments that probe the proper-

ties of these polypeptide sequences in their interactions with aqueous and lipid environments. These experiments utilize mutant signal sequences which are known to have altered in vivo functions. The conformational mobility of the signal amino acid sequences makes them models for other transient species such as the folding intermediates of the rest of the proteins.

The chapter from Linda Randall's laboratory (reprinted from *Science*) describes the necessity of staying unfolded in order to be competent for export from the bacterial cytoplasm; many folded proteins cannot be efficiently transported through the membrane channels leading to the outside world. Substantial evidence has recently accumulated for proteins which specifically recognize partially folded intermediates and maintain them in an export competent state, such as the secB gene product of *E. coli* (Watanabe and Blobel, 1989).

In the chapter from my laboratory, we show that single amino acid substitutions at certain sites in a polypeptide chain can prevent productive folding in vivo. The striking feature of these mutations is that they do not alter the function of the stability of the native protein once correctly folded. Thus they identify sequences within the polypeptide chains critical for in vivo folding intermediates but not important in the structure of the native state of the protein. The study of these mutations has also revealed that inclusion bodies form from folding intermediates and not from the native state, accounting for many of their properties.

The most abundant structural protein of vertebrates is the triple-helical collagen molecule described in chapter 5. The pathway of collagen maturation was one of the earliest examples of the complexity of in vivo folding processes in higher organisms. Within the cell, collagen chains are synthesized as much longer preprocollagen molecules, whose globular N- and C-terminal regions fold and associate prior to triple-helix formation. The repeating triplet amino acid sequence of collagen generates a serious registration problem among the chains. If the molecules are not in exact register, they form intermolecular helices, the basis of gel formation (collagen is the protein of "Jell-o" and traditional glues).

Peter Byers describes how defects in collagen metabolism cause a variety of developmental diseases in humans. Byers and his colleagues have identified the genetic defects in a number of these diseases which result in amino acid sequence changes in the collagen molecule. Particularly surprising is the discovery that single amino acid substitutions in the triple helical regions can disrupt maturation of the entire collagen molecule.

Since these chapters were written, a class of proteins referred to as chaperonins has been shown to consist of helper proteins in chain folding and assembly within cells (Ellis and Hemmingsen, 1989; Rothman, 1989). Originally identified as host proteins needed in bacteriophage assembly, the chaperonins have been found to be widely distributed in prokaryotes and eukaryotes and to be members of the heat shock class of proteins. The best characterized prokaryotic chaperonin is a tetradecameric complex of the *E. coli* GroE large subunit. This structure binds folding intermediates released from the ribosome. Release of the intermediates requires the GroE small subunit as well as ATP.

Similar proteins function in the maturation of ribulose 5 bisphosphate carboxylase in plants, and in the maturation of a variety of eukaryotic proteins including immunoglobulins and influenza virus hemagglutinin (Goloubinoff *et al.*, 1989; Hurtley and Helenius, 1989). These proteins probably function to prevent aggregation and other off pathway interactions, where intermediates need to be relatively long lived, either for transport or other requirements. Certainly many more such auxiliary proteins remain to be identified.

References

Ellis, R. J., and S. M. Hemmingsen, *TIBS* **14**, 339 (1989)..

Goloubinoff, P., J. T. Christeller, A. A. Gatenby, G. H. Lorimer, *Nature* **342**, 884 (1989).

Hurtley, S. M., and A. Helenius, *Ann. Rev. Cell Biol.* **5**, 277 (1989).

Mitraki, A., and J. King, *Bio/technology* **7**, 690 (1989).

Rothman, J. E., *Cell* **59**, 591 (1989).

Watanabe, M., and G. Blobel, *Cell* **58**, 696 (1989).

21

Conformations and Interactions of Signal Peptides

Approaches to Elucidating the Role of the Signal Sequence in Protein Secretion

Lila M. Gierasch

Targeting sequences mediate localization of nascent polypeptide chains to their sites of action within and outside of a cell. Several types of targeting sequence have been identified, including those that specify export from the cell (called signal or leader sequences), those that specify import into mitochondria, and those that direct chains to the nucleus (for reviews, see Verner and Schatz, 1988, and Silver and Goodson, 1989). While these cellular "zipcodes" must perform their targeting roles efficiently and selectively, they do not show primary structural homology within a given class. It appears that a pattern of residues and, most probably, a secondary structural motif signals their presence to the cellular components with which they interact.

This chapter will focus on the targeting sequences that direct nascent polypeptides for export from cells across either the cytoplasmic membrane (in prokaryotes) or the endoplasmic reticulum membrane (in eukaryotes). Signal sequences are interesting with respect to the protein folding problem for several reasons. First of all, they illustrate some of the principles of stabilization of folding units such as helices. Second, these sequences may be required to undergo conformational changes

as a function of environment. Third, they are implicated in the folding problem in vivo where there are temporal and spatial constraints on folding. Targeting sequences are directly involved in insuring that in vivo folding takes place productively, in the right place and at the right time (Wickner, 1989; Randall, chapter 22, this volume).

The secretory pathways of both prokaryotes and eukaryotes have been extensively studied (for recent reviews, see Randall *et al.,* 1987; Briggs and Gierasch, 1986; Walter and Lingappa, 1986; Rapoport, 1986). Despite the fact that a signal sequence is the most universal requirement for secretion, a detailed understanding of its roles remains elusive (Gierasch, 1989). Similar mechanisms are apparently operative in prokaryotes and in eukaryotes, but more extensive characterization of the components of the export apparatus has been achieved in eukaryotes.

As shown in Fig. 1, the nascent chain of a secreted protein is first recognized as being targeted to the endoplasmic reticulum and the secretory pathway by the signal recognition particle (SRP) that binds to the signal sequence near the N-terminus of the chain as it emerges from the ribosome. At this stage, the

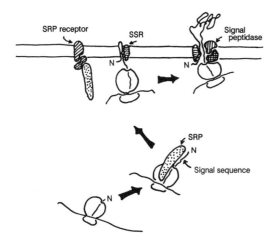

Fig. 1. The signal hypothesis, 1989 version. As the signal sequence emerges from the ribosome (after synthesis of approximately 70 residues), it is bound by the signal recognition particle (SRP), via the 54 kDa subunit, in combination with the ribosome. This secretion-competent complex is targeted to the endoplasmic reticulum (ER) membrane by specific binding of SRP and the SRP receptor (also known as the docking protein). This interaction releases the nascent chain, which then is proposed to interact with the ER membrane by binding to a signal sequence receptor (SSR), and a translocation apparatus as yet poorly defined. Cleavage of the signal peptide by the signal peptidase and continuing translocation of the nascent chain then ensue.

signal sequence is involved in a protein-protein interaction with the 54 kDa subunit of SRP (Kurzchalia et al., 1986; Krieg et al., 1986). SRP targets the nascent chain to the endoplasmic reticulum by virtue of its binding to the SRP receptor (also known as "docking protein"), which triggers its dissociation from the ribosome/nascent chain complex (Meyer et al., 1982; Gilmore et al., 1982; Gilmore and Blobel, 1983). The nascent chain then interacts with the membrane, possibly via a proteinaceous signal sequence receptor (SSR), whose existence has been proposed on the basis of cross linking experiments (Wiedmann et al., 1987). At this point, translocation of the chain across the membrane into the endoplasmic reticulum must occur in order for it to be correctly localized. Folding takes place, presumably concurrently, as the chain emerges on the opposite side of the membrane. The signal sequence is usually cleaved to form the mature protein, and the signal peptidase that carries

out this processing exists in a complex of polypeptide chains and apparently has its active site on the other side of the ER membrane (the luminal side) (Evans et al., 1986; Baker and Lively, 1987). Thus, the functions of the signal sequence are completed as translocation proceeds.

The mechanism of translocation is one of the major mysteries of protein export. The pathway of protein export in prokaryotes most likely involves species that correspond to SRP. Likely candidates are the products of either the secA (Oliver and Beckwith, 1981; Schmidt et al., 1988) or the ffh genes (Bernstein et al., 1989), the SRP receptor (SecA or SecY [Ito et al., 1983, 1984; Fandl et al., 1988]), and the translocation apparatus (possibly SecY [Bieker and Silhavy, 1989]). This brief overview of the steps in eukaryotic protein secretion clearly implies that the signal sequence may perform several roles.

Despite their lack of primary structural homology, signal sequences have some properties in common (von Heijne, 1985). They are generally 15 to 30 amino acids in length, and usually occur on the N-terminus. In most cases, they are cleaved from the precursor to form the mature protein product. The presence of the signal sequence is required for correct localization of the protein. A common feature of signal sequences is a stretch of hydrophobic residues about 10 to 12 residues long, which is called the hydrophobic core or the h-region. Near the N-terminus is a charged locus, which in prokaryotes is rigorously basic. At the C-terminal side of the hydrophobic stretch is a more hydrophilic locus that has been proposed to consist of turn-forming residues. The most homologous region is near the site of cleavage by the signal peptidase. It is interesting to note that, even though they lack homology, signal sequences are distinguishable as a class from other types of sequence (e.g., membrane-spanning sequences, segments of globular proteins) on the basis of the average length of their hydrophobic cores. Hydrophobic segments of globular proteins are shorter (about 7 residues) and of membrane-spanning sequences are longer (about 22 residues). In composition, the hydrophobic cores of signal sequences resemble the regions of transmembrane sequences that are in contact with lipid (Rees *et al.*, 1989).

Strategy: Biophysical Study of Isolated Synthetic Genetically Defined Signal Sequences

The strategy we are using to explore the properties of signal sequences that enable them to function effectively in vivo is to synthesize examples as isolated peptides. We select cases of fully functional (wild-type) signal sequences and mutated, defective versions for comparison. The examples are drawn from bacterial strains that have been characterized as defective in localization of a protein. If we see a loss of a property in the isolated signal peptide and a loss of function in the corresponding in vivo activity, we are encouraged that the specific property is important for signal sequence function. Ideally, this approach may lead to a model for the mechanism of signal sequence action in vivo. The properties that we have examined are conformations, including responses to different environments, and interactions with membranes. The family of sequences that we have focused on primarily comes from an outer membrane protein of *Escherichia coli*, LamB (Fig. 2). The wild-type sequence is typical: it is 25 residues in length

with a 10 residue hydrophobic segment flanked by a proline and a glycine. Silhavy and co-workers have isolated a number of LamB mutants with altered signal sequences that synthesize preLamB normally but fail to export it to the outer membrane, and the precursors accumulate in the cytoplasm (for a review, see Benson *et al.*, 1985). For example, Scott Emr and Tom Silhavy found a family of three sequences (Fig. 2) that have a deletion of four residues in the hydrophobic segment (Emr and Silhavy, 1983). Alone, this deletion causes a complete loss of function in vivo. These four residues are removed from the region that constitutes the most general characteristic of signal sequences, so it is not surprising that the altered sequence does not function as a signal sequence.

What was surprising was that there were two pseudorevertant strains that arose from the deletion mutant and had regained the ability to localize the protein correctly. The pseudorevertants retain the deletion within the hydrophobic core but have additional point mutations that compensate for that loss. In one case, glycine in position 17 has been changed to cysteine. In the other case, proline in position 9 has been changed to leucine. The activity of the Pro→Leu revertant is nearly wild type; that of the Gly→Cys revertant is about half of wild type. Examples of another type of mutation that has been found to cause

	1			5				10				15				20				25					
WT	M M I T L R K L P L A V A V A A G V M S A Q A M A /
Δ78	M M I T L R K L P ------- V A A G V M S A Q A M A /
Δ78r1	M M I T L R K L P ------- V A A <u>C</u> V M S A Q A M A /
Δ78r2	M M I T L R K L <u>L</u> ------- V A A G V M S A Q A M A /
G17R	M M I T L R K L P L A V A V A A <u>R</u> V M S A Q A M A /
A13D	M M I T L R K L P L A V <u>D</u> V A A G V M S A Q A M A /

Fig. 2. Amino acid sequences of LamB signal peptides discussed. Numbers indicate amino acid position from the N-terminus of the translation product; dashes represent deleted residues; slashes represent signal peptidase cleavage site. Underlined characters indicate residues differing from the wild type. [Reprinted from *The Journal of Biological Chemistry* **264**, no. 29, 17293 (1989) with permission. Copyright 1989, American Society for Biochemistry and Molecular Biology.]

defects in secretion also are illustrated in Fig. 2: the introduction of a charge in the middle of the hydrophobic segment causes a very severe defect (Stader *et al.*, 1986). If the charge is at the end of the hydrophobic segment, the defect is marked, but it is a kinetic defect and eventually all of the protein is exported.

Conformations of LamB Signal Peptides

When Emr and Silhavy isolated the deletion mutant and pseudorevertant strains, they put forth the hypothesis that a common secondary structure, namely α-helix, was required for function in signal sequences (Emr and Silhavy, 1983). Indeed, two helix-disrupting residues, Pro and Gly, are brought into proximity by the deletion, and the pseudorevertants each change one of these to a helix-favoring residue. Chou-Fasman predictions (Chou and Fasman, 1974a, 1974b) support the hypothesis that α helicity is essential for signal sequence function. We tested these predictions by synthesis of the wild-type, deletion mutant and pseudorevertant LamB signal peptides, and examined their tendencies to fold into secondary structures (Briggs and Gierasch, 1984; Briggs, 1986; McKnight *et al.*, 1989). By circular dichroism (CD), we found that these sequences are unstructured in aqueous solution (by contrast with those discussed by Marqusee and Baldwin, chapter 8, this volume). In helix-promoting environments such as sodium dodecyl sulfate micelles or trifluoroethanol/water mixtures, LamB signal peptides adopt helical conformations but to varying extents (Table 1).

Key to our analysis is the finding that the secondary structural tendencies of the different signal peptides correlate with their in vivo function: the tendency to adopt helix is greatly reduced in the case of the deletion mutant. The Pro→Leu revertant, which regains nearly wild-type levels of function, also regains nearly wild-type tendency to form α-helix. The Gly→Cys revertant, which functions at about 50 percent wild-type level, has a helix content that is also between that of the defec-

Table 1. Helix contents and in vivo activities of synthetic LamB signal peptides.

Signal peptide	α-helix content[a] %	In vivo activity[b] %
Wild type	70	100
Deletion mutant Δ78	35	0
Gly → Cys revertant	40	50
Pro → Leu revertant	75	90
A13D	60	10
G17R	70	40/100[c]

[a]In 40mM SDS, 25°C, with α-helix content determined by fitting to reference curves in Greenfield and Fasman (1969). [b]Activity is the amount of LamB localized to the outer membrane in 4 minutes (Stader *et al.*, 1986). [c]At longer times, this mutant exports wild-type levels of LamB.

tive deletion mutant and that of the wild type. Also shown in Table 1 are CD data for the two mutants that harbor a charge. These peptides behave similarly to the functional signal sequences in the helix-promoting environments, yet their phenotypes are distinct. Clearly, there are properties in addition to the capacity to fold into a helix that are required for function of signal peptides.

It is interesting to ask whether there is a critical length of the helical segment of a functional signal peptide. The family of LamB signal peptides—including the nonfunctional deletion mutant, the semifunctional Gly→Cys revertant, and the near wild-type Pro→Leu revertant—offer a useful case study to investigate the nature of the helical portion of a signal sequence required for function. By NMR, we find that it is the *stability* of the helix that correlates with function more than its length (Bruch and Gierasch, 1990).

Membrane Interactions of Signal Peptides

We next asked whether isolated signal peptides interact with lipid phases in a spontaneous fashion and whether this capability is a discriminator amongst functional and nonfunctional sequences. The experiment we used to assess membrane affinity is to spread a lipid monolayer on an aqueous solution and to vary the concentration of signal peptide in the aqueous subphase. We monitored the surface pressure of the monolayer; insertion of signal peptide into the monolayer causes an increased surface pressure. Data from these titrations (Fig. 3) reveal (i) that the isolated signal peptides that correspond to functional sequences in vivo have a strong tendency to insert (i.e., high affinity and substantial perturbation of the surface pressure) and (ii) nonfunctional signal peptides have lower affinity (the deletion mutant and the Ala13→Asp) and may show little tendency to insert (the deletion mutant) (Briggs *et al.*, 1985; McKnight *et al.*, 1989).

We can now state that the nonfunctional deletion mutant, in addition to having little tendency to form an α-helix, also has a very low tendency to insert into a lipid monolayer. The Pro→Leu revertant shows near wild-type behavior. Most importantly, the mutant that harbors a charge at the end of the hydrophobic segment and exports normal levels of LamB has near wild-type affinity for lipid, whereas the one that has a charge in the middle of the hydrophobic segment and a severe

export defect has a significantly reduced affinity for lipid. Hence, affinity for a lipid environment provides an additional discriminator among functional and nonfunctional signal sequences beyond conformation. From these results, it is not possible to infer that signal sequences interact directly with lipid in vivo. However, these results do argue that the properties that are characteristic of successful signal sequences confer upon them the ability to interact favorably with lipids and to insert spontaneously into a membrane. One can conclude that either signal sequences interact with lipids or with proteinaceous binding sites that look like lipid environments, or with both. The idea of a binding site that requires the same biophysical properties that are necessary for insertion into lipid phases is intriguing.

Conformations of Signal Peptides in Lipid Environments

The above results—that not only a propensity to adopt an α-helical conformation in interfacial environments but also a high affinity for lipid monolayers were properties of functional

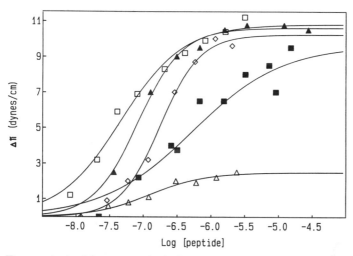

Fig. 3. Insertion of LamB signal peptides into monolayers. The initial monolayer was spread from a chloroform solution of 65 percent 1-palmitoyl-2-oleoylphosphatidyl-eth anolamine, 35 percent 1-palmitoyl-2-oleoylphosphatidylglycerol to a lateral pressure of 23.5 dynes/cm. Peptide solutions were injected using a Hamilton syringe into the aqueous subphase, and surface pressure increases were monitored using a du Nuoy tensiometer. The values plotted are the surface pressure rises after a constant pressure had been reached. The affinity of the peptide for the monolayer is indicated by the concentration necessary to cause a half-maximal surface pressure rise. The magnitude of the pressure rise indicates the nature of the lipid/peptide interaction: A surface pressure rise on the order of 10 dynes/cm suggests strongly that the peptide inserts into the acyl chain region. A surface pressure rise of 2–3 dynes/cm is indicative of a headgroup interaction. ☐, WT; △, ∆78; ◇, ∆78r2; ▲, G17R; ■, A13D. [Reprinted from *The Journal of Biological Chemistry* **264**, no. 29, 17293 (1989) with permission. Copyright 1989, American Society for Biochemistry and Molecular Biology.]

signal peptides—suggested that the peptides must take up a helix upon lipid interaction. Therefore, we explored the conformations of the LamB wild-type signal peptide in its lipid-interactive states (Briggs *et al.,* 1986; Cornell *et al.,* 1989). The peptide was injected beneath a lipid monolayer formed in a Langmuir trough. Prior to spreading the monolayer, solid supports made either of germanium (for Fourier transform, attenuated total reflectance infrared spectroscopy [ATR FT-IR]) or quartz (for CD) were suspended through the aqueous surface (Fig. 4a). Insertion of the signal peptide leads to a pressure rise (at constant area of the monolayer). Withdrawing the germanium or quartz plates while maintaining constant surface pressure results in the transfer of patches of the peptide/lipid monolayer at a known surface pressure (Fig. 4b). Transfers were quantitative, i.e., the area loss of the monolayer in the trough corresponded to the total area covered on the plates. We carried out the transfer, starting from lipid monolayers at high pressure where no insertion of peptide took place, or lower pressures where the peptide inserted and caused a pressure rise. Both IR and CD data were indicative of a state of association of the peptide with the lipid in the high pressure, noninserted case, with predominantly β-structure. IR spectra obtained with polarized radiation showed the β form to lie in the plane of the membrane.

Inserted peptide was largely helical, with some β-structure remaining, as judged by either CD or IR data. Polarization IR of the inserted peptide led to a model in which the helical, inserted peptides are colinear with the lipid acyl chains.

The signal peptide insertion into the acyl chain region of lipid monolayers has been confirmed in lipid bilayers in recent work with tryptophan-containing LamB signal sequences (C. J. McKnight, M. Rafalski, and L. M. Gierasch, unpublished results). Peptides were synthesized with Trp's at positions 5, 18, or 24 of the 25-residue signal peptide. A transmembrane orientation is indicated by the preferential quenching by an aqueous-resident quencher (iodide ion) of the Trp at position 24, followed by that at 5, then by Trp 18. By contrast, nitroxide-labeled lipids, where the spin label is on carbon 5, 12, or 16 of the acyl chain of a 1-palmitoyl-2-(5, 12, or 16-doxylstearoyl)-phosphatidylcholine quench the 18-position Trp better than that at position 5, which is, in turn, quenched better than that in position 24.

Working Model for the Role of the Signal Sequence in Initial Steps in Protein Secretion

Spectroscopic data have revealed two modes

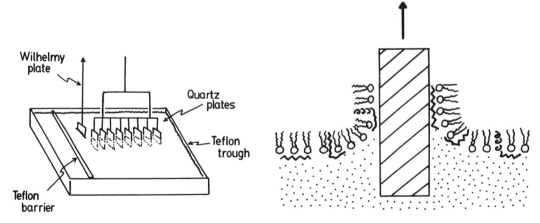

Fig. 4. **(A)** Transfer of a phospholipid monolayer to a solid support. (See text and Briggs *et al.,* 1986, for detailed description of experiment.) **(B)** Peptide/lipid monolayer was transferred to the hydrophilic surface (quartz for CD studies or germanium for IR studies) while maintaining surface pressure, such that the conformational states of the peptide were maintained for spectroscopy. [Reprinted from *Science* **233,** 206 (1986) with permission. Copyright 1986, AAAS.]

of interaction of the LamB signal peptide with a lipid monolayer, adsorbed to the headgroup region in a β-conformation (at high lipid lateral pressure) and inserted into the acyl chain region in a helical conformation (at moderate surface pressure). Studies in lipid vesicles confirm that the peptides can insert in a helical conformation that is probably transmembrane. From these results and consideration of the sequence similarities among signal sequences, we have suggested a model for possible steps in the initial interaction of a nascent chain with the membrane (cytoplasmic or endoplasmic reticulum) in vivo (Fig. 5) (Briggs *et al.*, 1986). The initial environment experienced by a signal sequence as the nascent chain emerges from the ribosome would be an aqueous one, although binding interactions, to either SRP or its prokaryotic equivalent, may sequester the signal region. After release of SRP (or its equivalent), the signal peptide may be briefly in an aqueous milieu where an unordered conformational distribution is suggested by our CD data. Our results would argue that, in any case, the signal peptide would partition readily into the membrane via interactions with lipids. We are postulating that this membrane association is made favorable by electrostatic interactions, since lipid affinity of the isolated signal peptides is reduced either at higher ionic strength or lower headgroup charge (J. Johnston and L. Gierasch, unpublished results). Steps 2 and 3 in Fig. 5 derive from our observation of a β form of the signal peptide that can bind the membrane surface. We are proposing that this conformation of the peptide could insert, with the characteristic 10 or so hydrophobic residues comprising the hydrophobic core spanning the hydrophobic region of the bilayer. Also, the more polar, turn-forming locus at the end of the hydrophobic core would be exposed in a bend on the opposite side of the membrane. The more stable conformation, once the peptide is inserted, however, is the transmembrane α-helix shown in Step 4. The conformational change from β to α would lead to insertion of the first part of the mature passenger protein. Subsequent translocation can not depend on the signal sequence because it

is cleaved at some point as the rest of the chain traverses the membrane.

An important test of the ability of the signal sequence to facilitate insertion of its passenger domain into a membrane via interaction directly with lipids has recently been carried out. We have synthesized the LamB signal peptide with 28 residues of the mature LamB protein attached (C. J. McKnight, S. J. Stradley, and L. M. Gierasch, unpublished results). This 53 residue-long peptide displays an affinity for membranes that is nearly the same as that of the signal peptide alone and markedly higher than that

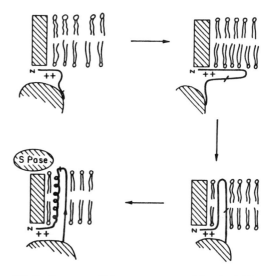

Fig. 5. Summary of the steps suggested for the initial interactions of a signal sequence with a membrane based on the conformations taken up by a synthetic LamB signal peptide in lipid monolayers. Our results suggest that signal sequences in aqueous medium would be unstructured. Upon approaching a lipid surface, the signal sequence may adopt β-structure. This form could be the conformation that initially inserts into the membrane. Ten to twelve consecutive hydrophobic residues could span the nonpolar region of the bilayer if in β-structure. Insertion should lead to a preference for an α-helical conformation, as indicated by our monolayer spectroscopy and by CD of our signal peptides in vesicles (McKnight *et al.*, 1989). The consequence of this conformational change, if the N-terminus stays anchored on the cytoplasmic face of the membrane, is entry of the first ten to fourteen residues of the mature protein into the membrane. Thermodynamically, this constitutes a coupling of the favorable insertion of the hydrophobic signal sequence with a potentially unfavorable insertion of the first portion of the mature protein. [Reprinted from *Science* **233**, 206 (1986) with permission. Copyright 1986, AAAS.]

of the mature portion alone. Furthermore, the signal sequence region of this longer peptide seems to fold into a helix in vesicles and micelles, as it did without the passenger. Detailed analysis of the residues adopting helical structure awaits nuclear magnetic resonance (NMR) analysis. But based on data obtained to date, it appears as though the properties of the isolated signal sequence overwhelm those of the segment of chain adjacent. This relative dominance of the signal sequence properties reflects an absence of strong conformational influences, high charge, or highly hydrophobic nature in the first part of the mature protein so that it is in effect a "passive," compliant passenger. Consistent with these implied requirements on the mature chain are several recent reports demonstrating that alterations within the N-terminal region of the mature chain can have profound impact on secretion. In vivo, these ideas would suggest that the behavior of the early portion of a nascent, secretory protein would be governed by the interactions and conformations of the signal sequence.

Conclusions

Our work with isolated signal peptides has provided some clues about important properties of signal sequences for their in vivo function and about possible mechanistic aspects of protein secretion. We can state that functional signal peptides have a high tendency to form a stable α-helical conformation in interfacial environments and that they have, in addition, a high affinity for lipid membranes. They insert spontaneously into lipid monolayers and bilayers, forming a transmembrane α-helix. Presence of the passenger segment representing the first 28 residues of mature LamB following the LamB signal sequence does not significantly alter the folding or membrane association of the signal peptide. The ability of the mature domain to interact with a membrane is thus markedly increased by the presence of the signal sequence. We suggest that the properties of signal peptides are "dominant" over adjacent sequences in a secretory protein; the consequence of this

relative importance is that the interactions of the nascent secretory chain with the export pathway are determined by the signal sequence.

Acknowledgments

The research described from my laboratory is the work of several people: Marty Briggs, Jamie McKnight, Sarah Stradley, Maria Rafalski, and Martha Bruch. We benefited from a number of fruitful collaborations: with Rich Dluhy of Batelle Laboratories and Don Cornell of the U. S. Department of Agriculture in Philadelphia on monolayer spectroscopy and with Tom Silhavy and co-workers on comparisons of LamB signal sequence functions in vivo. This research has been supported by grants from the National Science Foundation and the National Institutes of Health. We also appreciate the support of the Robert A. Welch Foundation.

References

Baker, R. K., and M. O. Lively, *Biochemistry* **26**, 8561 (1987).
Benson, S. A., M. N. Hall, T. J. Silhavy, *Ann. Rev. Biochem.* **54**, 101 (1985).
Bieker, K. L., and T. J. Silhavy, *Proc. Natl. Acad. Sci. U.S.A.* **86**, 968 (1989).
Briggs, M. S., Ph.D. Dissertation, Yale University (1986).
Briggs, M. S., and L. M. Gierasch, *Biochemistry* **23**, 3111 (1984).
_____, *Adv. Protein Chem.* **38**, 109 (1986).
Briggs, M. S., L. M. Gierasch, A. Zlotnick, J. D. Lear, W. F. DeGrado, *Science* **228**, 1096 (1985).
Briggs, M. S., D. G. Cornell, R. A. Dluhy, L. M. Gierasch, *Science* **233**, 206 (1986).
Bruch, M. D., and L. M. Gierasch, *J. Biol. Chem.* **265**, 3851 (1990).
Bruch, M. D., C. J. McKnight, L. M. Gierasch, *Biochemistry* **28**, 8554 (1989).
Chou, P. Y., and G. D. Fasman, *Biochemistry* **13**, 222 (1974a).
_____, *Biochemistry* **13**, 222 (1974b).
Cornell, D. G., R. A. Dluhy, M. S. Briggs, C. J. McKnight, L. M. Gierasch, *Biochemistry* **28**, 2789 (1989).

Emr, S. D., and T. J. Silhavy, *Proc. Natl. Acad. Sci. U.S.A.* **80,** 4599 (1983).

Evans, E. A., R. Gilmore, G. Blobel, *Proc. Natl. Acad. Sci. U.S.A.* **83,** 581 (1986).

Fandl, J. P., R. Cabelli, D. Oliver, P. C. Tai, *Proc. Natl. Acad. Sci. U.S.A.* **85,** 8953 (1988).

Gierasch, L. M., *Biochemistry* **28,** 923 (1989).

Gilmore, R., P. Walter, G. Blobel, *J. Cell Biol.* **95,** 453 (1982).

Gilmore, R., and G. Blobel, *Cell* **35,** 677 (1983).

Greenfield, N., and G. D. Fasman, *Biochemistry* **8,** 4108 (1969).

Ito, K., *et al., Cell* **32,** 789 (1983).

Ito, K., T. Yura, D. Cerretti, *EMBO J.* **3,** 631 (1984).

Kreig, U., P. Walter, A. Johnson, *Proc. Natl. Acad. Sci. U.S.A.* **83,** 8604 (1986).

Kurzchalia, T. V., *et al., Nature* **320,** 634 (1986).

McKnight, C. J., M. S. Briggs, L. M. Gierasch, *J. Biol. Chem.* **29,** 17293 (1989).

Meyer, D. I., E. Krause, B. Dobberstein, *Nature* **297,** 503 (1982).

Oliver, D. B., and J. Beckwith, *Cell* **30,** 311 (1982).

Randall, L. L., S. J. S. Hardy, J. R. Thom, *Annu. Rev. Microbiol.* **41,** 507 (1987).

Rapoport, T. A., *CRC Crit. Rev. Biochem.* **20,** 73 (1986).

Rees, D. C., L. DeAntonio, D. Eisenberg, *Science* **245,** 510 (1989).

Schmidt, M. G., E. E. Rollo, J. Grodberg, D. B. Oliver, *J. Bacteriol.* **170,** 3404 (1988).

Silver, P., and H. Goodson, *CRC Crit. Rev. Biochem. and Mol. Biol.* **24,** 419 (1989).

Stader, J., S. A. Benson, T. J. Silhavy, *J. Biol. Chem.* **261,** 15075 (1986).

Verner, K., and G. Schatz, *Science* **241,** 1307 (1988).

von Heijne, G., *J. Mol. Biol.* **184,** 99 (1985).

Walter, P., and V. Lingappa, *Annu. Rev. Cell Biol.* **2,** 499 (1986).

Wiedmann, M., T. V. Kurzchalia, E. Hartmann, T. A. Rapoport, *Nature* **328,** 830 (1987).

22

Modulation of Folding Pathways of Exported Proteins by the Leader Sequence

Soonhee Park, Gseping Liu, Traci B. Topping
William H. Cover, Linda L. Randall

Efficient transfer of proteins through membranes during the processes of secretion and mitochondrial assembly in eukaryotes and of export in prokaryotes requires that the polypeptide has not adopted the stably folded structure of the mature species (Maher and Singer, 1986; Eilers and Schatz, 1986; Randall and Hardy, 1986). The current models for the export process incorporate the effects of protein conformation in different ways. One hypothesis prevalent among workers studying eukaryotic systems is that cells contain factors that actively unfold structured precursors by using the hydrolysis of nucleotide triphosphates as a source of energy (Rothman and Kornberg, 1986; Verner and Schatz, 1987). A different notion, proposed for bacterial export, is that components within the cells bind to precursors before they fold into the final mature conformation and thereby maintain (or create) the export-competent state without having to disrupt established tertiary structure (Randall and Hardy, 1986; Crooke and Wickner, 1987). A defining and essential feature of a protein destined for export to the periplasm of *Escherichia coli* is that at its amino terminus, it contains a leader sequence that is proteolytically removed to generate the mature species upon translocation across the membrane. Although functional leader peptides have some common features, there is no sequence similarity among such peptides. In bacteria the leader peptide is likely to be involved in several phases of export, initially in mediating entry into the export pathway, and subsequently in establishing interaction with the membrane at export sites (Ryan and Bassford, 1985; Stader *et al.* 1986; Kaiser *et al.* 1987. For reviews, see Briggs and Gierasch, 1986; Randall *et al.*, 1987). The precise role of the leader sequence in these separate steps may differ. Gierasch and co-workers (Briggs and Gierasch, 1984; Zlotnick *et al.*, 1985; Briggs *et al.*, 1986) have suggested that during the encounter of the precursor with the membrane, the hydrophobicity and conformation of the leader are crucial for its proper insertion into the bilayer. We propose that, in addition, at an earlier step leader sequences allow the initial interaction with components of the export apparatus by modulating the folding pathways of precursor polypeptides,

This chapter is reprinted from *Science* **239**, 1033 (1988).

and we present evidence that the leader sequences of two periplasmic proteins from *Escherichia coli,* those of maltose-binding protein and ribose-binding protein, decrease the rates of folding of these proteins into their mature conformations.

Since we were interested in investigating the effect of leader sequences on the pathway of protein folding in the absence of interaction with any other cellular components, we purified the precursor and mature forms of the proteins[1] and compared the kinetics of their folding in vitro. Both maltose-binding protein (molecular weight 38,500) and ribose-binding protein (molecular weight 29,000) are monomeric and contain no disulfide bonds. Maltose-binding protein contains eight tryptophanyl residues and thus the reversible unfolding-folding transition could be monitored by changes in the intrinsic fluorescence of tryptophan (Lakowicz, 1983). In contrast, fluorescence spectroscopy could not be used to monitor the folding of ribose-binding protein, because that protein contains no tryptophan, and no change in the fluorescence of tyrosine was observed when the protein was denatured. Studies of the folding of ribose-binding protein were thus performed by measuring the resistance of the mature conformation to proteolytic degradation as the assay for folding.

Using fluorescence spectroscopy, we have investigated the equilibrium unfolding transition of maltose-binding protein induced by guanidinium hydrochloride (GuHCl) (G. Liu *et al.,* unpublished results) and have shown that the data can be approximated by a simple two-state model. We can represent the reaction as follows:

$$\text{Native} \underset{k_f}{\overset{k_u}{\rightleftharpoons}} \text{Unfolded}$$

The experimental approach that we have taken is based on the elegant work of Matthews and co-workers (Beasty, 1986; Beasty *et al.,* 1987). Purified maltose-binding protein either in a folded (no denaturant present) or unfolded (denaturant present) state was subjected to a rapid change in conditions that required the protein to achieve a new equi-

---

1   Mature maltose-binding protein was purified from *E. coli* strain MC4100 by affinity chromatography by using cross-linked amylose as the resin (Ferenci and Klotz, 1978). The maltose was removed from the pure protein by extensive dialysis against 10 mM tris-HCl, pH 7.6. To obtain precursor maltose-binding protein, we grew *E. coli* strain MM18 (Ito *et al.,* 1981) in M9 minimal salts medium supplemented with 0.4 percent glycerol. When the density reached 1.5×10^8 cells per milliliter, maltose was added (0.2 percent) and growth was continued for 3.5 hours. Cells were harvested by low-speed centrifugation, converted to spheroplasts (Witholt *et al.,* 1976), and the periplasm was removed. After the spheroplasts were disrupted by sonication, the suspension was centrifuged at 20,000g for 20 minutes. The pellet was suspended in 10 mM Hepes, pH 7.6, 3 percent Triton X-100, and 5 mM EDTA. After incubation for 15 minutes on ice, the suspension was centrifuged at 20,000g for 10 minutes. The pellet was solubilized in 10 mM Hepes, pH 7.6, 4M guanidinium hydrochloride (GuHCl) and incubated at 22°C for 15 minutes. The GuHCl was diluted to 0.15M and the solution was incubated at 22°C for 30 minutes. After the solution was centrifuged at 16,000g for 10 minutes, the supernatant was removed and concentrated to a minimal volume in an Amicon ultrafiltration cell with a PM10 membrane. The precursor was purified from this sample by affinity chromatography as described above for the mature species. Maltose was removed from the precursor maltose-binding protein by repeated dilution and volume reduction in an Amicon ultrafiltration cell (PM10 membrane).

     To facilitate purification of mature ribose-binding protein and the precursor form, the appropriate alleles of *rbsB* were cloned under the lambda P_L promoter on the plasmid vector pPLC2833. The procedures for cloning and purification are described in detail elsewhere (Park, 1987). The mature protein was purified from the periplasmic fraction obtained by osmotic shock of cells and the precursor was obtained from lysed spheroplasts. The purification procedure involved two sequential steps of ion-exchange column chromatography (DEAE-Sephadex and CM-Sephadex) followed by chromatofocusing (Pharmacia, Mono P). We were unable to obtain quantities of wild-type precursor sufficient for these studies. Therefore, we used a precursor with a mutated but functional leader sequence (see footnote 2).

librium mixture of the native and unfolded states. The relaxation time to reach the new equilibrium position was determined by monitoring the change in fluorescence with time. Experiments were carried out to determine the relaxation time as a function of the final concentration of GuHC1 (Fig. 1).

Comparison of the data for the mature protein with those for the precursor indicates that the presence of the leader sequence does not significantly alter the relaxation time for the unfolding transition but increases the relaxation time, τ, for the folding transition, which can be related to the rate constants as $\tau^{-1} = k_u + k_f$. For experiments where the concentration of denaturant is high, $k_u >> k_f$ and $\tau^{-1} \cong k_u$. Where the concentration of denaturation is low, $\tau^{-1} \cong k_f$. The data show that the presence of the leader decreases the rate of folding but has little effect on the rate of unfolding. The magnitude of the effect that might be physiologically significant is difficult to define precisely since we do not know what limits the rate of folding in vivo. The in vitro rate-limiting step, which is monitored by fluorescence, changes at approximately 0.5M GuHCl. Below that concentration, the relaxation time is independent of the concentration of denaturant, whereas above 0.5M, the relaxation time shows dependence on the final concentration of GuHCl. The denaturant-independent phase may reflect cis-trans isomerization of proline residues about X-Pro peptide bonds (for review, see Kim and Baldwin, 1982). The presence of the leader sequence increases the relaxation time for this phase by a factor of ~3. If the rate-limiting step in vivo were that reflected in the transitions above 0.5M GuHCl, the presence of the leader would have an even greater effect: extrapolation to 0M GuHCl shows that the leader increases the relaxation time of this step by about 40-fold, from 0.7 to 28 seconds (Fig. 1).

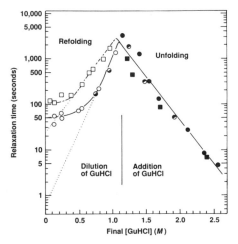

Fig. 1. Comparison of relaxation times for folding transitions of mature and precursor maltose-binding proteins. The relaxation times for folding (open symbols) and unfolding (closed symbols) transitions were obtained by monitoring the change in fluorescence of tryptophan. For unfolding transitions the protein was initially in 10 mM Hepes, pH 7.8, and guanidinium hydrochloride (GuHCl) was added to the final concentration shown. For refolding transitions, the protein was dissolved in 2M GuHCl, which was diluted to the final concentration shown. Fluorescence measurements were made with a Perkin-Elmer MPF-3L. The excitation and emission wavelengths used were 295 nm and 344 nm, respectively; mature maltose-binding protein (O); precursor maltose-binding protein (☐). The precursor species was purified by a procedure that includes one cycle of unfolding-refolding.[1] As a control, the mature species was subjected to a cycle of unfolding-refolding. Relaxation times determined with this material are represented by the half-closed circles; unfolding transition (◑); refolding (●).

The presence of a functional leader peptide on ribose-binding protein (Iida, 1985)[2] decreases the rate of folding of that precursor by a factor of 3 relative to the rate of folding of the corresponding mature protein (Figs. 2 and 3). Since analysis of folding of ribose-binding protein used the resistance to proteolytic degradation as the assay for the folded state (Fig. 2), refolding had to be monitored under conditions in which the folding was complete at equilibrium (that is, a rapid dilution of the

---

2   The precursor used in this study carries a functional leader that differs from the wild type at two positions. The substitution of a leucyl residue at position −17 by a prolyl residue caused a defect in export, and the second substitution of a seryl residue at −15 by a phenylalanyl residue restored export. The amount of mature protein in the periplasm of the revertant strain is equal to that in the wild type; however, the export of precursor in the revertant strain is slightly slower than normal.

urea from 6 to 0.1M). Thus, our analysis was in this case restricted to effects on the step that is rate limiting under these conditions. The folding pathway may include another step (as was the case for the folding of maltose-binding protein) that might also be influenced by the leader. Unfortunately, we could not investigate this possibility.

The final folded state achieved by each precursor polypeptide resembles that of the corresponding mature species because treatment with proteinase K removed only the leader sequence from each precursor and left the mature protein intact (see Fig. 2 and Randall and Hardy, 1986). In addition, precursor maltose-binding protein was purified by its ability to bind ligand, which suggests the achievement of native structure.

The export apparatus may not be capable of interacting with or translocating a precursor polypeptide after it has attained the

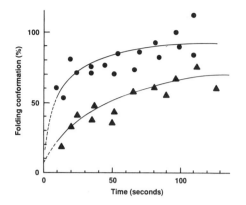

Fig. 3. Kinetics of folding of mature and precursor forms of ribose-binding protein. Purified protein was unfolded by incubation at 30°C for 30 minutes in 6M urea, 10 mM Hepes, pH 7.1. Folding was initiated at 12.5°C by dilution of the urea to a final concentration of 0.1M in 10 mM Hepes, pH 7.1. Samples were withdrawn at the times indicated and rapidly chilled by transfer into tubes held on ice. The resistance of ribose-binding protein to proteolytic degradation was assessed as described in the legend to Fig. 2. Quantification of the percent of protein that had folded was obtained from densitometric tracings of the Coomassie blue-stained gels. Samples withdrawn at 2 and 5 minutes indicated that the plateau levels of folding were 95 and 70% for the mature and precursor proteins, respectively. To determine the relative effect of the leader on folding, the times taken for the species to obtain half of the maximal folding observed were compared. Mature ribose-binding protein (●); precursor, ribose-binding protein (▲).

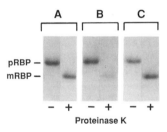

Proteinase K

Fig. 2. Assay of the folded state of ribose-binding protein by measuring resistance to proteolytic degradation. Purified precursor ribose-binding protein (molecular weight 31,000) was subjected to the following treatments before assessing the resistance to proteolytic degradation. (A) Native protein, no treatment, held on ice. (B) Unfolded by incubation with 6M urea, 10 mM Hepes, pH 7.1, for 30 minutes at 30°C. (C) Unfolded as described for (B) and subsequently refolded by dilution of the urea to 0.1 M with 10 mM Hepes, pH 7.1, and incubation at 30°C for 30 minutes. Following treatment, the samples were placed on ice and incubated without (−) or with (+) proteinase K (1.5 μg/ml) for 20 minutes. Proteolysis was terminated by addition of sample buffer for SDS-polyacrylamide gel electrophoresis (Randall and Hardy, 1986) containing phenylmethylsulfonyl fluoride (0.2 mM). After incubation at 100°C for 5 minutes, the samples were analyzed by SDS-13% polyacrylamide gel electrophoresis. Only the relevant portion of the Coomassie blue-stained gel is shown. Proteolytic digestion of the precursor when it is in a folded state results in removal of the leader; the mature portion, which is resistant to degradation, is recovered as a species that migrates during electrophoresis at the position of the mature protein.

conformation characteristic of the mature species. The slowing of the folding rate by leader sequences might reflect a function critical to export. Modulation of the folding pathway by the presence of the leader peptide could either expose or create an element of structure that is not accessible or not present in the mature species, but that is essential to allow functional interaction with the export apparatus as was originally proposed in the trigger hypothesis (Wickner, 1979). Such a role for leader peptides could explain the immense variation that exists among sequences that function to initiate export. In addition to the wide range of naturally occurring leader sequences, a surprisingly high frequency of randomly cloned sequences function in export in yeast (20 percent [Kaiser *et al.*, 1987]) and in bacteria (between 4 and 15 percent [Smith *et al.*, 1987]). It may be that many sequences, normally sequestered by the rapid folding of polypeptides, when moved out of their proper context and inserted at the beginning of an exported protein, can kinetically interfere with folding to the mature species and allow the protein to enter the export pathway.

Acknowledgments

We are grateful to F. W. Dahlquist for suggesting that leader peptides might have an effect on the kinetics of folding. We thank C. R. Matthews for constant advice and J. Knowles for critically reading the manuscript. This work was supported by a grant from the National Institutes of Health (GM29798) to L. L. R.

References

Briggs, M. S., and L. M. Gierasch, *Biochemistry* **23,** 3111 (1984).

———, *Adv. Protein. Chem.* **38,** 109 (1986).

Briggs, M. S., D. G. Cornell, R. A. Dluhy, L. M. Gierasch, *Science* **233,** 206 (1986).

Briggs, M. S., A. Zlotnick, J. D. Lear, W. F. DeGrado, *Science* **228,** 1096 (1985)

Beasty, A. M., *et al., Biochemistry* **25,** 2965 (1986).

———, in *Protein Engineering,* D. L. Oxender and C. F. Fox, Eds. (Liss, New York, 1987), p. 91.

Crooke, E., and W. Wickner, *Proc. Natl. Acad. Sci. U.S.A.* **84,** 5216 (1987).

Eilers, M., and G. Schatz, *Nature (London)* **322,** 228 (1986).

Ferenci, T., and U. Klotz, *FEBS Lett.* **94,** 213 (1978).

Iida, A., *et al., EMBO J.* **4,** 1875 (1985).

Ito, K., P. J. Bassford, Jr., J. Beckwith, *Cell* **24,** 707 (1981).

Kaiser, C. A., D. Preuss, P. Grisafi, D. Botstein, *Science* **235,** 312 (1987).

Kim, P. S., and R. L. Baldwin, *Annu. Rev. Biochem.* **51,** 459 (1982).

Lakowicz, J. R., *Principles of Fluorescence Spectroscopy* (Plenum, New York, 1983).

Maher, P. A., and S. J. Singer, *Proc. Natl. Acad. Sci. U.S.A.* **83,** 9001 (1986).

Park, S., Thesis, Washington State University, Pullman (1987).

Randall, L. L., and S. J. S. Hardy, *Cell* **46,** 921 (1986).

Randall, L. L., S. J. S. Hardy, J. R. Thom, *Annu. Rev. Microbiol.* **41,** 507 (1987).

Rothman, J. E., and R. D. Kornberg, *Nature (London)* **322,** 209 (1986).

Ryan, J. P., and P. J. Bassford, Jr., *J. Biol. Chem.* **260,** 14832 (1985).

Smith, H., S. Bron, J. van Ee, G. Venema, *J. Bacteriol.* **169,** 3321 (1987).

Stader, J., S.A. Benson, T. J. Silhavy, *J. Biol. Chem.* **261,** 15075 (1986).

Verner, K., and G. Schatz, *EMBO J.* **6,** 2449 (1987).

Wickner, W., *Annu. Rev. Biochem.* **48,** 23 (1979).

Witholt, B., *et al., Anal. Biochem.* **74,** 160 (1976).

23

Identification of Amino Acid Sequences Influencing Intracellular Folding Pathways Using Temperature-Sensitive Folding Mutations

Jonathan King, Bentley Fane, Cameron Haase-Pettingell
Anna Mitraki, Robert Villafane, Myeong-Hee Yu

Recent results on both the in vivo folding and in vitro refolding of proteins establish the existence of partially folded intermediates. It has often been assumed that such species are pauses on a continuum from an unfolded chain to the fully folded native state. In fact, the existing data suggest that within cells, folding intermediates have properties and functions of their own, not necessarily reflected in the native state. In the two-disulfide intermediate of bovine pancreatic trypsin inhibitor (BPTI), cysteines at the opposite ends of the native protein are joined in a disulfide bond (Creighton and Goldenberg, 1984; Creighton, chapter 16, this volume). Thus, this intermediate must have chain conformations that are absent from the native species. Similarly the identification of intracellular proteins that bind to newly synthesized, not yet native chains—sec B, SRP, GroEL/S, BIP—suggest that the partially folded intermediates that are recognized may have distinct sites and properties.

The conformation of these intermediates must be encoded in the genes and amino se-quences of these polypeptide chains. This grammar, through which sequence specifies structure, must specify temporal as well as spatial components of the processes—first form conformation a, then transform to conformation b, then interact with region c to form N. If the amino acid sequence does specify the conformation of folding intermediates, it will not generally be possible to deduce the nature of the rules simply by comparing native structure to amino acid sequence. The conformation of the intermediate will be needed.

To determine the rules through which sequence specifies structure requires describing not only the conformation of the intermediates but also the identity of those residues in the sequence that direct the conformation of the intermediates. For some polypeptide chains of interest, we have been involved in developing a methodology for identifying those residues and local sequences that direct the conformation of the intracellular folding intermediates.

Three formal models for the distribution of the folding pathway information through the polypeptide chain amino acid sequence are shown in Fig. 1.

In the conventional model, every residue contributes to determining the conformation. This model underlies most algorithms for predicting secondary structure. However, it cannot be correct: comparison of the sequences of members of structurally homologous protein families such as the hemoglobin reveal tolerance at many positions in the chain for different residues (Bashford *et al.*, 1987). Many positions must be silent with respect to determining folding and final conformation.

The second model, in which residues or groups of residues controlling folding are dispersed throughout the sequence, is consistent with the comparative studies. This dispersion also explains the success of protein engineering studies of active sites. The efforts to modify active sites involve recovering native-like species with amino acid substitutions at the active site. The recovery and partial enzymatic activity of such mutant proteins means that these active site residues were not making a significant contribution to the folding pathway or final conformation.

However, this grammar is still too simple. Kabsch and Sander (1984) have shown that identical pentapeptide sequences take different conformations in different proteins.

Thus, local sequences usually do not directly determine their own local conformation in proteins.

An interactive or context-dependent set of rules is more realistic. The figure is still simplistic, since it assumes contiguity of the essential residues. It is physically more likely that interacting residues are linearly dispersed.

Analyzing Control of Protein Folding Within the Cell

Our strategy has been to isolate mutations that specifically affect the folding pathway rather than the native protein and then characterize the mutant polypeptide chain to determine if, in fact, it has folded incompletely or incorrectly within the cell (Smith *et al.*, 1980; Goldenberg and King, 1981; Smith and King, 1981). For those mutants that are blocked in the chain folding pathway, mapping and sequencing identifies critical residues. Such mutants will only exist where there is an intracellular folding pathway in which intermediates are well differentiated from the native structure.

Mutants that prevent the folding of the polypeptide chain are generally absolute lethal mutations. Historically such mutants have

Fig. 1. Formal models for the amino acid sequence rules for protein folding. The strings represent an amino acid sequence that will form the helix-turn-helix conformation shown at the left. The "conventional" model at the right assumes that all residues in the sequence contribute to specifying chain conformation. The model in the center assumes that dispersed groups of residues direct the folding pathway while the intervening residues are passive, presumably awaiting their later role in the activity of the native protein. The model at the left, which we prefer, assumes that dispersed sequences direct the folding pathway but that these sequences are sensitive to their local environment so that identical sequences would specify different conformations, depending on context.

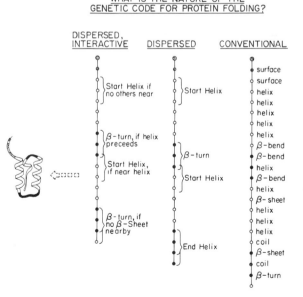

not been given much attention by molecular geneticists or microbial physiologists (King and Yu, 1986). However, with absolute mutants, no native form of the protein is available (Schwarz and Berget, 1989). Given that the analytical and conceptual basis of protein biochemistry is built on the features of a relatively homogenous, soluble native species, this causes serious problems.

Instead, we decided to isolate conditional lethal mutations — temperature-sensitive mutations — in which the folding defect was expressed at high temperature and not at low temperature (Edgar and Lielausis, 1964). One of the authors, Jonathan King, was a graduate student with Robert S. Edgar during the development of temperature-sensitive (*t*s) mutations as genetic tools. The mutants fell into two classes: TL for thermolabile protein and TSS for temperature-sensitive synthesis (Sadler and Novick, 1965). We thought that some of the TSS class might be defective in polypeptide chain folding or assembly. Once correctly folded and assembled, the sensitive stage would be passed, accounting for the thermostability of the mature forms.

Since the initial work of Anfinsen and coworkers (Anfinsen, 1973), it has been difficult to determine how unfolded chains successfully refold in vitro with little help. A problem frequently faced in refolding studies is off-pathway aggregation reactions, which compete with folding into the native conformation (Goldberg, see chapter 15, this volume). Biochemists traditionally solve this problems by working at the lowest chain concentrations possible. But, within cells actively synthesizing proteins, ribosomes are relatively densely packed and local protein concentrations are very high (Fig. 2). Yet, without urea, guanidine hydrochloride, or dilute conditions, polypeptide chains reach their native conformations. We have been particularly interested in how folding is assured under these intracellular conditions (Mitraki and King, 1989).

Properties of the Thermostable Tailspike Endorhamnosidase

To ascertain whether mutations interfere with the intracellular folding process requires a system in which the intracellular maturation intermediates can be conveniently discriminated from the native state. The protein that satisfied this requirement was the tailspike endorhamnosidase of Salmonella phage P22, the virion cell attachment or adhesion organelle

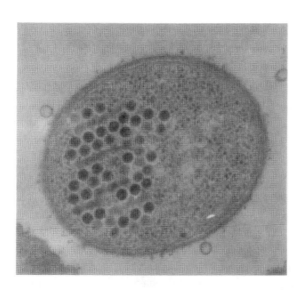

Fig. 2. Cross section of a Salmonella cell infected by phage P22. The particles on the outside of the cell injected their DNA into the cells prior to fixation of the culture. The large darkly stained particles are the newly assembled phage capsids, which are 50 percent protein, 50 percent DNA. The small dark dots around the cell periphery are ribosomes actively synthesizing both phage and bacterial proteins.

(Israel *et al.,* 1967; Iwashita and Kanegasaki, 1976; Berget and Poteete, 1980).

There are six tailspikes in a complete phage; each tailspike is itself a trimer of three identical polypeptide chains, the product of phage gene 9 (Botstein *et al.,* 1973; Goldenberg *et al.,* 1982). Each polypeptide chain has 666 amino acids (Sauer *et al.,* 1982). There is no known covalent modification; all the transformations are conformational. The tailspike recognizes the O-antigen, of the Salmonella surface and binds to it.

The three-dimensional structure has not yet been solved. However, crystals diffracting to 2.4 angstroms have been obtained by Tom Alber, and we expect the structure within a year or two. It is already clear from laser Raman spectroscopy carried out by George J. Thomas, Jr., and co-workers that the structure is dominated by β-sheet (Sargent *et al.,* 1988). Given the elongated morphology of the protein, its core is most likely a complex cross β rod, in which short lengths of β-strand are adjacent, connected by turns, and then two or more such segments form a cross β-sheet sandwich. Such structures often display a conformational repeat, though the amino acid sequence may not be obviously repetitive.

To study the folding of the tailspike chain into the soluble tailspike rather than the assembly of the tailspike onto the virion, we block the assembly of the virus shell by introducing an additional mutation that prevents assembly of the shell. Under these conditions, the DNA is not packaged and the synthesis of the tailspike increases tenfold over the wild-type level, so that it is a major protein of the infected cell (Adams *et al.,* 1985).

The binding of the tailspike to heads generating infectious particles is the last step in the assembly pathway. This reaction proceeds very efficiently in vitro and provides an activity assay for this structural protein (Israel *et al.,* 1967). The tailspikes are also good antigens and are the targets of the neutralizing antibody induced in animals. Bertrand Friguet and Lisa Djavadi in Michel Goldberg's group at the Pasteur Institute in Paris have raised over two dozen monoclonal antibodies directed against the tailspike.

An important feature of the proteins for these studies is the thermal stability of the mature tailspike. The T_m for thermal melting is 88°C (Sturtevant *et al.,* 1989; Sargent *et al.,* 1988). This probably reflects the tailspike's role as an external structural protein of a virus that has evolved to survive in the stomach, in the sewer, in the soil, and in the streets of Boston and Paris.

Its thermal stability is matched by resistance to other denaturants (Fig. 3). The protein is resistant to most proteases and is not denatured in concentrations of sodium dodecyl sulfate (SDS), which denature all other phage and host proteins to SDS polypeptide complexes (Goldenberg *et al.,* 1982). As a result, incompletely or incorrectly folded chains form SDS/polypeptide chain complexes, and these can be distinguished from the native conformation, which remains native and migrates much more slowly under the same conditions.

Recently, the tailspike has been successfully refolded in vitro, starting with chains fully unfolded in urea at low *p*H (Seckler *et al.,* 1989).

Identifying In Vivo Folding Intermediates

Unlike many of the experiments reported in other chapters of this volume, most of the experiments reviewed here are performed on polypeptide chains newly synthesized within cells, and often the characterization is performed within the crude cell extracts. The partially folded species do not come from denaturation but from biosynthesis off the ribosome. Cells are infected with P22 phage wild type or phage carrying a mutant of interest, and, late after infection, such cells fill up with phage components. Most of the experiments utilize a short pulse of radioactive amino acids, so that we detect polypeptide chains synthesized during a defined time period.

The use of phage infected cells rather than uninfected or plasmid carrying cells provides certain technical advantages. Late after

gp9 TAIL SPIKE ACTIVITIES AND CHARACTERISTICS

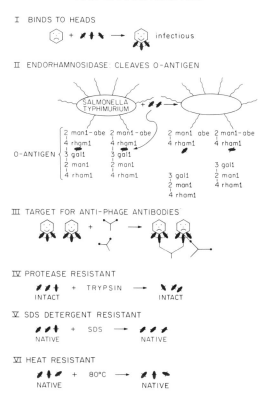

Fig. 3. Properties of the P22 tailspike endorhamnosidase.

infection, the phage genome directs the synthesis of a lysozyme so that the infected cells can be rapidly and easily lysed.

Proteins chosen for in vitro refolding structures have generally been small so that the partially folded intermediates would have limited structure. However, even a partially folded intermediate of something as large as the tailspike might have considerable local structure and, therefore, be relatively long lived.

David Goldenberg, when a graduate student, attempted to trap such intermediates by rapidly chilling samples of pulse-labeled infected cells and fractionating the proteins through an acrylamide gel in the cold in the absence of denaturants. In these experiments, the tailspike is being expressed at a sufficiently high rate that it is the major radioactively labeled species in these samples. Using these

procedures, Goldenberg was able to trap intermediates in chain folding and association and delineate the in vivo folding pathway shown in Fig. 4 (Goldenberg and King, 1982).

The results of such an experiment with cells infected with phage encoding wild-type tailspikes are shown in the first two lanes of the gels shown in Fig. 9 later in the text. On warming such samples, the "protrimer" species converts to the native tailspike (Goldenberg and King, 1982). The single-chain intermediate was identified in later work but is not long lived enough to migrate through the gel as a tight band (Goldenberg *et al.*, 1983; Haase-Pettingell and King, 1988).

These results led to the following model for the intracellular chain folding and association pathway shown in Fig. 4. Chains released from the ribosome form an early, partially folded, single-chain intermediate. This folds to a state sufficiently structured for specific chain recognition. These species associate into the protrimer, in which the chains are associated but not fully folded. The protrimer can be trapped in the cold and is sufficiently long lived to form a discrete band in a native acrylamide gel (Goldenberg and King, 1982). The protrimer transforms to the native spike in a presumed first-order reaction. It is in this last step that the stability of the native spike is attained.

Note that there is no species corresponding to a native monomer; chain folding and chain assembly are coupled as in collagen or myosin maturation. The half time for the reaction is 5 minutes at 30°C.

As noted above, when samples of lysed infected cells are applied to an SDS gel, the mature native tailspikes remain native in the presence of SDS and migrate much more slowly than the denatured extended SDS polypeptide chain complex, which is binding 1.4 grams of SDS gram protein (Reynolds and Tanford, 1970). Those chains that have not yet matured into native trimers are denatured by the detergent and easily distinguished from the native tailspikes. Though both single-chain and protrimer intermediates are melted out by detergents, fractionation of samples through an SDS gel in the absence of heating provides

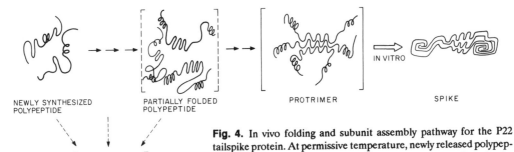

NEWLY SYNTHESIZED
POLYPEPTIDE

PARTIALLY FOLDED
POLYPEPTIDE

PROTRIMER

SPIKE

IN VITRO

AGGREGATED STATE

Fig. 4. In vivo folding and subunit assembly pathway for the P22 tailspike protein. At permissive temperature, newly released polypeptide chains form a partially folded single chain intermediate. In the productive pathway these single chains fold further into a state competent for chain/chain recognition. The product of the chain association reaction, the protrimer, is metastable and can be trapped in the cold (Goldenberg and King, 1982). The stability toward heat and chemical denaturants is achieved in the transformation of the protrimer to the native trimer.

a convenient tool for following the intracellular events and screening mutants.

Thermolabile Intermediates for a Thermostable Protein

Though the native tailspike is thermostable, intermediates in the pathway are thermolabile. Using the SDS sensitivity of the intermediates, we can measure what fraction of the chains released from the ribosome successfully reach the native conformation. As can be seen in Fig. 5, this fraction decreases with increasing temperature (Goldenberg *et al.*, 1982; Yu and King, 1984). Subsequent studies have shown that the early single-chain intermediate is the thermolabile species (Haase-Pettingell and King, 1988). This species or this step is thermolabile in the wild-type infected cells; as the temperature of maturation increases, the fraction of chains that reach the fully native state decreases quite sharply, so that by 40°C, only 20 percent of the completed chains reach the native state.

The rate and yield of native tailspikes from newly synthesized polypeptide chains also decreases at lower temperatures (Fig. 5). This reflects the cold sensitivity of the protrimer to native transition.

The chains that fail to reach the native state are not degraded, but will accumulate as inclusion bodies. We describe the process of inclusion body formation in more detail in a later section.

Isolation of Mutations Affecting Protein Folding Within the Cell

The isolation of mutations that prevent the chain from reaching the native structure causes an empirical and theoretical quandary. Most techniques of physical biochemistry depend on the existence of a soluble discrete native state. The conceptual frameworks of physical biochemistry also rest on the properties of native states. This is particularly the case for refolding studies where one measures transition and equilibria between native and unfolded states. As a result, if a mutant protein cannot reach its native state, standard physical biochemical methods may be difficult to apply. In fact, such absolute lethal amino acid substitutions have been described for the P22 tailspike by Schwarz and Berget(1989) and by Fane and King (1987).

To circumvent this problem, we have concentrated on conditional lethal mutants, namely, temperature-sensitive mutants, in which the mutation renders the folding *process* highly thermolabile. These mutations allow the production, by growth of the infected cell at low temperatures, of a fully native but mutant protein.

The *ts* mutations are isolated by conventional criteria. The phage forms a plaque at low temperatures but not at high temperatures. Such mutations occur in most of the genes of the phage (Edgar and Lielausis, 1964). Using the procedures of microbial genetics, we find the ones in gene 9 and then

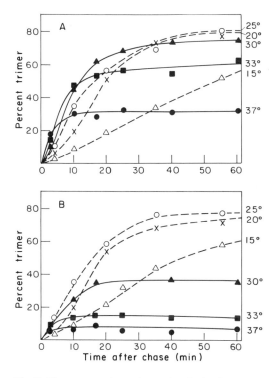

Fig. 5. Temperature dependence of the in vivo formation of mature tailspikes (Yu and King, 1984). The abscissa represents tailspike chains in the native trimeric conformation as fraction of total tailspike polypeptides synthesized during a pulse of radioactive amino acids. The upper panel shows the folding of the wild-type protein within phage infected cells. The lower panel shows the folding of a *tsf* chain within mutant infected cells. Bacteria were infected as 30°C with either (A) *wt,* 9 [+] /5−/13− or (B) *ts* H300/5− /13−. After 60 minutes ^{14}C-labeled amino acids were added to the infected cells and then chased for 1 minute with cold amino acids. One minute after chase, portions of the culture were transferred to 15 °C (open triangles), 20±C (X) 25°C (open circles), 30±C (filled triangles), 33°C (filled squares) and 37°C (filled circles). At various times afterwards, samples were withdrawn and lysed by freezing and thawing. The samples were electrophoresed through SDS/polyacrylamide gels without prior heating. The peaks corresponding to the mature trimer and the SDS/polypeptide chain complex were quantified.

order them. The steps are (Smith *et al.,* 1980): (i) random mutagenesis of mature phage (usually by ultraviolet light), (ii) isolation of strains that propagate at 28°C but are unable to propagate at 38°C, (iii) genetic complementation tests against amber mutations in the late phage genes, (iv) selection of those *ts* mutants that are in gene 9, (v) fine-structure mapping against deletions extending into gene 9 and by

two factor crosses, (vi) examination of the behavior of the mutant polypeptide chains, under both permissive and restrictive conditions (Goldenberg and King, 1981; Smith and King, 1981), (vii) intragenic complementation and dominance tests, and (viii) sequencing of restriction fragments most likely to contain nucleotide substitution (Yu and King, 1984; Villafane and King, 1988).

The selection for the folding defects comes not from an explicit experimental manipulation but from the initial choice of target — a gene whose product, the tailspike, is extremely thermostable. The thermostability acts as a natural barrier against picking up the TL class of *ts* mutants; single amino acid substitutions are unlikely to lower the melting temperature of a protein by 50°C. Of the more than 20 mutant proteins whose thermostability we have studied in detail, none lower the T_m by more than 8°C. Since, as we describe below, the defects are in intermediate steps in the chain folding pathway, we called these *ts* mutants temperature-sensitive folding (*tsf*) mutants.

More than 100 *ts* mutations in gene 9 have been isolated (Smith *et al.,* 1980; M.-P. Corr, K. Haubert, A. Marra, R. Seet, J. King, unpublished results). Genetic mapping and DNA sequencing indicate that they define some 30 sites in the central third of the gene and polypeptide chain. The map in Fig. 6 shows the distribution of the temperature-sensitive mutations along the gene and polypeptide chain. At the bottom, the distribution is summarized. All of the *ts* mutations map in the central region of the gene and polypeptide chain. No *ts* mutations have been recovered in the region from residue 1 to 150, and none in the C-terminal 500 to 666 region of the chain. Assuming the mutations to follow a Poisson distribution, we estimate that there are likely to be a total of 40 such sites, so that on the order of 75 percent of the possible sites of such *tsf* amino acid substitutions have been identified.

The identity of the sites of these mutations is quite nonrandom (Table 1). They fall predominantly at the sites of glycines and hydrophilic amino acids. Although the central

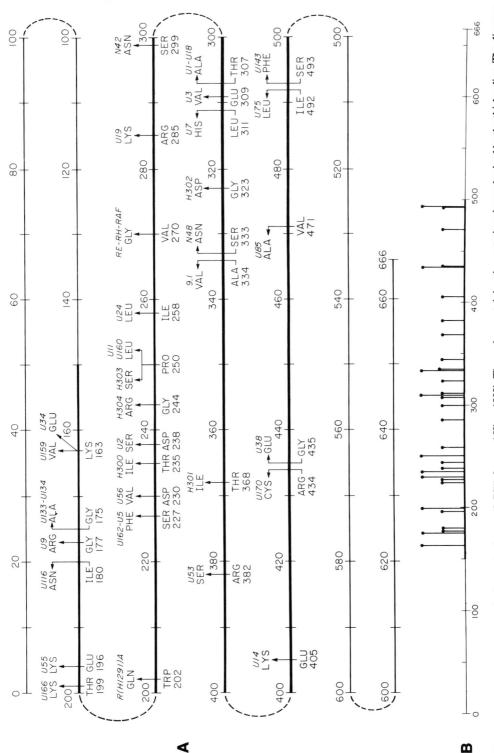

Fig. 6. Sites and substitutions of *tsf* mutation in gene 9 (Villafane and King, 1988). The region containing the mutations is emphasized by the thicker line. The diagram is calibrated in amino acid position coordinates, with 666 amino acids in the complete tailspike chain (Sauer *et al.*, 1982). The distribution of the sites is summarized on the bottom line.

Table 1. Sites of *tsf* mutations in the tailspike gene.

Allele	Codon no.	Amino acid substitution	Local sequence
tsU131	175	Gly > Ala	Ala · Lys · Phe · Ile · **Gly** · Asp · Gly · Asn · Leu
tsU134	175	Gly > Ala	Ala · Lys · Phe · Ile · **Gly** · Asp · Gly · Asn · Leu
tsU9	177	Gly > Arg	Phe · Ile · Gly · Asp · **Gly** · Asn · Leu · Ile · Phe
tsH304	244	Gly > Arg	Val · Lys · Phe · Pro · **Gly** · Ile · Glu · Thr · Leu
tsH302	323	Gly > Asp	Asn · Tyr · Val · Ile · **Gly** · Gly · Arg · Thr · Ser
tsU38	435	Gly > Glu	Leu · Leu · Val · Arg · **Gly** · Ala · Leu · Gly · Val
tsH303	250	Pro > Ser	Glu · Thr · Leu · Leu · **Pro** · Pro · Asn · Ala · Lys
tsU11	250	Pro > Leu	Glu · Thr · Leu · Leu · **Pro** · Pro · Asn · Ala · Lys
tsU160	250	Pro > Leu	Glu · Thr · Leu · Leu · **Pro** · Pro · Asn · Ala · Lys
tsU166	199	Thr > Lys	Met · Glu · Ser · Thr · **Thr** · thr · Pro · Trp · Val
tsH300	235	Thr > Ile	Gly · Tyr · Gln · Pro · **Thr** · Val · Ser · Asp · Tyr
tsH301	368	Thr > Ile	Thr · Trp · Gln · Gly · **Thr** · Val · Gly · Ser · Thr
tsU18	307	Thr > Ala	Asp · Gly · Ile · Ile · **Thr** · Phe · Glu · Asn · Leu
tsU1	307	Thr > Ala	Asp · Gly · Ile · Ile · **Thr** · Phe · Glu · Asn · Leu
tsU5	227	Ser > Phe	Thr · Leu · Lys · Gln · **Ser** · Lys · Thr · Asp · Gly
tsU162	227	Ser > Phe	Thr · Leu · Lys · Gln · **Ser** · Lys · Thr · Asp · Gly
tsN42	299	Ser > Asn	Ala · Asn · Asn · Pro · **Ser** · Gly · Gly · Lys · Asp
tsN48	333	Ser > Asn	Gly · Ser · Val · Ser · **Ser** · Ala · Gln · Phe · Leu
tsU143	493	Ser > Phe	Gln · Ile · Tyr · Ile · **Ser** · Gly · Ala · Cys · Arg
tsU19	285	Arg > Lys	Gly · Phe · Leu · Phe · **Arg** · Gly · Cys · His · Phe
tsU53	382	Arg > Ser	Asn · Leu · Gln · Phe · **Arg** · Asp · Ser · Val · Val
tsU170	434	Arg > Cys	Asn · Leu · Leu · Val · **Arg** · Gly · Ala · Leu · Gly
tsU159	163	Lys > Val	Asp · Phe · Gly · Gly · **Lys** · Val · Leu · Thr · Ile
tsU34	163	Lys > Glu	Asp · Phe · Gly · Gly · **Lys** · Val · Leu · Thr · Ile
tsU57	230	Asp > Val	Glu · Ser · Lys · Thr · **Asp** · Gly · Tyr · Glu · Pro
tsU56	230	Asp > Val	Glu · Ser · Lys · Thr · **Asp** · Gly · Tyr · Glu · Pro
tsU2	238	Asp > Ser	Pro · Thr · Val · Ser · **Asp** · Tyr · Val · Lys · Phe
tsU55	196	Glu > Lys	Gly · Val · Phe · Met · **Glu** · Ser · Thr · Thr · Thr
tsU3	309	Glu > Val	Ile · Ile · Thr · Phe · **Glu** · Asn · Leu · Ser · Gly
tsmU8	344	Glu > Lys	Asn · Gly · Gly · Phe · **Glu** · Arg · Asp · Gly · Gly
tsU14	405	Glu > Lys	Asp · Met · Asn · Pro · **Glu** · Leu · Asp · Arg · Pro
ts9.1	334	Ala > Val	Ser · Val · Ser · Ser · **Ala** · Gln · Phe · Leu · Arg
tsU86	224	Leu > Ser	Val · Val · Ala · Thr · **Leu** · Lys · Gln · Ser · Lys
tsU7	311	Leu > His	Thr · Phe · Glu · Asn · **Leu** · Ser · Gly · Asp · Trp
tsU116	180	Ile > Asn	Asp · Gly · Asn · Leu · **Ile** · Phe · Thr · Lys · Leu
tsU24	258	Ile > Leu	Lys · Gly · Gln · Asn · **Ile** · Thr · Ser · Thr · Leu
tsU75	492	Ile > Leu	Asn · Gln · Ile · Tyr · **Ile** · Ser · Gly · Ala · Cys
tsRAF	270	Val > Gly	Glu · Cys · Ile · Gly · **Val** · Glu · Val · His · Arg
tsRE	270	Val > Gly	Glu · Cys · Ile · Gly · **Val** · Glu · Val · His · Arg
tsRH	270	Val > Gly	Glu · Cys · Ile · Gly · **Val** · Glu · Val · His · Arg
tsU85	471	Val > Ala	Thr · His · Glu · Ser · **Val** · Phe · Thr · Asn · Ile

third of the chain contains 38 aromatic amino acids, none of the *tsf* sites fall at the positions of aromatic amino acids. We suspect that mutations in these residues would cause absolute lethal defects in protein folding. Absolute lethal mutations in gene 9 have been isolated by Schwarz and Berget (1989) at more than 20 sites in gene 9. Fane and King (1987) found that at 22 of 60 nonsense sites in gene 9, insertion of a missense amino acid caused lethal defects. A number of these sites are tyrosines and tryptophans (B. Fane, R. Villafane, J. King, unpublished results). The amber mutations map throughout the gene, showing that the distribution of the *tsf* mutations is a property of the polypeptide chain and not the nucleic acid sequences or organization.

Examination of the sites of the mutations reveals that they resemble those reported for turns (Chou and Fasman, 1978; Sibanda and Thornton, 1985). We describe additional biochemical evidence below, suggesting that the *tsf* mutations occur at sites that determine the occurrence or stabilization of β-turns.

Properties of the Native Forms of the *tsf* Mutant Proteins Formed at Low Temperature

An expected character of folding mutations is that the effect of the mutation is dependent on the history of the protein molecule and not just its current state. Thus, for each mutant, one must characterize two protein prepara-

tions: (i) those molecules released from the ribosome at low temperature that fold up into stable, biologically active peptide chains, and (ii) those molecules that are released from the ribosome at high restrictive temperature and fail to reach the active state. The character of these *tsf* mutations is that these polypeptide chains fail to reach the native conformations. They are not degraded; they form aggregates inside the cell-inclusion bodies.

The native forms of these proteins are fully biologically active They have all the activities of native protein binding to phage heads, endorhamnosidase, antigenicity, and infectivity, and they form viruses with infectivities not different from wild type (Goldenberg and King, 1981).

The native forms of some of the mutant proteins differ from wild type in only one clear cut manner: for those mutants in which the amino acid substitution causes a change of charge, both the electrophoretic mobilities and isoelectric points are altered (Fig. 7) (Yu and King, 1988). No such changes have been found for the neutral substitutions. If the change in mobility was due to a local conformational deformation, then some of the neutral substitutions should have displayed electrophoretic alterations. The absence of this phenotype indicates that the electrophoretic mobility changes associated with charge substitutions are due to the substitutions occurring at the solvent-accessible surface of the native protein.

In addition, turns are generally located at the surface of proteins (Richardson, 1981).

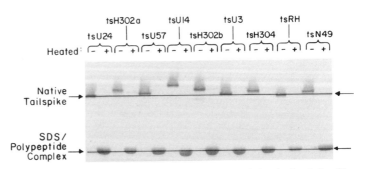

Fig. 7. Mobility of native and denatured forms of the mutant tailspike proteins. Samples of purified native tailspikes were electrophoresed through an SDS/polyacrylamide gel with and without prior heating to 100°C. The native spikes bind little SDS and display the mobility differences similar to those seen in native gels (Fig. 9). Except for *tsU14*, the mutant SDS/polypeptide chain complexes had the same mobilities as wild type, indicating that the altered mobilities of the native forms were not due to covalent scission in the chains. The *tsU14* denatured chains migrate faster than wild type. These chains may carry a small deletion in addition to the *tsU14* allele.

Combining the physical evidence for surface location with the sequence support for turns, we conclude that the most likely sites of the mutations are at surface turns. Since Raman spectra and x-ray results indicate that the protein is dominated by β-sheet structures, these are likely to be β-turns. Many such turns should occur in relatively close proximity in a cross β structure; this may account for the occurrence of more than 30 sites of *tsf* mutations in the central region of the chain.

Note that the surface location accounts for the ability of the protein to accommodate substitutions such as arginines for glycines and to remain fully functional once they have reached the native state.

The most striking feature of the native forms of the *tsf* mutant proteins is their thermostability. Calorimetric data were obtained by Julian Sturtevant on the melting temperature of native mutant tailspikes. The melting temperature of these *tsf* mutant proteins is indistinguishable from the native protein (Sturtevant *et al.,* 1989). At most, the mutants differ in a few degrees from wild type. These results can not account for the inability of the polypeptide chains to form native structure at 40°C.

The high temperature conformation of the native forms of the *tsf* proteins have also been studied by Raman spectroscopy, which allows the detection of partially disordered regions in an otherwise native protein (Sargent *et al.,* 1988). The Raman studies support the conclusion that the *tsf* amino acid substitutions have, at most, very subtle efforts on the native structures.

We conclude from these results that the *tsf* amino acid substitutions do not act by alter-ing the structure, function, or stability of the native proteins. The wild-type side chains at these positions appear to play no significant role in the native structure. However, at high temperature, they must be critical for stabilizing intermediates in the maturation pathway.

The mutant polypeptide chains synthesized at restrictive temperature are blocked in the folding of the single-chain intermediate. Infected cells incubated at restrictive temperature of 38–42°C with gene 9 *tsf* mutations fail to accumulate active native tailspikes. The tailspike polypeptide chains are synthesized at the same rate as wild type, but they fail to mature into the native state.

Smith and King (1981) analyzed the high temperature tailspike polypeptide chains of 15 different *tsf* mutants for the properties of the native proteins. The mutant chains were synthesized at the same rate as wild-type chains and were relatively stable within the infected cells. They were not associated with phage heads, lacked endorhamnosidase activity, and were sensitive to detergent and to protease digestion. Figure 8 shows the digestion of the partially folded intermediates from both *tsf* and wild-type infected cells by trypsin. That is, the single amino acid substitutions knocked out all of the activities of the native protein. How could single amino acid substitution prevent the expression of binding, antigenicity, and enzyme for 15 different sites through local effect? The simplest interpretation of these results was that the substitutions prevented the folding of the chain into the correct conformation.

Analysis of the samples by native gel electrophoresis, shown in Fig. 9, revealed that the mutations blocked maturation prior to as-

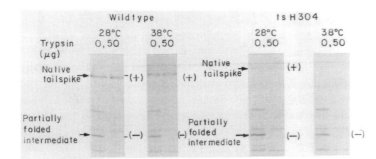

Fig. 8. Trypsin sensitivity of partially folded intermediates. Native newly synthesized tailspikes from infected cells are at the top of these gels and are completely resistant to proteolysis by trypsin. In contrast, the partially folded intermediates, both in the wild-type and mutant infected cells, are proteolyzed to small fragments (Haase-Pettingell and King, 1988).

Fig. 9. The *tsf* mutant-infected cells do not accumulate protrimers at restrictive temperature. Samples of the pulse-labeled infected cells were chilled and lysed by freezing and thawing. Samples of the lysate were electrophoresed through polyacrylamide gels under nondenaturing conditions at 4°C. The protrimer migrates more slowly than the native trimer. At the restrictive temperature, mature trimer does not form nor does the protrimer accumulate. Under the condition of these experiments the *tsf* single chain intermediates have aggregated into inclusion bodies and do not enter the gel.

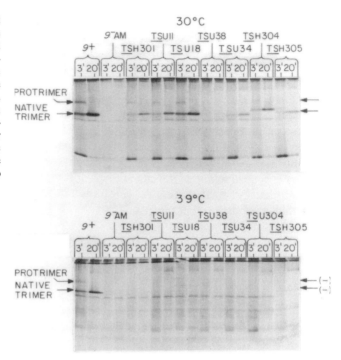

sociation into the protrimer (Goldenberg *et al.*, 1983). Given the long-lived nature of the tailspike folding intermediates, it seemed reasonable that the mutations were preventing the transformation of the early single-chain intermediate into the form capable of chain recognition. In fact, by shifting cultures from high temperature to permissive temperature, it was possible to rescue the mutant chains. After shift to permissive temperature, the protrimer appeared first and then the native protein, consistent with the block being at the stage of the folding of the single chain as shown in Fig. 10 (Goldenberg *et al.*, 1983).

Harrison and Durbin (1985), in defending a "no pathway" model for protein folding, recognized that this would mitigate against the existence of single amino acid substitutions that block folding. They suggested that the tailspike *tsf* mutations were blocking not the folding of the chain into a competent subunit but instead specific subunit-subunit interactions. In this sense, the mutations would be subunit-assembly mutations rather than chain folding mutations. However, if there are 30 sites of such mutations, the subunit-assembly model requires that each of those sites par-

ticipates directly in subunit association. Since, in this model, each mutation would only knock out the local site, leaving the remaining substantial number intact, it is difficult to explain how the single substitutions completely prevent subunit association. The data are far more easily understood by a sequential pathway, in which single substitutions prevent the chain from reaching the conformation needed for chain-chain recognition (Fig. 10).

Inclusion Bodies Form from Folding Intermediates

The high temperature chains did not remain rescuable for very long. As the time of incubation increased, the reversibility was lost (Haase-Pettingell and King, 1988). Investigation of the physical state of the *tsf* mutant chains revealed that they were aggregating into inclusion bodies and accumulating in the low speed pellet. Since no native spikes are formed in the mutant infected cells, the aggregates can not be formed from native tailspikes.

Haase-Pettingell and King (1988) fol-

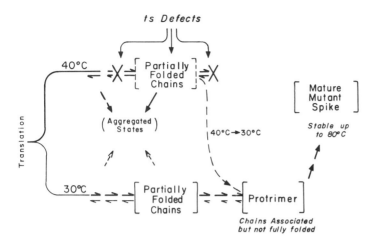

Fig. 10. Folding defects associated with temperature-sensitive folding mutations. Temperature-sensitive folding mutants further destabilize the early intermediate (Smith and King, 1981; Goldenberg *et al.*, 1983; Yu and King, 1984; Yu and King, 1988). The single-chain intermediate is initially soluble and can be rescued by shifting infected cells to permissive temperature. The mutant chains are blocked in the folding of the chain into a species competent for chain-chain association. The early intermediate aggregates at higher temperatures (Haase-Pettingell and King, 1988). This inclusion body state is a kinetic trap for both mutant and wild-type off-pathway chains.

lowed the kinetics of mutant and wild-type polypeptide chains under restrictive conditions. Early after synthesis, the high temperature wild-type and mutant *tsf* tailspike chains were soluble and remained soluble even after more than an hour of manipulation. As the time of maturation increased, the soluble chains decreased, with a resulting increase in the pelletable species (aggregates). These aggregates formed from a soluble non-native folding intermediate. This soluble species was not the protrimer, because this species is absent from the *tsf* infected cells at high temperature (Fig. 9).

The simplest model to explain these results is that the trigger for inclusion body formation is the partial melting of the partially folded single-chain intermediate. Consistent with this is the sharp dependence of inclusion body formation on temperature of folding, shown in Fig. 11. At lower temperature, the native tailspike is the predominant species formed. As the temperature increases, the native chains decrease, with a resulting increase in the aggregate. Essentially all the mutant chains are found in the aggregate at the higher temperatures. Because of the resemblance of a melting curve, we think of it as the local denaturation of the soluble thermolabile intermediate that forms the native, shifting the chains off the productive pathway to the aggregation pathway.

Temperature-Sensitive Folding Defects and β-Sheet Formation

The evidence presented here and elsewhere indicates that *tsf* mutations identify local sequences that stabilize early intermediates in chain folding such as the repeating section of β-sheet. Little is known of the mechanism of β-sheet formation. We think of the sites of these mutations as important in correctly locating or stabilizing the intermediate conformations in the formation of a cross β structure. It is quite possible that out-of-register, incorrect β-sheets can be formed by the mutant chains, leading to the aggregation pathway.

Our selection process requires that proteins function once they are correctly folded. Thus, the mutant amino acids must be able to be accommodated in the functional protein.

The surface is where all the large or most dramatic substitutions can be accommodated. Although the protein surface is often thought to be most tolerant of substitutions, the *tsf* sites are likely to correspond to conserved residues, since their functions are important in the folding intermediates. The conserved surface sites in the hemoglobin might have similar functions (Bashford *et al.*, 1987).

All this leads to the following model: there is a thermolabile intermediate in the intracellular folding of the thermostable tail-

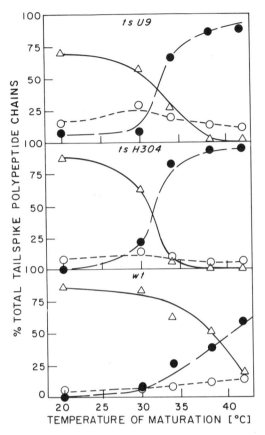

% TOTAL TAILSPIKE POLYPEPTIDE CHAINS

TEMPERATURE OF MATURATION [°C]

Fig. 11. Aggregation increases with temperature (Haase-Pettingell and King, 1988). The cells were infected and pulse labeled with wild-type, tsfH304, and tsfU9. After the chase with cold amino acids at 38°C, aliquots were shifted to the appropriate temperatures 20°C, 30°C, 34°C, 38°C, and 42°C. They were incubated for one hour, iced, and lysed by freezing and thawing two times. A pellet supernatant separation was performed. Then samples were applied to an SDS/polyacrylamide gel. The graph represents native, aggregated, and soluble intermediates as the percent of the total tailspike polypeptide chains synthesized during the pulse. (open triangles) soluble native tailspike; (filled circles) pelleted aggregated partially folded species; (open circles) partially folded soluble intermediates.

spike protein. Residues in the central part of the chain provide the interactions stabilizing this intermediate. The *tsf* mutations identify residues whose interactions stabilize the intermediate at the high end of the temperature range of phage growth but have little or no role in stabilizing the native protein.

Experiments with Synthetic Peptides

Adam Stroup and Lila Gierasch have studied peptides corresponding to sequences surrounding the *tsf* loci to address whether these sequences are turn forming. Cysteines were introduced at the ends of the sequence, such that they could form cyclic disulfide peptides. Cyclic disulfide decapeptides corresponding to wild type and *ts* H304 were carefully characterized using CD, NMR, and disulfide exchange methods. The *ts* H304 mutation corresponds to a substitution of arginine instead of glycine in position 244, the surrounding sequence being Val-Lys-Phe-Pro-Gly-Ile-Glu-Thr-Leu. The NMR characterization suggested that those peptides can adopt a type II β-turn conformation, for both Pro-Gly (wild-type) and Pro-Arg (mutant) sequences., with the Gly (or Arg) residues being at the i + 2 position (Stroup, 1989). The disulfide-exchange methods indicated that the wild-type sequence prefers the intramolecular disulfide bond formation with an equilibrium constant of 20 mM, while the one for the mutant sequence was only 5 mM.

Stroup and Gierasch suggest that the major difference between the wild-type and mutant sequences seems to be the steric hindrance conferred by the arginine replacement at the i + 2 position of the β-turn. Furthermore, they propose that additional interactions may be important for turn formation, such as a putative Lys– – –Glu salt bridge that may be destabilized by the presence of the charged arginine side chain. These results indicate that peptide models of the *tsf* tailspike sites may be a very useful experimental tool for understanding the formation of β-turns and their possible role as folding units in the tailspike.

Summary

The most straightforward structural model accounting for these results is that these *tsf* sites

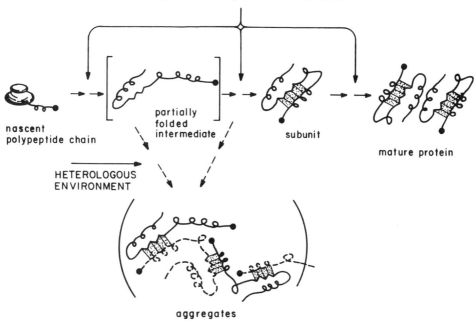

NATIVE ENVIRONMENT
IONS, COFACTORS, CHAPERONES etc.

nascent
polypeptide chain

partially
folded
intermediate

HETEROLOGOUS
ENVIRONMENT

subunit

mature protein

aggregates

Fig. 12. In vivo hypothetical folding and maturation pathway for an oligomeric protein. (Mitraki and King, 1989) The outcome of the intracellular pathway depends on the presence of the proper environmental conditions, including cofactors, chaperones, etc. An heterologous environment—found with cloned proteins—can influence the passage of partially folded intermediates towards the aggregated state. This schematic representation tries to emphasize the aggregation steps and, therefore, does not represent conformational refinements and isomerization steps that may occur as late events in the folding pathway.

are involved in the formation of the repeated features of the β-sheet, such as strand-strand interactions or β-turns. Destabilization of the folding intermediates results in the formation of intracellular aggregates (inclusion bodies), perhaps representing incorrect β-sheets. Formation of inclusion bodies often occurs during the expression of recombinant proteins into heterologous hosts. As illustrated in Fig. 12, evidence is accumulating that aggregate formation in both homologous and heterologous hosts is due to partial intracellular denaturation of folding intermediates (Mitraki and King, 1989).

Since the native forms of the mutant proteins are perfectly stable, stability of the native state is not a sufficient criterion for reaching the native state. The properties of the intracellular intermediates are equally critical.

These experiments show that there are sequences within polypeptide chains that function primarily in determining conformations of intermediates. Presumably there is also a variety of cellular information such as the recently described chaperonin proteins that interact with such intermediate states to insure that the chains reach their correct conformation under intracellular conditions.

Acknowledgments

This work was supported by grant GM17,980 from the National Institute of General Medical Sciences and grant DMB 8704126 from the National Science Foundation.

References

Adams, M. B., H. R. Brown, S. Casjens, *J. Virol.* **53**, 180 (1985).
Anfinsen, C. B., *Science* **181**, 223 (1973).

Bashford, D., C. Chothia, A. M. Lesk, *J. Mol. Biol.* **196,** 199 (1987).

Berget, P. B., and A. R. Poteete, *J. Virol.* **34,** 234 (1980).

Botstein, D., C. H. Waddell, J. King, *J. Mol. Biol.* **80,** 669 (1973).

Chou, P. Y., and G. D. Fasman, *Ann. Rev. Biochem.* **47,** 251 (1978).

Creighton, T. E., and D. P. Goldenberg, *J. Mol. Biol.* **179,** 497 (1984).

Edgar, R. S., and I. Lielausis, *Genetics* **49,** 649 (1964).

Fane, B., and J. King, *Genetics* **117,** 157 (1987).

Goldenberg, D., and J. King, *Proc. Natl. Acad. Sci. U.S.A.* **79,** 3403 (1982).

———, *J. Mol. Biol.* **145,** 633 (1981).

Goldenberg, D. P., P. B. Berget, J. King, *J. of Biol. Chem.* **257,** 7864 (1982).

Goldenberg, D. P., D. H. Smith, J. King, *Proc. Nat. Acad. Sci. U.S.A.* **80,** 7060 (1983).

Haase-Pettingell, C., and J. King, *J. Biol. Chem.* **263,** 4977 (1988).

Harrison S. C., and R. Durbin, *Proc. Natl. Acad. Sci. U.S.A.* **82,** 4028 (1985).

Israel, J. V., F. Anderson, M. Levine, *Proc. Natl. Acad. Sci. U.S.A.* **57,** 284 (1967).

Iwashita, S., and S. Kanegasaki, *Eur. J. Biochem.* **65,** 87 (1976).

Kabsch, W., and C. Sander, *Proc. Natl. Acad. Sci. U.S.A.* **81,** 1075 (1984).

King, J., and M.-H. Yu, in *Enzyme Structure,* C. W. H. Hirs and S. Timashiff, Eds. (Academic Press, New York, 1986), pp. 250–266.

Mitraki, A., and J. King, *Bio/Technology* **7,** 690 (1989).

Reynolds, J. A., and C. Tandford, *J. Bio. Chem.* **245,** 5161 (1970).

Richardson, J. S., *Adv. Prot. Chem.* **34,** 168 (1981).

Sadler, J. R., and A. Novick, *J. Mol. Biol.* **12,** 305 (1965).

Sargent, D., J. M. Benevides, M.-H. Yu, J. King, G. J. Thomas, Jr., *J. Mol. Biol.* **199,** 491 (1988).

Sauer, R. T., W. Krovatin, A. R. Poteete, P. B. Berget, *Biochem.* **21,** 5811 (1982).

Schwarz, J. J., and P. B. Berget, *Genetics* **121,** 635 (1989).

Seckler, R., A. Fuchs, J. King and R. Jaenicke, *J. Biol. Chem.* **264,** 11750 (1989).

Sibanda, B. L., and J. M. Thornton, *Nature (London)* **316,** 170 (1985).

Smith, D. H., and J. King, *J. Mol. Biol.* **145,** 653 (1981).

Smith, D. H., P. B. Berget, J. King, *Genetics* **96,** 331 (1980).

Stroup, A., Ph.D. Thesis, University of Texas Southwestern Medical Center (1989).

Sturtevant, J., Yu, M.-H, C. Haase-Pettingell, J. King, *J. Biol. Chem.* **264,** 10693 (1989).

Villafane R., and J. King, *J. Mol. Biol.* **204,** 607 (1988).

Yu, M.-H., and J. King, *Proc. Natl. Acad. Sci. U.S.A.* **81,** 6584 (1984).

———, *J. Biol. Chem.* **263,** 1424 (1988).

24

Folding of Collagen Molecules Containing Mutant Chains

Peter H. Byers

Human genetic diseases may be considered models of protein folding errors. Mutations in collagen genes provide excellent examples of how alterations in the normal folding pathways of complex multidomain molecules have major phenotypic effects (Byers, 1989). Mutations in collagen genes produce recognizable clinical phenotypes at a relatively high frequency, somewhere between one in 5000 and one in 40,000 births, depending on the population that is examined and the number of collagen genes studied. Mutations in collagen genes are known to produce inherited disorders of bone formation, of cartilage growth and development, and of integrity of skin, bowel, vessels, and uterus; the site of the clinical abnormality depends on the tissue distribution of the collagens affected (Byers, 1989; Mayne and Burgeson, 1987).

Collagen Is a Large Family of Proteins

More than 12 types of collagen molecules that contain more than 20 different chains have been identified (Mayne and Burgeson, 1987). Collagens have a characteristic three-chain, triple-helical structure and are secreted to the extracellular matrix. There are several families of collagens, including the highly abundant and ubiquitously distributed fibrillar collagens, the basement membrane collagens, and the less common collagens that differ in the size of molecules from their more common homologues. The fibrillar collagens are best studied and understood; the mutations that affect molecular assembly have been identified only among these genes. This discussion of folding mutations is limited to those in fibrillar collagens.

Collagens Are Multidomain Proteins

Collagens are synthesized as precursors, procollagens, which have a complex structure (Bornstein and Traub, 1979; Bornstein, 1974; Fessler and Fessler, 1978). In fibrillar collagens, the predominant structural motif of the core is a triple-helix, which is 1014 amino acids in length. There is a cysteine-rich domain that forms intrachain disulfide bonds at the amino-terminal end of the chain, followed by a short triple-helical domain, which is separated by a telopeptide domain of about 18 residues from the major triple-helix. The triple-helix is terminated by a short telopeptide domain of about 28 residues and is followed by a globular carboxyl-terminal extension of about 250 residues.

The functions of the domains external to the major triple-helix are partially understood. The telopeptides contain sequences that are recognized by the proteolytic enzymes that convert procollagen to collagen. The carboxyl-terminal propeptide extension contains both intrachain and interchain disulfide bonds and is the region that contains interchain recognition regions to facilitate molecular assembly. Intermolecular cross links occur between chains of the same and different types via lysine- and hydroxylysine-derived oxidation products (Eyre *et al.*, 1984). Residues involved in cross link formation are located both in the telopeptide domains and in the major triple-helix. The precise functions of the amino-terminal propeptide domains are not understood, although it is clear that the signal sequence on each precursor chain permits transport across the rough endoplasmic reticulum (RER) membrane during its synthesis.

Features of Triple-Helix Structure and Sequence

The triple-helical domain of fibrillar collagen chains contains glycine in every third position (Gly-X-Y). The X and Y positions often contain proline and hydroxyproline, respectively, and exclude cysteine and tryptophan. The hydroxylated amino acids hydroxyproline and hydroxylysine are limited to the Y-position by the specificity of the enzymes that perform the modifications. Most amino acids can appear in either the X or Y position, although phenylalanine is limited to the X-position and leucine is found only once in the Y-position, apparently because of steric considerations. The triple-helix formed by three chains of the collagen molecule has a structure that is very similar to the Gly-Pro-Pro triple-helix (Bornstein and Traub, 1979).

The stability of the triple helix is provided by interchain hydrogen bonds involving the carbonyl group of glycine and the amide groups of adjacent residues on neighboring chains. The hydroxyl group of hydroxyproline is involved in hydrogen bond formation and provides additional stability, as do, to some extent, charge interactions (Bornstein and Traub, 1979).

Collagen Gene Structure

Collagen gene structure is complex and, to some degree, reflects the domain structure of the protein (Ramirez *et al.*, 1985). The genes of the chains of type I procollagen contain more than 50 exons each, 42 of which encode the triple-helical domain. In the triple helical domain, the exons range in size from 45 to 162 base pairs. The majority are either 54 or 108 base pairs in length; each starts with a glycine codon and ends with the codon for a Y-position residue. The structure of the gene and the protein suggests that many point mutations could produce substitutions for glycine residues; that splicing mutations might be frequent, simply by virtue of the number of splice junctions; and that internal deletions might be common because of the repetitive nature of the coding sequences. Genomic deletions and insertions are rare and usually involve intron-to-intron rearrangements; point mutations that result in substitutions for glycine residues in the triple-helix are relatively common, and several splicing mutations have been characterized (Byers, 1989).

The Biosynthesis of Collagen

The biosynthesis of collagen is complex and chain association and molecular folding are a consequence of structural features (Fig. 1). The genes (COL1A1 and COL1A2) that encode the chains of type I procollagen — proα1(I) and proα2(I), respectively — are located on different chromosomes, and their expression is coordinately regulated through mechanisms that are not entirely understood (Bornstein and Sage, in press). The transcripts are spliced in the nucleus, and the message is transported to the cytoplasm and translated on membrane-bound ribosomes. Transport through the RER membrane is facilitated by the amino terminal signal sequence. As cotranslational and posttranslational events, a number of important modifications occur to the nascent chains (Kivirikko and Myllyla, 1982). Virtually all prolyl and some lysyl resi-

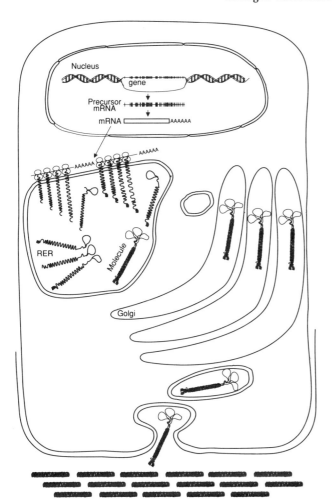

Fig. 1. Biosynthesis of procollagen. The chains of type I procollagen are encoded by nonsyntenic genes, the precursor mRNA molecules are extensively spliced and modified in the nucleus and transported to the cytoplasm where they are translated on membrane-bound ribosomes. Chain synthesis and passage across the membrane of the rough endoplasmic reticulum parallel the processes of other proteins destined for extracellular transport. Assembly of two proα1(I) and a single proα2(I) chain into a trimer begins with folding of the individual chains, stabilization of the intrachain folding by formation of disulfide bonds, and association of the three chains through domains located in the carboxyl-terminal propeptide domain. Triple-helix formation is initiated near the carboxyl-terminus and propagated toward the amino-terminus of the molecule. Peptidyl proline isomerase may be important in facilitating cis-trans isomerization of prolyl residues in the triple-helical domain. Posttranslation prolyl hydroxylation, lysyl hydroxylation, and hydroxylysyl glycosylation can occur until a stable triple-helical conformation is achieved. Molecules are transported through the Golgi to the extracellular matrix where the amino-terminal and carboxyl-terminal propeptides are cleaved and fibril formation occurs adjacent to the cell of origin of the molecules.

dues that precede glycines within the triple-helical domain are hydroxylated. In the absence of prolyl hydroxylation, the mature procollagen molecule has a melting temperature of about 27°C while, following hydroxylation, the melting temperature is 43°C. Lysyl hydroxylation is important for the subsequent formation of stable intermolecular cross links. The two hydroxylating enzymes, lysyl and prolyl hydroxylase, and enzymes responsible for hydroxylysyl glycosylation recognize chains in nontriple-helical array as substrates and can no longer modify residues in chains that are in stable triple-helical array.

The proα chains of type I procollagen are not assembled into molecules until the complete chain is synthesized. During synthesis, the intrachain disulfide bonds at the amino-

terminal end of the chains are formed. Following completion of the chains and release from the ribosomes, intrachain disulfide bonds form in the carboxyl-terminal propeptide extension of each chain to produce a loop structure (Doege and Fessler, 1986). The loop is stabilized by a disulfide bond that links residue 80 to 242 and 151 to 195 in the proα1(I) chain and residue 84 to 245 and 153 to 198 in the proα2(I) chain (Koivu, 1987). Four additional cysteines are available in each proα1(I) chain and three in the proα2(I) chain in the carboxyl-terminal propeptide region. Following loop formation, the chains of type I procollagen, two proα1(I) chains, and a single proα2(I) chain assemble through domains in the carboxyl-terminal propeptide, probably in the amino-terminal end of the peptide, where interchain disulfide bonds stabilize the interaction. Protein disulfide isomerase, the β-chain of prolyl 4-hydroxylase, probably facilitates the formation of appropriate interchain and intrachain disulfide bonds. Once chain aggregation occurs, triple-helix is propagated from the carboxyl-terminus toward the amino-terminus of the molecule (Bachinger et al., 1980; Fessler et al., 1981). The process may be limited by the rate of proline cis-trans isomerization (Bachinger, 1987), a reaction that is presumably enzymatically catalyzed. Studies of the denaturation of type III collagen suggest that there may be multiple folding domains along the triple helix (Bachinger, 1987). The mature protein is transported from the RER to the Golgi and then to the extracellular space. At the cell surface fibrils form, the final step in collagen molecular assembly.

Mutations in the Carboxyl-Terminal Propeptide Affect Chain Association

An important step in the stabilization of folded chains is the formation of intramolecular disulfide bonds in the carboxyl-terminal propeptide domain. Two mutations, both of which prohibit assembly of chains that carry the mutation into molecules, affect molecular assembly. One changes the reading frame near the end of the proα2(I) chain to delete the last cysteine (Deak et al., 1983; Pihlajaniemi et al., 1984) and change the sequence of the final dozen residues. The second frameshift mutation occurs in the codons 11 and 12 residues from the carboxyl-terminus of the proα1(I) chain. This frameshift changes the cysteine at position 242 and then extends the chain an additional 84 residues beyond the normal termination site (Willing et al., in press). In both instances, the mutant chain is not included in type I procollagen molecules, which suggests that loop formation is an essential prerequisite for chain assembly, either because it increases interacting surfaces or removes an inhibitory peptide from the region.

Deletions Within the Triple-Helix Affect Folding

Multiexon deletions within the triple helical domain of both proα1(I) (Chu et al., 1985; Barsh et al., 1985) and proα2(I) (Willing et al., 1988) have been identified and found to result from intron-to-intron genomic deletions. Deletion of the coding material for single exons in proα2(I) usually result from splicing defects (Tromp and Prockop, 1988,) but in some instances, they may result from partial deletion of an exon as well (Kuivaniemi et al., 1988). Because each exon within the triple-helical domain encodes a multiple of three amino acids, and because each begins with a glycine codon and ends with a Y-position codon, deletion of a single or of multiple exons in that region assures the synthesis of a structure with an intact Gly-X-Y structure, albeit shorter than normal.

Genomic multiexon deletions are probably all lethal, but the phenotypic effect of single exon deletions may depend on the region deleted and the chain in which the deletion occurs. All deletions appear to have a similar effect on folding, but the most remarkable, and probably best characterized in terms of effects on the molecule, is the multiexon deletion that removes the 180 residues from 586-765 in the triple-helical domain of the proα2(I) chain (Willing et al., 1988). The mutation affects only a single allele, and both the normal and mutant allele are normally expressed and are assembled into molecules with equal efficiency. Because a type I procollagen molecule contains one proα2(I) and two proα1(I) chains, half the molecules synthesized by cells that carry the deletion are normal, and the others contain the defective chain. Thus, in the same cell, it is possible to observe and compare the folding and behavior of both molecules. These cells secrete some normal type I procollagen but retain a population of type I procollagen within the RER. The retained molecules consist entirely of those that contain the mutant chain. Furthermore, the retained molecules undergo increased posttranslational modification amino-terminal to the deletion junction in all three chains in the molecules. Because the modifying enzymes recognize only chains that are not in triple-helical array as substrates, these findings indicate that the structure of the molecule changes at the junction. From these data, then, it appears that triple-helix is propagated normally from its site of initiation and for the next 250 residues. At that point, the residue in the proα2(I) chain that normally is at 585 is juxtaposed to residue 766, and, although the Gly-X-Y triplet repeat structure is maintained, a triple-helix of normal stability is not formed. Similar effects are seen with single exon deletions in the proα2(I) chain and with a multiexon deletion from one COL1A1 allele.

These findings suggest that triple-helix is not equivalent for production of a stable structure throughout its length and that some regularity of information must reside in sequence. The distribution of hydrophobic residues in the two chains is not conserved, but that of charged groups is highly conserved. Thus, it appears that charge interactions may make a far greater contribution to triple-helix propagation and stability than previously recognized. It is not yet clear how triple-helix is altered in these regions and whether the alteration in modification reflects a delay in propagation or the production of a slightly more open structure, which is accessible to modifying enzymes.

The triple-helix that is formed has a lower thermal denaturation temperature than normal, but this does not allow discrimination between the two possibilites. The cell can discriminate very well between the properly folded type I procollagen and the aberrant molecule by mechanisms that we do not understand.

Point Mutations Affect Folding

Several point mutations that result in substitutions for glycine residues along the length of the triple-helix of the proα1(I) chain have now been identified, and others have been created by site-directed mutagenesis (Stacey et al., 1988). Many of these mutations produce

severe phenotypes of deforming bone disease, affect folding of type I procollagen molecules into which the abnormal chains are incorporated, decrease the thermal stability of the molecules, and delay their secretion. Examples of the now characterized mutations include substitutions for glycine at positions 988 (Cohn et al., 1986), 904 (Constantinou et al., 1989), 748 (Vogel et al., 1987), 718 (B. J. Starman et al., 1989), 526 (B. J. Starman et al., 1989), 175 (D. Hollister, personal communication) and 94 (B. J. Starman et al., 1989) by cysteine; at positions 664 (Bateman et al., 1988) and 391 (Bateman et al., 1987); by arginine; and at 883 (Cohn et al., in press) by aspartic acid. The frequency of cysteine for glycine substitutions in the α1(I) chains represents a bias of ascertainment because the substitution creates a disulfide-bonded dimer of α1(I) chains, which permits the ready identification, localization, and characterization of the mutation because cysteine is normally absent from triple-helical domain of the chain.

Cells that are heterozygous for these point mutations synthesize some normal molecules and other type I procollagen molecules in which all chains in molecules that carry the defective molecule are overmodified amino-terminal to the site of the mutation (Fig. 2). Although it might be supposed that substitution for a single glycine out of the 338 in the triple-helical domain would have little effect, many of those in the α1(I) chain are lethal.

Substitutions for the glycine should alter packing of chains into a triple-helix, but it is not clear how that explains the alteration in thermal stability and the polar increase in posttranslational modification of the abnormal molecules. Molecular modeling of such substitutions provide several alternative models, some of which predict little disarray amino-terminal to the substitutions (Traub and Steinmann, 1986), others of which suggest that chain order may be altered and thus propagate an irregularity in structure (Vogel et al., 1988).

The latter is more consistent with the observations of overmodification along the entire length of the molecule amino-terminal to

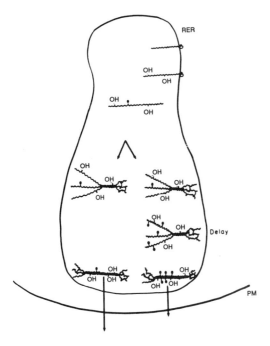

Fig. 2. Aberrant folding of molecules that contain mutations within the triple-helical domain of the chains of type I procollagen. Chains that contain substitutions for glycyl residues within the Gly-X-Y triplets of the triple-helical domains as well as those that have deletions of exons within the same domain appear to fold in an abnormal fashion once chain assembly occurs. Triple-helix propagation is normal to the site of the mutation, but, amino-terminal to that domain, an abnormal structure is propagated that permits continued exposure to the modifying enzymes and results in molecules that may be asymmetrically over-modified (largely increased lysyl hydroxylation and hydroxylysyl glycosylation) prior to transport beyond the rough endoplasmic reticulum. Some molecules that contain mutant chains are not released from the rough endoplasmic reticulum but are slowly degraded; others are rapidly degraded.

the substitution and with the alterations in substrate conformation for the amino-terminal propeptidase (Vogel et al., 1988). The peptidase cleaves three chains in the amino-terminal telopeptide domain as part of the extracellular conversion of procollagen to collagen and requires that all chains be in register (Tuderman and Prockop, 1982). Deletions within the triple-helical domain of either proα1(I) or proα2(I) and point mutations can affect the efficiency of cleavage, indicating that even point mutations produce an altered structure that is propagated along the length of the molecule.

Summary

Collagens are very complex molecules that fold domains of chains prior to assembly of three chains to form a molecule and then fold two triple-helical domains. The folding of the triple-helix is easiest to monitor, and a variety of mutations in that region, ranging from single amino acid substitutions to large deletions, may have dramatic effects on folding and phenotypic effects that range from mild bone fragility to death in the perinatal period. The phenotypic outcome of such mutations emphasizes that, although the protein folding problem is important in many areas, alterations in protein assembly and folding may have enormous implications for the health of the organisms of which they are part, whether those organisms be phage or human.

Acknowledgments

Supported in part by a grant from the National Institutes of Health (AR 21557) and a Clinical Research Grant from the March of Dimes Birth Defects Foundation (6-298).

References

Bachinger, H. P., J. Biol. Chem. **262**, 17144 (1987).

Bachinger, H. P., P. Bruckner, R. Timpl, D. J. Prockop, J. Engel, Eur. J. Biochem. **106**, 619 (1980).

Barsh, G. S., C. L. Roush, J. Bonadio, P. H. Byers, R. E. Gelinas, Proc. Natl. Acad. Sci. U.S.A. **82**, 2870 (1985).

Bateman, J. F., D. Chan, I. D. Walker, J. G. Rogers, W. G. Cole, J. Biol. Chem. **262**, 7021 (1987).

Bateman, J. F., S. R. Lamande, H.-H. M. Dahl, D. Chan, W. G. Cole, J. Biol. Chem. **263**, 11627 (1988).

Bornstein, P., Annu. Rev. Biochem. **43**, 567 (1974).

Bornstein, P., and H. Sage, Prog. Nucleic Acid Res. Mol. Biol., in press.

Bornstein, P., and W. Traub, in The Proteins, R. Hill and H. Neurath, Eds. (Academic Press, New York, 1979), 3rd ed., vol. 4, pp. 412–605.

Byers, P. H., in The Metabolic Basis of Inherited Disease, C.R. Scriver, A. L. Beaudet, W. S. Sly, D. Valley, Eds. (McGraw-Hill, New York, 1989), 6th ed., pp. 2805–2842.

Chu, M.-L., V. Gargiulo, C. Williams, F. Ramirez, *J. Biol. Chem.* **260**, 691 (1985).

Cohn, D. H., P. H. Byers, B. Steinmann, R. E. Gelinas, *Proc. Natl. Acad. Sci. U.S.A.* **83**, 6045 (1986).

Cohn, D. H., B. J. Starman, B. Blumberg, P. H. Byers, *Am. J. Hum. Genet.,* in press.

Constantinou, C. D., K. B. Nielson, D. J. Prockop, *J. Clin. Invest.* **83**, 574 (1989).

Deak, S. B. M., A. C. Nicholls, F. M. Pope, D. J. Prockop, *J. Biol. Chem.* **258**, 15192 (1983).

Doege, K. J., and J. H. Fessler, *J. Biol. Chem.* **261**, 8924 (1986).

Eyre, D. R., M. A. Paz, P. M. Gallop, *Annu. Rev. Biochem.* **53**, 717 (1984).

Fessler, J. H., and L. I. Fessler, *Annu. Rev. Biochem.* **47**, 129 (1978).

Fessler, L. I., R. Timpl, J. H. Fessler, *J. Biol. Chem.* **256**, 2531 (1981).

Kivirikko, K. I., and R. Myllyla, *Methods Enzymol.* **82A**, 245 (1982).

Koivu, J., *FEBS Lett.* **212**, 229 (1987).

Kuivaniemi, H., C. Sabol, G. Tromp, M. Sippola-Thiele, D. J. Prockop, *J. Biol. Chem.* **263**, 11407 (1988).

Mayne, R., and R. E. Burgeson, Eds. *Structure and Function of Collagen Types* (Academic Press, Orlando, 1987).

Pihlajaniemi, T. *et al., J. Biol. Chem.* **259**, 12941 (1984).

Ramirez, F., *et al., Ann. N.Y. Acad. Sci.* **460**, 117 (1985).

Stacey, A., *et al. Nature* **332** 131 (1988).

Starman, B. J., *et al., J. Clin. Invest.* **84**, 1206 (1989).

Traub, W., and B. Steinmann, *FEBS Lett.* **198**, 213 (1986).

Tromp, G., and D. J. Prockop, *Proc. Natl. Acad. Sci. U.S.A.* **85**, 5254 (1988).

Tuderman, L., and D. J. Prockop, *Eur. J. Biochem.* **125**, 545 (1982).

Vogel, B. C., R. R. Minor, M. Freund, D. J. Prockop, *J. Biol. Chem.* **262**, 14737 (1987).

Vogel, B. E., *et al., J. Biol. Chem.* **263**, 19249 (1988).

Willing, M. C., *et al., J. Biol. Chem.* **263**, 8398 (1988).

_____, *J. Clin. Invest.,* in press.

Part VI

Modeling Protein Folding and Structure

Jiri Novotny

In this section, the reader will find four chapters that sample, more or less randomly, the present-day approaches to modeling protein structure. In the broader sense, this "modeling" also includes development of theoretical concepts for the process of protein folding; hence, the article by Donald Bashford, Martin Karplus, and David Weaver on the diffusion-collision model of protein folding.

The folding problem, most fundamentally stated, seeks to unravel the formal code that relates the amino acid sequence of the protein polymer to its three-dimensional structure. In practice, only partial solutions to this problem can be attempted. It has been known that the two torsional degrees of freedom of the polypeptide backbone, ϕ and ψ, suffice to define the chain fold (Pauling, 1951; Flory, 1953) and that only a small fraction of the torsional space is populated by the protein backbone. These are the regions of extended (trans) β conformation and the right-handed, compact helical (gauche) α-conformation (Ramachandran and Sasisekharan, 1968).

Side chain character of the 20 different types of amino acids often imparts strong conformational preferences on the backbone. Thus, numerous empirical and statistical procedures have been developed to determine secondary structure preferences (i.e., α and β conformational tendencies) from the primary structure alone. These algorithms have recently been critically reviewed (Schulz,

1988) and are not dealt with here. Nevertheless, some interesting aspects of structure prediction (e.g., the work addressing space-related and time-related problems of the assembly of secondary structure segments into compact folds) are discussed in this volume by Fred Cohen, Scott Presnell, Lydia Gregoret, and Irwin D. Kuntz, and by Donald Bashford and colleagues.

An entirely different approach to folding consists of the sampling of the conformational space (Moult and James, 1986; Bruccoleri and Karplus, 1987). Although conceptually simple, this approach faces the practical difficulty of sampling an enormously large, multidimensional space (e.g., 24^{10} different conformations are to be sampled if the backbone of a decapeptide is examined using a 30° torsional grid). Modern computers have made this approach possible, and promising results have recently been obtained with the method (see chapter 26, this volume).

The importance of computing technology for protein folding theory and modeling can not be overestimated. To keep readers up to date, we included in this volume the review article by Larry Smarr. The chapter emphasizes nationwide computing networks that are becoming available to an increasing number of users.

The chapters by Cohen *et al.* and by Bruccoleri *et al.* have one aspect in common: they use potential energy functions to evaluate energetics of generated protein models. In protein structure modeling, it is assumed that the "natural" structure is the most stable one; that is, the native fold will be the one with the lowest potential energy. Thus, the concept of empirical potential energy function becomes the pivotal point of protein modeling. Levitt and Lifson (1969) first introduced a molecular-mechanical energy potential that described the protein molecule as a collection of hard, impenetrable spheres (atoms) held together by elastic strings (covalent bonds). The atoms possessed partial electric charges that acted through space according to the Coulomb law. The atoms were also capable of hydrogen bonding, although hydrogen atoms were not explicitly present. The potential has become a useful and an increasingly popular computational tool (e.g., the computer programs AMBER, Weiner and Kollman, 1981; CHARMM, Brooks *et al.*, 1983; DISCOVER, Hagler, 1984; ECEPP, Nemethy *et al.*, 1983; GROMOS, Berendsen *et al.*, 1981) despite the fact that its use for understanding protein folding is inherently very limited because of its total neglect of solvent effects. The incorporation of water into our theoretical schemes of protein mechanics and energetics is perhaps the most exciting theoretical development that is happening today. The interested reader is referred to recent articles by Hagler and Moult, 1978; Jorgensen *et al.*, 1983; Eisenberg and McLachlan, 1986; Bash *et al.*, 1987; Levitt and Sharon, 1988; Novotny *et al.*, 1989; and Shen *et al.*, 1989.

References

Bash, P. A., U. C. Singh, F. K. Brown, R. Langridge, P. A. Kollman, *Science* **235**, 574 (1987).

Berendsen, H. J. C., J. P. M. Postma, A. di Niola, W. F. van Gunsteren, J. R. Haak, *J. Chem. Phys.* **81**, 3684 (1981).

Brooks, B., *et al., J. Comput. Chem.* **4**, 187 (1983).

Bruccoleri, R. E., and M. Karplus, *Biopolymers* **26**, 137 (1987).

Eisenberg, D., and A. D. McLachlan, *Nature* **319**, 199 (1986).

Flory, P. J., *Principles of Polymer Chemistry* (Cornell University Press, Ithaca, NY, 1953).

Hagler, A., in *Molecular Dynamics and Protein Structure*, J. Hermans, Ed. (Polycrystal Book Service, Western Springs, IL, 1984), pp. 133–139.

Hagler, A., and J. Moult, *Nature* **272**, 222 (1978).

Jorgensen, W. L., J. Chandraskhar, J. D. Madura, R. W. Impey, M. L. Klein, *J. Chem. Phys.* **79**, 926 (1983).

Levitt, M., and S. Lifson, *J. Mol. Biol.* **46**, 269 (1969).

Levitt, M., and R. Sharon, *Proc. Natl. Acad. Sci. U.S.A.* **85**, 7557 (1988).

Moult, J., and M. N. G. James, *Proteins* **1**, 146 (1986).

Nemethy, G., M. S. Pottle, H. Scheraga, *J. Phys. Chem.* **87**, 1883 (1983).

Novotny, J., R. E. Bruccoleri, F. Saul, *Biochemistry*, in press.

Pauling, L., R. B. Corey, H. R. Branson, *Proc. Natl. Acad. Sci. U.S.A.* **37**, 205 (1951).

Ramachandran, G. N., and V. Sasisekharan, *Adv. Prot. Chem.* **23**, 283 (1968).

Schultz, G. E., *Ann. Rev. Biophys. Biophys. Chem.* **17**, 1 (1988).

Shen, J., S. Subramaninam, C. F. Wong, J. A. McCammon, *Biopolymers*, in press.

Weiner, P. K., and P. A. Kollman, *J. Comput. Chem.* **2**, 287 (1981).

25

Theoretical Approaches to Protein Structure Prediction

Fred E. Cohen, Lydia M. Gregoret
Scott R. Presnell, Irwin D. Kuntz

The amino acid sequence of a protein specifies the blueprint for chain folding (Anfinsen *et al.*, 1961). Deducing this blueprint from a study of the amino acid sequence is the main thrust of the protein folding problem. Confronted with a sequence, how well can we produce an approximate tertiary structure? In this chapter, we describe some successes and some failures in this arena. Hopefully, a critical analysis of our successes and failures will help derive the next generation of protein structure prediction algorithms.

Basic Approaches to Folding an Extended Chain

There are two fundamental approaches to the problem of folding an extended chain. One is to first write out some potential function and then hope to follow the gradients of that potential function to the energy minimum (Levitt and Warshel, 1975; Nemethy and Scheraga, 1977; Weiner *et al.*, 1984). That approach, although fundamentally correct and conceptually pleasing, encounters considerable trouble (Hagler and Honig, 1978; Cohen and Sternberg, 1980b). Scheraga and coworkers have spent a great deal of time examining the multiple minima problem. In two dimensions, the problem is equivalent to

trying to cross the maxima that separates one minima from another on a polynomial curve. Most gradient minimizers will never sample far enough away from a local minima to encounter additional minima. Considering that the problem is not in two dimensions, but closer to a thousand dimensions, this surface is hopelessly complex. Unless one were to start near the actual answer, the chance of encountering the native structure is vanishingly small. Some time ago, we decided that it would be more sensible to divide the problem up into more tenable bits (Cohen *et al.*, 1979). One might imagine starting with an amino acid sequence, using that sequence to predict secondary structure, taking the secondary structure and packing it to form an approximate tertiary structure, and then finally using that approximate structure as a starting point for energy calculations to generate a complete tertiary structure (Fig. 1).

Many investigators have focused on secondary structure prediction, locating α-helices, β-strands, and turns from an analysis of a protein sequence. First-generation algorithms of this type have achieved approximately 70 percent accuracy (Chou and Fasman, 1974, 1977; Lim, 1974). Unfortunately, this is not accurate enough to help with the folding problem. A series of second-generation algorithms is being developed by Taylor

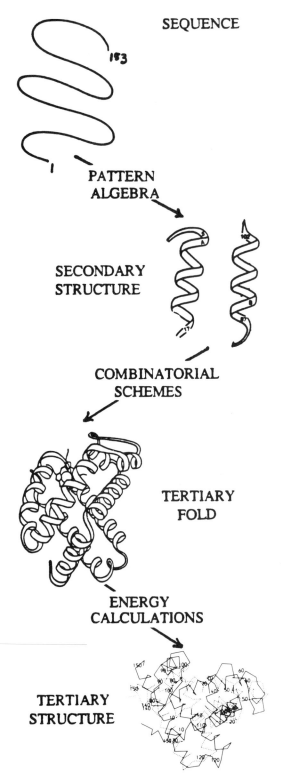

SEQUENCE

183

PATTERN
ALGEBRA

SECONDARY
STRUCTURE

COMBINATORIAL
SCHEMES

TERTIARY
FOLD

ENERGY
CALCULATIONS

TERTIARY
STRUCTURE

Fig. 1. Schematic overview of the hierarchic condensation model for protein structure prediction.

and Thornton (1984) and Cohen *et al.* (1983, 1986a). Although there are some interesting conclusions, there is still no algorithmic crank to turn that will reliably assign secondary structure when confronted with a sequence. This chapter will focus on all-helical proteins, although similar work has been done on α/β and β/β proteins (Cohen *et al.*, 1980, 1982).

An α-helix is a periodic polypeptide structure with 3.6 residues/turn and a pitch of 1.5 Å/residue. Side chains form ridges and grooves on the helix surface, which mediate helix-helix packing (Chothia *et al.*, 1977). If one knew the locations of all the helices and the packing sites that mediate the interactions between the helices in the all-helical protein myoglobin, then presumably it should be possible to reconstruct the molecule.

Helix Interaction

By studying helix-helix interactions, we can gain insight about the formation of a protein hydrophobic core. Helix interaction sites fall into geometric categories. Some fit the perpendicular category, which has an inter-helical angle of approximately − 80°, but there is a much more populated category at approximately − 60°. Finally, there is a parallel category at about + 20°. Richards and co-workers noted that there seemed to be restrictions on the size of residues that were allowed to be at these interaction sites (Richmond and Richards, 1978; Cohen *et al.*, 1979). Smaller side chains allow helices to pack closer together. As the side chain volume increased, the spacing between the helices enlarged. There were some angular preferences as well.

The helix-helix interface is composed largely of hydrophobic residues. Accessible surface area is lost when the two helices are brought together. Richmond and Richards (1978) recognized that one could write down a reasonably simple algorithm to locate possible helix-packing sites. Although it was over-predictive, this algorithm had the benefit of locating all helix-packing sites in myoglobin.

The ability to place all the potential helix-packing sites facilitates the conceptually simple combinatoric calculation. All one needs to do is to pair all the possible type I ($-80°$) sites with type I sites, type II ($-60°$) sites with type II sites, and type III ($+20°$) sites with type III sites to build up a helix structure that would eventually become myoglobin. There are 3.4×10^8 possible helix arrangements to examine—outside the realm of human patience, but quite managable for a computer (Cohen *et al.*, 1979). A construction of one possible model for myoglobin using

these helix-helix interactions is shown in Fig. 2. Structures generated should satisfy some physical constraints: they should contain no unreasonable steric interactions and should form a continuous polypeptide chain. It turns out that if one applies steric and connectivity constraints to this problem, only 20 structures of the 10^8 structures remain. Among the 20 remaining structures, only 2 can bind a heme group in a sterically reasonable fashion between His 63 and His 94 (Fig. 3) (Cohen and

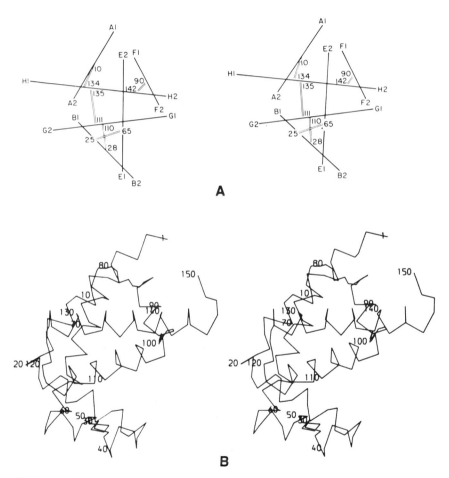

Fig. 2. (A) Helical axis representation of a candidate for the myoglobin fold from the work of Cohen *et al.* (1979). On inspection, this structure most resembles myoglobin. Helices are labeled alphabetically with 1 corresponding to the N-termini and 2 to the C-termini. The double lines represent the contact normal used in the construction of this model. The numbers of the residues central to the helix-helix interaction mark the ends of the contact normals. (B) Alpha carbon representation of the structure shown in (A). The idealized geometry of an α-helix, a pitch of 1.5 Å per residue with 3.6 residues per turn so that each alpha carbon lay 2.29 Å from the helix axis is used. The relative phasing of residues on interacting helices follows from the position of the contact normal and the magnitude of the skew angle (Cohen *et al.*, 1979). Residues in the chain joining 2 helices were placed so that the distance between consecutive α carbons is 3.81 Å. [Reprinted from *J. Mol. Biol.* **132**, 275 (1979) with permission.]

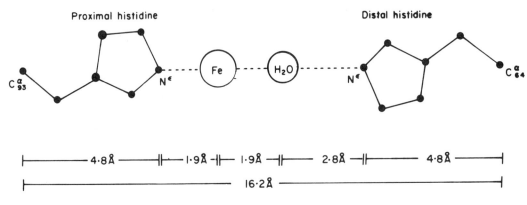

Proximal histidine

Distal histidine

A

Fig. 3. **(A)** Ultraviolet, visible and infrared spectroscopy of myoglobins and hemoglobins have been used to identify an imidazole ring as the iron-protein or proximal ligand (Brill and Sandberg, 1967). Electron spin resonance studies of myoglobin in H2170 indicate that a water is bound to the porphyrin ring (Vuk-Pavolic and Siderer, 1977) whose titration behavior suggests a hydrogen bond to a histidine Ne (Antonin and Brunori, 1971). Sequence studies demonstrate that His93 must be the proximal histidine, and His64 the distal histidine. These assignments are confirmed by the work of Johnson *et al.* (1978) on leghemoglobin. The maximum distance between C^{α} and N^{ε} of a histidine is 4.8 Å. The separation between proton donor and acceptor in a hydrogen bond is 2.8 Å (Pauling, 1960) and the length of an iron ligand is approximately 1.9 Å, from crystallographic studies of nickel etioporphyrin by Crute (1959). **(B)** The octahedrally liganded heme iron is shown with 2 of the 4 nitrogens (N) from the porphyrin ring and the nitrogen of the histidene imidazole N^{ε}. The ligand length is 1.9 Å. The van der Waals' radii of the Ca (2.0 Å) and the half-thickness of the aromatic rings (1.7 Å) allows a C^{α} to approach within 4.0Å of the iron atom when 90% of the appropriate van der Waals' radii are used. Thus the C^{α} atom of the histidine is 3.33 Å from the nitrogens. [Reprinted from *J. Mol. Biol.* **137**, 9 (1980) with permission.]

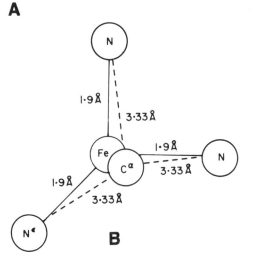

B

Sternberg, 1980a). The root mean square (RMS) difference between those two structures is about 0.3 Å (Fig. 4). They are effectively the same structure from our perspective. The crystal structure of myoglobin is shown overlaid on the predicted structure in Fig. 4B and C. The RMS difference between the model and the native structure is about 4.5 Å, an encouraging result. But much of this work was developed with myoglobin in mind. The key question is what these algorithms yield for a sequence of unknown structure.

Interleukin-2 provides an interesting example (Cohen *et al.*, 1986b). Turns were located using a pattern-based algorithm (Cohen

et al., 1986a) and four helical regions were located using a scheme currently under development. If the myoglobin calculation is valid, then similar calculations should produce a structure for the core helices of interleukin-2. In this case, about 10^5 structures were generated. Twenty-six structures were produced, falling into four families: (i) right-handed, four-fold α-helical bundles, (ii) left-handed, four-fold helical bundles, (iii) zigzag structures, which are suboptimal from an electrostatic perspective, and (iv) a miscellaneous category that had an excessively large surface area and lacked a substantial hydrophobic core (Fig. 5).

A

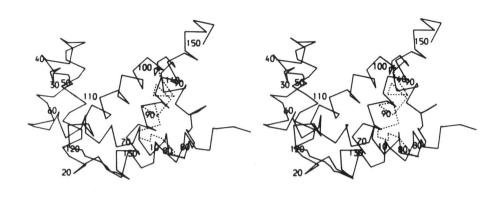

B

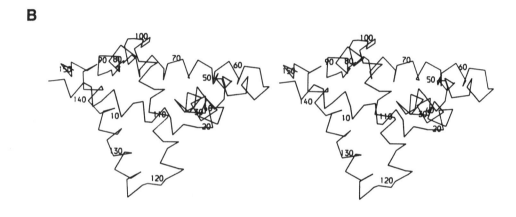

C

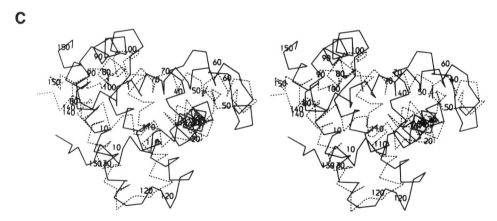

Fig. 4. A stereo diagram of the 2 structures remaining as a result of the heme constraint. An alpha carbon representation of I97 in solid lines with the differences of I88 overlaid in dotted lines. **(B)** An alpha carbon representation I97 rotated into the reference frame of the myoglobin coordinates (Bernstein *et al.,* 1977). **(C)** The superimposition of the predicted myoglobin structure I97 seen here in solid lines on the crystallographically determined alpha carbon coordinates connected by dotted lines. [Reprinted from *J. Mol. Biol.* **137,** 9 (1980) with permission.]

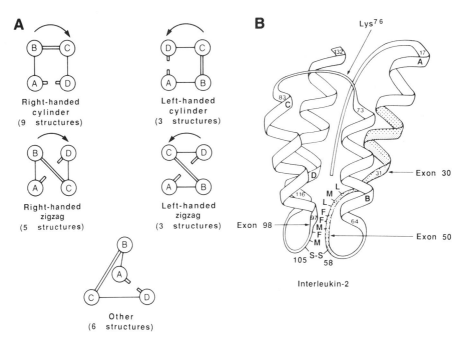

Fig. 5. **(A)** Schematic drawings of the helical topologies for the five families of predicted IL-2 structures. α-Helices are represented by circles and labeled sequentially A through D. They are shown end on. Connecting loops are shown as single or double lines. Double lines represent connections in front of the page and single connections behind the page. Arrows highlight the sequential rotation of the helices. **(B)** Ribbon diagram of a member of the right handed cylinder family of predicted IL-2 structures. Helical boundaries are located by a pattern based turn scheme (Cohen *et al.*, 1986a) with most turns located by the patterns pppp, pxppp, ppxpp, or pppxp where p is a hydrophilic residue and x is any amino acid. Helices are segments bounded by turns with the patterns hqqhhqqh, hhqqhh, hqqqhhqqh, or hqqhhqqqh, where h is a hydrophobic residue and q tends to be hydrophilic. Helical boundary predictions have implied errors of ± 3 residues. Helices are labeled A (17–31) B (64–73) C (83–97), D (116–132) and the amino- and carboxy-terminii are numbered. Strong sites for helix-helix packing were determined by the method of Richmond and Richards (1). Interaction classes pertain to helix-helix docking angles II = − 60° (residues 86, 128), III = 19° (residues 23, 24, 25, 69, 92, 93, 118, 122). For further details see Cohen *et al.* (1979). The disulfide bridge between Cys[58] and Cys[105] is indicated. A collection of hydrophobic residues in the loop between helices A and B which may be important in receptor binding is marked. Exon boundaries are marked with arrows. The region of binding for monoclonal antibodies to 23–41, 27–41, and 42–60, which neutralize activity, are shown. Lys[76], a site of limited proteolysis, is also marked. [Reprinted from *Science* **234**, 349 (1986) with permission. Copyright 1986, AAAS.]

Experimental Tests

These model structures became candidates for experimental tests. With Ciardelli, Smith, and co-workers, we devised, constructed, and evaluated a series of IL-2 analogs (Ciardelli *et al.*, 1988). Focusing on the putative C-terminal α-helix, analogs were designed that would stabilize and destabilize this secondary structure. Native IL-2 contained nadirs in the circular dichroism (CD) spectra at 208 and 222 nm, implying α-helical structure. The prediction that IL-2 was an all-helical protein seemed correct. A more stringent test of the model of

IL-2 would be the predictable enhancement or depression of α-helical content as measured by CD. This was accomplished with a pair of analogs that probed the structure of the C-terminal helix. Exchanging residues that enhanced the amphipathicity of the putative helix resulted in a stronger helical signal for the analog when compared to the native. Presumably, this exchange improved packing at the helix-helix interface. The insertion of two prolines significantly decreased the apparent helicity of the protein. Had these residues been in a loop region, presumably no change would have resulted. Soon after the

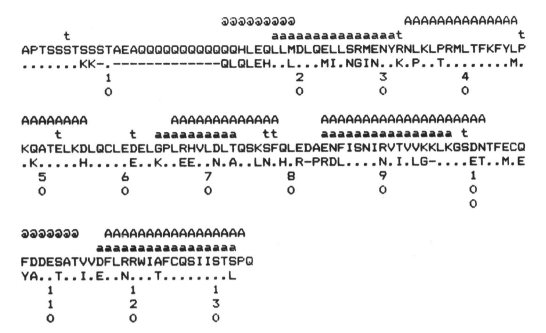

Fig. 6. Mouse (**top**) and human (**bottom**) interleukin-2 sequences. Numbers pertain to the human interleukin-2 sequence. (.) implies homology, and (-) implies deletion or insertion. Predicted alpha helical regions are labeled aaaa. AAAA indicates alpha helical regions in x-ray structure of human Il-2 and ∂∂∂∂∂ are non-core alpha helices in x-ray structure of human IL-2. Each t locates a turn identified by the algorithm of Cohen *et al.* (1983).

completion of these experiments, the crystallographic structure was solved at intermediate resolution. Highlighted in Fig. 6 are the predicted α-helices and the crystallographic α-helices. Three core helices were correctly located, but one was completely missed. The region where the N-terminal α-helix was incorrectly identified was re-examined. Turns had parsed the sequence into two regions that were candidates for the N-terminal helix. The subsequence 17–31 contains a classical α-helical pattern. Position I is a leucine, I + 1 is hydrophilic, I + 2 is hydrophilic, I + 3 and 4 are hydrophobic, 5 is hydrophilic, 6 is hydrophilic, and 7 is hydrophobic, suggesting an amphiphilic helix; however, no helical structure was found. The reason why this region does not form an α-helix remains obscure. By contrast, the true helix 33–46 has the sequence LPRMLTFK. Proline at position i + 2 could kink the helix, and i + 6 is hydrophobic and i + 7, hydrophilic. Hopefully, detailed structural information will help rationalize this error in the prediction. On the positive side, two helix-helix interfaces and the disulfide bridge were correctly modeled.

Another aspect of this structure that was incorrectly modeled was the topology of the four-helix bundle. The computer program suggested a variety of left- and right-handed bundles. We simply assumed that right-handed helical structures were most likely correct because this motif appeared in cytochrome b_{562}, hemerythrin, and several other proteins (Weber and Saleme, 1982). Until that time, no left-handed bundles had been reported. As it turns out, IL-2 forms a left-handed, four-helix bundle (Brandhuber *et al.*, 1987). We emphasize that the combinatorial algorithm generated left-handed structures; however, we rejected these structures on historical grounds. Clearly, this historical perspective was flawed (Presnell and Cohen, 1989). Although theoretical considerations proved to be of little help at this juncture in the modeling effort, experimental tests could have conceivably resolved structural ambiguities.

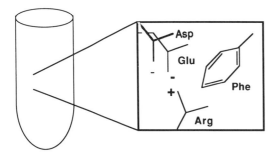

Fig. 7. A schematic of a molecular test tube. The protein polypeptide backbone forms the framework on which side chains are arrayed. Site-directed mutagenesis can be used to investigate the proximity of residues which could participate in interatomic interactions.

What is the nature of the difference between a correctly and incorrectly modeled structure? Our models all share good secondary structure, hydrogen bonding, and packing; electrostatic considerations are satisfied reasonably well. Yet a number of alternative structures remain. Perhaps the answer lies in learning how to blend theory and experiment. If we think of a protein as a molecular test tube, mutagenesis technology facilitates the redesigning of proteins (Fig. 7). One can devise mutagenesis experiments that can sort between the alternative structures predictively generated. Perhaps we can combine theory and experiment to turn a series of low-resolution experiments into a moderate-resolution structure.

Acknowledgments

This work was supported by a grant from the Searle Foundation/Chicago Community Trust (F. E. C.) and the Defense Advanced Research Projects Agency (F. E. C., I. D. K.). L. M. G. was supported by an National Science Foundation Graduate Student Fellowship. We wish to express our thanks to the Computer Graphics Laboratory (National Institutes of Health: RR-1081) and Professor R. Langridge.

References

Anfinsen, C. B., E. Haber, M. Sela, F. H. White, *Proc. Natl. Acad. Sci. U.S.A.* **47,** 1309 (1961).

Antonini, E., and M. Brunori, *Hemoglobin and Myoglobin in Their Reactions with Ligands* (North-Holland, Amsterdam, 1971), pp. 40–54.

Bernstein, F. C., et al., *J. Mol. Biol.* **112,** 535 (1977).

Brandhuber, B. J., T. Boone, W. C. Kenney, D. B. McKay, *Science* **238,** 1707 (1987).

Brill, A. S., and H. E. Sandberg, *Proc. Natl. Acad. Sci. U.S.A.* **57,** 136 (1967).

Chothia, C., M. Levitt, D. Richardson, *Proc. Natl. Acad. Sci. U.S.A.* **74,** 4130 (1977).

Chou, P. Y., and G. D. Fasman, *Biochemistry* **13,** 211 (1974).

———, *J. Mol. Biol.* **115,** 135 (1977).

Ciardelli, T. L., et al., *J. Molec. Recognition* **1,** 42 (1988).

Cohen, F. E., and M. J. E. Sternberg, *J. Mol. Biol.* **137,** 9 (1980a).

———, *J. Mol. Biol* **138,** 321 (1980b).

Cohen, F. E., R. A. Abarbanel, I. D. Kuntz, R. J. Fletterick, *Biochemistry* **22,** 4894 (1983).

———, *Biochemistry* **25,** 266 (1986a).

Cohen, F. E., T. J. Richmond, F. M. Richards, *J. Mol. Biol.* **132,** 275 (1979).

Cohen, F. E., M. J. E. Sternberg, W. R. Taylor, *Nature (London)* **285,** 378 (1980).

———, *J. Mol. Biol.* **156,** 821 (1982).

Cohen, F. E., et al., *Science* **234,** 349 (1986b).

Crute, M. B., *Acta Crystallogr.* **12,** 24 (1959).

Hagler, A. T., and B. Honig, *Proc. Natl. Acad. Sci. U.S.A.* **75,** 554 (1978).

Johnson, R. N., J. H. Bradbury, C. A. Appleby, *J. Biol. Chem.* **253,** 2148 (1978).

Levitt, M., and A. Warshel, *Nature* **253,** 694 (1975).

Lim, V. I., *J. Mol. Biol.* **88,** 857 (1974).

Nemethy, G., and H. A. Scheraga, *Quart. Rev. Biophys.* **10,** 239 (1977).

Pauling, L., *The Nature of the Chemical Bond* (Cornell University Press, Ithaca, 1960).

Presnell, S. R., and F. E. Cohen, *Proc. Natl. Acad. Sci. U.S.A.* **86,** 6592 (1989).

Richmond, T. J., and F. M. Richards, *J. Mol. Biol.* **119,** 537 (1978).

Taylor, W. R., and J. M. Thornton, *J. Mol. Biol.* **173,** 487 (1984).

Vuk-Pavlovic, S., and Y. Siderer, *Biochem. Biophys. Res. Commun.* **79,** 885 (1977).

Weber, P. C., and F. R. Salemme, *Nature (London)* **287,** 82 (1982).

Weiner, S. J., et al., *J. Am. Chem. Soc.* **106,** 765 (1984).

26

Using Conformational Search to Predict Polypeptide Segments

Robert E. Bruccoleri, Edgar Haber, Jiri Novotny

After most proteins are synthesized on the ribosome as a polymer of amino acid subunits, they spontaneously and reproducibly fold into a compact, three-dimensional structure. Although genetic sequencing technologies are rapidly increasing our knowledge of the amino acid sequences of proteins, structure determination techniques (e.g., x-ray crystallography, Nuclear Magnetic Resonance spectroscopy) are not keeping pace. With the stupendous increase in computing power anticipated in the future, computer-based prediction of protein folding has the potential to provide structural information for all the genetic sequences to be discovered. However, such predictions are extraordinarily difficult because the number of conformational possibilities present in a protein is very, very large. Even the most optimistic estimate, 1.4^N (Dill, 1985), is too large for complete search of conformational space for even a small protein such as myoglobin (153 residues, $1.4^{153} = 2.3 \times 10^{22}$). In addition, since we believe that the native, folded structure of a protein is the lowest energy conformation (Anfinsen, 1973), computer predictions of protein folding require an accurate calculation of the Gibbs free energy in solution. Such accurate calculations are not yet possible.

However, if we wish to make some progress on the prediction of protein folding, we can consider protein folding problems where a complete conformational search is feasible (Némethy and Scheraga, 1977; De Coen and Ralston, 1977; Hall and Pavitt, 1985; Dygert *et al.*, 1975; Moult and James, 1986). Because of the molecular basis of evolution, such problems abound — there are many examples of homologous families of proteins where the structures differ only in small regions, corresponding to variations in sequence. The conformational freedom in such small segments is usually low enough to be explored thoroughly in a reasonable amount of computer time. Given such a complete search, it is then possible to test free-energy functions by simply comparing the lowest energy conformation found in the search against experimentally determined structures.

Our conformational search procedure is very simple in principle — we uniformly sample the free torsion angles of a polypeptide segment (Bruccoleri, 1984; Moult and James, 1986; Bruccoleri and Karplus, 1987). These segments may adopt any structure that is sterically allowed; helices, sheets, turns, and loops are all permissible. Provided the sampling grid is not too fine, the number of generated conformations is manageable. This sampling does not depend on any statistics of known protein structures, but only on the chemical structure of the protein. Therefore, it is applicable to any system. However, the computer time and space required for such a sampling grows exponentially with the number of free torsion angles, so we are limited in practice to a relatively small polypeptide segment.

The evaluation of the free energy of the generated conformations is more problematic. Because there are many conformations to evaluate and because part of the generation process depends on energetic information, it is necessary for the energy evaluation to work very quickly. Although considerable strides have been made in the determination of the free energy of a protein (Rashin, 1984; Pettitt and Karplus, 1985; Mezei and Beveridge, 1986; Eisenberg and McLachlan, 1986; Bruccoleri et al., 1986; Bash et al., 1987; Novotny et al., 1988; Novotny et al., 1989), none of these methods is rapid enough for use in our searches. Thus, we are using the CHARMM potential energy function (Brooks et al., 1983) as our primary energy evaluator, but we have supplemented it with other criteria in order to improve its predictive accuracy.

Although we are limited to small polypeptide segments, our conformational search algorithm has great practical value. We can apply it toward many homology modeling problems (Browne et al., 1969; Padlan et al., 1976; Blundell et al., 1978; Feldmann et al., 1978; Greer, 1980; Furie et al., 1982; Inana et al., 1983). It can also be applied to site-directed mutagenesis problems (Razin et al., 1978; Hutchinson et al., 1978; Wilkinson et al., 1984) where one wishes to determine the effect of a localized change.

In the future, our work may be applied to the general folding problem by substituting our exhaustive conformational searching techniques with other secondary and tertiary structure prediction methods (Chou and Fasman, 1974; Schulz et al., 1974; Anfinsen and Scheraga, 1975; Tanaka and Scheraga, 1976; Wu et al., 1978; Sternberg and Thornton, 1978; Lim et al., 1978; Cohen et al., 1981, 1982, 1983; Ptisyn and Finkelstein, 1983; Taylor and Thornton, 1984) to generate possible conformations, which are then ranked by their energies.

In the remainder of this chapter, we describe the conformational search program in some detail. Next, we show examples from tests to demonstrate the program's capabilities. We then briefly describe the reconstruction (Bruccoleri et al., 1988) of an antibody molecule, McPC 603 (Satow et al., 1986), using CONGEN, and finally summarize our results.

CONGEN: The Conformational Search Program

CONGEN samples the conformational space of a polypeptide segment. It has been described in detail in other publications (Bruccoleri, 1984; Bruccoleri and Karplus, 1985, 1987), but we will summarize its function below as well as illustrate new features not previously published.

CONGEN has been written to assume that the endpoints of the loop are fixed in space. The surrounding protein influences the search through its excluded volume and other nonbonded interactions (such as electrostatics and hydrogen bonds). The sampling of the loop proceeds in two phases, backbone and side chains. The backbone construction depends on the Go and Scheraga chain closure algorithm. (Go and Scheraga, 1970). Given two fixed endpoints, stereochemical parameters for the construction of a polymer, and six adjustable torsion angles, this algorithm will calculate values for the six torsion angles in order to perfectly connect the polymer from one endpoint to the other. In our sampling of the backbone, we assume that only torsion angles are free to move, and in addition, the ω torsion angle is fixed planar (either cis or trans). Since each backbone residue has two free torsion angles, three residues are required for the application of the Go and Scheraga algorithm. For sampling conformations where more than three residues are involved, we sample the conformations of all but three residues and use the Go and Scheraga procedure to close the backbone.

We have modified the Go and Scheraga algorithm to allow small changes in the peptide bond angles (Bruccoleri and Karplus, 1985). After the first implementation of the algorithm, we tested it by deleting three residue segments in several different proteins and calling the algorithm to reconstruct the peptide backbone. In the helices in flavodoxin (Burnett *et al.*, 1974), the algorithm failed to find any closure for a large number of these segments. Apparently, the normal variations in position due to the limits of crystallographic resolution were interfering with the algorithm. By allowing the algorithm to adjust the bond angles by small amounts, typically less than 5°, we were able to find closures for all the helices (Bruccoleri and Karplus, 1985).

The free sampling of backbone torsion angles is done with the aid of a backbone energy map. We have calculated the energetics of constructing the backbone for three different classes of amino acids: glycine, proline, and all the rest. This information is stored as a map (Ramachandran *et al.*, 1963), which gives the energy as a function of discrete values ϕ, ψ where ω can only be 0° (cis) or 180° (trans). We have a set of maps corresponding to different grids; typically, a 30° sampling is sufficiently fine for good agreement.

With regard to the peptide ω angle, we normally allow only the proline ω angle to sample cis values. The ω angle for all other amino acids is always trans.

After each backbone conformation is determined, the position of side chains is constructed. Since the backbone construction provides the position of the C_β carbon and because an exhaustive search of the side chain conformations is generally not feasible, we use an iterative approach that begins by finding a side chain conformation, not necessarily of low energy, which has no large repulsive contacts. Then, each side chain in turn is deleted and a complete conformational search over its χ_i angles is performed to find the lowest energy conformation. The algorithm continues with each succeeding side chain until the energies no longer change. It is also possible to search side chain conformations for the best agreement to another structure instead of the lowest energy. This feature is useful in testing, when one wishes to know how close a sampling can approach the native, experimentally determined structure.

A new feature in the construction of side chains is the van der Waals avoidance option.

In earlier versions of CONGEN, the values used for side-chain torsion angles, χ_i, were sampled on a grid. If any bad contacts occurred, that sample would have been discarded. However, it is a straightforward geometrical problem to determine the range of torsion angles that will avoid constructing an atom within a given distance of other atoms in the system. As a side chain torsion angle, χ_i, varies, it specifies a circular locus of points on which atoms can be constructed (Bruccoleri and Karplus, 1987). If we examine the atoms in the vicinity of this circle, we can calculate the sectors of the circle, which will result in the repulsive overlap of the constructed atom with its spatial neighbors. The complement of these sectors can be used to determine values for the χ_i angles that avoid bad contacts.

Finally, after all the backbone and side chain atoms have been constructed, the energy of the conformation is evaluated. The atomic coordinates and the energy are written to a file for later analysis.

Testing

One of our key guiding principles is testing. A predictive tool is useful only if it is known to be accurate from prior experience. There are a number of questions to be answered by testing. First, can we come close to the native structure even though CONGEN is discretely sampling conformational space? This question determines how much computer time will be needed, since fine sampling is very expensive. Second, how close is the lowest energy structure to the native structure? Assuming a satisfactory answer to the first question, this reflects on the quality of energy function.

In Table 1, the first column of numbers answers the first question, the second column addresses the second. We can see that a 30° sampling can get us conformations well within 1 Å, and that the CHARMM energy function is a useful predictor. Figure 1 shows calculated and x-ray coordinates for the conformation described in the last line of Table 1. Note the very close agreement of the backbone. In addition, the first proline is predicted to be

Table 1. Congen test cases.[a]

Type	Protein segment	RMS (Å) of best match	RMS (Å) of lowest energy
Helix	Flavodoxin 127–131	0.444	0.944
Sheet	Plastocyanin 80–84	0.652	0.652
Turn	McPC 603 Light 95–99	1.209	1.579
Turn	McPC 603 Light 95–103	1.880	3.660
Turn	McPC 603 Light 98–102	0.871	1.371
Turn	KOL Heavy 41–45	0.650	2.031
Turn	KOL Heavy 41–46	0.685	0.789
Turn	KOL Heavy 41–47	0.743	0.951

[a]Tests of CONGEN performed on a variety of known structures. The first column of Root Mean Square (RMS) values displays the deviation for the conformation which came closest to the crystal. The searches over the side chains were guided by the agreement to the crystal rather than the energy. Thus, this column gives the theoretical lower bound for agreement to the x-ray data given the sampling grid. The second column is the lowest energy conformation found using an energy-directed search, and it measures the quality of the prediction. Coordinates for the molecules were obtained from the Brookhaven Data Bank (Bernstein *et al.*, 1977). The crystal structure for flavodoxin was solved by Burnett *et al.*, 1974; plastocyanin was solved by Colman *et al.*, 1978; McPC 603 was solved by Satow *et al.*, 1986; and Kol by Marquart *et al.*, 1980.

cis, as found in the crystal. The side chains contribute more to the difference between prediction and reality.

Besides these general questions, there are a number of specific questions concerning the options that control the search process. They affect both the number of conformations generated and their quality, and we have explored the variation of these options in great detail (Bruccoleri and Karplus, 1987). We have examined the effect of adjusting the maximum allowed van der Waals repulsion for any constructed atom, the coarseness of the ϕ, ψ maps, the side chain torsion angle sampling, the effect of energy minimizing the generated conformations, and of variations in the non-bonded energy calculation. The results described here use optimal values determined from our previous work.

We have performed some tests on the van der Waals avoidance option. In many cases, it has provided lower energy conformations than were found without it. Although it takes significant computational resources to compute the avoidance angles, we can lower the maximum permitted van der Waals avoidance so fewer conformations need to be generated in order to achieve good results.

Antibody Reconstruction

The antibody molecule (Padlan, 1977; Amzel and Poljak, 1979; Novotny and Haber, 1985; Davies *et al.*, 1988) is an excellent system for understanding the folding of short polypeptide segments. All antibody molecules possess variable domains that consist of two β-sheet barrels that are noncovalently associated (Novotny *et al.*, 1983; Chothia *et al.*, 1985; Novotny and Haber, 1985).

The antigen-combining site is composed of six hypervariable loops (three per barrel) (Edelman, 1970; Kabat *et al.*, 1987), all situated together in a patch that covers the interface between the two barrels. Each loop is typically less than 10 residues long, although some loops are found with up to 20 residues. The endpoints of each of these loops is fixed in a framework that varies very little from one antibody to another, typically less than 1 Å. (Novotny *et al.*, 1983; Novotny and Haber, 1985). For our reconstruction, we used McPC 603, a phosphorylcholine-binding antibody (Satow *et al.*, 1986).

Because the hypervariable loops interact with one another, it would be desirable to search over all loops simultaneously. How-

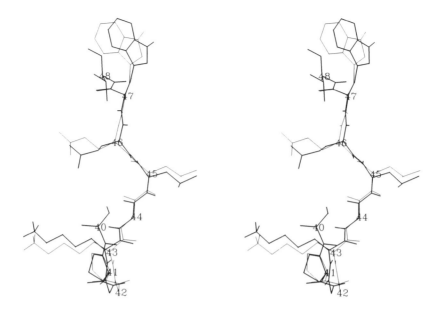

Fig. 1. A stereo line drawing showing the x-ray structure for residues 41 through 47 (light lines) in the heavy chain of Kol (Marquart *et al.,* 1980) and the lowest energy structure generated by CONGEN (heavy lines). Residues 40 and 48 are also included. The sequence of residues 41–47 is Pro Gly Lys Gly Leu Glu Trp. [Adapted from Bruccoleri and Karplus, 1987]

ever, this is not yet feasible because CONGEN is capable of a thorough search only over a single loop of moderate size. Thus, we must construct the combining site one loop at a time by building each loop onto the structure predicted for the others. This approach is fraught with difficulty because if one loop is constructed incorrectly, succeeding loops are very likely to be incorrect as well. In addition, since our free-energy function is the in vacuo potential of CHARMM (Brooks *et al.,* 1983), we would not expect it to correctly rank the generated conformations in all cases. In this reconstruction, we examined all the conformations generated for each loop, and we found an additional rule to supplement the energy ranking. This rule states that we should examine all the conformations within 2 kcal/mole of the lowest and select the one with the lowest accessible surface as computed within the context of the framework and other constructed loops.

Our sequential construction commenced from the framework underlying the combining site, constructing in layers until the outermost loops are formed. The construction order we

used was L2, H1, L3, H2, H3, L1 (Fig. 2). We were able to construct the four shortest loops (L2, H1, L3, and H3) using the simple rule above. In two of these cases, the lowest energy conformation was selected by the surface rule; in the other two, the next lowest energy was selected.

The remaining two loops (H2 and L1) were too long to be searched in reasonable time. Here, the search was broken up into several smaller searches, where the best conformations found a few residues are used as endpoints for searching succeeding residues. This approach, "real space renormalization" (Pincus and Klausner, 1982; Pincus *et al.,* 1982), worked successfully with L1 but not with H2.

For all six loops, we used a grid size of 30° on the backbone torsion angles. For the side chain torsion angles, we used 30° when the loops were short, and larger grids when this was impractical because of computer time. We experimented with smaller backbone grids and, in general, got better energies and agreements to the crystal, but the improvements did not justify the tremendous increase in com-

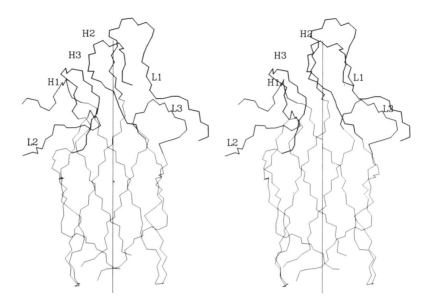

Fig. 2. Stereoscopic view of the hypervariable loops of McPC 603 with the underlying β sheets. By tight, noncovalent association, two curved β-sheets from the VL and VH domains create a twisted, elliptical β-barrel (Richardson, 1981; Chothia *et al.,* 1985; Novotny and Haber, 1985). The polypeptide backbone of this barrel can be approximated by mathematical hyperboloidal surfaces (Novotny *et al.,* 1984), and the long axis of the least-squares-fitted surface becomes a convenient reference axis of the β-barrel. The fitted axis of the β-sheet backbones are drawn in thin lines (the VL domain sheet is in front, the VH domain sheet is in back), and the 6 hypervariable loops (heavy chain loops H1, residues 28–32; H2, residues 50–58; H3, residues 102–109; light chain loops L1, residues 26–37; L2, residues 56–61; L3, residues 97–102, consecutive numbering system) are drawn with heavier lines. Note that the three shorter loops, H1, L2, and L3, drawn in moderately thick lines, have lower average axis coordinates, i.e., closer to the center of the barrel, than the other three loops, H2, H3, and L1, drawn in the heaviest thickness. In our construction protocol, the low loops were constructed before the high loops. [Adapted from Bruccoleri *et al.,* 1988]

puter time (e.g., for L2, a 100-fold increase in computer time improved the Root Mean Square (RMS) agreements by 20 percent). Also, we experimented with the order of construction within each loop and used the run that gave the lowest energy.

The calculation of the electrostatic interaction presented some difficulties, in particular, in the selection of the dielectric constant (Brooks *et al.,* 1983; Warshel and Levitt, 1976). Our initial plan was to use a dielectric constant of 50, because this approximates the dielectric constant of water and was suggested in a model by Warshel (Warshel *et al.,* 1984). This contrasts with the typical distance dielectric constant used for many previous molecular mechanics simulations (Brooks *et al.,* 1983), namely $\varepsilon = r$ where r is the distance between the interacting charges. The distance-dependent dielectric

better simulates the protein interior and is also computed efficiently, since no square root is needed for the distance factor.

The constant dielectric of 50 gave good results for the first three loops, L2, H1, and L3. However, in the real space renormalization used for H2, it was not until we used a constant dielectric constant for the first three residues (50–52) and the distance-dependent dielectric for the remaining residues (53–58) that we could construct a reasonable conformation for H2. The distant-dependent dielectric was used for the succeeding loops. We attempted to reconstruct the first three loops using the distance-dependent dielectric, but we failed to get good results with L3. Obviously, this is not consistent, and we are exploring improvements to the electrostatic calculation which will avoid such inconsistencies.

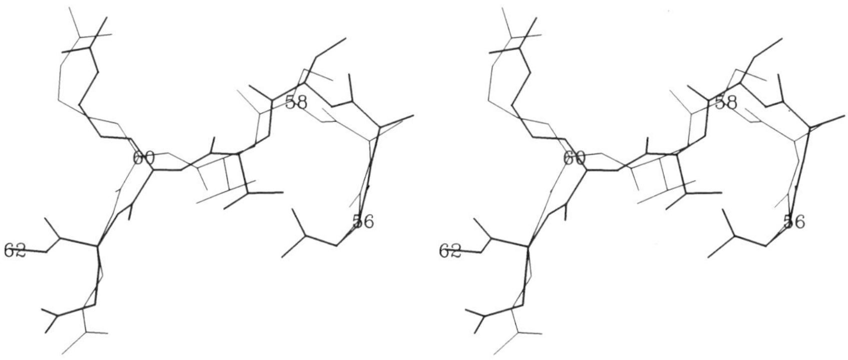

Fig. 3. A comparison of the x-ray and CONGEN-generated structure for the L2 loop, residues 56–61 (Gly-Ala-Ser-Thr-Arg-Glu) in the light chain of McPC 603. The x-ray structure is in thin lines and the CONGEN-generated structure is in thick lines.

Details of Loop Construction

In the L2 loop (Table 2, Fig. 3), two conformations were found within 2 kcal of the lowest energy. The second lowest energy structure had a better match to the crystal and had a smaller surface area, so we selected this conformation for the next stage. The biggest difference between the selected conformation

Table 2. Construction of L2 loop[a].

| Loop | Energy (kcal) | RMS (Å) | | Surface (Å²) |
		Total	Backbone	
L2	−16.1	2.4	2.0	397
	−14.6	**1.9**	**1.6**	**360**

[a]The selected conformation is shown in boldface. Residues 61 through 59 were searched in the C → N direction with chain closure applied to residues 56 through 58.

and the crystal is a shift in the backbone of about 1.5 Å at worst. Both the orientation of the side chains and their position in space are well preserved.

In H1 (Table 3, Fig. 4), the lowest energy conformation was separated by 6.4 kcal from the next lowest energy structure. Thus, we did not consider any other conformations. The character of the agreement here is a little different than with L2. Here, there is less shift in

Table 3. Construction of H1 loop[a].

| Loop | Energy (kcal) | RMS (Å) | | Surface (Å²) |
		Total	Backbone	
H1	**−17.1**	**1.7**	**0.7**	**344**
	−10.7	1.6	0.7	329

[a]The selected conformation is shown in boldface. Residues 28 and 32 were constructed by free backbone sampling followed by chain closure on residues 29 through 31.

the backbone but more changes in orientation. Residues Thr 28 and Phe 32 agree well, but Phe 29, Ser 30, and Asp 31 are shifted by as much as 2 Å.

L3 (Table 4, Fig. 5) is similar to L2 in that the second lowest energy structure has a much better agreement to the crystal than the best energy structure (the difference between the

Table 4. Construction of L3 loop[a].

| Loop | Energy (kcal) | RMS (Å) | | Surface (Å²) |
		Total	Backbone	
L3	−21.8	3.0	1.5	375
	−20.8	**1.4**	**0.8**	**320**

[a]The selected conformation is shown in boldface. L3 was built in the N → C direction.

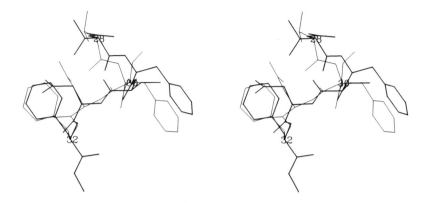

Fig. 4. A comparison of the x-ray and CONGEN-generated structure for the H1 loop, residues 28–32 (Thr-Phe-Ser-Asp-Phe) in the heavy chain of McPC 603. The x-ray structure is in thin lines and the CONGEN-generated structure is in thick lines.

two being 1 kcal/mole). The accessible surface of the second lowest is about 15 percent lower and, thus, it was selected. The agreement between the generated conformation and the crystal is very good, with only one side chain (Asp 97) being out of place. There is only a small shift in the backbone, and the orientations are all well preserved. Note that the cis

Table 5. Construction of H2 loop[a].

Loop	Energy (kcal)	RMS (Å)		Surface (Å²)
		Total	Backbone	
H2 50–52	−18.8	2.1	2.0	101
	−18.5	2.2	2.2	126
	−18.2	2.1	2.1	100
	−17.9	2.2	2.1	123
	−17.8	**1.6**	**1.0**	**80**
	−17.8	1.7	1.0	96
H2 53–58	**−39.6**	**2.4**	**1.9**	**550**
	−33.8	4.0	1.5	584

[a]The H2 loop was constructed in two parts, residues 50 to 52 first, followed by 53 to 58. In the upper part of the table is shown the energy, backbone, total Root Mean Square deviations, and accessible surface for the six conformations within 1 kcal/mole of the lowest. The fifth conformation in the list was selected because it had the smallest accessible surface. This conformation was then used to construct the remaining residues in the loop as shown in the lower part of the table. Here, the lowest energy conformation was 5.8 kcal/mole lower in energy than the nearest candidate.

proline at position 101 is correctly predicted.

H2 (Table 5, Fig. 6) was the most difficult loop to construct, as we described earlier. Many combinations of searches on the amino and carboxy termini were attempted, and the only construction that gave acceptable agreement to the x-ray structure began with a three-residue search on the amino terminal (residues 50–52) using a constant dielectric of 50.

There were six conformations for residues 50 to 52 within 2 kcal of the lowest energy. The fifth lowest, which has the lowest accessible surface, had a good agreement with the crystal. Starting with this conformation and using the distance-dependent dielectric constant $\varepsilon = r$, we were able to search the remaining six residues in reasonable time and get the conformation shown in Fig. 6.

The backbone of the constructed H2 is shifted in space by about 1.5 Å. In addition, some of the side chains are reoriented, but two of the largest shifts (Lys 54 and Lys 57) occur on the surface, where such rearrangements would be expected. Other residues such as Asn 53 and Tyr 58 superimpose better.

The H3 loop (Table 6, Fig. 7) was the longest loop we were able to search in one construction. It required seven days of CPU time. There were two low-energy conformations within 2 kcal of each other, and the lowest surface area corresponded with the lowest energy.

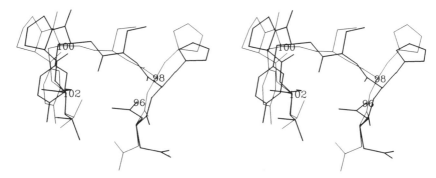

Fig. 5. A comparison of the x-ray and CONGEN-generated structure for the L3 loop, residues 97–102 (Asp-His-Ser-Tyr-Pro-Leu, note the cis proline, residue 101) in the light chain of McPC 603. The x-ray structure is in thin lines and the CONGEN-generated structure is in thick lines. [From Bruccoleri *et al.,* 1988.]

The agreement of this structure is quite good except for the tyrosine 103 residue, whose side chain makes a very large contribution to the total RMS. The backbone occupies the same space as the crystal, but many of the peptides are shifted along the chain. Most of the side chains are oriented correctly, except for the tyrosine 103 and tryptophan 107.

The L1 loop (Table 7, Fig. 8), having 12 residues, had to be searched using real space normalization. However, real space renormalization worked quite well in this case. We started by constructing the first two amino-terminal residues (Ser 26 and Gln 27). The lowest energy structure matched the crystal to 1.2 Å.

Using this and the next three low-energy conformations, we constructed residues Ser 28 and Leu 29. The lowest energy conformation for the first four residues was 1.3 Å. We took the lowest four energy structures and used these to start the next two (Leu 30 and Asn 31), getting an agreement of 1.8 Å. At this point, the real space renormalization broke down, as we were unable to find conformations that continued from the lowest energy starting points.

Table 6. Construction of H3 loop[a].

Loop	Energy (kcal)	RMS (Å)		Surface (Å²)
		Total	Backbone	
H3	**−64.5**	**2.9**	**1.1**	**369**
	−62.2	2.7	0.9	394

[a]The selected conformation is shown in boldface. H3 was built in the N → C direction.

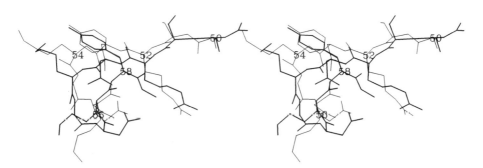

Fig. 6. A comparison of the x-ray and CONGEN-generated structure for the H2 loop, residues 50–58 (Ala-Ser-Arg-Asn-Lys-Gly-Asn-Lys-Tyr) in the heavy chain of McPC 603. The x-ray structure is in thin lines and the CONGEN-generated structure is in thick lines.

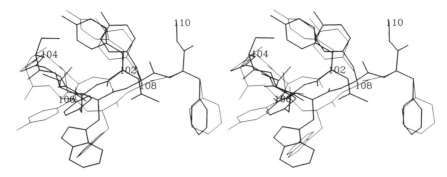

Fig. 7. A comparison of the x-ray and CONGEN-generated structure for the H3 loop, residues 102–109 (Tyr-Tyr-Gly-Ser- Thr-Trp-Tyr-Phe) in the heavy chain of McPC 603. The x-ray structure is in thin lines and the CONGEN-generated structure is in thick lines.

Table 7. Construction of L1 loop[a].

Residues	Energy (kcal)	RMS (Å)	
		Total	Backbone
26–27	− 27.2	1.2	0.3
28–29	− 47.0	1.3	0.6
30–31	− 65.3	1.8	1.6
37–36	− 30.9	1.7	1.9
31–36	− 49.0	4.0	3.8
Total	−105.9	3.0	2.7

[a]The L1 loop was constructed stepwise, i.e., using real space renormalization. First, six residues at the amino terminus were constructed two at a time. The four lowest energy conformations from one step were used as starting conformations for the next step. Next, the two carboxy terminal residues were constructed. Finally, the middle residues of the loop were constructed, using the earlier constructions as starting points.

We now constructed residues Asn 37 and Lys 36 in the reverse direction, and the lowest energy conformation agreed to 1.7 Å. Finally, we took the lowest energy construction from each end, deleted the final residue in each case (residue Asn 31 and residue Lys 36), and constructed the final six residues to complete the loop. The overall agreement was 3.0 Å. The agreement of this structure is quite good. The rest of the loop did not match very well. However, according to R. P. Davies, the electron density in this region is very weak, and the coordinates are no more than a stereochemically good guess (Satow et al., 1986).

The overall agreement is shown in Table 8. The results are good enough to give a rough impression of the binding site, but not good enough to predict the binding of antigen. Color Plate XXIII shows a space-filling view of both the x-ray structure and the model. It is possible to see the rearrangements of heavy chain residues tyrosine 103 (the yellow side

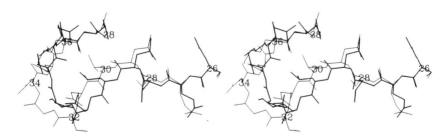

Fig. 8. A comparison of the x-ray and CONGEN-generated structure for the L1 loop, residues 26–37 (Ser-Gln-Ser-Leu-Leu-Asn-Ser-Gly-Asn-Gln-Lys-Asn) in the light chain of McPC 603. The x-ray structure is in thin lines and the CONGEN-generated structure is in thick lines.

Table 8. Summary of agreements for all loops[a].

Loop	Length	RMS (Å)		CPU (μVax II)
		Total	Backbone	
H1	5	1.7	0.7	4 h.
H2	9	2.1	1.6	5 d.
H3	8	2.9	1.1	7 d.
L1	12	3.0	2.6	7 d.
L2	6	1.9	1.6	8 h.
L3	6	1.4	0.8	5 h.
Totals	46	2.4	1.7	20 d.

[a]The RMS deviations for the loops (complete and backbone only) as well as the loop lengths and CPU times for the searches are given for each loop individually and for the six loops jointly.

chain pointing up in the model) and tryptophan 107 (the tilted side chain in the combining site).

Concluding Remarks

We are very encouraged by the good agreements found for all of the loops that were constructed in a single CONGEN run. The use of real-space renormalization remains a problem, as seen with the difficulties in reconstructing H2. We are not yet ready to reliably construct an entire combining site using our methods, since we need to be able to predict all six loops in a consistent manner, and we must further explore the construction of interacting loops. We hope that as we improve the efficiency of the search and the quality of energy function, we will ultimately be able to construct any loop accurately and reliably.

References

Amzel, L. M., and R. J. Poljak, *Ann. Rev. Biochem.* **48**, 961 (1979).

Anfinsen, C. B., *Science* **181**, 223 (1973).

Anfinsen, C. B., and H. A. Scheraga, *Adv. Prot. Chem.* **29**, 205 (1975).

Bash, P. A., U. C. Singh, F. K. Brown, R. Langridge,

P. A. Kollman, *Science* **235**, 574 (1987).

Bernstein, F. C., *et al., J. Mol. Biol.* **112**, 535 (1977).

Blundell, T. L., S. Bedarkar, E. Rinderknecht, R. E. Humbel, *Proc. Natl. Acad. Sci. U.S.A.* **75**, 180 (1978).

Brooks, B., *et al., J. Comput. Chem.* **4**, 187 (1983).

Browne, W. J., *et al., J. Mol. Biol.* **42**, 65 (1969).

Bruccoleri, R. E., Ph.D. thesis, Harvard University, Cambridge, MA, 1984.

Bruccoleri, R. E., and M. Karplus, *Biopolymers* **26**, 137 (1987).

_____, *Macromolecules* **18**, 2767 (1985).

Bruccoleri, R. E., E. Haber, J. Novotny, *Nature* **335**, 564 (1988).

_____, *Nature* **336**, 266 (1988).

Bruccoleri, R. E., J. Novotny, P. Keck, C. Cohen, *Biophys. J.* **49**, 79 (1986).

Burnett, R. M., *et al., J. Biol. Chem.* **249**, 4383 (1974).

Chothia, C., J. Novotny, R. E. Bruccoleri, M. Karplus, *J. Mol. Biol.* **186**, 651 (1985).

Chou, P. Y., and G. D. Fasman, *Biochemistry* **13**, 211 (1974).

Cohen, F. E., R. M. Abarbanel, I. D. Kuntz, R. J. Fletterick, *Biochemistry* **22**, 4898 (1983).

Cohen, F. E., M. J. E. Sternberg, W. R. Taylor, *J. Mol. Biol.* **148**, 253 (1981).

_____, *J. Mol. Biol.* **156**, 821 (1982).

Colman, P. M., *et al., Nature* **272**, 319 (1978).

Davies, D. R., S. Sheriff, E. A. Padlan, *J. Biol. Chem.* **263**, 10541 (1988).

De Coen, J-L., and E. Ralston, *Biopolymers* **16**, 1929 (1977).

Dill, K. A., *Biochemistry* **24**, 1501 (1985).

Dygert, M., N. Go, H. A. Scheraga, *Macromolecules* **8**, 750 (1975).

Edelman, G. M., *Biochemistry* **9**, 3197 (1970).

Eisenberg, D., and A. D. McLachlan, *Nature* **319**, 199 (1986).

Feldmann, R. J., D. H. Bing, B. C. Furie, B. Furie, *Proc. Nat. Acad. Sci. U.S.A.* **75**, 5409 (1978).

Furie, B., *et al., J. Biol. Chem.* **257**, 3875 (1982).

Go, N., and H. A. Scheraga, *Macromolecules* **3**, 178 (1970).

Greer, J., *Proc. Natl. Acad. Sci. U.S.A.* **77**, 3393 (1980).

Hall, D., and N. Pavitt, *Biopolymers* **24**, 935 (1985).

Hutchinson, C. A., III, *et al., J. Biol. Chem.* **253**, 6551 (1978).

Inana, G., J. Piatorgsky, B. Norman, C. Slingsby, T. Blundell, *Nature* **302**, 310 (1983).

Kabat, E. A., T. T. Wu, M. Reid-Miller, H. M. Perry, K. S. Gottesman, *Sequences of Proteins of Immunological Interest,* Public Health Service, National Institutes of Health, Bethesda, MD (1987).

Lim, V. I., A. L. Mazanov, A. V. Efimov, *Molekilyarnaya Biologiya* **12**, 219 (1978).

Marquart, M., J. Deisenhofer, R. Huber, *J. Mol. Biol.* **141**, 369 (1980).

Mezei, M., and D. L. Beveridge, *Ann. N.Y. Acad. Sci.*. **482**, 1 (1986).

Moult, J., and M. N. G. James, *Proteins* **1**, 146 (1986).

Némethy, G., and H. A. Scheraga, *Q. Rev Biophys.* **10**, 239 (1977).

Novotny, J., and E. Haber, *Proc. Natl. Acad. Sci. U.S.A.* **82**, 4592 (1985).

Novotny, J., R. Bruccoleri, J. Newell, *J. Mol. Biol.* **177**, 567 (1984).

Novotny, J., R. E. Bruccoleri, F. Saul, *Biochemistry* **28**, 4735 (1989).

Novotny, J., A. A. Rashin, R. E. Bruccoleri, *Proteins* **4**, 19 (1988).

Novotny, J., *et al., J. Biol. Chem.* **258**, 14433 (1983).

Padlan, E. A., *Quart. Rev. Biophys.* **10**, 35 (1977).

Padlan, E. A., D. R. Davies, I. Pecht, D. Givol, C. Wright, *Cold Spring Harbor Symp. Quant. Biol.* **41**, 627 (1976).

Pettitt, B. M., and M. Karplus, *J. Chem. Phys.* **83**, 781 (1985).

Pincus, M. R., and R. D. Klausner, *Proc. Natl. Acad. Sci. U.S.A.* **79**, 3413 (1982).

Pincus, M. R., R. D. Klausner, H. A. Scheraga, *Proc. Natl. Acad. Sci. U.S.A.* **79**, 5107 (1982).

Ptisyn, O. B., and A. V. Finkelstein, *Biopolymers* **22**, 15 (1983).

Ramachandran, G. N., C. Ramakrishnan, V. Sasisekharan, *J. Mol. Biol.* **7**, 95 (1963).

Rashin, A. A., *Biopolymers* **23**, 1605 (1984).

Razin, A. T., K. Hirose, K. Itakura, A. D. Riggs, *Proc. Natl. Acad. Sci. U.S.A.* **75**, 4268 (1978).

Richardson, J., *Adv. Prot. Chem.* **34**, 167 (1981).

Satow, Y., G. H. Cohen, E. A. Padlan, D. R. Davies, *J. Mol. Biol.* **190**, 593 (1986).

Schulz, G. E., *et al., Nature* **250**, 140 (1974).

Sternberg, M. J. E., and J. M. Thornton, *Nature* **271**, 15 (1978).

Tanaka, S., and H. A. Scheraga, *Macromolecules* **9**, 142 (1976).

Taylor, W. R., and J. M. Thornton, *J. Mol. Biol.* **173**, 487 (1984).

Warshel, A., and M. Levitt, *J. Mol. Biol.* **103**, 227 (1976).

Warshel, A., S. T. Russell, A. K. Churg, *Proc. Natl. Acad. Sci. U.S.A.* **81**, 4785 (1984).

Wilkinson, A. J., A. R. Fersht, D. M. Blow, P. Carter, G. Winter, *Nature* **307**, 187 (1984).

Wu, T. T., S. C. Szu, R. L. Jernigan, H. Bilofsky, E. A. Kabat, *Biopolymers* **17**, 555 (1978).

27

Supercomputing Opportunities for the Protein Sciences

Larry Smarr

Science has historically relied on two basic methodologies: theory and observation/experiment. In addition to these two modes, which are many centuries old, a third mode has arisen in the last half century: computational science. Computational science involves the use of digital computers to manipulate either equations or data. Although theory provides the equations, the analytic tools of theory are only adequate for obtaining solutions for special geometries or for simplified versions (linearized or perturbations) of the equations. Solutions of these equations that exhibit the realistic complexity seen in nature require numerical computations. Massive data sets, arising from modern laboratory instruments, are meaningless by themselves until analyzed by numerical means. Not only can computational science serve as a strong link between theory and experiment, it can also lead to new insights and knowledge in its own right.

The power of digital computers has increased exponentially for decades and should continue to do so for decades to come. This means that the computational scientist must gain access to new equipment on a time scale of every few years or fall behind competitively. The United States has been struggling with how to provide such technological access to university researchers for the last three decades.

In the 1960s, the federal government provided the funds needed to set up first-rate university computing centers. However, for the 15 years between 1970 and 1985, the federal government removed itself from maintaining these facilities at the state of the art. During that period of "feudalism," scientists were on their own in obtaining computing resources. Very few had access to the newest computational technologies. There was a radical reversal of this policy of "benign neglect" in 1985 when the National Science Foundation (NSF) formed the national supercomputer centers and began the national NSFNET network. That this change will also transform American industry, and thereby the national economy, has been explicitly recognized. Both the Executive Branch (Office of Science and Technology Policy, 1989) and the Congress (U.S. Congress, 1989; Senate Bill 1067, 1989) have issued strong calls for a national initiative in high-performance computing and networking. These programs in the 1990s will involve new forms of collaboration between government, universities, and industries.

In the last four years, more than 20,000 university scientists, engineers, social scientists, and humanists at over 250 universities and colleges have gained access to virtually all forms of frontier computing technologies housed in the national centers. Such access requires peer review of proposals in order to maintain a high standard of research excellence. There is a factor of 100 to 1000 times the computing speed, memory, and storage capacity in the national centers as is available in the desktop computer of the typical individual scientist. The national network, which allows the researcher to "reach out" and grab that extra power when needed, has 1000 times the bandwidth of a user's access path four years ago. There are roughly 100 staff at each of the five NSF supercomputer centers to support the remote user and to provide a high level of training and consulting.

By the mid 1990s, the computing power on both the desktop computers and on the central supercomputers will be at least 100 times what it is today. The bandwidth of the national network will rise by another factor of 1,000. We are also seeing a fundamental change in software. User interfaces are moving from command line, character-oriented, single screens to menu-driven, bit-mapped, multiple-windowed environments. Easy-to-use tool sets in the public domain are being developed to handle routine tasks in file management, graphics, and telecommunications. Many important concepts in computer science (e.g., object-oriented programming, distributed computing, data structures) are becoming practical tools for computational scientists. Finally, a wide range of visualization technologies are changing the primary unit of information from number to image. Because of this enormous rate of technological change and the great democratization of access that the NSF has provided, the period in which we are now is one of historical change in computational science.

This chapter will give an overview of the emerging national information infrastructure that will enable many exciting discoveries in the computational sciences, including the protein sciences. The near future will see most researchers having access to powerful and flexible desktop computers linked over a national network. "Supernodes" on this network will contain high-value resources such as supercomputers and national data banks. Scientific visualization capabilities will be ubiquitous. The ability to bring together on the desktop the results of both complex simulations and detailed observations, and to be able to interact with each data set visually as well as quantitatively, could profoundly influence the progress of the protein sciences.

Computational Protein Sciences

There are many current applications of advanced computing to the protein sciences, some of which are described in detail in other chapters in this volume. Since my research area is relativistic astrophysics, I will not presume to review the biology or biochemistry involved, but will instead give a brief overview of some of the research areas in the protein sciences in which I see computational progress being made: imaging of biological polymers, genome sequencing, determination of protein structure and function, and the protein folding process.

The direct imaging of the polymers of proteins and nucleic acids is bringing new technologies such as the scanning tunneling microscope into the biological laboratory. These images of individual molecules are digital and require image processing to reveal fine details of structure. Because imaging instruments create digital data sets, "multisensor fusion" is becoming practical. This approach combines data from various modalities such as optical, x-ray, and scanning tunneling microscopy into a single, digital, synthetic "object" that can be explored interactively on a workstation. It would be very desirable to make these data sets available electronically to the national community.

The rapid rise of interest in genome sequencing is producing ever larger numbers of the amino acid sequences that code for proteins. Steps are being taken in the community to assure that these sequences are available to all researchers in national data banks. However, the sequences require annotations in order to be scientifically useful. In many cases researchers would also like to see the original gel images. Thus, the need arises for a single file structure that can accommodate symbolic, numerical, and image data. Furthermore, a new generation of application software is being written to allow for comparisons and searches among the accumulating data banks.

The three-dimensional (3D) atomic structure is known for some 300 proteins. Since this is only 10 percent of the number of genes on a single bacterial DNA (which itself is only 1/1000 of the length of the human genome), it is clear that researchers will soon have far more linear sequences than they will have the folded 3D structure for proteins. Hence the interest in computational protein folding. Nonetheless, advances in x-ray crystallography and 2D nuclear magnetic resonance (NMR) hold out the hope for many more structures to be revealed experimentally. Some supermolecular structures such as viruses and protein/nucleic acid complexes have been solved as well. For the largest structures, supercomputers are required to reconstruct the 3D structure from the experimental data. The researcher again requires remote electronic access to national data banks (such as at Brookhaven National Laboratory). In addition, workstations capable of running 3D graphics software interactively are necessary to comprehend the hierarchical, organized complexity of protein structures.

An increasingly common use of supercomputer time is the determination of protein function from protein structure. Proteins carry out their function in an aqueous solution. In such an environment, they continuously flex and interact with other molecules. Molecular dynamics software can calculate the motions of the atoms in the protein, and computer graphics software can translate these computed trajectories into visual animation. However, even thousands of hours of time on the fastest supercomputers can compute only a tiny fraction of the possible motions of a large protein. Quantum chemistry codes can approximately determine the electronic structure of proteins. From this structure, researchers are beginning to study chemical interactions between molecules and electron or proton tunneling within molecules.

The one key area that is missing from the computational protein sciences today is the capability to predict the three-dimensional folded protein structure from the linear amino acid sequence. This seminar has been very useful for bringing together many of the leading researchers in the field to exchange views on how to proceed. It seems clear that there is not one "royal road" to the solution of the protein folding problem. Instead, I expect to see new algorithms brought into this field from other disciplines such as statistical mechanics (Wolynes, in press), computer science, and mathematics that will qualitatively change the computational approach. In any case, for the foreseeable future, this central problem of biology will require immense computing resources. Since other chapters in this volume deal with some specific techniques for computational protein folding, I will not discuss details of the relevant algorithms further here.

Rather, I will describe the wide variety of computational and communications technologies necessary to support the broad range of protein sciences described above. From these thumbnail sketches of the major subfields of the protein sciences, we can see a number of common technologies are required. Remote digital access to data banks of images, sequences, and structures as well as applications software, electronic mail, and the scientific literature itself needs to be easily available. Both local and remote storage capacity for exponentially increasing data sets must be provided.

A wide range of visualization capabilities—from x-y plots to color three-dimensional, real-time animations—are required to probe the complexity of proteins. All of the computers used by the researcher should be transparently integrated by distributed system software. A computational environment on a workstation configured with a Graphical User Interface (GUI) should tie together all the software tools and remote computing resources needed to perform protein research. One might term this device a "protein workstation."

In addition to these technological requirements, a higher level of human teamwork is necessary. Modern computational science demands not only detailed knowledge of the science itself but also of the computer science and technology that is being used to solve the problem computationally. Therefore, consulting, training, and education services covering all aspects of the computational technologies and their applications to scientific research should be available to the end user. Particularly in the protein sciences, research progress will also require a high level of interdisciplinary collaboration between individuals and institutions in universities, industry, and the government.

These computational infrastructure needs of the researcher are not specific to the protein sciences. Indeed, it is their universality that makes it possible to design a national information system by spreading the total cost over all areas of science and engineering in both pure and applied research.

The Emerging National Information Infrastructure

The 1990s will witness the establishment of a fiber optic network that will link together most major research facilities, whether in universities, industry, or government, to provide a comprehensive national computational environment with the capabilities described above. The beginnings of this infrastructure have already been laid. As mentioned above, NSF has created a number of national supercomputing centers to serve the university community and begun a national network, NSFNET, which today hooks most research universities together through over 1000 local, regional, and state networks tied to the national backbone (Fig. 1). In addition, nearly 20 universities have purchased their own supercomputers, and many more have created campus networks. Other government agencies with national laboratories as well as many large corporations have supercomputers with limited access to the university community but with strong in-house research groups. Personal computers and workstations are becoming very widespread on researchers' desktops. Finally, there is a rapidly improving family of application software in both public domain and commercial forms that can attack most of the problems that arise in protein science.

In this section, I will review some of the key computational technology trends that protein researchers should be aware of as this infrastructure emerges. I will divide the discussion into desktop computers, networks, and supernodes.

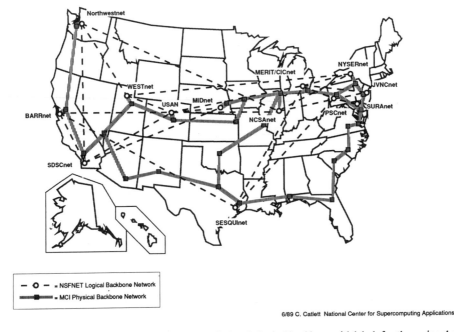

6/89 C. Catlett National Center for Supercomputing Applications

Fig. 1. The NSFNET national network. Shown is the logical and physical backbone with labels for the regional networks.

Desktop computers

In 1989, there are well over 20 million personal computers and workstations on desktops in America. Although the great majority of these are engaged in business activities, an increasing number are being used by researchers. Originally, these machines were character oriented and command line driven single screens, but, in the last few years, they have moved to bit-mapped graphics, "point and click" interface, with multiple windows. These desktop computers, which have previously been used primarily as stand-alone machines, are increasingly being used as "smart ports" into a networked distributed computing environment. As the speed of all the computers in the network increases exponentially, users are turning to visual representations of the massive data sets they are producing.

A key trend for all of the major vendors of desktop computers is to provide a standard GUI with a "cut and paste" capability across all application software. At this writing, this is complete only for the Apple Macintosh. Therefore, I will focus below on what can be achieved in this environment. During the next 18 months, the other major vendors will complete their transition over to this type of advanced interface. Complete GUIs are now emerging for each major operating system, for instance: Microsoft's Windows for DOS personal computers, Presentation Manager for IBM's OS/2 operating system, and OPEN-LOOK (AT&T, Sun Microsystems, Inc., and others), Motif (Open Software Foundation — IBM, DEC, HP, and others), and NextStep (NeXT and IBM) for UNIX workstations. Since the industry has not standarized on a complete GUI, many third-party application software developers have not yet modified their codes to tie tightly into the GUI. In the interim, most vendors have agreed to a partial GUI, "X-Windows," as a standard windowing system, but one which docs not provide as easily for moving across applications.

These desktop machines run commercial productivity software such as word processing, data bases, spreadsheets, and modem communication software, which plays a crucial role in the day-to-day life of a researcher. In addition, one can purchase a variety of 2D and 3D computer graphics software packages. Except on the Macintosh, these are stand-alone applications. While extremely valuable and powerful, they will become even more so when one can uniformly move data, images, and annotations easily across applications. This will result not only in greater productivity for the end user but also in a much reduced training barrier than exists today.

I will illustrate some of the potential capabilities of such future software tools, integrated with a standard GUI, by describing the current National Center for Supercomputing Applications (NCSA) software suite. These are general tools needed by anyone computing in today's distributed environment. These tools link personal computers, remote workstations, and supercomputers into a cooperative computing environment to enable the researcher to do computations, share files and data across machines, generate images from data sets, analyze and animate those images, produce color maps, and create presentation-quality graphics. Because these software tools were not available commercially, NCSA has created a software development group to produce public domain[1] software tools for the desktop. This group consists of computer scientists and computer professionals who receive functional design input from the computational scientists using the facilities of NCSA.

In today's distributed computing environment, the most fundamental need is for connectivity. As local ethernets, campus networks, and regional networks merge with the national backbone, a user needs to be able to run multiple computers simultaneously from

---

1   The NCSA software suite is released into the public domain and may be downloaded at no charge from an anonymous file transfer protocol (FTP) server at NCSA (via Internet addresses ftp ftp.ncsa.uiuc.edu or ftp 128.174.20.50), or ordered through the NCSA Technical Resources Catalog. To obtain an NCSA Technical Resources Catalog, contact: NCSA Documentation Orders, 152 Computing Applications Building, 605 E. Springfield Avenue, Champaign, IL 61820 (217) 244-0072.

his or her desktop and transfer files between them. Fortunately, NSF has insisted that all NSFNET access follow the standard "TCP/IP" protocols. NCSA Telnet provides the user with TCP/IP connections from DOS, Macintosh, and UNIX workstations to remote hosts with multiple window sessions, FTP file transfer, and Tektronix and raster image capabilities. Figure 2 shows a photo of a Macintosh II screen running NCSA Telnet. Each window is running a session on a different computer on the national network (here, a remote Cray Research, Inc., supercomputer, a DEC VAX superminicomputer, and a Sun Microsystems network server) and each session is independently scrollable in each window. The information in the window can be cut and pasted into any other Macintosh application package. We estimate that NCSA Telnet has tens of thousands of users today.

Once one has data sets, either from computation, experiment, or observation with modern sensors, the user needs a simple set of tools to explore the data visually and quantitatively. At this writing, the available NCSA software can handle two-dimensional data sets, of which I will give examples below. We have similar tools for three-dimensional data sets in development. NCSA Datascope can be used to create a color raster image representation of 2D data by simply pulling down a menu.

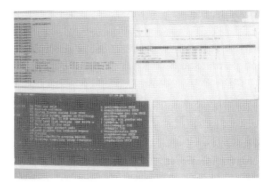

Fig. 2. NCSA Telnet running three sessions on different remote computers.

Figure 3 shows a fluid flow computation being explored on a Macintosh II using Datascope. (The original screen was in color but is printed as black and white in this volume.) Note that the data are held in electronic spreadsheet form, so that the numbers remain "live." An electronic notebook allows one to compute functions of the data by simply writing down the desired formula. The mouse can be used to pick out any subset of the data and this area is simultaneously shown on the image.

This image can be easily moved into NCSA Image, which allows one to obtain line graphs of cuts through the data, contour and 3D surface plots of the data, or animations of a series of images. Rudimentary image

Fig. 3. NCSA Datascope analyzing a vortex fluid flow.

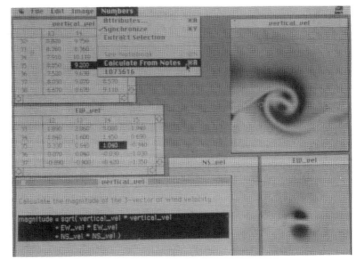

processing can be achieved by manipulations of the color transfer function, which is the method by which data values are turned into colors. These are all mouse driven and require no programming. NCSA PalEdit is another tool with which one can construct custom color transfer functions or "palettes." Finally, NCSA Layout allows one to design presentation graphics containing raster images. Again, one can cut and paste all these images, palettes, graphs, words, and equations into any Macintosh application. This allows one to create an "electronic research notebook."

In order to make the capabilities of the NCSA suite available on other vendor platforms which do not yet have a complete GUI, NCSA has developed a set of tools (e.g., NCSA X Image, X DataSlice) that run on any workstation that supports the X-windows standard. Figure 4 shows a screen where a user is studying another fluid flow simulation with NCSA X Image. This greatly extends the number of end user desktop computers that can work in the modern bit-mapped, multiple-windowed environment. However, until the other vendors GUIs are complete, one will not be able to move as freely among all application software on these machines as one can today on the Macintosh.

Today these tools handle only 2D data sets, which are being used by protein biologists and chemists to study such widely varying topics as sequencing gels, electronic orbitals, and microscopic images. The study of protein structure and function, of course, requires a 3D visualization capability. There are many powerful, stand-alone commercial packages for molecular graphics, many of which are demonstrated in figures elsewhere in this volume. Both these software developers and NCSA will be working to integrate these capabilities into future standard GUIs.

The cost of desktop computers capable of not only displaying 3D graphics but interacting with them as well has recently decreased to the point where most researchers can afford one. The introduction of the Personal Iris, from Silicon Graphics, Inc., in fall 1988, is indicative of this important trend. As very large systems integration (VLSI) drives specialized chip prices ever lower, this situation will continue to improve rapidly. It is still too computationally intensive to have full digital real-time 3D dynamics on an inexpensive desktop machine. Some high-end graphics workstations are entering the market and some centers like NCSA have experimental "numerical laboratories" for real-time interactivity with dynamical systems. This capability will be widely available by the mid 1990s.

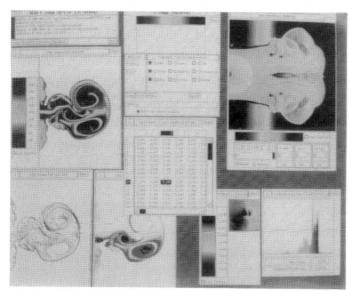

Fig. 4. NCSA X Image software used on a fluid flow simulation.

Finally, one needs a method for storing and transferring multi-object files across different machines on the network. For example, multidimensional floating point data arrays, palettes, images, and annotations are preferably kept together under one file name, as in the genome example mentioned above. Furthermore, one does not want to have to bundle and unbundle these objects by hand. NCSA developed the Hierarchical Data Format (HDF) to accomplish this. Figure 5 shows how the HDF allows different vendors' computers on the network to automatically access these combined files from selected software. The user's application code can read and write HDF files. NCSA's HDF is not yet a national standard, but we are working with others to create such a standard file format to ease the data exchange problem between researchers and computers.

A hardware breakthrough is going to radically alter the power of the desktop computer very soon in certain aspects of protein science. Parallel arrays of microprocessors called "transputers" can now be placed on add-in boards for workstations. Mature applications codes such as molecular modeling

or genome sequencing are beginning to be mapped onto these transputers. The computational speed of these boards can approach that of a supercomputer, for a price of tens of thousands of dollars[2]. Of course, they do not have the flexibility of a general-purpose supercomputer, but, for certain molecular design or sequencing studies that do not require the large memory of supercomputers, they can allow a researcher to interact rapidly with the molecule under study. When these transputers are combined with 3D interactive graphics software by the early 1990s, we will be close to the dream protein workstation described in the first section of this chapter.

Networks

Even if one can increase the speed of specialized applications on desktop machines to near supercomputer speeds, total memory and storage is still a limitation on the science. A "full-up" personal computer will have 8 megabytes of memory and 100 megabytes of disk. A much more expensive high-end workstation may have as much as 128 megabytes of memory and 1000 megabytes of disk storage. Our Cray-2 supercomputer has 1000 megabytes of memory and our central on-line disk storage has a capacity of 100,000 megabytes. In order to provide the end user with this dynamic range in speed, memory, and storage of several orders of magnitude, a high bandwidth national network is essential.

The network connection originates in the building in which the researcher is working. Here Ethernet (1 megabit/sec) has become the standard for computational scientists. Many campuses are providing connectivity between buildings with higher bandwidth (such as the 80 megabit/sec Proteon backbone on our campus). Host computers designated as "campus gateways" are then hooked together by the many regional and NSF supercomputer centers networks shown in Fig. 1. Finally, the NSFNET backbone (1.5 megabits/sec) hooks

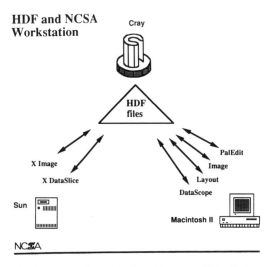

Fig. 5. NCSA Hierarchical Data Format and Distributed Computing.

2   Those interested in this approach should contact: Professor Klaus Schulten, Beckman Institute for Advanced Science and Technology, 405 North Mathews Avenue, Urbana, IL 61801

the regional nets together with the national supercomputer centers. By early 1989, the entire national network had "jelled," and service is now quite reliable.

Clearly, we have not finished the job. The backbone should have a greater bandwidth than the "tributaries" flowing into it. Therefore, plans are under way to take some legs of the backbone to about 45 megabits/sec during 1990. Other government agencies, such as the National Aeronautics and Space Administration (NASA), the Department of Energy (DOE), the Department of Defense (DOD), and the National Institutes of Health (NIH) have networks and major data repositories that need to be merged with NSFNET. All this is in the implementation stage. By the mid to late 1990s, a national fiber optic "superhighway information system" will be in place to link all these sites at bandwidths in excess of 1000 megabits/sec.

During the past few years, much attention on this critical issue has been focused by the bill introduced in Congress by Senator Albert Gore, Jr., to create such a national network. In September 1989, the Executive Branch (Office of Science and Technology Policy) joined this effort with its plan to establish the National Research and Education Network (NREN). This network would extend NSFNET to researchers at universities, national laboratories, private companies involved in government-supported research and education, and facilities such as supercomputers, experimental remote instruments, data bases, and research libraries.

Going from 1200 bits/sec (modems) in 1985 to 1,000,000,000 bits/sec (fiber) in 1995 will qualitatively change the ways in which humans interact with computers. To attempt to see into this future, NCSA has installed an Ultranet (800 megabit/sec) network in our central facility. This connects a high-resolution frame buffer to our Cray-2 and Cray X-MP supercomputers. We are experimenting with selected scientists (including protein scientists) to see how such a "personal supercomputer" can allow us to tackle interactive simulations at a new level. This bandwidth is becoming an industry standard (called the High Speed Channel (HSC)), which will start to become commercially available on a wide range of nonsupercomputers in the years ahead.

The net effect of such high bandwidth is that it eliminates distance as a consideration in computation. As a result, this will alter not only remote computing but also scientific collaboration. Essentially, all researchers and their scientific instruments will be tightly linked in a National Collaboratory (Lederberg and Uncapher, 1989). Again, a very synergetic interaction between computer scientists and computational scientists will produce the new research paradigms for working in this digital world.

Supernodes

As mentioned earlier, specialized centers are currently on the national network and more will arise in the future. These include not only general purpose supercomputers, but also novel architecture computers, high-end visualization facilities, massive file storage capacity, and specialized data centers. I will refer to any such nationally shared network node as a "supernode" (Press, 1981). They make sense whenever it is more cost effective to place specialized capabilities centrally rather than to distribute them. This approach is much the same as that used in astronomy, where there are many small telescopes available at universities (for routine work or for training observers) and a few national observatories such as the Space Telescope or Very Large Array radio telescope (for frontier research allocated by peer review). One cannot do the same science with 1000 pairs of binoculars as can be done with a single large aperture telescope, even though the combined light-gathering power of the binoculars is equal to that of the large instrument!

The modern supercomputer achieves its speed through vector and parallel processing. Vector processing allows the computer to process arrays of numbers ("vector") instead of single numbers ("scalar"). Parallel processing allows multiple tasks to occur simultaneously. The vector compilers of today have had more than a decade to develop in a highly competitive marketplace, so the user does not have to do much in the way of special programming to take advantage of this feature. Parallelism is much more complex. First, there are many types of hardware implementation of the idea of parallelism. Second, the "smart compilers" for these hardware designs are just emerging into the marketplace. Thus, it is more difficult today for the end user to take advantage of parallelism than it is of vector architectures. This is rapidly changing; the NSF national centers are playing a key role in this process by providing access to different computer architectures. This will allow application codes in many fields to be redeveloped with new algorithms that are most efficient on each architecture.

To give the reader some idea of what to expect in the way of speed and memory increases during the next five years, Fig. 6 shows the proposed upgrade path of NCSA's supercomputers through 1995. The units on the left are in units (of memory and speed) of the Cray 1 supercomputer of 1980. To obtain this increase in performance for the end user, I am assuming that the user's code has been rewritten to take advantage of both the parallel and vector hardware. Currently the top Cray Research, Inc., supercomputers have either four (Cray-2) or eight (Cray Y-MP) processors. Future machines from Cray Research, Inc. and other vendors will have 16 (1992) and later 64 (1994) processors. Furthermore, the speed of each processor in 1995 will be at least six times faster than those available today.

Massive parallelism is just emerging as an alternative approach to supercomputing in the marketplace. NCSA took delivery in 1989 of a 32,000 processor Connection Machine (CM) from Thinking Machines, Inc. The speed of this machine is comparable to (or in some cases faster than) current supercomputers that possess only a few processors because, even though each CM processor is very slow compared to a conventional supercomputer processor, the massive number of processors overcomes the slower speed. In addition, the CM is aircooled rather than having the com-

NCSA PROPOSED UPGRADE PATH

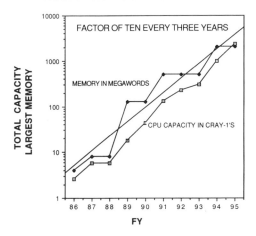

Fig. 6. Proposed upgrade path for supercomputers at NCSA. Units at left are in terms of a 1 megaword Cray 1 supercomputer of 1980.

plex liquid cooling required for conventional design supercomputers. The software environment on such radical architectures is, of course, not as highly "battle tested" as on decade-old architectures.

Balancing this lack of application software is the fact that today's user has much more powerful code development environments than 10 years ago. Thus, I expect the 1990s to see a real race between supercomputers built around a few powerful processors and those built around hundreds to thousands of slower processors. The end user will once again be the winner as a wider array of capabilities becomes available.

As the unrelenting exponential increase of supercomputer power continues, the need for novel approaches to storage is becoming acute. Centers such as NCSA use mainframes to act as file servers for the hundreds to thousands of remote users. The on-line capacity is around 100 gigabytes and the off-line capacity is over a terabyte (tera = 1000 giga). These figures will grow by at least an order of magnitude by 1995. In addition to this, one needs to have random access to individual numbers in massive data sets. For this purpose, laser disk jukeboxes or optical tape with capacities of a terabyte or more are coming into use. At the desktop, CD-ROMs, read-write laser disks, and high-density videotape are being used to provide massive local storage. Although visualization was a response to how to scan large amounts of data, the storage of thousands of images (each 1 megabyte) for animations is itself becoming a new driver of mass storage needs. In this field, as in desktops, networks, supercomputers, and algorithms, the next five years will see a great deal of experimentation with new technologies.

With the enormous increase in available information comes an increased need for sophisticated human interface systems to allow the user to search this information. The Computer and Genomic Systems Laboratory (CGSL) at the University of Arizona, led by Bruce Schatz, is implementing an advanced "digital library" interface system using data related to molecular biology, including the scientific literature itself. While at Bell Communications Research, Schatz developed a prototype digital library system (Schatz, 1985) from which he coined the word telesophy or "wisdom at a distance." The telesophy system provides a mechanism whereby the entire search or selected portions of the search can be stored as an additional information object, complete with links to the collected information. Thus, the insight of the individual performing the search is selectively preserved for other users of the telesophy system. NCSA is working with Schatz and the CGSL to construct an initially limited telesophy system, but with a continually expanding scope to include various scientific disciplines and with a goal of incorporating this important technology into the interdisciplinary environment.

Finally, the most important aspect of supernodes may lie in human factors. Because a large staff (NCSA has over 200 staff members) is aggregated around the specialized resources of supernodes, there is a critical mass effect. This allows visitors to the supernodes to learn about many new technologies simultaneously, using them in a working environment on their own research problems. National workshops, training sessions, vendor presentations, and interdisciplinary seminars are almost a daily occurrence.

For instance, NCSA has recently joined 20 other interdisciplinary research teams in the new Beckman Institute. These teams of faculty, postdocs, graduate students, and nonacademic staff not only cover genome sequencing, molecular recognition, protein dynamics, and tunneling microscopy, but also many other areas in the physical, biological, engineering, and computer sciences. Included in this mix are also major industrial partners to NCSA, including Kodak, Amoco, Eli Lilly & Co., Motorola, FMC Corp., Dow Chemical, and Caterpillar. By having a constant stream of national and international visitors in a state-of-the-art computational facility, we are able to identify many of the emerging trends in computational science. This, in turn, allows NCSA to provide better education and training to our many remote users.

The bottom line is that the next five years are going to be ones of great change in computational science. The critical factor is to keep our minds open and flexible, so that we can all take advantage of these new technologies and methodologies and apply them to our own scientific specialities. I believe that protein sciences will be one of the fields of research most affected. I look forward with a keen sense of anticipation to the new discoveries that will occur.

Acknowledgments

I would like to thank the members of the NCSA Software Development Group and networking groups for providing the figures, and many NCSA staff and UIUC faculty for comments on the manuscript. Radha Nandkumar and Janus Wehmer were particularly helpful during the final editing. NCSA is supported by the National Science Foundation, the State of Illinois, the University of Illinois, and corporate partners.

References

Lederberg, J., and K. Uncapher, cochairs, *Towards a National Collaboratory*. Report of an Invitational Workshop (Rockefeller University, 1989).

Office of Science and Technology Policy, *The Federal High Performance Computing Program* (Executive Office of the President, Washington, DC, 1989).

Press, W.H., *Prospectus for Computational Physics.* Report by the Subcommittee on Computational Facilities for Theoretical Research to the Advisory Committee for Physics (Division of Physics, National Science Foundation, Washington, DC, 1981).

Schatz, B.R., *Telesophy Project Report #1* (Bell Communications Research, 1985).

Senate Bill 1067 "National High Performance Computer Technology Act," *Congressional Record* **135,** no. 64 (1989).

U.S. Congress, Office of Technology Assessment, *High Performance Computing and Networking for Science Background Paper.* OTA-BP-CIT-59 (U.S. Government Printing Office, Washington, DC, 1989).

Wolynes, P.G., in *Spin Glasses and Biology* (World Scientific Publishing Co., Inc., Teaneck, NJ) in press.

28

The Diffusion-Collision Model of Protein Folding

Donald Bashford, Martin Karplus, David L. Weaver

The diffusion-collision model describes the formation of protein tertiary structure in terms of the diffusion, collision, and coalescence of fluctuating structural elements, such as α-helices and β-sheets, that are not stable in isolation (Karplus and Weaver, 1976, 1979). It differs from most other models in that it focuses on the dynamics of the folding process and permits an estimation of the folding times and the nature of the intermediate states. This is of particular interest at present because experiments making use of nuclear magnetic resonance (NMR) and fragment constructs are beginning to probe the details of protein folding dynamics (Roder *et al.*, 1988; Udgaonkar and Baldwin, 1988; Wright *et al.*, 1988; Oas and Kim, 1988). Further, other models that have been discussed recently, such as the "framework" (Kim and Baldwin, 1982) and "jigsaw puzzle" (Harrison and Durbin, 1985) models, emphasize special aspects of the diffusion-collision model.

To introduce the diffusion-collision model, we apply it to the formation of the first detected intermediate in the folding of cytochrome c (Roder *et al.*, 1988), which corresponds to an example of a single diffusion-collision step. Next, an application to the complete folding of a protein, apomyoglobin, is given. This is a multistep process in which a small number of alternative pathways are significant. Finally, some remarks on current and future directions in the development of the model and its range of applicability are outlined.

Early Refolding of Cytochrome c

In the refolding of GuHCl-denatured cytochrome c, the reformation of hydrogen bonding has been measured by a NMR technique that makes use of proton exchange and its control by pH (Roder and Wuthrich, 1986). It was found that the first H-bonds seen in refolding (Roder *et al.*, 1988) are in the N- and C-terminal helices and that these form essentially simultaneously in about 20 milliseconds.

These findings can be interpreted by a simple application of the diffusion-collision model. Figure 1 illustrates the model for this first step in the folding process. Following Karplus and Weaver (1976, 1979), regions of the unfolded chain near the N- and C-termini are assumed to fluctuate between helical and condensed random coil states but spend much of their time in the latter, since the helices are not stable in isolation. These nascent helices move diffusively until a collision leads to their coalescence and mutual stabilization by favorable helix-helix interactions due to hydrophobic, electrostatic, and/or van der Waals terms (Privalov and Gill, 1988). This picture is consistent with the experimental observation that H-bonded structure appears simultaneously in the N- and C-terminal re-

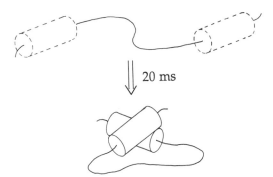

Fig. 1. The elementary step in the diffusion-collision model. Two nascent helices move diffusively until a collision results in their coalescence and mutual stabilization. The nascent helices in the upper figure are drawn with dashed lines to indicate a rapid equilibrium between helical and condensed random coil states.

gions. It is assumed that collisions can only lead to coalescence if both nascent helices are at least partly in helical states and they are appropriately oriented. The orientation need not be precisely that of the native state, since even a loose association could be sufficient to stabilize the helix pair. Indeed, there is experimental evidence that suggests intermediate states in folding contain loosely associated secondary structure (Semisotnov *et al.*, 1987). The diffusive motion of the helices prior to coalescence is assumed to be force-free diffusion, there being no long-range attraction between them. The intervening polypeptide chain restricts the diffusion space by keeping the nascent helices from drifting apart to more than a maximum distance.

To obtain an analytically soluble model, which captures the essential characteristics of the process, this description of the folding is idealized further. The nascent helices are modeled as spheres whose motion is governed by the Smoluchowski (diffusion) equation, and the connecting polypeptide chain is modeled as a string, which does not impose any drag on the motion of the spheres. Thus, the space in which diffusion takes place is delimited by R_{min}, the sum of the radii of the spheres, and R_{max}, the distance imposed by the string (Fig. 2). These simplifications, which may appear rather drastic, have been compared with the results of more complex

and realistic models. Lee *et al.* (1987) have done Brownian dynamics calculations on the relative motion of two eight-residue helices connected by an eight-residue chain. These calculations, which did not include the helix-coil equilibrium, showed that times required for collision in the Brownian dynamics simulation were in order of magnitude agreement with the times calculated from the simple diffusion model used here.

Superimposed on the diffusive motion is a fluctuation of the entire system between "reflecting" and "absorbing" states (Bashford, 1986). If a collision between spheres takes place while the system is in the absorbing state, coalescence occurs and the elementary folding step is complete. If the collision takes place in the reflecting state, the spheres separate again and continue their diffusive motion. This two-state fluctuation model represents the effects of the helix-coil fluctuations of the nascent helices and their mutual orientation. The absorbing state is the state in which both nascent helices are in their helical state and their relative orientation is suitable for coalescence.

The equation governing the dynamics of the system is:

$$
\frac{\partial}{\partial t}
\begin{bmatrix} \rho_a(r, t) \\ \rho_r(r, t) \end{bmatrix}
= D\nabla^2
\begin{bmatrix} \rho_a(r, t) \\ \rho_r(r, t) \end{bmatrix}
+
$$

$$
\begin{bmatrix} -k_{ar} & k_{ra} \\ k_{ar} & -k_{ra} \end{bmatrix}
\begin{bmatrix} \rho_a(r, t) \\ \rho_r(r, t) \end{bmatrix}
\tag{1}
$$

The first two terms are the force-free Smoluchowski equation representing the diffusive motion. A two-component quantity appears in place of the usual density function. The upper component, $\rho_a(r, t)$, is the probability of finding the system in the absorbing state with the spheres having a relative displacement r at time t; and the lower component, $\rho_r(r, t)$, is the corresponding probability in the reflecting state. The second term on the right-hand side introduces the fluctuation between absorbing and reflecting states through the rates k_{ar} and k_{ra} for the absorbing-to-reflecting transition and the reflecting-to-absorbing transition,

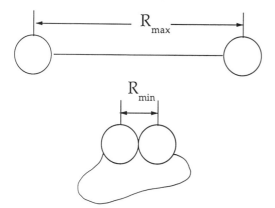

Fig. 2. The nascent helices of Fig. 1 are idealized as spheres and the connecting polypeptide as a string.

respectively. The space in which the equation applies is the annular spherical volume shown in Fig. 3. The outer boundary is imposed by the length of the polypeptide chain. Here, the boundary condition is always reflecting; that is,

$$\frac{\partial \rho}{\partial r} = 0 \tag{2}$$

At the inner boundary, either reflection or absorption can take place, depending on the state of the system, so a mixed boundary condition is applicable; i.e.,

$$\rho_a = 0; \quad \frac{\partial \rho_r}{\partial r} = 0 \tag{3}$$

It is convenient to introduce the parameters β and τ that are defined in terms of the transition rates,

$$\beta = \frac{k_{ra}}{k_{ra} + k_{ar}}; \quad \tau_r = \frac{1}{k_{ra} + k_{ar}} \tag{4}$$

Here, β is the equilibrium probability of finding the system in the absorbing state; that is, in the absence of coalescence, β is the probability of finding both nascent helices in their helical states and correctly oriented for coalescence. The quantity τ_r is the characteristic time for fluctuations between the absorbing and reflecting states.

The coalescence of the two helices appears as the depletion of probability from the volume in Fig. 3 by "absorption" at the inner boundary. The probability of finding the sys-

tem uncoalesced at time t is then

$$P(t) = \int_{R_{min}}^{R_{max}} \left[\rho_a(r, t) + \rho_r(r, t) \right] d^3r \tag{5}$$

The characteristic time for coalescence, τ_b, is the decay time or first passage time (Adam and Delbruk, 1968) of P(t); that is,

$$\tau_b = \int_0^\infty P(t) \, dt \tag{6}$$

An advantage of having thus simplified the model is that it can be solved analytically for τ_b (Bashford, 1986). The result is

$$\tau_b = \frac{G}{D} + \frac{LV(1 - \beta)}{\beta DA} \tag{7}$$

where

$$G \equiv \frac{R^2_{max}}{3} \frac{1 - (9/5)\varepsilon + \varepsilon^3 - (1/5)\varepsilon^6}{\varepsilon(1 - \varepsilon^3)}$$

$$\frac{1}{L} \equiv \frac{1}{R_{min}} +$$

$$\alpha \frac{\alpha R_{max} \tanh \left[\alpha(R_{max} - R_{min}) \right] - 1}{\alpha R_{max} - \tanh \left[\alpha(R_{max} - R_{min}) \right]}$$

$$\alpha \equiv \left(D\tau_r \right)^{-1/2}$$

In these formulae, $\varepsilon = R_{min} / R_{max}$, V is the annular spherical volume in Fig. 3, and A is the area of the partially absorbing inner sphere. For the case $R_{min} << R_{max}$ and

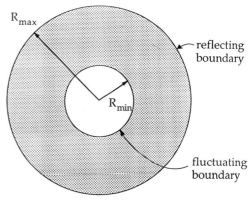

Fig. 3. The diffusive motion of the system in Fig. 2 is governed by a diffusion equation in an annular spherical volume. The tendency toward coalescence and the presence of the string are expressed as boundary conditions.

$(D\tau_r)^{1/2} << R_{min}$, Eq. 7 becomes

$$\tau_b = \frac{R^3_{max}}{3DR_{min}} + \frac{1-\beta}{\beta} \frac{V}{DA} \left(D\tau_r\right)^{1/2}$$

(8)

Although not exact, this formula gives order of magnitude agreement with Eq. 7 for the present case, and its simple structure makes it more convenient for discussion. In the actual calculations, we use Eq. 7.

Several observations concerning the dependence of the model on the parameters of interest can be made from Eq. 8. When β is small (as it is in most cases), the second term on the right-hand side dominates and is inversely proportional to β. For this case, the dependence on viscosity is complex. Superficially, it would appear that the second term depends on the inverse square root of the diffusion constant and thus on the square root of the viscosity. However, if τ_r is linear in the viscosity, as may well be the case, the first passage time will also depend linearly on the viscosity.

As can be seen from Eqs. 7 or 8, the characteristic time τ_b depends on five parameters: R_{min}, R_{max}, D, τ_r, and β. To apply the model, we need to estimate their values for cytochrome c. The first four are relatively straightforward. If 10 Å is taken as an estimate for the radius of a spherical model of a helix, R_{min} is 20 Å. There are 73 residues separating the native N- and C-terminal helices, so R_{max} $\approx$ 73 × 3.5 Å + 20 Å = 276 Å. The relative diffusion constant of two 10 Å spheres in water is calculated from the Stokes formula to be 70 Å²/nanosecond. Helix-coil transition times are not well established, but experimental and theoretical studies suggest values ranging from 10^{-7} to 10^{-10} seconds, so $\tau_r = 10^{-8}$ seconds is chosen here.

The parameter β is the most difficult to estimate directly. The relative stabilities of the isolated N- and C-terminal helices of cytochrome are unknown, as are the limits on the orientation required for coalescence. Consequently, we fit β to the experimental data and then examine whether the resulting value of β is physically appropriate.

With a value of β equal to 10^{-4}, Eq. 7

gives τ_b = 28 milliseconds, close to the 20 millisecond time observed experimentally. This value for β is in the range used in previous applications of the diffusion-collision model (Bashford et al., 1988) and is physically reasonable. For example, if each of the two helices is present 10 percent of the time and if the target size for correct orientation is 10 percent of each helix's surface, the product of these four 10 percent values would give β = 10^{-4}.

Although the model gives a satisfactory interpretation of the rate of formation of the framework-type interaction of the N- and C-terminal helices, it does not explain why they are the first to come together and be stabilized by coalescence. There are two other helices in the native structure and three helix-helix contacts. All of these have a smaller interchain distance than does the N- and C-terminal pair. In terms of the diffusion-collision model, a possible reason is a variation in the parameter β. If other helices are substantially less stable, the β values for the steps associated with them may be small enough to cause them to be slower than the C-N coalescence in spite of the smaller R_{max} value. For example, R_{max} for the two middle helices is 37.5 Å, giving τ_b = 0.13 ms in Eq. 7; thus, a 200-fold decrease in β would be required to compensate for the decrease in R_{max}. To test this possibility, it would be of considerable interest to have measurements of the individual helix stabilities (Kim and Baldwin, 1984). There may also be factors involved that are beyond the scope of the model as it is applied here, such as proline isomerization or ligand interaction with the heme iron (Babul and Stellwagen, 1972; Brems and Stellwagen, 1983; Roder and Elove, personal communication)

Apomyoglobin

Application of the diffusion-collision model to apomyoglobin (Bashford et al., 1988) requires consideration of a multistep pathway, each element of which is of the diffusion-collision type. The elementary steps in the folding process are taken to be the formation of native-like helix-helix pairings. The folding process described here involves interactions similar to those considered by Ptitsyn and Rashin (1975) in their attempt to predict the fold of myoglobin. Six major helix-helix pairings in sperm whale myoglobin have been identified (Richmond and Richards, 1978); they are AH, BD, BE, BG, FH, and GH. For the calculation, the state of the system during folding is defined in terms of the presence or absence of these contacts. With six contacts, there are 2^6 or 64 states. The present model takes no account of the possible effects of intermediates with non-native contacts. The contacts may form in any order, so the model is, in principle, a multipathway description, as in the jigsaw puzzle model (Harrison and Durbin, 1985). It will be seen however, that only a small number of the possible paths are followed to a significant extent.

Figure 4 illustrates a few steps along one possible pathway. The term "microdomain" as used here represents a unit of structure, which may be a helix, a nascent helix, or a cluster of helices, involved in any elementary diffusion-collision step.

The overall dynamics of the system is approximated by a first-order chemical kinetics equation,

$$\frac{dp_i}{dt} = \sum_{j=1}^{N} R_{ij} p_j \quad (i = 1,2...N) \tag{9}$$

where p_i (t) is the probability of finding the system in state i at time t and R_{ij} is the transition rate from state j to state i. The R_{ij} are $1/\tau_b$ where the τ_b are calculated using Eq. 7 for the microdomain pair corresponding to the j-to-i transition. The only nonzero, off-diagonal R matrix elements are those for which states i and j differ by one helix-helix contact. Because of the difficulty of estimating β, different sets of β values were examined to determine their effects on the overall rate and the important intermediates along the folding pathways. The other parameters were chosen by a procedure similar to that used in the cytochrome example (Bashford *et al.*, 1988).

Once a set of β values is selected and the transition matrix, R, is calculated, Eq. 9 can be solved by standard techniques of linear al-

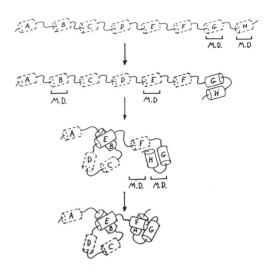

Fig. 4. A few possible steps in the diffusion-collision model for multihelix proteins such as apomyoglobin. Each step involves the coalescence of two *microdomains* (indicated by M.D.) which may be individual nascent helices, such as the G and H helices in the first step, or clusters of helices, such as the GH pair in the third step.

gebra. Figure 5 shows the results of one such set of calculations; only the states whose probability rises above 2 percent are shown. The β value for a microdomain pair is the product of β_m values for the individual microdomains. For a one-helix microdomain, β_m is chosen as 0.01 on the assumption that individual helices are unstable; and for any multihelix microdomain (two or more helices), β_m is chosen as 1.0 on the assumption that the microdomain helices are fully stabilized when at least one pair-wise interaction is present. State 62 appears in the long-time behavior because backward (unfolding) reactions were included in the rate matrix and adjusted to give an equilibrium probability of 0.95 for the folded state (Bashford *et al.*, 1988).

The present choice of β values leads to a nucleation-like behavior in which intermediate states are suppressed. The first steps in folding, the pairing of nascent helices, have the smallest β values and thus the longest first passage times. Once they have taken place, the folding proceeds rapidly. Intermediate states are short-lived and relatively unpopulated.

The major transient intermediates appearing in Fig. 5 contain the BDE and/or

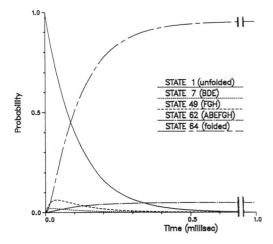

Fig. 5. The results of a diffusion-collision calculation for apomyoglobin using the choice of B values described in the text. Notation of the form "FGH" indicates that helices F, G, and H have coalesced into a single micro-domain as in the fourth state shown in Fig. 4, but no other helix-helix contacts are formed.

FGH helix clusters. From this, one can see that the main pathways being followed involve pairings between helices that are nearest neighbors along the chain. This occurs because all helices are treated equally with respect to the choice of β values. Making the β values associated with one helix substantially higher than the others would produce nucleation around that helix. There is experimental evidence that the nascent H helix has a relatively high stability (Wright, private communication).

The overall β value for the first steps is 10^{-4}, the same value used in the cytochrome c calculation. However, since folding in the apomyoglobin model proceeds by nearest neighbors, the R_{max} values are smaller and the folding time is only 0.1 to 0.2 milliseconds instead of 28 milliseconds.

The apomyoglobin folding calculations were repeated with several methods of choosing β_m values. All of the methods treated all helices equally. A variety of intermediate states were produced, and total folding times ranged from 50 nanoseconds when $\beta_m = 1.0$ was chosen for all microdomains, to 0.5 millisecond when $\beta_m = 0.01$ was chosen for all microdomains (Bashford et al., 1988). Nuclea-

tion-like behavior was found mainly when β_m values for multihelix microdomains were significantly greater than the β_m values for single-helix microdomains. Selections that differentiated less between one-helix and multihelix microdomains gave more intermediate states.

Analysis of the results led to the delineation of a common two-branch folding pathway shown in Fig. 6. In this pathway, nearest neighbor helix pairs form the first contacts leading to three-helix microdomains in the N- and/or C-terminal half of the protein. Next, these two microdomains join, and finally, the contact between helices A and H is formed. It is particularly interesting that relatively simple dominant folding pathways can result from a model that includes a large number of possible pathways.

Currently, there are no experimental data for comparison with the apomyoglobin calculations. Thus, the calculations we have described here serve as an exploration of the folding pathways and intermediate states implied by the diffusion-collision theory and the effect of variation of parameters.

Future Directions

Work on the diffusion collision model is continuing (Yapa et al., unpublished results). Calculations similar to that described for apomyoglobin are being carried out for the synthetic four-helix-bundle protein designed by DeGrado and co-workers (Ho and De-Grado, 1987). In addition, Brownian dynamics simulations are being done for three- and four-helix systems to provide a more rigorous check on their dynamics. Brownian dynamics studies are also being carried out on antiparallel β-sheets, as part of an effort to extend the model to proteins containing β-structure.

Another area for development is the inclusion of non-native secondary structure and non-native pairings in the model. To do this completely would be to confront the full combinatorial complexity of the protein folding problem. But on a more modest scale, one could construct models containing varying

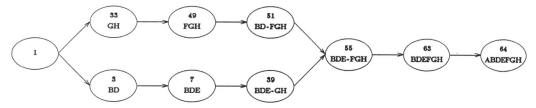

Fig. 6. The general pathway for the folding of apomyoglobin derived from analysis of diffusion-collision calculations. Only states rising above a probability of 0.02 are shown.

numbers of hypothetical "wrong" helix pairings and test their effect on the time scale, intermediate states, and pathways of folding.

As measurements on the stability of microdomains (Kim and Baldwin, 1984) and the time development of intermediates in protein folding become available, more detailed applications and tests of the diffusion-collision model will be made.

Conclusions

The diffusion-collision model provides a consistent picture of early events in the folding process. It suggests that, in the absence of complicating features such as disulfide bond formation or proline isomerization, proteins acquire at least a roughly folded structure on the millisecond time scale. Times and pathways can be strongly influenced by the stability of nascent secondary structures and by the separation distance of these structures along the polypeptide chain. In the case of cytochrome c, the model provides a quantitative interpretation of experimental measurements of the first observed step in folding. The model is also consistent with several recent experimental observations of refolding in which secondary and/or loosely packed tertiary structures are formed on the millisecond time scale (Semisotnov et al., 1987; Gilmanshin and Ptitsyn, 1987; Kuwajima et al., 1987). Full recovery of native-like structure and activity typically takes much longer and would appear to involve more localized structural changes that are beyond the scope of the diffusion-collision model.

The diffusion-collision model encompasses a number of qualitative models that have

been discussed in the literature; they include the so-called "framework," "jigsaw puzzle" and "sequential" models. It has been suggested, for example, that the framework model (Kim and Baldwin, 1982) is supported by several recent experiments (Udgaonkar and Baldwin, 1988; Oas and Kim, 1988; Dobson and Evans, 1988), including the cytochrome c results described above (Roder et al., 1988). This model postulates that the initial step in folding is the formation of elements of H-bonded secondary structure. Thus, it is in accord with the diffusion-collision model in which native-like elements of secondary structure are identified as the microdomains that form in the earliest stages of folding. Our finding that folding times in agreement with experiment are obtained with small β values suggests that these secondary elements need be only marginally stable. Harrison and Durbin have proposed a jigsaw model of folding in which there are multiple pathways by which puzzle pieces of the protein structure can be assembled into a unique structure (Harrison and Durbin, 1985). They point out that their model corresponds closely to the diffusion-collision model, since no a priori order of microdomain assembly is imposed. However, the apomyoglobin calculations summarized here show that, depending on the model parameters and protein geometry, one or two pathways can dominate the folding because they are much faster than the alternate pathways. Thus, the kinetics can be similar to the sequential model (Kim and Baldwin, 1982), in which folding proceeds by well-defined steps along a unique pathway. It would, of course, be of great interest to follow the folding kinetics of mutants that can fold but in which the stability of a microdomain (e.g., a helix) is significantly altered from that of the wild type.

There is some experimental evidence (e.g., for the bovine pancreatic trypsin inhibitor)(Creighton, 1988) that the rate-determining step occurs near the end of the folding pathway. These experiments have been interpreted in terms of a strained, native-like transition state. Indeed, the same experimental study that detected the rapid early-folding step in cytochrome c analyzed here also detected subsequent slower steps (Roder *et al.*, 1988). In such cases, the diffusion-collision model is most pertinent to the early steps in folding. However, these early steps are of great interest because they may lead to the formation of approximately native-like secondary and tertiary structure.

The recent experimental studies of the kinetics of early steps in protein folding represent an important development in the field. A simple context for the interpretation of such data is provided by the diffusion-collision model. The detection of native-like secondary structure in peptide fragments is of particular interest (Wright *et al.*, 1988; Kim and Baldwin, 1984). These can help to determine appropriate β values in the diffusion-collision model, so that it can be applied in a more rigorous fashion. By a combination of such experimental and theoretical techniques, one may hope that an understanding of the broad outline of protein folding dynamics will be obtained in the not-too-distant future.

References

Adam, G., and M. Delbruck, in *Structural Chemistry and Molecular Biology,* N. Davidson, Ed. (W. H. Freeman, San Francisco, 1968), p. 199.

Babul, J., and E. Stellwagen, *Biochemistry* **11**, 1195 (1972).

Bashford, D., *J. Chem. Phys.* **85**, 6999 (1986).

Bashford, D., F. E. Cohen, M. Karplus, I. D. Kuntz, D. L. Weaver, *Proteins* **4**, 211 (1988).

Brems, D. N., and E. Stellwagen, *J. Biol. Chem.* **258**, 3655 (1983).

Creighton, T. E., *Proc. Nat. Acad. Sci. U.S.A.* **85**, 5082 (1988).

Dobson, C. M., and P. A. Evans, *Nature* **335**, 666 (1988).

Gilmanshin, R. I., and O. B. Ptitsyn, *FEBS Lett.* **223**, 327 (1987).

Harrison, S. C., and R. Durbin, *Proc. Natl. Acad. Sci. U.S.A.* **82**, 4028 (1985).

Ho, S. P., and W. F. DeGrado, *J. Am. Chem. Soc.* **109**, 6751 (1987).

Karplus, M., and D. L. Weaver, *Nature* **260**, 404 (1976).

_____, *Biopolymers* **18**, 1421 (1979).

Kim, P. S., and R. L. Baldwin, *Ann. Rev. Biochem.* **51**, 459 (1982).

Kim, P. S., and R. L. Baldwin, *Nature* **307**, 329 (1984).

Kuwajima, K., H. Yamaya, S. Miwa, S. Sugai, T. Nagamura, *FEBS Lett.* **221**, 115 (1987).

Lee, S., M. Karplus, D. Bashford, D. L. Weaver, *Biopolymers* **26**, 481 (1987).

Oas, T. G., and P. S. Kim, *Nature* **336**, 42 (1988).

Privalov, P. L., and S. J. Gill, *Adv. Prot. Chem.* **39**, 191 (1988).

Ptitsyn, O. B., and A. A. Rashin, *Biophys. Chem.* **3**, 1 (1975).

Richmond, T. J., and F. M. Richards, *J. Mol. Biol.* **119**, 537 (1978).

Roder, H., and K. Wuthrich, *Proteins* **1**, 34 (1986).

Roder, H., G. A. Elove, S. W. Englander, *Nature* **335**, 700 (1988).

Semisotnov, G. V., *et al., FEBS Lett.* **224**, 9 (1987).

Udgaonkar, J. B., and R. L. Baldwin, *Nature* **335**, 694 (1988).

Wright, P. E., H. J. Dyson, R. A. Lerner, *Biochemistry* **27**, 7167 (1988).

Part VII

Protein Design: What Can We Get Away With?

Lynne Regan

Simple model systems are extremely desirable in order to simplify the study of protein folding and to investigate the forces determining protein structure. Several systems have been employed for the study of α-helix formation, from the classical host-guest studies of Scheraga and colleagues (for example, Sueki *et al.*, 1984) to the more recent work on monomeric helix formation in short peptides, predominantly from Baldwin's group (see Marqusee and Baldwin, chapter 8, this volume). These provide tractable experimental systems in which to study the factors influencing α-helix formation in aqueous solution. Similar simple systems have been lacking for β-sheet structures, as insoluble multisheet arrays have been a commonly encountered problem.

The elegant approach of Daniel Kemp and Benjamin Bowen uses a conformationally constrained analogue of a segment of β-structure to form the central two strands of a four-strand β-sheet. The rationale is that this rigid segment will provide two sets of correctly oriented H-bonding groups and thus act as a nucleation center for β-sheet formation. At the ends of this central template, turn sequences are attached, followed by two amino acids, which are the "test positions" at which to study the propensity of different amino acids to form β-structure.

Using primarily ^{1}H nuclear magnetic resonance (NMR) methods, Kemp and Bow- en demonstrate that, at least in certain solvents, their model system does show monomeric β-sheet formation. They are also able to show a clear requirement for strong turn-forming elements and to detect some difference in propensity to form β-sheets between the amino acids they have tested so far.

Thus, this system meets many of the criteria required for a model of β-sheet formation and should provide a useful test system. To date, Kemp and Bowen have concentrated on hydrophobic amino acids, with the result that their peptide is insoluble in greater than 60 percent water in dimethylsulfoxide. In the future, modifications to their design might allow the synthesis of a fully water-soluble derivative, which will be of great interest.

An important aim of protein biochemistry is to achieve an understanding of protein structure and function, which will allow the design of novel proteins and enzymes. Although this problem is not yet solved, it is now possible to qualitatively predict the effects of certain small changes on protein function. Such approaches have been used successfully to modify the specificity of catalysis in enzymes such as trypsin, carboxypeptidase, and alcohol dehydrogenase. In these examples, the modification of activity has been achieved by changing specific residues of the enzyme that are involved in substrate binding.

In their chapter, Paul Carter and James Wells describe a novel approach in which they actually replace a catalytically important side chain in the active site of the enzyme with the same side chain provided by the peptide substrate.

Much is known about the catalytic mechanism of the protease subtilisin, from x-ray crystallography as well as biochemical and kinetic studies. The important residues are the catalytic triad Asp^{32}, His^{64}, and Ser^{221}. Carter and Wells describe how, if a peptide substrate is modeled at the active site, His^{64} can be replaced by a His side chain from the residue -2 from the cleaved peptide bond in the substrate. Indeed, when His^{64} of subtilisin was replaced by Ala, proteolytic activity was only detected against peptides with His in the -2 position, as the modeling had predicted. The enzymatic activity of this "substrate-assisted" enzyme was significantly diminished relative to that of wild-type subtilisin. This is presumably due to less-than-perfect positioning of the substrate His in the catalytic triad and will perhaps be improved by further changes.

The results described in this chapter provided an innovative example of the use of protein engineering to generate an enzyme with novel substrate specificity.

Although progress is being made in rational protein design, the answers obtained are limited by the questions asked, and the results are certainly not always as predicted. Therefore, it is useful to exploit genetic techniques as a complementary approach to the protein folding problem.

In their chapter, Jon Beckwith and colleagues describe the use of a clever technique that enables them to determine the topography in the membrane of proteins of unknown structure. The basis of the technique is to use two marker enzymes that function best in opposite milieux. Alkaline phosphatase is unable to assemble in the cytoplasm, but shows high activity in the periplasm. Conversely, β-galactosidase can not transverse the membrane, but is active in the cytoplasm. Using either in vivo or in vitro techniques, a set of fusions of these "tester proteins" to various C-terminal positions in the membrane protein under study are generated. High alkaline phosphatase activity indicates fusion to a periplasmic domain, whereas high β-galactosidase activity implies fusion to a cytoplasmic domain. Thus, cytoplasmic or periplasmic domains can be identified along the primary structure of the protein. In this chapter, the authors describe the successful application of this technique to several membrane proteins.

This approach is remarkable for its elegance and ease of application. The results are somewhat surprising, as the fusions mostly appear to insert correctly into the membrane despite missing various C-terminal regions. This suggests that interactions between the different domains of the protein are not required for efficient insertion into the membrane. Such an observation is important, as it opens the door for many adventurous protein engineering studies on membrane proteins.

Reference

Sueki, S., *et al., Macromolecules* **17,** 148 (1984).

29

Diacylaminoepindolidiones
as Templates for β-Sheets

Daniel S. Kemp and Benjamin R. Bowen

Study of protein β-structure has been hindered by the lack of simple models that exhibit well-defined sheet structure in solution (Creighton, 1983). In this study, we demonstrate sheet structure in short peptides linked to a complementary sheet-nucleating template in the form of an acylamino-functionalized epindolidione shown in Fig. 1.

The concept of a template that can selectively nucleate a specific class of secondary structure deserves brief discussion. The success of the simple Ising models for describing the random coil–α-helix interconversions of polyamino acids (Zimm and Bragg, 1959; Scheraga, 1978) led us to search for such templates. In these models, initiation of secondary structure is described by a parameter σ that is typically three or four orders of magnitude smaller than the propagation parameter s, which is close to unity. In water, helices are thus propagated within a partially helical peptide strand by a marginally favorable addition of single residues to a helical core that is initially very difficult to generate. The difficulty is easy to understand. Initiation of secondary structure requires surrender of internal freedom of bond rotation by at least three contiguous amino acid residues without a compensating stabilization from hydrogen bonding or other interactions internal to the forming helix. Although the model is derived for helices, similar factors doubtless underlie the formation of sheets, with the important

difference that sheet nucleation must arise intermolecularly or, in the case of antiparallel sheets, through mediation of other secondary structural elements such as β-turns.

As used in this discussion, a template is defined as a molecule that can be attached to a normal peptide and that contains a set of rigidly oriented carbonyl or NH groups. These mimic the hydrogen bonding pattern of a nucleation site for a particular type of secondary structure. Although this discussion is concerned with models for antiparallel β-sheets, elsewhere we have reported helix formation in a series of short peptides attached to a constrained tricyclic molecule that contains the bonded linkages of acetyl-L-prolyl-L-proline (Kemp and Curran, 1988).

All of our peptide-template conjugates are tests of the efficacy of hydrogen bonding for conveying conformational signals to attached, freely orientable peptides. The role of hydrogen bonds in the nucleation and stabilization of secondary structure has long been controversial (for a review, see P. Schuster *et al.,* 1976). Simple experimental models for the free energy of hydrogen bond formation to single peptide amides in water demonstrate an almost exact energetic trade-off between single hydrogen bonds broken to water and formed within secondary structure (Klotz and Franzen, 1962). Extrapolations from properties of single amide residues to the linked amides of a polypeptide rest on an

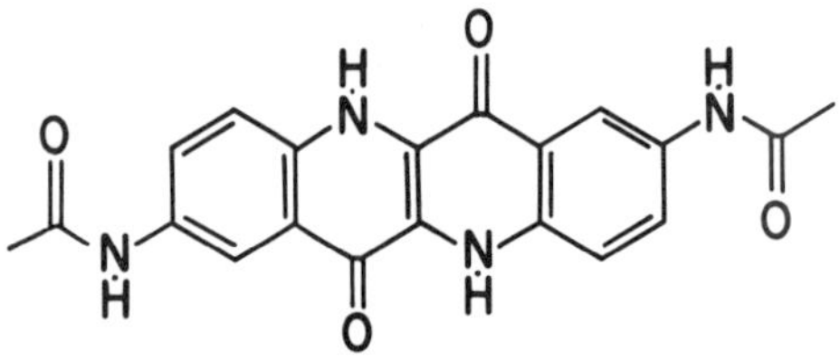

Fig. 1. The structure of the 2,8-diacylaminoepin-
dolidione designed as a nucleation site for formation of
β-sheet conformations in linked polypeptides.

assumption of independent solvation and
backbone stabilization for each amide residue.
Almost certainly this assumption is invalid,
since local concentration effects within the
peptide chain and within the structure of
water itself are likely to create overriding
entropy contributions when the linked amide
residues of a peptide are considered. For this
reason, experiment is probably the best test of
the relevance of hydrogen bonding to the
stabilization of secondary structure, and this
aim has motivated our design of nucleation
sites for secondary structure.

Models of the Zimm-Bragg type treat
every amino acid residue as an isolated con-
tributor to the helix stability and make no
allowance for the stabilizing packing interactions contributed by tertiary structure, the
polar interactions that may arise between
pairs of side chain residues, or the interactions
between side chain residues and the backbone
of the helix itself. Baldwin and co-workers
have recently noted that fragments and
analogs of the S-peptide of RNAse A exhibit
an unexpectedly high helicity at low temperatures in water (Bierzynski *et al.*, 1982). Polar
interactions between pairs of charged side
chain functions and between charged side
chain groups and the global dipole of the helix
appear to add sufficient additional stabilization to allow the helix ensemble to be detected
by circular dichroism (CD) and nuclear magnetic resonance (NMR) methods (Schoemaker *et al.*, 1985). Moreover, by NMR criteria, a
variety of short proline-containing peptides
have detectable β-turn structures in water
(Stimson *et al.*, 1968; Dyson *et al.*, 1988). These
studies demonstrate tractable models for
studying the effects that stabilize or destabilize

helices and turns, two of the three key elements of secondary structure in proteins.

By contrast, there are no satisfactory
models for studying the properties of β-sheets.
Under proper conditions, polylysine yields a
high molecular weight aggregate that has been
assigned β-structure by circular dichroism
(Hartman, 1974), and highly associated β-
structure has been observed for specific short
peptides conjugated with polyethylene glycol
(Schmitt and Mutter, 1983), but neither of
these systems permits detailed structural assignment or study of local stability effects.

Sheets are extended structures with large
surface areas, and thus it can be argued that
formation of aggregates is an intrinsic property of either parallel or antiparallel β-struc-
tures. If so, no tractable models can be
expected, since aggregation voids the prospect
of easily interpretable structural analysis.

As with helices and turns, sheet structures
in proteins display a moderately strong bias
for and against specific amino acids (Chou
and Fasman, 1977; Levitt, 1978), but interpretation of these biases requires unraveling
of the tangled skein of cause and effect that
governs the architecture of protein interiors.
Sheets in proteins are almost invariably buried
structures (Richardson, 1981), and it can be
argued that the bias against polar residues and
toward the amino acids with aromatic side
chains or β-branches is more the consequence
of location of sheets in the uncharged, relatively hydrophobic interiors of proteins than
an intrinsic feature governing the formation of
sheets themselves. The latter can only be
learned from study of an unaggregated model.

The first aim of this study is the construction of peptide conjugates of a rigid template
of hydrogen bond donors and acceptors that
mimics the hydrogen bonding signature of a
tripeptide sequence in a sheet conformation.
A demonstrated lack of self-association of
such conjugates, when considered with conformational study of the peptide portions,
should answer the fundamental questions of
whether hydrogen bonding sites alone can
nucleate β-structure and whether such structures can have an independent existence in
solution. Preparation of tractable, unaggre-

gated β-structures should then permit assessment of the intrinsic stabilizing effects of changes in solvent and amino acid, developing, in effect, a grammar for the formation of β-structures.

Design Considerations

As noted in Fig. 1, a 2,9-di(acylamino)-epindolidione has the hydrogen bonding pattern of a polypeptide chain in its extended conformation, with distances between hydrogen bonding sites that are very similar to those of an antiparallel β-sheet (Kemp and Bowen, 1988). The perspective drawings of Figs. 2 and 3 shown relationships between the classical antiparallel β-sheet and the peptide-epindolidione complex. The epindolidione preserves the hydrogen bonding relationships of the sheet while maintaining a minimum steric profile, generating no interactions with the amino acid side chain functions that lie substantially above and below the plane of the rings and hydrogen bonds. The complex should therefore test whether ordered hydrogen bonding alone is sufficient to nucleate secondary structure.

A number of different epindolidione-peptide conjugates are potentially attractive sheet models, but, for this first exercise, we selected the C_2-symmetric, urea-containing antiparallel structure shown in Fig. 4. Several features of this structure are noteworthy. The C_2 symmetry permits ease of synthesis and spectroscopic assignment, since the resulting epindolidione function has only four ^{1}H NMR resonances. The rigid, 2,8-functionalized

epindolidione is linked to a dipeptide that is likely to assume a β-turn conformation, and this is followed by a urea that reverses the direction of the peptide chain and permits formation of an antiparallel sheet structure. (Attachment of a normal tetrapeptide sequence to the epindolidione can result in the formation of a parallel sheet structure, which will be the subject of later reports.) The final pair of amino acids provide the laboratory for exploring the nucleation of antiparallel sheets. In this first exploration of sheet formation, we have confined attention to uncharged amino acids, and thus a neutral N,N-dimethylamide is used to terminate the amino acid sequence. The resulting tertiary amide lacks the capacity for edge-wise intermolecular hydrogen bond formation of a secondary amide, thereby minimizing one type of association.

Simple epindolidiones are microcrystalline materials with exceptionally high melting points and are soluble only in aggressive solvents such as concentrated sulfuric acid (Jaffee and Matrick, 1968). Strong intermolecular hydrogen bonding can be demonstrated for them in the solid state, and these properties might seem to vitiate their candidacy as templates. However, we expected that much more tractable properties would be exhibited by template-peptide conjugates that can mutually satisfy most of the hydrogen bonding valences of both template and peptide within the expected β-structure.

As reported elsewhere (Kemp and Bowen, 1988, and submitted), our synthetic studies confirm this expectation. The syntheses have proceeded by four successive steps involving diacylations of 2,8-diamino-

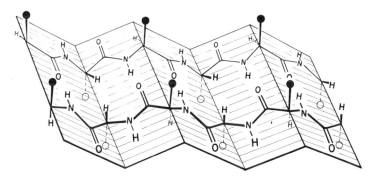

Fig. 2. A pair of polypeptide chains in hydrogen-bonded antiparallel β-pleated sheet conformations. Bonds to amino acid substituents are perpendicular to the average plane of the sheet structure and are alternately above and below it. The perspective representation is drawn from Kendrew models that were constructed from exact sheet parameters (Ashida *et al.*, 1981).

Fig. 3. A hybrid antiparallel sheet structure containing one polypeptide chain and one 2-acylaminoepindolidione function, showing the distance between the peptide substituents and the atoms of the epindolidione rings.

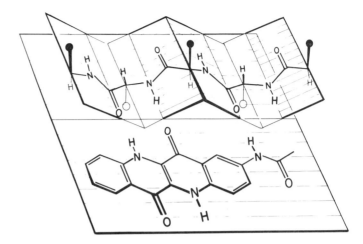

epindolidione by N- or C-protected amino acid derivatives, followed by protective group removal. The starting diaminoepindolidione itself and 2,8-di-(t-butoxycarbonyl-D-alanylamido)-epindolidione formed from it are insoluble substances, but the final tetra-amino acid conjugates have normal solubilities in common organic solvents and can be purified uneventfully to 99 + percent purity by high-performance liquid chromatography (HPLC) on reverse phase columns and chromatography on Sephadex LH-20. A total of 12 con-

jugates have been prepared for this study. For the purposes of this discussion, an abbreviation derived from the one-letter amino acid code is used in which, for example, the structure shown in Fig. 4B is designated as F · G : P · dA.

Proton NMR spectroscopy is the primary structural tool for these studies, and the ^{1}H NMR spectrum of the bellwether structure F · G : P · dA is shown in Fig. 5 in the region from 7 to 12 δ, where NH and aryl CH resonances appear. The cleanness and simplicity

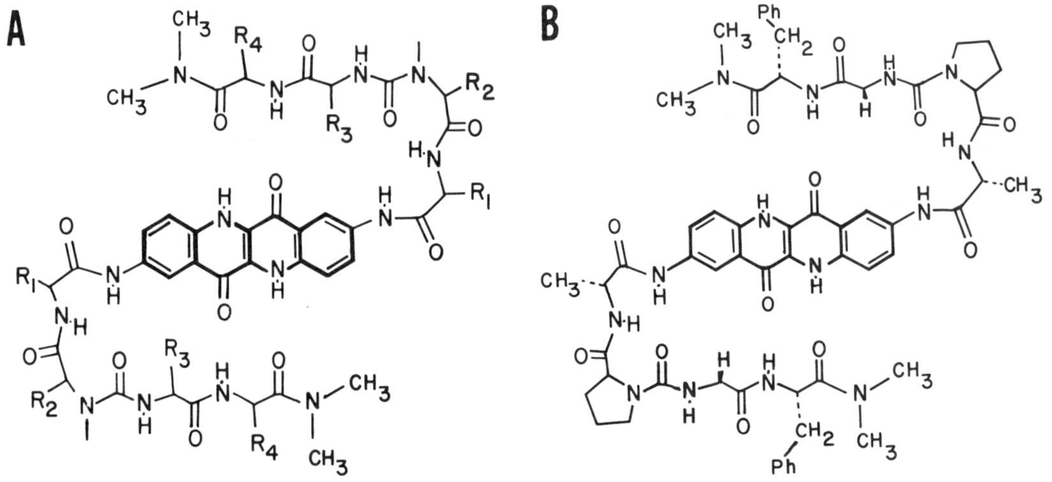

Fig. 4. (A) The backbone structure of the peptide-epindolidione conjugates used in these studies, showing the position of the substituents R_1 and R_2 of the β-turn region and the substituents R_3 and R_4 of the β-sheet region. (B) The structure of F · G : P · dA, the archetype of the peptide-epindolidione conjugates. In this structural abbreviation, the residue linked to the epindolidione appears last, the dots symbolize a normal peptide bond, and the colon symbolizes the chain-reversing urea function.

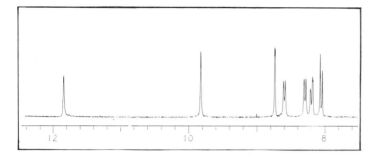

Fig. 5. An ^{1}H NMR spectrum of F · G : P · dA in DMSO-d$_6$ at 300 mHz. From left to right, the resonances correspond to heteroaryl NH, aryl NH, aryl 1-CH, dA NH, F NH, aryl 3-H, and aryl 4-H.

of this spectrum greatly facilitated the spectroscopic interpretations leading to assignments of conformation.

Association Behavior of Epindolidione-Peptide Conjugates

A necessary precondition for an unambiguous assignment of their conformations in solution is a demonstration that epindolidione-peptide conjugates do not associate. The simple epindolidiones display a rich, long-wavelength electronic-absorption spectrum. For example, F · G : P · dA in THF (tetrahydrofuran) shows major bands at 303 mn (58,000), 340 nm (9000), 452 nm (6800), and 480 nm (7800). Layered packings of associated sheet structures must juxtapose chiral amino acid functions with π orbitals of the heteroaryl rings, generating large CD effects. Rich CD absorption in the near UV and visible spectra is, in fact, observed for nearly all epindolidione-peptide conjugates. Relatively weak bands appear at 440 and 470 nm that are solvent- and concentration-independent and that appear to correlate with formation of the β-turn conformation that is discussed in the next section. For selected derivatives in nonpolar solvents, intense bands appear at 295, 304, and 312 nm, together with a weak band at 505 nm that is probably an emission band. These are strongly dependent on concentration, solvent, temperature, and amino acid sequence. They are only observed for structures X · G : P · Y in which the amino acid X has the same chirality as the proline residue, and they are observed in solvents such as benzene, ethanol, and THF, but

not in dimethylformamide (DMF), dimethylsulfoxide (DMSO), or water. As little as 2 percent of water in THF or ethanol abolishes these bands, which are depicted in Fig. 6.

The pronounced concentration dependence of these bands is apparent in Fig. 6, and the data are quantitatively described over more than three orders of magnitude in concentration by a simple monomer-dimer equilibrium. A face-to-face dimerization with parallel or perpendicular epindolidione axes explains the structural requirement of a glycine at site 3, and the observed 4 kcal/mol association energy is reasonable for a van der Waals interaction that can be abolished by polar solvents. The intensity of these long-wavelength CD bands proves that the epindolidione function can be a sensitive reporter of a neighboring chiral environment, and the successful quantitative modeling of CD concentration dependence by a simple dimerization establishes that more complicated association phenomena can not be occurring in the concentration range of 10^{-7} to $10^{-3}M$ in any of these solvents with F · G : P · dA, or by inference with the majority of epindolidione-peptide conjugates that lack intense, long-wavelength CD absorption. As an independent test of this important point, vapor-phase osmometric measurements on millimolar solutions in THF of F · G : P · dA give values consistent with simple dimerization at this concentration.

Other than the solvent and structural dependences cited above, there are few clues to the structure of the dimer of F · G : P · dA, whose formation is accompanied by only modest changes in the proton NMR spectrum or the electronic absorption spectrum. The conjugate F · G : P · dA is unique among its 12 analogs in being highly crystalline, and it seems likely that the dimeric structure persists in the solid state. Its crystals have been subjected to x-ray diffraction, but the resulting data await refinement.

The Structure of F · G : P · dA in Solution in DMSO and Water-DMSO Mixtures

Data from proton NMR spectroscopy have been widely used to assign conformations of cyclic peptides (Kessler, 1982; Gierasch et al., 1981), and we have built our conformational study of F · G : P · dA and its analogs on this prior art. Unlike the time scale for most other forms of spectroscopy, that of NMR observations is relatively slow. Consequently, an ensemble of many equally stable, rapidly equilibrating molecular conformations will show sharp resonances that are averages of chemical shifts over the available conformations. The first task of an NMR-based conformational study is to prove that a single structural or a group of closely related conformations dominates the conformational population. This point is best established from a series of independent NMR parameters, each of which differs from the value expected for the conformational average of a random coil.

A variety of features of the proton NMR spectrum of F · G : P · dA in DMSO-d_6 solution in the temperature range of 295–340°C (300 MHz) are consistent with dominance of the expected β-sheet conformation. The chemical shifts of the diastereotopic hydrogens of the glycine residue differ by 0.47 δ, implying a large difference in shielding environment, and their $J_{geminal}$ value of 16.7 Hz corresponds to a ψ dihedral angle of $\pm$ 20° or $\pm$ 150° (Bystrov, 1976, 1978), in accord with an expected antiparallel sheet value of $-140°$ (Ashida et al., 1981). Consistent with a dominant sheet conformation, the vicinal coupling constants $J_{\alpha CH-NH}$ for D-alanine and phenylalanine are respectively 7.0 Hz and 8.4 Hz expected for a random coil. Application of a Karplus curve (Tardi et al., 1984) gives ϕ dihedral angle values of either $+80°$ or $+165°$ for dA (expected for β-turn: $+80°$), $\pm$ 140° for G (expected for extended sheet, $- 145°$), and $- 90°$ or $- 150°$ for F (expected for antiparallel sheet, $- 140°$).

The ^{13}C NMR resonances for the β and γ-carbons of the proline appear at 29.32 and 24.53 δ, respectively, allowing assignment (Grathwol and Wuthrich, 1976; Siemion et al., 1975) of the s-trans conformation at the

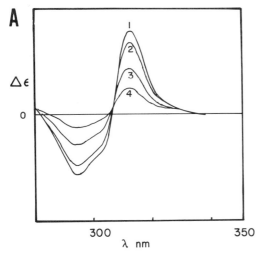

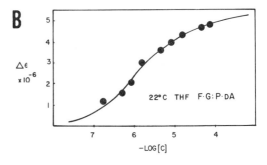

Fig. 6. (A) The temperature-dependent circular dichroism of F · G : P · dA in ethanol at 0°C (curve 1), 13.8°C (curve 2), 34.0°C (curve 3), and 48.1°C (curve 4). The curves can be quantitatively fitted to a two-species model and correspond to a value of −4.3 kcal/mol for Δ H° and +13 cal/mol for ΔS°. (B) Evidence for a simple monomer-dimer equilibrium. The dots show the experimental concentration dependence of the circular dichroism of F · G : P · dA in tetrahydrofuran at 312 nm, 22°C. The solid line is calculated for a simple dimerization equilibrium for which the molar ellipticity of the dimer is assumed to be 8.6 × 10₅ mdegcm^2/mmol and that of the monomer is zero.

proline amide bond consistent with calculated ψ angles at P of either $+172°$ or $-50°$ (expected for a β-turn, $-60°$).

In the strong hydrogen bond–forming solvent DMSO, the temperature dependences of δ values for the NH resonances provide a well-tested criterion for the formation of intramolecular hydrogen bonds (Llinás and Klein, 1975; Kessler, 1982). The respective values for the aryl NH, the dA NH, the G NH, the F NH, and the heteroaryl NH in units of -10^{-3} ppm/K are as follows: 1.5, 3.9, 4.7, 1.8, and 4.5. Values below 3 are expected for intramolecular hydrogen bonds, and by this criterion, the dA and G NHs, which are expected to be hydrogen bonded to solvent, exhibit δ values above 3, while those of the aryl NH (β-turn) and the F NH (the first of the sheet hydrogen bonds) are, in fact, intramolecularly hydrogen bonded. The heteroaryl NH poses special problems in interpretation, since this function is at least five orders of magnitude more acidic than a normal amide NH. Therefore, rules for the interpretation of this parameter had to be developed through study of a series of analogs.

The chemical shifts of the aryl NH and the heteroaryl NH resonances also carry unique structural information (Rose *et al.*, 1985). The least reliable of these is the F NH, since structural assignments based on chemical shift changes require a statistically significant data base for assigning the unperturbed δ value, and here the base is only a few derivatives. For the remaining three cases, the δ values belong to protons in regions of constant local environment, and at least 10 conformationally random acylaminoepindolidione derivatives are available for the data base. This demonstrates a near invariance of chemical shift for derivatives that lack β-structure.

For the $F \cdot G : P \cdot dA$ derivative, the following values for $(\delta-\delta_{std})$ are observed: -0.36 for the aryl NH, $+0.30$ for the aryl H-3, $+0.18$ for F NH, and -0.25 for the heteroaryl NH. The change in δ for the aryl H-3 is not shared with H-1, which shows only modest structure-dependent δ changes, nor with H-4, which appears at 8.08 ± 0.02 δ in 20 peptide-epindolidione conjugates. Almost certainly, the large δ increase for the aryl H-3 reflects a conformational restriction at the bond linking the aryl amido function to the ring, with a resulting fixation of the carbonyl oxygen near H-3 (Martin *et al.*, 1965). As noted in Fig. 7, the structural condition for this fixation involves formation of a β-turn with near coincidence of the plane of the turn with that of the epindolidione nucleus. Large values of $(\delta-\delta_{std})$ for H-3, therefore, report formation of the first hydrogen bond of an antiparallel sheet structure.

The most revealing demonstration of intact β-structure was provided by nuclear Overhauser difference spectroscopy (NOE), which reveals nonbonded hydrogens that are proximate and whose spins can interact through space (Billeter *et al.*, 1982). An exceptionally rich NOE spectrum was observed for $F \cdot G : P \cdot dA$ in DMSO-d_6. Figure 8 depicts by arrows the NOE's that are observed between hydrogens that are separated by seven or more bonds. The NOE's between both H's of the G CH_2 and H-1 of the epindolidione establish the presence of the sheet structure up to its first hydrogen bond, and the reciprocal NOE's seen between the epindolidione H-10 (H-10 is identical with H-4) and the F amido N-methyls establishes the integrity of the sheet structure through its second hydrogen bond.

Over the range of 295–340°C, the large diastereotopic δ values for G persist, and coupling constants and other δ values show only minor changes, a fact which can be interpreted as consistent with the presence of a single dominant conformation for $F \cdot G : P \cdot dA$ under these conditions. NMR spectra run in DMSO that is titrated with increasing amounts of either $CDCl_3$ or D_2O up to 60 mole percent (at which point precipitation occurs in the DMSO-water system) show the δ changes expected for the homogeneous β-structure and no measurable changes in coupling constants. By these standard criteria, the conformational equilibrium for $F \cdot G : P \cdot dA$ in these solvents appears to be dominated by a β-turn, β-sheet conformation.

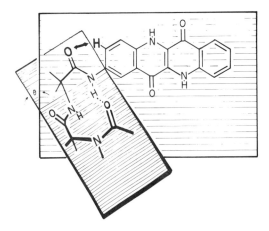

Fig. 7. The dihedral angle θ between average planes of the epindolidione and β-turn functions. Anomalous shielding of the aryl 3-H by the acylamino carbonyl oxygen (solid arrow) is possible only if θ is near zero. Near-zero values of θ are attributed to the structural constraint of hydrogen bonding in the sheet region (not shown).

Conjugates of Diacylamino-epindolidiones with Peptides That Cannot Form Sheets

It is also instructive to examine analogs of F · G : P · dA that may form secondary structures with difficulty or that are incapable of completing an antiparallel β-sheet. An example of the former is provided by F · A : Sar · G, in which the conformationally mobile sarcosine residue (N-methylglycine) has replaced a proline, which has a φ angle constrained to − 60°. Values near − 3.0 × 10 $^{-3}$ ppm are seen for Δδ/ΔT for all NH's, and the (δ–δ$_{std}$) values for NH's fall in the range of 0.0 to − 0.1 δ for this compound. In striking contrast to all other derivatives studied, the CD spectrum for F · A : Sar · G in a variety of solvents exhibits no bands in the range of 300–500 nm, indicating no significant interaction between the two amino acid chiral centers and the epindolidione. In solvents ranging in polarity from THF to DMSO, this substance thus behaves as a conformationally mobile random coil. Evidently, the conformation constraint of a pair of amino acids biased toward β-turn formation must link the epindolidione to the test peptide for nucleation of a β-sheet to occur.

Inspection of Fig. 2 reveals that, owing to interchain steric interactions, polypeptide chains containing both L and D amino acids can not form stable antiparallel β-sheets. To explore this point, the species F · dA : P · dA and dF · A : P · dA were studied, as well as the α-aminoisobutyric acid (Aib) derivative F · Aib : P · dA, in which the Aib group can be viewed as having the steric bulk of a composite of L and D alanines.

The (δ–δ$_{std}$) values for the F · Aib : P · dA derivative are zero for H-3 and the heteroaryl NH, consistent with absence of either hydrogen bond that defines the sheet region. Also significant are the − Δ/ΔT values of 5.0 and 5.5 × 10 $^{-3}$ ppm and the F and heteroaryl NH groups, which imply the absence of intramolecular hydrogen bonds. A weak β-turn hydrogen bond is hinted by the temperature factor for the aryl NH of 3.0 and its (δ–δ$_{std}$) value of − 0.35 δ. As expected, the bulky Aib residue at site-3 thus blocks sheet formation.

F · dA : P · dA and dF · A : P · dA may both be able to form the first hydrogen bond of the sheet structure, but neither can complete the sheet by forming the second. In fact, (δ–δ$_{std}$) for the heteroaryl NH is zero for both derivatives, and its temperature coefficients both lie in the range of − 4.6 × 10^{-3} ppm, consistent with an absence of intramolecular hydrogen bonding. Evidence for the first two

Fig. 8. Nuclear Overhauser effects (solid arrows) observed for F · G : P · dA in DMSO-d$_6$ at 22°C. Reciprocal NOE's are signified by double-headed arrows. Only NOE's that extend over seven or more linked bonds and that define β-structure are shown.

hydrogen bonds is relatively strong in the case of dF · A : P · dA $(\delta-\delta_{std})$ and values of −0.35 and + 0.38 for the aryl NH and H-3 resonances, together with − $\Delta\delta/\Delta T$ values for 1.3, 4.7, 4.5, and 2.7 × 10 $^{-3}$ ppm for the aryl NH, dA NH, and F NH, are consistent with a relatively robust structure defined by the β-turn and the first of the β-sheet hydrogen bonds. The corresponding values for the F · dA : P · dA analog are all consistent with a weaker doubly hydrogen bonded secondary structure that is subject to a greater degree of conformational averaging.

Given the considerable conformational freedom of glycine residues, it was of interest to compare the sequence F · G · P · dA that was examined in the preceding section with the more mobile sequences F · G : P · G and G · G : P · G. The NH NMR signatures of the latter resemble that of the conformationally averaged F · dA : P · dA except that they demonstrate small but significant $(\delta-\delta_{std})$ values of −0.08 and −0.12 δ for their heteroaryl NH's, suggesting weak, triply hydrogen bonded structures that are in mobile equilibrium with more random conformations. Evidently, the structural freedom allowed by glycine in the β-turn and β-sheet regions loosens global structure but does not abolish it.

Conformational Analysis of F · A : P · dA and dF · dA : P · dA; Evidence for Averaging with Strong Sheet Formers

By the criteria of the previous sections, the NMR signature for the sequences F · A : P · dA and dF · dA : P · dA in DMSO show these to be strongly dominated by sheet conformations. It is striking that both should be able to form sheets. Either of these structures can assume a conformation containing a β-turn and antiparallel β-sheet, but the chiral sense of the sheet region must be opposite in the two cases. Therefore, the relative stability of these structures tests the degree to which the chiral bias of the turn region,

which is the same for both derivatives, influences, through the urea spacer, the stability of sheet regions of either LL or DD chirality. As shown in Fig. 9, models imply that the DD structure allows less distortion of the turn region, although both structures are favorable. NOE experiments and measurements of J values give results similar to those observed for F · G : P · dA and consistent with the turn-sheet secondary structures. The respective values in −10^{-3} ppm of $\Delta\delta/\Delta T$ for the LL and DD cases in DMSO are as follows: aryl NH, 1.2 and 0.9; dA NH, 5.1 and 4.7; A or dA NH, 5.5 and 2.5; F or dF NH, 2.5 and 1.8; heteroaryl NH, 3.1 and 1.2. Values for $(\delta-\delta_{std})$ are larger than for other epindolidione-peptide conjugates studied to date: aryl NH, − 0.40 and − 0.42 δ; aryl H-3, +0.46 and +0.58 δ; heteroaryl NH, − 0.28 and − 0.50 δ.

It can be argued that the chemical shift changes that have been observed for the peptide-epindolidione conjugates that exhibit β-structure imply that each amino acid sequence has a distinct conformation with its own local shielding parameters and chemical shift values. The strongest piece of evidence supporting this view is the relatively small changes in NMR parameters with temperature increase. However, it should be noted that for conformational changes with small $\Delta G°$ (and therefore $\Delta H°$) values, only correspondingly small changes in K_{conf} are expected for temperature variations in the range of 295–340 K.

It is more likely that the interconversion of the random coil and sheet conformations of a peptide-epindolidione conjugate can be described by a series of equilibria, each of which generates one of the three hydrogen bonds of the complete structure. Almost certainly, the corresponding $\Delta G°$ values for these individual steps are small, with the consequence that rapid equilibration among an ensemble of conformations is the intrinsic feature of structures of this type. Although a single sheet conformation is the dominant form of F · G : P · dA and the analogs of this section, its quantitative contribution to the ensemble may still vary substantially. The data of Fig. 10 demonstrate strong linear correlations of the heteroaryl NH chemical shift with its

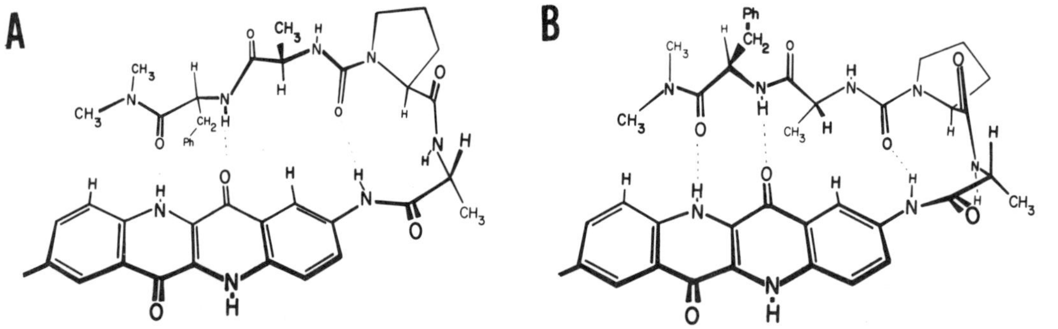

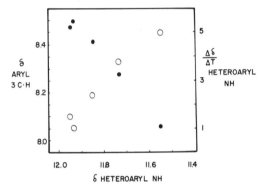

Fig. 9. (A) A perspective representation of a likely conformation of F · A : P · dA, drawn from Kendrew models that were constructed using standard values for torsional angles in the β-turn and β-sheet regions. (B) An analogous representation of a likely conformation of dF · dA : P · dA.

Fig. 10. Linear correlations between the ^{1}H chemical shift of the heteroaryl NH (horizontal axis), the chemical shift of aryl 3 C-H (left vertical axis, open circles), and the temperature dependence in units of -10^3 ppm/K of the chemical shift of the heteroaryl NH (right vertical axis, filled circles). The five derivatives are, from left to right, G · G : P · G,   F · G : P · G,   F · G : P · dA, F · A : P · dA, dF · dA : P · dA. The expected δ values for the aryl 3 C-H and heteroaryl NH in a derivative that shows no β-structure are respectively, 7.9 ppm and 12.0 ppm.

temperature dependence and with the chemical shift of aryl H-3. The latter correlation between δ values of protons in separate parts of the structure is most plausibly explained as a result of different degrees of conformational averaging, and with this interpretation, the largest values of $(\delta - \delta_{std})$ must correspond to the most stable structures.

Under the assumptions of this model, the following structures, ranked in order of stability, form identifiable δ-turn-δ-sheet conjugates:

dF · dA : P · dA > F · A : P · dA >
F · G : P · dA > F · G : P · G >>
G · G : P · G.

Other experiments are in progress to extend this analysis to a more complete list of amino acids and to explore the degree of stabilization of β-structure in these models by quantitative methods. Ultimately we hope to develop syntheses of chimeric analogs of proteins that contain secondary structure-nucleating templates imbedded in regions of natural amino acid sequences. Syntheses of these chimeras will require a breakthrough in the art of chemical synthesis of small proteins, and experiments are in progress to that end (Fotouhi et al., 1989).

Summary

The following conclusions result from this initial study of peptide-epindolidione conjugates:

(i) Short, antiparallel β-sheets have been nucleated in DMSO and water-DMSO mixtures linked templates bearing three oriented sites for hydrogen bonding, and the resulting structures have been shown to be unassociated in polar solvents up to millimolar concentrations.

(ii) Null hypotheses have been successfully demonstrated, showing an absence of sheet structure for amino acid substitutions that are sterically inconsistent with sheet formation.

The presence of a strong β-turn forming signal in the region linking the epindoldione and sheet peptide has been shown to be a precondition for sheet formation.

(iii) The linear dependence of NMR parameters that are observed for sheet-forming sequences has been explained as the result of equilibration among an ensemble of turns and partial sheets in which a fully formed turn, sheet conformation is dominant in the most stabilized cases.

(iv) The chirality of the δ-turn region has been shown to provide only a weak constraint on sheet chirality, and modest but detectable differences among the sheet-forming tendencies of G, A, and F have been demonstrated.

Acknowledgment

Financial support from GM 40547-02 is gratefully acknowledged.

References

Ashida, T., I. Tanaka, T. Yamane, *Int. J. Peptide Protein Res.* **17**, 322 (1981).

Bierzynski, A., P. S. Kim, R. L. Baldwin, *Proc. Natl. Acad. Sci. U.S.A.* **79**, 2470 (1982).

Billeter, M., W. Braun, K. Wuthrich, *J. Mol. Biol.* **155**, 321 (1982).

Bystrov, B. F., *J. Magn. Resonance.* **30**, 151 (1978).
_____, *Progress in NMR Spectroscopy* **10**, 41, (1976).

Chaiken, I. M., J. M. Stewart, R. L. Baldwin, *Proc. Natl. Acad. Sci. U.S.A.* **82**, 2349 (1985).

Chou, P., and G. Fasman, *J. Mol. Biol.* **135**, 135 (1977).

Creighton, T. E., *Proteins—Structure and Molecular Properties* (W. H. Freeman, San Francisco, 1983), p. 191.

Dyson, H. J., M. Rance, R. A. Houghten, R. A. Lerner, P.E. Wright, *J. Mol. Biol.* **201**, 161 (1988).

Fotouhi, N., N. G. Galakatos, D. S. Kemp, *J. Org. Chem.,* **54**, 2803 (1989).

Gierasch, L. M., C. M. Deber, V. Madison, C. Niu, E. R. Blout, *Biochem.* **20**, 4730 (1981).

Grathwol, N., and K. Wuthrich, *Biopolymers* **15**, 2025 (1976).

Hartman, R., R. C. Schwaner, J. Hermans, *J. Mol. Biol.* **90**, 415 (1974).

Jaffee, E. E., and H. Matrick, *J. Org. Chem.* **33**, 4004 (1968).

Kemp, D. S., and B. R. Bowen, *Tetrahedron Lett.* **4970**, 4975 (1988).

Kemp, D. S., and T. P. Curran *Tetrahedron Lett.* **4931**, 4935 (1988).

Kessler, H., *Angew. Chem. Int. Ed. Eng.* **21**, 512 (1982).

Klotz, I. M., and J. S. Franzen, *J. Am. Chem. Soc.* **84**, 3461 (1962).

Levitt, M., *Biochem.* **17**, 4277 (1978).

Llinás, M., and M. P. Klein, *J. Am. Chem. Soc.* **97**, 4731 (1975).

Martin, R. H., N. Defay, F. Greets-Evrard, *Tetrahedron* **20**, 1505 (1965).

Rasasekharian Pillai, V. N., and M. Mutter, *Accts. Chem. Res.* **14**, 122 (1983).

Richardson, J. S., *Adv. Protein Chem.* **34**, 167 (1981).

Rose, G. D., L. M. Gierasch, J. A. Smith *Adv. Protein Chem.* **38**, 1, (1985).

Scheraga, H., *Pure Applied Chem.* **50**, 315 (1978).

Schmitt, J., and M. Mutter, *Biopolymers* **22**, 1849, (1983).

Schoemaker, K. R., et al., *Proc. Natl. Acad. Sci. U.S.A.* **82**, 2349 (1985).

Schuster, P., G. Zundel, C. Sandorfy, Eds., *The Hydrogen Bond: Recent Developments in Theory and Experiments* (North-Holland, Amsterdam, 1976).

Siemion, I. Z., T. Wieland, K. H. Pook, *Angew. Chem. Int. Ed. Eng.* **14**, 702 (1975).

Stimson, E., Y. Meinwald, G. Montelione, H. Scheraga, *Int. J. Peptide Protein Res.* **27**, 569 (1968).

Tardi, A., M. Billeter, K. Wuthrich, *J. Mol. Biol.* **180**, 741 (1984).

Zimm, B., and J. Bragg, *J. Chem. Phys.* **31**, 526 (1959).

30

Engineering Enzyme Specificity by "Substrate-Assisted Catalysis"

Paul Carter and James A. Wells

Rational design of enzyme specificity by protein engineering should expand the range and utility of biological catalysts. Site-directed mutagenesis techniques (Smith, 1985; Carter, 1986) have already been applied to modify the substrate specificity of subtilisin (Estell *et al.,* 1986; Wells *et al.,* 1987a, 1987b), trypsin (Craik, 1985), tyrosyl-tRNA (transfer RNA) synthetase (Fersht *et al.,* 1985), carboxypeptidase (Winther *et al.,* 1985), alcohol dehydrogenase (Murali and Creaser, 1986), and aspartate aminotransferase (Cronin *et al.,* 1987). These studies have focused on altering specificity by changing residues that make direct contact with the substrate. Here we present an alternative approach, termed "substrate-assisted catalysis," in which part of the catalytic machinery of the enzyme is removed and appropriately supplied by a similar functionality from a bound substrate. In this way substrates are distinguished primarily by their ability to actively participate in the catalytic mechanism permitting the design of extremely specific enzymes.

We have chosen subtilisin, a serine class endopeptidase, as a model to test the concept of substrate-assisted catalysis. In the hydrolysis of peptide bonds by subtilisin, His^{64} acts both as a catalytic base and acid in the formation of the acyl-enzyme intermediate and in a similar fashion in the subsequent deacylation step (Stroud *et al.,* 1975; Kraut, 1977). A model of a substrate containing a histidine residue at the P2 position[1] bound to subtilisin (Color Plate XXIV) indicated that the $N\delta1$ and $N\varepsilon2$ nitrogens can almost be superimposed (to about one angstrom unit) on the corresponding nitrogens of the catalytic histidine (His^{64}). This suggested that if the histidine in the catalytic triad of subtilisin was replaced by an alanine by means of site-directed mutagenesis, a histidine from the substrate might supply the missing catalytic functional group.

Construction and Expression of His64Ala Mutant Subtilisin

Maturation of the primary subtilisin gene

This chapter is reprinted from *Science* **237**, 394 (1987).

1   Peptide substrate nomenclature may be represented as:

$$NH_2\text{-Pn}...P2\text{-}P1\text{-}\overset{\overset{\text{O}}{\|}}{C}\text{-}\overset{\overset{\text{H}}{|}}{N}\text{-}P1'\text{-}P2'...Pn'\text{-}COOH$$

where the scissile bond is between the P1 and the P1' substrate residues (Schechter and Berger, 1967).

product (preprosubtilisin) to subtilisin in *Bacillus subtilis* is believed to be mediated by autoproteolysis that involves trace amounts of active subtilisin (Power *et al.*, 1986). The His64Ala mutation[2] caused a severe reduction in secretion of mature subtilisin that was presumed to result from a large reduction in catalytic activity (P. Carter and J. A. Wells, unpublished results). However, it was possible to process and subsequently purify the weakly active His64Ala enzyme by co-culturing *B. subtilis* cells harboring the His64Ala mutant gene with *B. subtilis* cells carrying an active subtilisin gene (helper)[3]. Stringent precautions were taken to ensure the purification of His64Ala subtilisin away from helper subtilisin and any other contaminating proteases. First, the mutant subtilisin was expressed in the *B. subtilis* host BG2036 (Yang *et al.*, 1984), which is deficient in chromosomal copies of the genes for alkaline protease (subtilisin) and neutral protease. To minimize helper contamination, the ratio of helper cells to His64Ala cells in the fermentation culture was adjusted to 1:1000. A functionally silent Ser24Cys mutation that is located on the surface of subtilisin (Wells *et al.*, 1986) was introduced into the His64Ala mutant. This accessible cysteine permitted reversible attachment to an activated thiol Sepharose column that enabled purification of the His64Ala mutant away from the cysteine-free helper subtilisin. Finally, the helper subtilisin contained a functionally silent Ala48Glu mutation (J. Wells, unpublished data) that altered its electrophoretic mobility relative to the Ser24Cys:His64Ala double-mutant subtilisin on native and sodium dodecyl sulfate (SDS)–polyacrylamide gels (P. Carter and J. A. Wells, unpublished data). After purification, the Ser24Cys:His64Ala mutant was judged to be more than 99 percent pure by silver-stained SDS (Morrissey, 1981; Laemmli, 1970) and native polyacrylamide gel electrophoresis (P. Carter, unpublished results).

---

2   The designation His64Ala refers to a mutation where the His residue at position 64 in wild-type subtilisin is mutated to Ala. The designation Ser24Cys:His64Ala refers to a double mutant protein in which the wild-type residues Ser[24] and His[64] are converted to Cys and Ala, respectively. The His64Ala mutation was constructed with the use of the oligonucleotide: 5'-CAACAACTCCGCGGGGAACTCAC-3' (asterisks denote mismatches to the wild-type sequence and underlined is a unique Sac II site) and a pSS5 single-stranded plasmid template (B. Cunningham, D. Powers, J. Wells, unpublished) containing the subtilisin gene (Wells *et al.*, 1983) using a previously described method (Carter *et al.*, 1985). The double-mutant Ser24Cys:His64Ala was constructed from the His64Ala and Ser24Cys single mutants by a three-way ligation with the use of the following fragments: 6-kb Eco RI-Bam HI vector fragment from pSS5, 0.5kb Eco RI-Cla I from Ser24Cys (Wells and Powers, 1986), and 1.0-kb Cla I-Bam HI from His64Ala. The entire coding sequence of the Ser24Cys:His64 Ala mutant was then verified by dideoxy sequencing (Sanger *et al.*, 1977). Transformation of *B. subtilis* BG2036 (Yang *et al.*, 1984) with *Escherichia coli-B. subtilis* shuttle plasmids has been described (Wells and Powers, 1986).

3   Separate *B. subtilis* BG2036 cultures, containing the Ser24Cys:His64Ala double-mutant subtilisin plasmid and a functionally silent Ala48Glu mutant subtilisin plasmid (J. Wells, unpublished data), were grown in 2 × TY media (Miller, 1972) containing chloramphenicol (12.5 μg/ml) at 37°C for 18 to 20 hours. Co-cultures were inoculated by diluting Ser24Cys:His64Ala 1 to 100 (v/v) and Ala48Glu 1 to 100,000 (v/v) in 2 × TY containing chloramphenicol (12.5 μg/ml) with 10 m*M* CaCl$_2$, and grown at 37°C for 20 to 24 hours with vigorous aeration. Co-cultures (2 liters) were centrifuged (8000*g*, 15 minutes, 4°C) and three volumes of ethanol (− 20°C) was added to the supernatant. After centrifugation (8000*g*, 15 minutes, 4°C) the pellet was resuspended in 50 m*M* tris-HCl (pH 8.0), 5 m*M* CaCl$_2$, 10 m*M* dithiothreitol (DDT). After centrifugation (40,000*g*, 30 minutes, 4°C), the supernatant was dialyzed against 2 liters of 10 m*M* 2-[*N*-morpholino]ethanesulfonic acid (MES) (*p*H 6.2), 5 m*M* CaCl$_2$, 10 m*M* DDT (S buffer) overnight at 4°C. The dialyzate was passed over a 50-ml DE52 column, and the flow through was placed on a 50-ml CM Trisacryl (LKB) column. Subtilisin was eluted with a 600-ml gradient of S buffer containing NaCl from 0 to 100 m*M*. Pooled subtilisin-containing fractions were dialyzed against 2 liters of deaerated 10 m*M* MES (*p*H 6.2), 5 m*M* CaCl$_2$, 100 m*M* NaCl (T buffer). Samples were loaded onto an activated thiol Sepharose matrix (Pharmacia), washed extensively with T buffer, and eluted with T buffer containing 20 m*M* DTT. The elute was concentrated with Centricon 10 microconcentrators (Amicon) and dialyzed against four changes of 2 liters of 10 m*M* MES (*p*H 6.2), 5 m*M* DTT. The concentration of subtilisin was determined from the measured absorbance at 280 nm ($\varepsilon^{0.1\%}$ = 1.17) (Matsubara *et al.*, 1965). The Ser24Cys mutant was cultured in the absence of helper and was purified as for Ser24Cys:His64Ala. Purified enzymes were flash frozen in aliquots and stored at − 70°C.

Kinetic Analysis of Ser24Cys:His64Ala

The kinetic parameters of Ser24Cys and Ser24Cys:His64Ala were determined for the substrates N-succinyl-l-Phe-l-Ala-l-[X]-l-Phe-p-nitroanilide (abbreviated sFAXF-pNA), where X is Ala, Gln, or His (Table 1). Wild-type and Ser24Cys subtilisins have essentially identical kinetic parameters for these substrates (D. A. Estell and T. P. Graycar, unpublished results), indicating that the Ser24Cys mutation is kinetically silent. By comparison, the His64Ala mutation causes a 10^6-fold decrease in the k_{cat}/K_m ratio for the Ala and Gln P2 substrates. Almost all of the decrease in catalytic efficiency is caused by a decreased k_{cat} value (up to 10^6 times), although significant increases appear in K_m (up to four times). The relatively small changes in K_m may reflect changes in the enzyme-substrate dissociation constant (K_s), although it may also reflect a shift in the rate-determining step of the reaction (Gutfreund and Sturtevant, 1956);[4] we have not determined whether acy-

lation is rate limiting for the His64Ala mutant, as it is for the wild-type enzyme (Wells et al., 1986).[5] In any case, the catalytic histidine contributes a factor of about 10^6 to the enzymatic rate enhancement (Table 1).

Unlike wild-type or Ser24Cys subtilisin, the Ser24Cys:His64Ala enzyme was completely resistant to inhibition by the active site reagent, phenylmethylsulfonyl fluoride (PMSF). This suggests that the catalytic histidine is critical for stable sulfonylation by PMSF. Although the proportion of functional active sites in Ser24Cys:His64Ala enzyme preparations could not be determined directly by such active site labeling, enzyme that was purified further by native gel electrophoresis (P. Carter and J. A. Wells, unpublished results) had identical kinetic parameters to Ser24Cys-His:64Ala (Table 1) purified as described (see footnote 3).

For the Ser24Cys enzyme, the Ala P2 substrate is preferred over the Gln and His P2 substrates by about four times (ratio of k_{cat}/K_m terms, Table 1). Most of this difference is the result of larger K_m values for the

Table 1. Kinetic analysis of mutant subtilisins with the substrates, N-succinyl-L-Phe-L-Ala-L-X-L-Phe-p-nitroanilide, when X is Ala, Gln, or His. Six hydrolysis assays were performed simultaneously against corresponding substrate blanks in 0.10M tris-HCl (pH 8.6), 10 mM dithiothreitol at 25° ± 0.2°C with a Kontron Uvikon 860 spectrophotometer. Initial reaction rates were determined from the increase in absorbance caused by the release of p-nitroaniline [$\varepsilon 410$ nm $= 8480 M^{-1}$ cm^{-1} (Del Mar et al., 1979)] and fitted by linear regression to an Eadie-Hofstee plot to calculate V$_{max}$ and K$_m$. The k_{cat} values were calculated from V$_{max}$; the spectrophotometrically determined enzyme concentration was used (Matsubara et al., 1965). Enzyme concentrations in the assays were about 50 μg/ml for Ser24Cys:His64Ala enzyme and 1 μg/ml for the Ser24Cys enzyme. Standard errors in all determinations were below 20 percent. Slight variation in the absolute kinetic values has been observed between batches of enzyme, but the relative values among substrates have remained constant.

Substrate P2 residue	Ser24Cys			Ser24Cys:His64Ala		
	k_{cat} (sec^{-1})	K_m (μM)	k_{cat}/K_m (sec$^{-1} M^{-1}$)	k_{cat} (sec^{-1})	K_m (μM)	k_{cat}/K_m (sec$^{-1} M^{-1}$)
Ala	8.1	10	8.0×10^5	8.1×10^{-6}	32	0.25
Gln	7.0	39	1.8×10^5	3.0×10^{-5}	150	0.20
His	4.6	23	2.0×10^5	1.6×10^{-2}	380	42

4   For the two-step reaction mechanism of serine proteases,

$$E + S \underset{}{\overset{K_s}{\rightleftharpoons}} E \cdot S \underset{Pr_1}{\overset{k_2}{\rightleftharpoons}} E - Ac \underset{H_2O}{\overset{k_3}{\rightleftharpoons}} E + Pr_2$$

(where E is enzyme, S is substrate, E − Ac is the acyl-enzyme, and Pr1 and Pr2 are the products), $K_m = K_s k_3/(k_2 + k_3)$. When acylation is rate determining (that is, $k_3 >> k_2$) $K_m \sim K_s$; when deacylation is rate-determining (that is, $k_2 >> k_3$) $K_m = K_s (k_3/k_2)$.

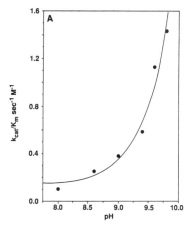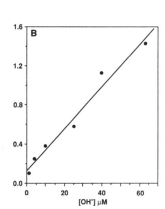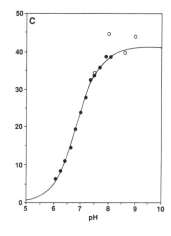

Fig. 1. The pH dependence of hydrolysis of p-nitroanilide peptide substrates by Ser24Cys:His64Ala subtilisin. Analysis of Ser24Cys:His64Ala against sFAAF-pNA (A) was determined as in Table 1 except that we used 100 mM tris-HCl or 100 mM 3-[cyclohexylamino]-1-propane sulfonic acid (CAPS) buffer. The data were fitted on the basis of a linear relation with hydroxide ion concentration (solid lines in A and B). Analysis of Ser24Cys:His64Ala against sFAHF-pNA (C) was determined as for Table 1, except that we used 100 mM 3-[N- morpholino]propanesulfonic acid (MOPS) buffer (closed circles) or 100 mM tris-HCl (open circles) and then normalized the ionic strength with KCl. The data were fitted to a sigmoid curve (solid line) with the use of a least-squares fit procedure.

Gln and His P2 substrates. For the Ser24Cys:His64Ala enzyme, the relative differences in k_{cat}/K_m toward the Ala and Gln P2 substrates are similar to Ser24Cys.

In contrast, the Ser24Cys:His64Ala enzyme hydrolyzes the His P2 substrate more efficiently by factors of 170 and 210 times k_{cat}/K_m, respectively. Essentially all of the increase in k_{cat}/K_m for the His compared to the Ala and Gln P2 substrates results from the k_{cat} term being larger by a factor of 2000 and 500, respectively. The larger K_m values for the His and Gln P2 substrates compared to Ala may reflect reduced binding affinity. Apparently, the catalytic advantage of the His P2 side chain is only realized in the context of the catalytic groups provided by the Ser24Cys:His64Ala enzyme, because the nonenzymatic hydrolysis rates for the His and non-His substrates are essentially the same (P. Carter, unpublished data). Thus, the drop in k_{cat}/K_m caused by the His64Ala mutation is partially restored when cleaving a His P2 substrate. The net effect is a marked increase in substrate preference for a His P2 side chain brought about primarily at the level of catalysis rather than binding.

The pH Dependence of Amide Bond Hydrolysis by Ser24Cys:His64Ala

The pH dependence of k_{cat}/K_m for wild-type subtilisin shows a sigmoidal increase from pH 6 to 8 (Glazer, 1967; Thomas et al., 1985) that reflects the titration of the catalytic His$_{64}$ (pK_a = 7.1 ± 0.1). The wild-type pH profile remains relatively flat over the range of pH 8 to 10 and declines thereafter (Ottesen and Svendsen, 1970).

The pH dependence of k_{cat}/K_m is markedly different for the Ser24Cys:His64Ala enzyme. For the sFAAF-pNA substrate, there is a 15-fold increase in k_{cat}/K_m between pH 8 and pH 10 (Fig. 1A). The k_{cat}/K_m ratio shows a linear dependence on hydroxide ion concentration (Fig. 1B), suggesting that a hydroxide ion can act as a catalytic base in the absence of a catalytic histidine side chain. If we extrapolate from the increase in k_{cat}/K_m as a function of hydroxide concentration (2×10^4 sec^{-1} M^{-2}), to the k_{cat}/K_m for Ser24Cys with the same Ala P2 substrate (8×10^5 sec^{-1} M^{-1}), then the equivalent concentration of the hydroxide ion would be about 40M.

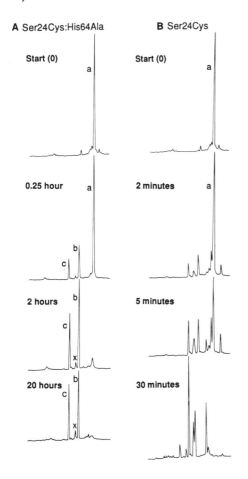

A Ser24Cys:His64Ala

Start (0)

0.25 hour

2 hours

20 hours

B Ser24Cys

Start (0)

2 minutes

5 minutes

30 minutes

Fig. 2. Hydrolysis of a polypeptide substrate (inhibin β chain) by subtilisin mutant Ser24Cys:His64Ala or Ser24Cys. The synthetic peptide substrate: TVIN-HYRMRGHSPFANLKSC (100 μg) was digested with 10 mg of the Ser24Cys:His64Ala enzyme (A) or with 0.13 μg of Ser24Cys enzyme (B). Reaction mixtures (total volume of 250 μl) contained 20 mM tris-HCl (pH 8.0), 10 mM dithiothreitol, 5 percent (v/v) dimethyl sulfoxide, and 1 mM PMSF (Ser24Cys:His64Ala only). After indicated times at 37°C, digestion products (monitored at 214 mm) were eluted from a reversed phase HPLC column (Waters, C18) with a gradient (from left to right) of 0 to 50 percent (v/v) acetonitrile in 0.1 percent (v/v) tri-fluoroacetic acid. Peaks a, b, c in (A) refer to the starting peptide, fragment TVINHY and fragment RMRGHSPFANLKSC, respectively. Peak X has a composition identical to the starting peptide.

In contrast, k_{cat}/K_m for hydrolysis of the sFAHF-pNA by Ser24Cys:His64Ala shows a sigmoidal pH dependence between pH 6 and 8 (Fig. 1C) that is similar to wild-type subtilisin.

The pK_a of the activity-dependent group is 6.8 ± 0.1, and almost all of the pH-dependent changes in k_{cat}/K_m result from changes in k_{cat}. For the sFAHF-pNA substrate, there is not a strong linear increase in k_{cat}/K_m with hydroxide above pH 8 as observed for hydrolysis of sFAAF-pNA. These data therefore suggest that the His P2 substrate side chain or hydroxide ion can substitute functionally for the missing catalytic His[64].

The data presented in Table 1 (measured at pH 8.6) underestimate the substrate preference for His over Ala (and Gln) because the k_{cat}/K_m for the sFAHF-pNA is maximal at pH 8.0 (Fig. 1C), whereas for the sFAAF-pNA substrate, it is significantly lower at pH 8.0 (Fig. 1A). Thus, for Ser24Cys:His64Ala at pH 8.0, we estimate the substrate preference is up to ~ 400 times for the His P2 substrate over the corresponding Ala or Gln substrates.

Many lines of evidence indicate that the activity we attribute to the Ser24Cys:His64Ala enzyme is not the result of any other protease contamination. First, the extreme substrate preference for His at the P2 position is unlike wild-type subtilisin or any known *Bacillus* protease. Furthermore, the mutant has K_m values that are significantly different from wild-type subtilisin, suggesting differences in substrate binding or catalysis. In addition, unlike other serine proteases, the mutant is completely resistant to inhibition by PMSF. In fact, the kinetic determinations and polypeptide digestion experiments with the Ser24Cys:His64Ala mutant (Table 1 and Fig. 1) were routinely made in the presence of PMSF to exclude any possibility of active helper subtilisin.

Moreover, the substrate-dependent pH profiles are unlike any protease we are aware of. In addition, preparations of Ser24Cys:His64Ala are extremely pure on the basis of analysis by SDS and native gels (99 percent). Finally, the kinetic values determined for Ser24Cys:His64Ala that was further purified by native gel electrophoresis (P. Carter, unpublished results) are essentially the same as those reported in Table 1.

Hydrolysis of Polypeptide Substrates by Ser24Cys:His64Ala

To evaluate further the specificity of Ser24Cys:His64Ala in comparison with Ser24Cys, we incubated both enzymes with a 20-residue fragment of the inhibin β chain at pH 8.0. The choice of the peptide was based on the presence of two histidines (position 5 and 11) along with 16 other amino acids including various large hydrophobic amino acids that are preferred amino acids at the P1 position of wild-type subtilisin (Estell *et al.,* 1986). The peptide (Fig. 2A, peak a) at ~120-fold molar excess over Ser24Cys:His64Ala was cleaved into only two pieces (Fig. 2A, peaks b and c) to more than 95 percent after incubation for 2 hours. Amino acid composition analysis of these two peptide fragments indicated cleavage had occurred between Tyr[6] and Arg[7], as would be expected for substrate-assisted catalysis by His[5] located at the P2 position relative to the cleavage site. After a longer (10 times) period of digestion (20 hours), a minor third peak appeared (Fig. 2A, peak X). Analysis showed it to have the same composition as the undigested inhibin peptide. This minor product also appeared in a nonenzymatic blank incubation. No digestion was observed at the second histidine site.

In contrast to the two fragments produced by Ser24Cys:His64Ala, the Ser24Cys enzyme produced at least seven fragments (Fig. 2B) at a similar extent of digestion of starting material (compare five-minute digestion with Ser24Cys to two-hour digestion with Ser24Cys:His64Ala). Although none of these seven fragments was sequenced, the first two produced eluted from the high-performance liquid chromatogram (HPLC) at the same positions as peaks b and c in Fig. 2A. Digestion to 95 percent completion of the starting peptide by Ser24Cys (Fig. 2C, 30-minute incubation) produced more than 10 different peptide fragments.

Digestion experiments for this and five other peptides are summarized in Table 2. A 10-residue fragment of human adrenocorticotropic hormone (ACTH) was quantitatively cleaved at a single site by Ser24Cys:His64Ala. Analysis of the amino acid composition of the two digestion products confirmed that the cleavage had occurred with a His residue at the P2 position of the substrate as expected. However, digestion of this peptide with Ser24Cys also gave specific cleavage at the same position. This probably resulted because Phe provides a very favorable P1 residue, and the two short peptides liberated are relatively poor substrates for subtilisin. The four other peptides tested (three containing His and one which did not) were not cleaved by Ser24Cys:His64Ala, but were cleaved at several sites by the Ser24Cys mutant.

These experiments establish much about the activity, specificity, and utility of the Ser24Cys:His64Ala mutant. In addition to *p*-nitroanilide substrates, the enzyme can cleave normal peptide bonds. Unlike the Ser24Cys enzyme, the specificity of Ser24Cys:His64Ala appears to be limited to sites containing a histidine side chain located at the P2 position of the cleavage site.[6] Furthermore, additional specificity determinants are required because not all His P2 sites are cleaved. We believe that this reflects the normal specificity determinants in the wild-type enzyme, which extend at least from P4 to P2' (Ottesen and Svendsen, 1970). Peptide substrates were chosen to have His followed by a large hydrophobic amino acid, which is preferred for the P1 site in subtilisin (Estell *et al.,* 1986; Ottesen and Svendsen, 1970). The potential cleavage sites for ACTH and the BOP (Table 2) peptide are very similar, except that the uncleaved BOP site contains a Glu at the P1' position. Little is known about P1' specificity, but the absence of cleavage at the other His sites may reflect

---

5   For wild-type enzyme, the ratio of the acylation rate (k_2) to the deacylation rate constant (k_3) is at least 1:33 for the substrate succinyl-L-Ala-L-Ala-L-Pro-L-Phe-*p*-nitroanilide.

6   In the context of some amino acid sequences, we have subsequently found that a histidine residue at the P1' position can also promote polypeptide cleavage (P. Carter, S. Braxton, D. Vandlen, J. Wells, unpublished results).

Table 2. Digestion of peptide substrates by Ser24Cys:His64Ala subtilisin. Various synthetic peptides (200 μg) shown were digested with Ser24Cys:His64Ala subtilisin (10 μg) in 20 mM tris-HCl (pH 8.0), 10 mM DTT, 5 percent (v/v) dimethyl sulfoxide, 1 mM PMSF (250 μl, total volume) for 20 hours at 37°C. Digestion products were analyzed by reversed-phase HPLC as described in the legend to Fig. 3. Digestion products recovered by HPLC were hydrolyzed for 24 hours in 6N HCl, 1% (v/v) phenol before amino acid analysis, with norleucine as an internal standard. The Cys residues in bovine insulin A and B chains were oxidized to cysteic acid. Sequences are designated by the single letter amino acid code, and arrows indicate potential His P2 cleavage sites. ACTH, adrenocorticotropic hormone; BOP is an open reading frame from the complementary strand to the gene for bacterial rhodopsin of *Halobacterium.* Single-letter abbreviations for the amino acid residues are: A, Ala; C, Cys; D, Asp; E, Glu; F, Phe; G, Gly; H, His; I, Ile; K, Lys; L, Leu; M, Met; N, Asn; P, Pro; Q, Gln; R, Arg; S, Ser; T, Thr; V, Val; W, Trp; and Y, Tyr.

Peptide source	Sequence	Cleavage peptides with Ser24Cys:His 64 Ala
Inhibin β chain (residues 61–80)	TVINHYRMRGHSPFANLKSC	TVINHY + RMRGHSPFANLKSC
ACTH (residues 1–10)	SYSMEHFRWG	SYSMEHF + RWG
Ubiquitin (residues 62–76)	CKESTLHLVLRLRGRR-NH2	Not cleaved
BOP gene product (residues 68–86)	GYEHFENLRRRAASFQGKY	Not cleaved
Bovine insulin B chain (oxidized)	FVNQHLCGSHLVEALYLVCGERGFFYTPKA	Not cleaved
Bovine insulin A chain (oxidized)	GIVEQCCASVCSLYQLENYCN	Not cleaved

the presence of a Val, a Pro, or a negatively charged residue (Glu or cysteic acid), all of which are very poorly hydrolyzed P1 amino acids (Estell *et al.,* 1986; Philipp and Bender, 1983; Svendsen, 1976).

Proteolytic instability of heterologous gene products (particularly small proteins) sometimes necessitates their expression as larger fusion polypeptides and recovery by chemical or enzymatic cleavage. The Ser24Cys:His64Ala mutant, or variant thereof, may be especially useful in site-specific proteolysis of fusion polypeptides. First, the enzyme is extremely specific for a P2 histidine compared to its closest isosteric homolog, glutamine. Furthermore, histidine is the third least abundant amino acid in proteins having an average abundance of 2.1 percent in proteins (Klapper, 1977). In addition, specificity determinants at the other subsites in subtilisin further restrict the cleavage specificity among possible histidine sites. If necessary, the

specificity of the P1 binding site in subtilisin can be further restricted by protein engineering (Estell *et al.,* 1986; Wells *et al.,* 1987a, 1987b). Moreover, subtilisin is unusually stable in denaturants often necessary for solubilization of fusion proteins. Finally, the surface thiol (Ser24Cys) permits easy immobilization or separation.

Substrate-Assisted Catalysis in Design and Evolution of Serine Proteases

The fact that the catalytic efficiency of the Ser24Cys:His64Ala enzyme for the His P2 substrate is 5000 times less than that of wild-type subtilisin suggests that the His provided by the substrate functions poorly in catalysis. Indeed, the model of the His P2 side chain does not exactly match the catalytic His[64] (Color Plate XXIV and Table 3). When the distances for the His P2 and His[64] imidazoyl nitrogens are matched to the catalytic Ser and Asp (Table 3, model S1), dihedral angles for the His P2 side chain differ from ideality (that is, $\chi_1 = \pm 60°, - 180°; \chi_2 = \pm 90°$) and the corresponding imidazoyl nitrogens from His[64] and His P2 are separated by more than an angstrom. In addition, the planes of the histidine side chains from the enzyme and substrate are nearly perpendicular to each other (Color Plate XXIV). This model does not appear to have a detrimental effect on the hydrogen bond angle between the Ser and His (Table 3) or lead to bad steric contacts. However, the modeled hydrogen bond angle between His and Asp is less favorable. Further mutagenesis experiments are under way to determine whether Asp[32] has a significant catalytic role in the His64Ala enzyme. When the dihedral angles are constrained to ideality, only $\chi_1 = 180°$ and $\chi_2 = -90°$ give approximate superposition of His[64] and His P2 (Table 3, model S2). The hydrogen bond distances, dihedral angles, and steric contacts are much less favorable when the substrate imidazoyl ring is rotated 180° (opposite to that of His[64] or model S1 in Table 3) to pair the Nδ1 with Ser[221] and Nε2 with Asp[32]. X-ray crystallographic studies will be necessary to clarify the precise mode of binding for the His P2 substrate. Further mutagenesis studies are directed toward producing more efficient substrate-assisted catalysis by a His P2 side chain.

The strategy for altering substrate specificity by changing substrate (or transition-state) binding contacts (Estell *et al.*, 1986; Wells *et al.*, 1987a, 1987b; Craik *et al.*, 1985; Fersht *et al.*, 1985; Winther *et al.*, 1985; Murali and Creaser, 1986; Cronin *et al.*, 1987) has general applicability in that contacts to any part of the substrate can be engineered to change their binding properties. The substrate-assisted catalysis approach is particularly applicable where removal of a catalytic group (such as a nucleophile, or an acidic or basic group) from an enzyme can be precisely replaced by a similar functional group from a bound substrate. Thus, enzymes (such as proteases) that react with substrates having potential catalytic functional groups may be especially good candidates for this approach to engineering specificity.

There are at least two distinct families of serine proteases, the "subtilisin-like" and "trypsin-like," which evolved the catalytic triad from two entirely separate genes (Stroud *et al.*, 1977). It is highly unlikely that the precise positioning of the catalytic triad (Ser-His-Asp) evolved in one step but more likely involved intermediates. Model building from a complex between bovine pancreatic trypsin inhibitor (BPTI) and bovine trypsin shows a His side chain substituted at the equivalent P2 position (Cys[14]) of BPTI can be reasonably superimposed upon the catalytic histidine (Color Plate XXV). Moreover, the dihedral angles, hydrogen bond angle, and relevant distances between the Nδ1 and Nε2 imidazoyl nitrogens from the enzyme or P2 substrate histidines to the catalytic Asp[102] and Ser[195] are reasonable (Table 3, model T1). Constraining χ_1 and χ_2 to ideality (Table 3, model T2) or rotating the His P2 through 180° (to pair the Nδ1 with Ser[195] and Nε2 with Asp[102]) gives less favorable hydrogen bond distances, angles, and steric contacts.

Model building and experimental data presented above show that the function of the catalytic histidine in subtilisin can be partially replaced by a His side chain from the P2 position of the substrate. We suggest that similar experiments in the trypsin family of proteases may yield similar results. There is no compelling mechanistic reason why a His at the P2 position should be so poised in close proximity to the catalytic histidine in two convergently evolved enzymes. Instead, we speculate that this could represent an evolutionary vestige of when serine proteases operated by substrate-assisted catalysis.

Nature provides a possible example of a serine protease in which the catalytic base is donated from another molecule. In the autoproteolytic maturation of the human rhinovirus coat protein VP0 to VP2 and VP4, it has been proposed that an RNA base acts as a proton acceptor-donor by inserting between a catalytic serine and carboxylate (Rossmann *et al.*, 1985; Arnold *et al.*, 1987). It is plausible that enzymes may evolve by taking maximal

Table 3. Pertinent bond angles and distances modeled for substrate-assisted catalysis by a His P2 side chain in subtilisin or trypsin as described in Figs. 1 and 4, respectively. Dihedral angles for the His side chains are defined by χ_1 (N–Cα–Cβ–Cγ) and χ_2 (Cα–Cβ–Cγ–Cδ). The hydrogen bond angles [Oγ(Ser)–Hδ(Ser)–Nϵ2(His)] were calculated from the measured Cβ(Ser)–Oγ(Ser)–Nϵ2(His) angle, the Nϵ2(His)–Oγ(Ser) distance and the known Oγ(Ser)–Hδ(Ser) distance (0.96 Å) and the Cβ(Ser)–Oγ(Ser)–Hδ(Ser) bond angle (108.5°) (Weiner et al., 1984). The hydrogen bond angles Nδ1(His)–Hϵ(His)–Oδ2(Asp) were measured after positioning Hϵ(His) in the structure using the known distances: Cγ(His)–Nϵ2(His) (1.39 Å), Cϵ(His)–Nϵ2(His) (1.34 Å) and Nϵ2(His)–Hϵ(His) (1.01 Å) and the known angles Cϵ(His)–Nϵ2(His)–Hϵ(His) (125.35°), Cγ(His)–Nϵ2(His)–Hϵ(His) (126.35°) (Weiner et al., 1984). Hydrogen bond distances were measured from the catalytic Ser (Oγ) and Asp (Oδ1 and Oδ2) to the Nϵ2 and Nδ1, respectively, of the enzyme His or the substrate His P2. The distances are given between the enzyme His and the modeled substrate His P2 Nϵ2 and Nδ1 nitrogens. Model 1 (shown in Figs. 1 and 4 for subtilisin and trypsin, respectively) has the His P2 side chain optimized for hydrogen bond distances between the imidazoyl nitrogens, Nϵ2 and Nδ1, to the catalytic Ser and Asp, respectively. Model 2 has idealized χ angles for the His P2 side chain. Molecular dynamics and energy minimization procedures were not applied to any of these models.

| | Angles | | | | Distances (Å) | | | | |
| | Dihedral | | H bonds | | Nϵ2(His) →Oγ(Ser) | Nδ1(His) → | | Catalytic His → His P2 | |
	χ_1	χ_2	(Ser → His)	(His → Asp)		Oδ1(Asp) or	Oδ2(Asp)	Nϵ2/Nϵ2	Nδ1/Nδ1
Subtilisin									
Catalytic His[64] (actual)	−167°	85°	148°	156°	3.17	3.34	2.72		
His P2 side chain									
Model S1	−164°	−50°	149°	98°	3.17	3.55	2.72	1.39	1.35
Model S2	−180°	−90°	144°	84°	3.25	3.59	3.34	0.37	1.57
Trypsin									
Catalytic His[57] (actual)	71°	85°	170°	129°	2.70	3.25	2.70		
His P2 side chain									
Model T1	−155°	−79°	179°	83°	2.78	4.78	3.28	0.98	2.10
Model T2	−180°	−90°	158°	122°	2.48	5.09	3.76	0.58	2.09

advantage of catalytic groups present in their environment, whether located on a co-factor or on the substrate. Some enzymes may remain dependent upon substrate functional group(s), perhaps because the enzymes are too "young," or the substrate functional group(s) cannot be adequately mimicked by an amino acid side chain (or a posttranslational modification thereof) of the enzyme, or because it serves an important regulatory function. Other enzymes, such as the serine proteases, may eventually dispense with the requirement for a substrate functional group because the latter can be adequately replaced by its own amino acid side chain allowing the enzyme to relax substrate specificity.

Acknowledgments

We thank J. Burnier for synthetic peptides, peptide substrates, and helpful discussions, R. Bott for providing crystallographic data prior to publication and help with computer graphics, M. Winkler for helpful discussions, B. Nivens for technical assistance with amino acid analysis, the organic chemistry department at Genentech for oligonucleotide synthesis, W. Anstine for manuscript preparation, and colleagues at Genentech and Genencor for support and encouragement. P. C. is on leave of absence from Gonville and Caius College, Cambridge, UK.

References

Arnold, E., *et al.*, *Proc. Natl. Acad. Sci. U.S.A.* **84**, 21 (1987).

Carter, P., *Biochem. J.* **237**, 1 (1986).

Carter, P., H. Bedouelle, G. Winter, *Nucleic Acids Res.* **13**, 4331 (1986).

Craik, C. S., *et al.*, *Science* **228**, 291 (1985).

Cronin, C. N., B. A. Malcolm, J. F. Kirsh, *J. Am. Chem. Soc.* **109**, 2222 (1987).

Deisenhofer, J., and W. Steigemann, *Acta Crystallogr. B.* **31**, 238 (1975).

Del Mar, E. G., C. Largman, J. W. Brodrick, M. C. Goekas, *Anal. Biochem.* **99**, 316 (1979).

Estell, D. A., *et al.*, *Science* **233**, 659 (1986).

Fersht, A. R., *et al.*, *Nature (London)* **314**, 235 (1985).

Glazer, A. N., *J. Biol. Chem.* **242**, 433 (1967).

Gutfreund, H., and J. M. Sturtevant, *Biochem. J.* **63**, 656 (1956).

Jones, T. A., *J. Appl. Crystallogr.* **11**, 268 (1978).

Kraut, J., *Annu. Rev. Biochem.* **46**, 331 (1977).

Klapper, M. H., *Biochem. Biophys. Res. Commun.* **78**, 1018 (1977).

Laemmli, U. K., *Nature (London)* **227**, 680 (1970).

Matsubara, H., C. B. Kaspar, D. M. Brown, E. L. Smith, *J. Biol. Chem.* **240**, 1125 (1965).

Miller, J. H., in *Experiments in Molecular Genetics* (Cold Spring Harbor Laboratory, Cold Spring Harbor, NY, 1972).

Morrissey, J. H., *Anal. Biochem.* **117**, 307 (1981).

Murali, C., and E. M. Creaser, *Prot. Eng.* **1**, 55 (1986).

Ottesen, M., and I. Svendsen, in *Methods in Enzymology*, C. Perleman, Ed. (Academic Press, New York, 1970), vol. 19, p. 199.

Philipp, M., and M. L. Bender, *Mol. Cell. Biochem.* **51**, 5 (1983).

Power, S. D., R. M. Adams, J. A. Wells, *Proc. Natl. Acad. Sci. U.S.A.* **83**, 3096 (1986).

Rossmann, M. G., *et al.*, *Nature (London)* **317**, 145 (1985).

Sanger, F., S. Nicklen, A. R. Coulson, *Proc. Natl. Acad. Sci. U.S.A.* **74**, 5463 (1977).

Schechter, I., and A. Berger, *Biochem. Biophys. Res. Commun.* **27**, 157 (1967).

Smith, M., *Annu. Rev. Genet.* **19**, 423 (1985).

Stroud, R. M., M. Krieger, R. E. Koeppe, A. A. Kossiakoff, J. L. Chambers, in *Proteases and Biological Control*, E. Reich, D. B. Rifkin, E. Shaw, Eds. (Cold Spring Harbor Laboratory, Cold Spring Harbor, NY, 1975), p. 13.

Svendsen, I., *Carlsberg Res. Commun.* **41**, 237 (1976).

Thomas, P. G., A. J. Russell, A. R. Fersht, *Nature (London)* **318**, 375 (1985).

Weiner, S. J., *et al.*, *J. Am. Chem. Soc.* **106**, 765 (1984).

Wells, J. A., and D. B. Powers, *J. Biol. Chem.* **261**, 6564 (1986).

Wells, J. A., B. C. Cunningham, T. P. Graycar, D. A. Estell, *Philos. Trans. R. Soc. London, Ser. A* **317**, 415 (1986).

———, *Proc. Natl. Acad. Sci. U.S.A.* **84**, 5167 (1987a).

Wells, J. A., E. Ferrari, D. J. Henner, D. A. Estell, E. Y. Chen, *Nucleic Acids Res.* **11**, 7911 (1983).

Wells, J. A., D. B. Powers, R. R. Bott, T. P. Graycar, D. A. Estell, *Proc. Natl. Acad. Sci. U.S.A.* **84**, 1219 (1987b).

Winther, J. R., M. C. Kielland-Brandt, K. Breddam, *Carlsberg Res. Commun.* **50**, 273 (1985).

Yang, M. Y., E. Ferrari, D. J. Henner, *J. Bacteriol.* **160**, 15 (1984).

31

Use of Gene Fusions to Study Membrane Protein Topology

Dana Boyd, Colin Manoil, Susan Froshauer, Jose-Luis San Millan
Neil Green, Karen McGovern, Catherine Lee, Jon Beckwith

This chapter describes a genetic approach to analyzing membrane protein topology in which a sensor protein, alkaline phosphatase or β-galactosidase, is fused to cytoplasmic or external domains of a membrane protein. The properties of the sensor protein differ, depending on the kind of domain to which it is fused. In this way, the position of hydrophilic domains can be determined. The approach has been used successfully with three proteins of known topology, Tsr, MotB, and leader peptidase. Analysis of the MalF protein by this approach has not only yielded information on its topology but also has revealed an important role in determining structure for the charged amino acids in hydrophilic domains.

Integral membrane proteins can span the lipid bilayer many times. For instance, bacterial rhodopsin, a cytoplasmic membrane protein, contains seven hydrophobic transmembrane stretches tightly packed together (Leifer and Henderson, 1983). Bacterial membrane proteins of this sort also contain a series of hydrophilic domains, alternatingly protruding into the cytoplasm and the periplasmic space. Determining the arrangement of this class of proteins in the membrane is essential for the study of the relationship between their structure and function and for studying the mechanism of their incorporation into the membrane.

Gene Fusions and Membrane Protein Topology

We have described a genetic approach to analyzing the arrangement of integral membrane proteins in the lipid bilayer (Manoil and Beckwith, 1986). In this approach, we use the technique of gene fusion to attach sensor proteins to various portions of the membrane protein. These sensor proteins have properties that allow us to distinguish whether they are attached to a cytoplasmic or to a periplasmic domain of the membrane protein.

One of the proteins used in such fusion studies is *E. coli* alkaline phosphatase. Alkaline phosphatase, when localized to the cytoplasm, can not assemble into active enzyme; however, the protein is enzymatically active in the periplasmic space, its normal location (Michaelis *et al.*, 1983). Thus, when alkaline phosphatase is fused to a cytoplasmic domain of a membrane protein, it is inactive; when it is fused to a periplasmic domain, it is active (Fig. 1).

A sensor protein with different properties is found in β-galactosidase (Fig. 2). This enzyme is normally localized to the cytoplasm. When a protein export signal is attached to β-galactosidase, initiation of the export process results in the protein becoming embedded in the cytoplasmic membrane (Beck-

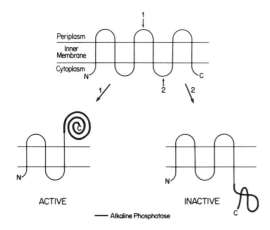

Fig. 1. Fusions of alkaline phosphatase to an hypothetical membrane protein.

with and Ferro-Novick, 1986). In this location, β-galactosidase can not assemble into active enzyme. As a result, when β-galactosidase is fused to periplasmic domains of a membrane protein, it has low enzymatic activity; when fused to cytoplasmic domains, it is highly active (Froshauer *et al.*, 1988). Together, these two sensor proteins provide a new approach to studying the topology of membrane proteins.

There are both in vivo and in vitro approaches to generating fusions of alkaline phosphatase and β-galactosidase to other proteins. In the cases described here, the fusions are obtained such that the amino-terminus of the sensor protein is replaced by amino-terminal sequences of the target protein. Many of our alkaline phosphatase fusions are obtained in vivo using the transposon, Tn*phoA* (Manoil and Beckwith, 1985). When

this transposon inserts into a gene in the proper orientation and proper reading frame, it creates a gene fusion between alkaline phosphatase and the gene product. A linker of 17 amino acids between the two proteins is coded for by a sequence of bases at the end of the transposon (Fig. 3).

It is important to note that in all of these fusions, the sensor protein is *replacing* the carboxy-terminal portion of the target protein. This aspect of our analysis places a limitation on the interpretation of results. Our ability to distinguish periplasmic and cytoplasmic domains depends on the assumption that amino-terminal portions of the protein are sufficient to direct localization of the carboxy-terminal sensor protein in the same fashion as with the native protein. Our results so far suggest that this assumption may be true in many cases. However, as discussed below, we also find cases where the absence of carboxy-terminal sequences does alter the pattern of membrane protein assembly.

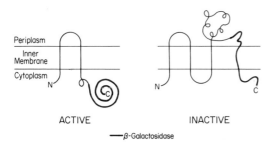

Fig. 2. Fusions of β-galactosidase to a cytoplasmic domain and a periplasmic domain of a membrane protein

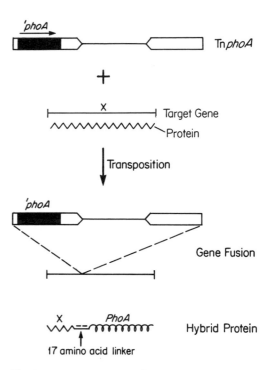

Fig. 3. Transposition of Tn*phoA* into a structural gene for a protein.

Alkaline Phosphatase Fusions to Membrane Proteins

Tsr protein

The alkaline phosphatase fusion approach has been tested on several proteins, the topology of which was established by other techniques. The first such protein to be studied was the Tsr protein of *E. coli*, a chemoreceptor involved in the process of chemotaxis (Manoil and Beckwith, 1986). The arrangement of this protein in the cytoplasmic membrane had been previously deduced from several lines of evidence (Fig. 4). We isolated alkaline phosphatase fusions to this protein using Tn*phoA*. Nine fusions with high alkaline phosphatase activity all had their fusion joints within or very close to the periplasmic domain of the protein. Seven fusions with much lower activity (2–3 percent of high-activity fusions) had their fusion joints in the cytoplasmic domain.

Several points emerge from the studies with Tsr protein. First, there is a strict correlation between the domain of the protein to which alkaline phosphatase is fused and the level of enzymatic activity. At least for this membrane protein of simple structure, the properties of fusions correctly predict the topology. Secondly, fusions to cytoplasmic domains, while quite low in activity, did still exhibit some level of alkaline phosphatase enzymatic activity. This is a result we have found consistently in all our studies with membrane proteins. Even though alkaline phosphatase may be fused to a cytoplasmic domain of a membrane protein, as long as that domain is preceded by a transmembrane segment, there is always a residual level of enzymatic activity.

This activity is due to a small fraction of the alkaline phosphatase that crosses the cytoplasmic membrane, not to a residual activity of the cytoplasmically localized form of the protein. This we have shown in several cases by fractionation and proteolysis studies, demonstrating that the enzymatic activity is always found on the periplasmic face of the membrane (Lee and Boyd, in preparation). Thus, the hybrid proteins represent a heterogeneous population of molecules; the major

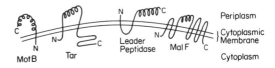

Fig. 4. Actual or proposed topological structure of membrane proteins analyzed by the gene fusion approach.

portion of the protein is correctly arranged with alkaline phosphatase in the cytoplasm, while, with a small portion of the molecules, alkaline phosphatase is exported to the periplasm.

These results suggest that alkaline phosphatase may not be an entirely neutral sensor protein. Even when anchored to a normally cytoplasmic domain of a membrane protein, the presence of any hydrophobic segments in the sequence of the target protein preceding alkaline phosphatase still allows some export of the latter. In contrast, fusions of alkaline phosphatase to cytoplasmic proteins or to a membrane protein in which all hydrophobic segments are missing give essentially no enzymatic activity (Hoffman and Wright, 1985; Manoil and Beckwith, 1985; Boyd *et al.*, 1987).

Leader peptidase

Leader peptidase is the enzyme responsible for the cleavage of signal sequences from secretory proteins during their traversal of the cytoplasmic membrane (Dalbey and Wickner, 1987). Proteolytic studies carried out with spheroplasts suggest that the topology of this protein in the membrane is the converse of the Tsr protein (Fig. 4). Both proteins have two transmembrane segments. However, Tsr has its amino-terminus protruding into the cytoplasm, while that of leader peptidase may face the periplasm.

Alkaline phosphatase fusions to this protein were obtained by both in vivo and in vitro techniques. Here again, all fusions to the periplasmic domain of the protein had high enzymatic activity (San Millan *et al.*, 1989). Fusions to the cytoplasmic domain had lower activity. In the case of a fusion where alkaline phosphatase followed directly after the end of the cytoplasmic domain, the relative amount of alkaline phosphatase activity was similar to that seen with Tsr cytoplasmic fusions. However, when alkaline phosphatase was fused directly to the first transmembrane segment with none of the cytoplasmic domain present, much higher levels of activity were observed. This difference in activity depending on the position of the fusion joint within the cytoplasmic domain was studied much more systematically in our analysis of the MalF protein, reported on below. We will discuss the implications of those results in conjunction with the MalF studies.

MotB

Studies on the MotB protein were carried out in the laboratory of Sandy Parkinson (Chun and Parkinson, 1988). The gene for MotB was sequenced in 1986, and, from the sequence, a topology for the protein was proposed (Stader *et al.*, 1986). Chun and Parkinson tested this model by using Tn*phoA* to obtain alkaline phosphatase fusions. Among high-activity fusions, many were found to lie in a region of the protein thought to be cytoplasmic based on the topological model. The finding suggested that either the model was wrong or that the fusion approach gave incorrect answers. To distinguish between these two explanations, proteolytic studies in spheroplasts were carried out. The results obtained were consistent with the model predicted from the fusion

analysis, not that proposed in the original sequencing paper.

MalF

These studies with three membrane proteins of relatively simple structure suggest that the fusion approach can be used successfully to analyze membrane protein topology. We have extended this analysis to a protein of more complex structure, the MalF protein. MalF is an integral protein of the cytoplasmic membrane, which is a component of the maltose transport system. The amino acid sequence deduced from the DNA sequence suggests that there may be eight transmembrane stretches in the protein (Froshauer and Beckwith, 1984). A model has been presented for the topology of this protein based on its sequence (Fig. 5). However, there is no biochemical evidence for this structure.

In the absence of other evidence, we have obtained both alkaline phosphatase and β-galactosidase fusions to MalF to see whether their properties yield a coherent picture of its topology in the membrane. Alkaline phosphatase fusions to MalF were first obtained using Tn*phoA* (Boyd *et al.*, 1987). We found that most of these fusions, which exhibited high levels of alkaline phosphatase activity, had their fusion joints in only four of the nine hydrophilic domains of the protein. These four hydrophilic domains were those proposed to be periplasmic in our model. Two

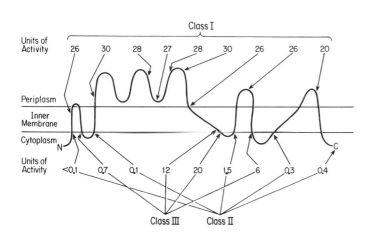

Fig. 5. Activities of alkaline phosphatase fusions to MalF. The potential transmembrane segments all correspond to uncharged and hydrophobic stretches of at least 18 amino acids. Those transmembrane stretches that are drawn at an angle are ones considerably longer than 20 amino acids (Froshauer and Beckwith, 1984).

additional fusions with somewhat lower levels of activity had alkaline phosphatase attached to the end of a transmembrane segment that precedes a domain proposed to be in the cytoplasm. Extensive use of the TnphoA approach failed to yield any additional fusions with end points in proposed cytoplasmic domains.

The failure to find significant numbers of fusions to proposed cytoplasmic domains may be explained in several ways. These are relatively short amino acid sequences and, therefore, the corresponding DNA is a small target for transposon insertion. Since there is some degree of specificity for transposition, either these sequences may not be preferred sites, or most fusions to cytoplasmic domains may have very low alkaline phosphatase activity and, thus, be missed on indicator plates where the fusions are usually detected. (The detection of fusion colonies depends on the expression of enough alkaline phosphatase activity to cleave the indicator dye 5-bromo-3-chloro-indolyl-phosphate, XP, to give a blue color.) To distinguish between these possibilities and to analyze the topology of MalF in a more systematic fashion, we have constructed in vitro a series of fusions of alkaline phosphatase to each of the proposed cytoplasmic domains, of this membrane protein. Furthermore, within each of these domains, we obtained fusions to both the beginning and the end of the hydrophilic sequences.

The results of these fusion studies can be summarized as follows (Fig. 5). Fusions with high alkaline phosphatase activity were obtained in each of the proposed periplasmic domains of MalF (class I). Fusions with junction points at the carboxy-terminal end of each proposed cytoplasmic domain (class II) gave activities 17 to 250 times lower than the average class I fusion. (Fusion A, which includes only the amino-terminal hydrophilic sequence of MalF, produced no detectable enzymatic activity.) These results are quite similar to those obtained with Tsr fusions. However, those strains in which alkaline phosphatase was fused to the end of a transmembrane segment that just preceded a proposed cytoplasmic domain (class III) gave significantly higher activities than class II fusions, although, in most cases, still lower than class I fusions.

These studies have led us to the following tentative conclusions. The topology of MalF is as described in Fig. 5. This conclusion is further supported by the studies described below with β-galactosidase fusions. Alkaline phosphatase is firmly anchored in the cytoplasm when it follows the cytoplasmic domain of a membrane protein. However, when a fusion does not contain any of the cytoplasmic domain, but rather has alkaline phosphatase fused directly to the transmembrane segment that precedes that domain, the sensor protein is exported to the periplasm to a significant extent. It appears that there are amino acid sequences within the cytoplasmic domains that are important for stably holding alkaline phosphatase in the cytoplasm. A possible explanation for these results is suggested by the finding of von Heijne (1986) that cytoplasmic membrane proteins have cytoplasmic domains that are more positively charged than their periplasmic domains. The charge differential around the transmembrane segment could be important in insuring the proper orientation of that segment in the membrane. It may be that transmembrane segments are most stably integrated into the membrane when their net dipole moment is in the opposite direction from that of the cytoplasmic membrane potential. Alternatively (or additionally), the relatively greater difficulty of membrane penetration by positively charged amino acids may impose kinetic constraints on the mode of insertion of transmembrane segments that those amino acids follow (von Heijne, 1986).

Thus, in those alkaline phosphatase fusions where the cytoplasmic sequences, including the positively charged amino acids, are not present, the sensor protein may no longer be stably resident in the cytoplasm. We have recently used oligonucleotide mutagenesis to test this idea and the results suggest that it is, in fact, the net positive charge of the cytoplasmic amino acid sequences that is important in maintaining a cytoplasmic location for alkaline phosphatase (Boyd and Beckwith, 1989).

In a number of these fusions, we have verified that the observed enzymatic activity of alkaline phosphatase corresponds to alkaline phosphatase exported to the periplasm. Furthermore, we have shown that the lower activity fusions exhibit a slower kinetics of alkaline phosphatase translocation across the membrane (Lee and Boyd, in preparation).

Another factor that plays a role in the amount of alkaline phosphatase export seen in different fusions is the linker sequence, which joins the sensor protein to the target protein (Fig. 3). We note that this sequence has a net negative charge of two. These charges may contribute to a reduction in the stability of cytoplasmic anchoring of alkaline phosphatase in certain of the fusion strains. We are currently using in vitro mutagenesis to eliminate one of these positive charges in order to see if this altered Tn*phoA* has different properties.

SecY

A similar study to the one described above has been done with another complex membrane protein, SecY (Akiyama and Ito, 1987). In this case, the properties of alkaline phosphatase fusions obtained in vivo presented a consistent pattern, allowing the formulation of a topological model.

β-Galactosidase Fusions to MalF

We have obtained a series of fusions of β-galactosidase to the MalF protein, using both in vivo and in vitro techniques (Froshauer *et al.*, 1988; K. McGovern and J. Beckwith, unpublished results). These include fusions to three of the four proposed periplasmic domains and to or near each of the proposed cytoplasmic domains. The β-galactosidase enzymatic activities of these fusions are shown in Fig. 6. A pattern complementary to that seen with alkaline phosphatase fusions emerges. Fusions to the proposed periplasmic domains give activities considerably lower than the

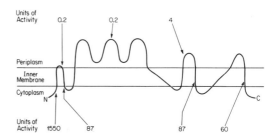

Fig. 6. Activities of β-galactosidase fusions to MalF. Except for the fusion with 1550 units of β-galactosidase activity, all hybrid proteins are made in similar amounts. The higher activity of this earliest fusion represents a comparably higher level of synthesis of the hybrid protein. This difference in levels of synthesis is related to a still not understood regulatory phenomenon which involves sites within the *malF* gene (Froshauer *et al.*, 1988).

cytoplasmic fusions. We assume that the higher activity fusion proteins have β-galactosidase attached to a cytoplasmic domain in such a way that the entire amino acid sequence of the sensor protein is in the cytoplasm. In this location, the protein can assume its proper conformation, including tetramerization, required for enzymatic activity. Proteolysis studies with 102, one of the fusions to a presumed periplasmic domain, show that some portion of the β-galactosidase molecule is protruding into the periplasm. Various lines of evidence suggest that hybrid proteins of this sort have a part of the β-galactosidase molecule stuck in the membrane (Fig. 2). In this location, the protein is unable to assemble into an active conformation.

We interpret these results as supporting the topological model for MalF derived from studies on alkaline phosphatase fusions.

Summary

We and others have shown that the gene fusion approach gives the correct topology for proteins whose arrangement in the membrane has been studied by other means. These proteins are the Tsr protein, leader peptidase, and the MotB protein. We have extended this analysis to a complex membrane protein, MalF, for which no other evidence exists indicating its topology. The alkaline phosphatase and the β-galactosidase fusion studies suggest the same topological structure. Currently, we are using other approaches to study some of the structural features of the intact MalF protein to determine if this way of analyzing membrane protein topology is applicable to such a complex protein. Certainly, at this point, the model for MalF topology must be considered tentative until additional evidence is obtained. However, if this model is shown to be correct, it will strongly support the utility of this approach.

It is perhaps surprising that the gene fusion approach does work to the extent shown already. First, all fusion proteins are missing carboxy-terminal sequences of the target protein. Yet the hybrid proteins appear to be arranged in the membrane in the same way as the native protein. One might have expected that the assembly of these proteins in the membrane would depend on interactions between different domains. If this were the case, separating amino-terminal from carboxy-terminal domains of the protein could conceivably result in completely aberrant structures. Since, so far, this does not seem to be generally the case, it suggests that the signals for proper assembly of the proteins into the membrane for each domain can act independently of sequences carboxy-terminal to them. However, it may be that in the native proteins both amino-terminal and carboxy-terminal signals contribute to topogenesis by ensuring the most efficient assembly and maximum stability.

It is not entirely the case that different domains of membrane proteins are assembled independently. We describe fusions of alkaline phosphatase to the cytoplasmic end of transmembrane segments of leader peptidase and MalF, which have unexpected properties. In the absence of the sequence of amino acids located in the cytoplasmic loop following such transmembrane segments, the alkaline phosphatase is not stably anchored in the cytoplasm. From a mutational study, we have obtained evidence that it is the positively charged amino acids in the cytoplasmic loop that are essential in keeping alkaline phosphatase in the cytoplasm. So, in this case, we have disrupted the normal structure of the protein by separating amino-terminal domains (the trans-membrane segment) from carboxy-terminal domains (the cytoplasmic loops).

The results suggest that these positively charged amino acids are important in determining the stable orientation of transmembrane segments, as von Heijne (1986) has proposed. Thus, the hydrophobic sequence and the adjacent basic residues may act together as a topological determinant. Fusions with end points within this determinant may give ambiguous or misleading results. However, as shown in these studies, further investigation of these results can lead to new insights into the mechanism of membrane protein assembly.

A second, perhaps surprising aspect of the success of the gene fusion technique is that alkaline phosphatase and β-galactosidase, both of which require oligomerization of the original gene product to achieve activity, can oligomerize when attached to membrane proteins. However, it is not unreasonable to think that membrane fluidity might allow efficient interaction between monomers in the membrane. In the case of alkaline phosphatase fusions, there is a linker sequence of 17 amino acids between it and the target protein, possibly allowing considerable flexibility.

While we believe that the gene fusion approach is of great utility in studying membrane protein topology, there are several cautions to be kept in mind. As pointed out above, separating amino-terminal from carboxy-terminal domains may, in some cases, disrupt the structure. Then, the fusion approach, in the absence of more detailed studies, could give incorrect answers. In addition, many membrane proteins, including MalF (Treptow and Shuman, 1985), interact with other proteins in complexes in the membrane. Those interactions may, in some cases, alter the topology of the protein. The fusion approach might then give a picture of the arrangement that the protein would take in the membrane if it were isolated from its compatriots, but this would not represent an accurate description of the protein when functionally part of a complex.

If the rates of insertion of the parts of a membrane protein play a crucial role in the determination of topological structure, properties of the sensor proteins could interfere with proper assembly. We know from our studies with fusions to MalF that the rate of translocation of alkaline phosphatase depends on the portion of MalF to which it is fused. We suspect that rates of insertion may be critical in the analysis of β-galactosidase fusions. If β-galactosidase were fused to a "slow" (in the kinetic sense) export signal, enough time may elapse before translocation to allow the enzyme to fold into a stable native structure in the cytoplasm. β-galactosidase, in this form, may not follow the export signal into the membrane. In this case, the fusion would exhibit high enzymatic activity and would appear to define a cytoplasmic domain. A mistaken conclusion would be drawn. While we do not know directly of any examples of this sort, this possibility should be kept in mind in such topological analyses. The issue probably does not arise in the case of alkaline phosphatase, since this protein does not appear to fold into a native structure in the cytoplasm (Michaelis *et al.*, 1986).

For the proteins we have examined so far, the gene fusion studies suggest a simple two-stage picture of how they assemble in the membrane. This picture is, in part, analogous to that proposed by Blobel (1980). Topological information may be read initially in a linear fashion. A hydrophobic stretch preceded by a cytoplasmic positively charged amino terminus may function as an export signal-promoting transfer of the following hydrophilic segment. A subsequent hydrophobic sequence followed by basic residues would be stably anchored in the membrane with its carboxy-terminus in the cytoplasm. This would allow the third hydrophobic stretch to function as an export signal for the next portion of the protein.

The unstable cytoplasmic localization of alkaline phosphatase in certain fusions, as revealed by slow kinetics of export, may reflect processes occurring in the native protein. If this is the case, then kinetic constraints may determine the correct topological structure prior to stable folding. In this view, the two classes of topological determinants exert their effects simply by influencing the rates of export of the various parts of the protein. Final folding into a structure stabilized by protein-protein interactions may then follow after the topological arrangement has been achieved. Despite the likelihood that the fusion technique will disrupt protein-protein interactions, the technique appears to reveal the correct topology. Therefore, it may be that protein-lipid interactions are primarily responsible for the kinetic factors that determine topology.

Acknowledgments

This work was supported by grants from the National Science Foundation, American Cancer Society and National Institutes of Health to J. B., C. M., and N. G. were supported by Arthritis Foundation Fellowships and C. L. by a Medical Foundation Fellowship.

References

Akiyama, Y., and K. Ito, *EMBO J.* **6**, 3465 (1987).

Beckwith, J., and S. Ferro-Novick, *Current Topics in Microbiology and Immunology* **125**, 5 (1986).

Blobel, G., *Proc. Natl. Acad. Sci. U.S.A.* **77**, 1496 (1980).

Boyd, D., and J. Beckwith, *Proc. Natl. Acad. Sci. U.S.A.* **86**, 9446(1989).

Boyd, D., *et al.*, *Proc. Natl. Acad. Sci. U.S.A.* **84**, 8525 (1987).

Chun, S. Y., and J. S. Parkinson, *Science* **239**, 276 (1988).

Dalbey, R. E., and W. Wickner, *Science* **235**, 783 (1987).

Froshauer, S., and J. Beckwith, *J. Biol. Chem.* **259**, 10896 (1984).

Froshauer, S., N. Green, D. Boyd, K. McGovern, J. Beckwith, *J. Mol. Biol.* **200**, 501 (1988).

Hoffman, C., and A. Wright, *Proc. Natl. Acad. Sci. U.S.A.* **82**, 5107 (1985).

Lee, C., and D. Boyd, in preparation.

Leifer, D. and R. Henderson, *J. Mol. Biol.* **163**, 451 (1983).

Manoil, *Proc. Natl. Acad. Sci. U.S.A.* **82**, 8129 (1985).

_____, and J. Beckwith, *Science* **233**, 1403 (1986).

Michaelis, S., J. Hunt, J. Beckwith, *J. Bacteriol.* **167**, 160 (1986).

Michaelis, S., H. Inouye, D. Oliver, J. Beckwith, *J. Bacteriol.* **154**, 366 (1983).

San Millan, J.-L., D. Boyd, R. Dalbey, W. Wickner, J. Beckwith, *J. Bacteriol.* **171**, 5536 (1989).

Stader, J., P. Matsumura, D. Vacante, G. E. Dean, R. C. Macnab, *J. Bacteriol.* **166**, 244 (1986).

Treptow, N. A., and H. A. Shuman, *J. Bacteriol.* **163**, 654 (1985).

von Heijne, G. *EMBO J.* **5**, 3021 (1986).

List of Authors

Stephen Anderson, *Rutgers University, Center for Advanced Biotechnology and Medicine, Piscataway, NJ*

Padmanabhan Balaram, *Molecular Biophysics Unit, Indian Institute of Science, Bangalore, India*

Robert L. Baldwin, *Department of Biochemistry, Beckman Center, Stanford University, Stanford, CA*

Donald Bashford, *Molecular Biology Department, Research Institute of Scripps Clinic, La Jolla, CA*

Jon Beckwith, *Department of Microbiology and Molecular Genetics, Harvard Medical School, Boston, MA*

Benjamin R. Bowen, *Department of Chemistry, Massachusetts Institute of Technology, Cambridge, MA*

Dana Boyd, *Department of Molecular and Cell Biology, University of California, Berkeley, CA*

David N. Brems, *Lilly Corporate Center, Eli Lilly & Co., Inc., Indianapolis, IN*

Barbara Brodsky, *Department of Biochemistry, University of Medicine and Dentistry of New Jersey, Robert Wood Johnson Medical School, Piscataway, NJ*

Robert E. Bruccoleri, *Squibb Institute for Medical Research, Princeton, NJ*

Peter H. Byers, *Department of Pathology, University of Washington, Seattle, WA*

Paul Carter, *Genentech, Inc., South San Francisco, CA*

Fred Cohen, *Department of Pharmaceutical Chemistry, University of California, San Francisco, CA*

William Cover, *Merck Chemical Manufacturing Division, Merck & Co., Inc., Elkton, VA*

Thomas E. Creighton, *Laboratory of Molecular Biology, Medical Research Council, University Medical School, Cambridge, England*

William F. DeGrado, *E. I. du Pont de Nemours and Company, Central Research and Development Department, Wilmington, DE*

H. Jane Dyson, *Department of Molecular Biology, Research Institute of Scripps Clinic, La Jolla, CA*

Bentley A. Fane, *Department of Biology, University of California, La Jolla, CA*

Jacquelyn Fetrow, *Whitehead Institute, Cambridge, MA*

Susan Froshauer, *Pfizer Central Research, Groton, CT*

Lila M. Gierasch, *Department of Pharmacology, University of Texas, Health Science Center, Dallas, TX*

Michel E. Goldberg, *Unité de Biochimie des Régulations Cellulaires, Institut Pasteur, Paris, France*

Antonio M. Gotto, Jr., *Department of Medicine, Baylor College of Medicine, The Methodist Hospital, Houston, TX*

Neil Green, *Department of Biochemistry, School of Medicine, University of California, San Francisco. CA*

Lydia M. Gregoret, *Department of Pharmaceutical Chemistry, School of Pharmacy, University of California, San Francisco, CA*

Cameron Haase-Pettingell, *Biology Department, Massachusetts Institute of Technology, Cambridge, MA*

Edgar Haber, *The Squibb Institute for Medical Research, Princeton, NJ*

Siew Peng Ho, *E. I. du Pont de Nemours and Company, Central Research and Development Department, Wilmington, DE*

Alfred Holtzer, *Department of Chemistry, Washington University, St. Louis, MO*

Marilyn Emerson Holtzer, *Department of Chemistry, Washington University, St. Louis, MO*

Isabella L. Karle, *Laboratory for the Structure of Matter, Naval Research Laboratory, Washington, DC*

Martin Karplus, *Department of Chemistry, Harvard University, Cambridge, MA*

Daniel S. Kemp, *Department of Chemistry, Massachusetts Institute of Technology, Cambridge, MA*

Peter S. Kim, *Whitehead Institute, Cambridge, MA*

Jonathan A. King, *Department of Biology, Massachusetts Institute of Technology, Cambridge, MA*

Joanna K. Krueger, *Department of Chemistry, Princeton University, Princeton, NJ*

Irwin D. Kuntz, *Department of Pharmaceutical Chemistry, University of California, San Francisco, CA*

Catherine Lee, *Department of Microbiology and Immunology, Stanford University Medical School, Stanford, CA*

Richard A. Lerner, *Department of Molecular Biology, Research Institute of Scripps Clinic, La Jolla, CA*

Gseping Liu, *Biochemistry/Biophysics Program, Washington State University, Pullman, WA*

Colin Manoil, *Department of Genetics, University of Washington, Seattle, WA*

Susan Marqusee, *Department of Biology, Massachusetts Institute of Technology, Cambridge, MA*

C. Robert Matthews, *Department of Chemistry, The Pennsylvania State University, University Park, PA*

Karen McGovern, *Department of Microbiology and Molecular Genetics, Harvard Medical School, Boston, MA*

Anna Mitraki, *Department of Biology, Massachusetts Institute of Technology, Cambridge, MA*

Barry T. Nall, *Department of Biochemistry, University of Texas Health Science Center, San Antonio, TX*

Björn Nilsson, *Department of Biochemistry, Royal Institute of Technology, Stockholm, Sweden*

Jiri Novotny, *Squibb Institute for Medical Research, Princeton, NJ*

Terrence G. Oas, *Whitehead Institute for Biomedical Research, Cambridge, MA*

Soonhee Park, *Cell Biology Laboratory, Korea Institute of Science and Technology, Seoul, Korea*

Scott R. Presnell, *Department of Pharmaceutical Chemistry, University of California, San Francisco, CA*

Leonard Presta, *Department of Biomolecular Chemistry, Genentech, Inc., South San Francisco, CA*

Linda L. Randall, *Biochemistry and Biophysics Program, Washington State University, Pullman, WA*

Lynne Regan, *Medical Research Council, Molecular Genetics Unit, Cambridge, England*

Jane S. Richardson, *Duke University Medical Center, Durham, NC*

David C. Richardson, *Duke University Medical Center, Durham, NC*

George Rose, *Department of Biological Chemistry, College of Medicine, The Pennsylvania State University, Hershey, PA*

Jose-Luis San Millan, *Unidad de Genetica Molecular, Servicio de Microbiologia, Hospital Ramon y Cajal, Madrid, Spain*

Clarence E. Schutt, *Department of Biology and Chemistry, Princeton University, Princeton, NJ*

Jeffrey Skolnick, *Scripps Clinic and Research Foundation, Molecular Biology Department, La Jolla, CA*

Larry L. Smarr, *National Center for Supercomputing Applications, University of Illinois at Urbana-Champaign, Champaign, IL*

James T. Sparrow, *Department of Medicine, Baylor College of Medicine, The Methodist Hospital, Houston, TX*

Ann M. Stock, *Molecular Biology Department, Princeton University, Princeton, NJ*

Jeffry B. Stock, *Biology Department, Princeton University, Princeton, NJ*

Martha M. Teeter, *Department of Chemistry, Boston College, Chestnut Hill, MA*

Traci B. Topping, *Biochemistry/Biophysics Program, Washington State University, Pullman, WA*

Dan W. Urry, *Laboratory of Molecular Biophysics, University of Alabama at Birmingham, Birmingham, AL*

Robert Villafane, *Department of Microbiology, University of Tennessee-Knoxville, Knoxville, TN*

Jonathan P. Waltho, *Department of Molecular Biology Research Institute of Scripps Clinic, La Jolla, CA*

Zelda Wasserman, *E. I. du Pont de Nemours and Company, Central Research and Development Department, Wilmington, DE*

David L. Weaver, *Department of Physics, Tufts University, Medford, MA*

James A. Wells, *Department of Biomolecular Chemistry, Genentech, Inc., South San Francisco, CA*

Peter E. Wright, *Department of Molecular Biology, Research Institute of Scripps Clinic, La Jolla, CA*

Myong-Hee Yu, *Genetic Engineering Center, Korea Institute of Science and Technology, Seoul, Korea*

Color Plates

Plate I. (A) A pair of origami flowers, in two traditional folds (Gray and Kasahara, 1977). (B) The two similar domains of γ crystallin (Blundell *et al.*, 1981).

Plate II. (A) An origami lobster (Honda, 1959) and the triangular piece of paper from which it is folded. (B) The three-dimensional structure of bovine pancreatic trypsin inhibitor or BPTI (Wlodawer *et al.*, 1984), with a ribbon following its backbone (Carson and Bugg, 1986) and side chains as stick figures. At the bottom is the amino acid sequence (in one-letter code) from which BPTI folds up.

Plate III. (A) An origami kitten (Honda, 1959) made from one black and one gray part, which are folded separately. Many additional multipart origami pieces are described in Kasahara (1988). (B) p-hydroxy benzoate hydroxylase (Schreuder *et al.*, 1988), with its three domains colored.

Plate IV. (A) Two positions of an eight-part origami figure that can make a concerted transition between a ring and a pinwheel shape (Gray and Kasahara, 1977). (B) The four domains in the F_{AB} portion of an immunoglobulin molecule (Saul *et al.*, 1978), which can undergo hinge motions both between the top and bottom halves shown here and between this part and the F_C part of the immunoglobulin.

Plate V. (A) Two different origami swans (Grimm, 1987; Montroll, 1985). Still other swan folds can be found in Honda (1959) and in Kasahara (1988). (B) A superposition of active site Ser, His, and Asp residues (in the center) for the convergently related serine proteases trypsin (Bode, 1975) in pink and subtilisin (Alden *et al.*, 1971) in blue.

Plate VI. A three-step illustration of how the paper is turned inside-out in making the traditional "petal fold" (Montroll, 1979).

Plate VII. Steps in folding an origami swan (Grimm, 1987). The character of the bird appears only at the final step when the head is formed.

Plate VIII. (A) Four different origami figures that have been unfolded to show the pattern of creases. (B) The amino acid sequence of staphylococcal nuclease, laid out to show hydrophobic (red) versus hydrophilic (green) structures (zigzag for β strands and scallops for α-helices).

Plate IX. (A) The same four origami pieces as in Plate VIII(A), in their folded forms (Grimm, 1987; Honda, 1959; Gray and Kasahara, 1977). (B) Backbone ribbon showing the folded structure of staphylococcal nuclease (Arnone *et al.*, 1971), with a ball for the bound Ca^{++} and a stick figure for the thymidine diphosphate inhibitor.

Plate X. An Attic white lekythos, ca. 470–460 B.C., with a Greek key motif around the shoulder. [From the National Museum, Athens.]

Plate XI. Schematic ribbon drawing of Cu,Zn superoxide dismutase (Tainer *et al.*, 1982), showing the eight-stranded barrel of antiparallel β-sheet. [Stained glass by Karen Williams, Alpine, Texas.]

Plate XII. (A) Steps in folding the little cube traditionally called a "balloon" (e.g., Gray and Kasahara, 1977). Its fully three-dimensional nature involves 90° corners. (B) View looking down a β strand; the two surrounding, parallel β strands are at either side, with backbone in blue, carbonyls (CO groups) red, and H bonds yellow. Within the β structure, alternate carbonyls point to the left and to the right, hydrogen bonding within the plane of the sheet. The transitional residue that starts the strand, however, is preceded by a carbonyl that points straight up, perpendicular to the plane of the sheet and to the next CO.

Plate XIII. An α-helix, with backbone in blue, carbonyls (CO groups) in red, and H-bonds in yellow. In the body of the helix all carbonyls point toward the C-terminus and are approximately parallel to each other, while the transitional (N-cap) residue that starts the helix has surrounding carbonyls at right angles.

Plate XIV. Sixteen superimposed examples of Asn in the N-cap position (side chains in yellow), showing that most of them have perpendicular carbonyls and that the side chain Oδ hydrogen bonds to an exposed backbone NH in the first turn of the helix.

Plate XV. λ repressor protein dimer (ribbons) binding to its operator-sequence DNA (blue stick figures). [Coordinates courtesy of Carl Pabo.]

Plate XVI. Superposition of four DNA-binding helix lap-joints (in blue) and four Ca-binding lap-joints (in orange). Note that their chains go in opposite directions (Richardson and Richardson, 1988b).

Plate XVII. (A) Symmetrical, five-pointed origami star folded from an uncut square of paper (Montroll, 1985); (B) Ribbon schematic of the structure expected for felix, a designed four-helix cluster protein.

Plate XVIII. (A) An origami ostrich (Montroll, 1985), a bird with the usual twofold wing structure but without the central function of flight. (B) Ribbon schematic of the structure expected for betabellin, a protein designed to have a twofold β-sheet structure but no function. [Drawing colored by Michael E. Zalis.]

Cover. The aesthetic relationship between (A) an origami wild goose folded from a triangular piece of paper, and (B) the backbone "fold" of a subunit of STNV (satellite tobacco necrosis virus (Jones, 1984), a β-sheet protein which forms trimers that pack together into the icosahedral shell of the virus.

Plate XIX. Stereoview of a typical loop from cytochrome c (residues 40–54).

Plate XX. Typical loops from cytochrome c (residues 40–54) and thermolysin (residues 188–203). (A and B) Space-filling representtion of the cytochrome c loop, with the same orientation as Plate XIX. Backbone atoms are shown in red and side chain atoms in blue. The loop main chain forms an internal cavity that is filled by side chain groups from loop residues. (C and D) Space-filling representation of the thermolysin loop with backbone atoms shown in red and side chain atoms in blue; (C) without the metal ligand, and (D) with the metal ligand, shown in green.

Plate XXI. Stereoview showing clustering of loops in superoxide dismutase.

Plate XXII. A representative α-helix, 12 residues in length, flanked by adjacent turns. Backbone nitrogen atoms are shown in green, backbone oxygen atoms in red. The eight intrahelical N–H · · · O = C hydrogen bonds are indicated by broken lines. N1, N2, N3 are the initial three residues of the helix proper while C3, C2, C1 are the final three residues. Residues N and C have nonhelical dihedral angles but contribute one additional hydrogen bond to the helix. Residues N″, N′, N and C, C′, C ″ are classified with the preceding and succeeding turns, respectively. Hydrogens in the initial four >N–H groups are indicated by stippled green surface; oxygens in the final four >C = O groups are indicated by stippled red surface. These eight groups can not be satisfied by intrahelical main chain partners.

Plate XXIII. A space-filling view of the x-ray structure (left) and the results of our reconstruction (right) for McPC 603. The color code is as follows: The heavy chain framework is in gray. The light chain framework is in white. The heavy chain hypervariable loops—H1, H2, and H3—are in pink, green, and yellow, respectively. The light chain hypervariable loops—L1, L2, and L3—are in blue, red, and orange, respectively. The residues that contact phosphorylcholine, the antigen, are in purple.

Plate XXIV. Stereo view of B. amyloliquefaciens subtilisin (blue) containing a modeled bound peptide substrate (pink) having the sequence L-Phe-L-Ala-L-His-L-Tyr-L-Gly-L-Phe representing residues P4 to P2′ of the substrate (Schechter and Berger, 1967). For model building we used the program FRODO (Jones, 1978) and an Evans and Sutherland PS300 graphics system. The model was based upon a 2.0 Å x-ray crystallographic study of the product complex (NH2-L-Phe-L-Ala-L-Ala-Leu-COOH) bound to subtilisin (R. Bott and M. Ultsch, unpublished data). The Ala P2 side chain was replaced by a His side chain fixing the main chain position and allowing the His side chain dihedral angles to vary (Table 3) (page 312). The catalytic triad (Asp[32], His[64], and Ser[221]) is shown in green with the His P2 side chain from the substrate superimposed upon the catalytic His[64] (model corresponds to model S1 in Table 3).

Plate XXV. Stereo view of a complex (Deisenhofer and Steigemann, 1975) between bovine trypsin (blue) and bovine pancreatic trypsin inhibitor (BPTI) complex (pink) in which the equivalent P2 substrate side chain (Cys[14] in BPTI) is replaced by His and superimposed upon His[57] in trypsin. The main chain position of BPTI remained fixed while the dihedral angles for the His side chain (substituted for Cys[14]) were varied. The catalytic triad of trypsin (Ser[195], His[57], Asp[102]) is shown in green and the carbonyl carbon of Lys[15] at the P1 position in BPTI is labeled (the model corresponds to model T1 in Table 3, page 312). [Coordinates for trypsin-trypsin inhibitor complex taken from the Brookhaven Protein Data Bank entry 2PTC deposited by R. Huber and J. Deisenhofer, September 1982.]

Plate I. (A)

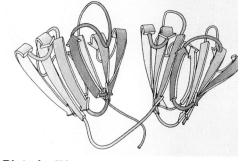

Plate I. (B)

Plate II. (A)

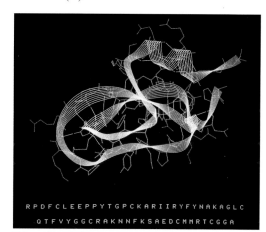

RPDFCLEEPPYTGPCKARIIRYFYNAKAGLC
QTFVYGGCRAKNNFKSAEDCMMRTCGGA

Plate II. (B)

Plate III. (A)

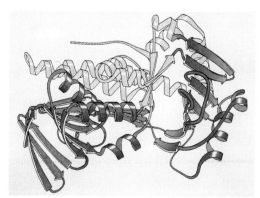

Plate III. (B)

Plate IV. (A)

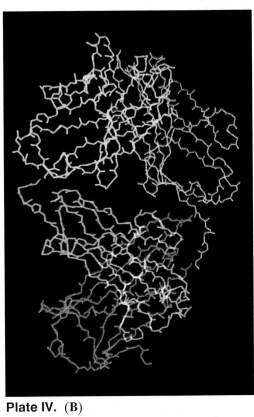

Plate IV. (B)

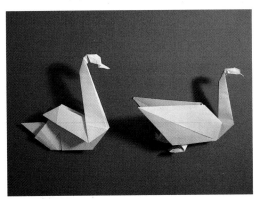

Plate V. (A)

Plate V. (B)

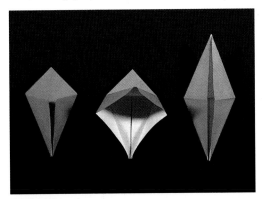

Plate VI.

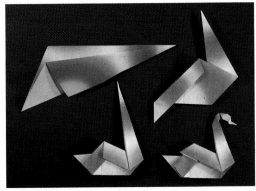

Plate VII.

Plate VIII. (A)

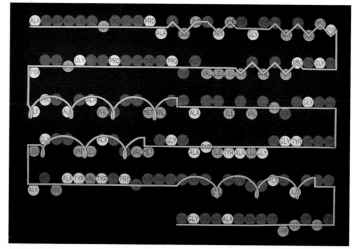

Plate VIII. (B)

Plate IX. (A)

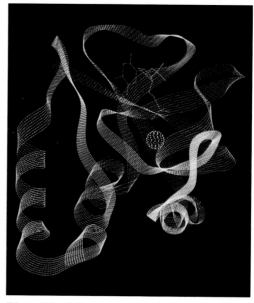

Plate IX. (B)

Plate X.

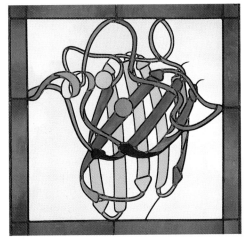

Plate XI.

Plate XII. (A)

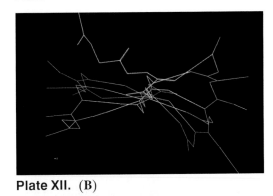

Plate XII. (B)

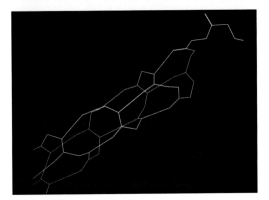

Plate XIII.

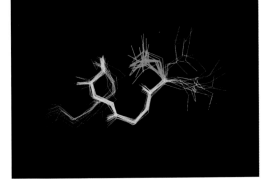

Plate XIV.

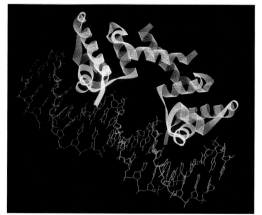

Plate XV.

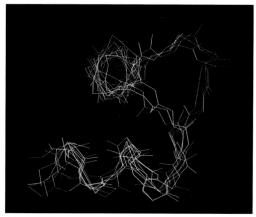

Plate XVI.

Plate XVII. (A)

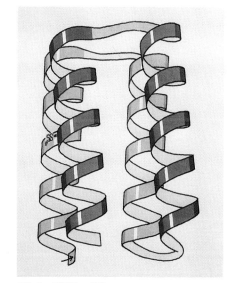

Plate XVII. (B)

Plate XVIII. (A)

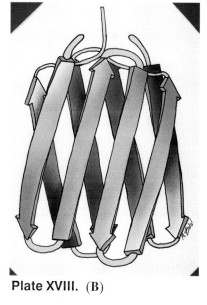

Plate XVIII. (B)

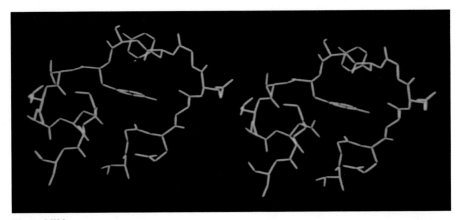

Plate XIX.

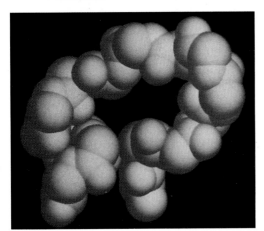

Plate XX. (A)

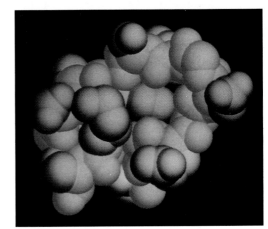

Plate XX. (B)

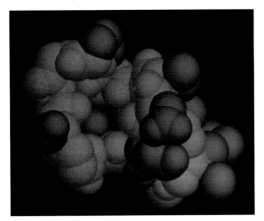

Plate XX. (C)

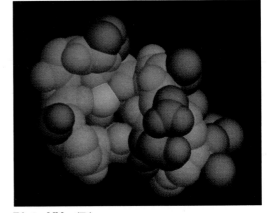

Plate XX. (D)

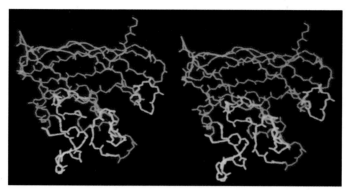

Plate XXI.

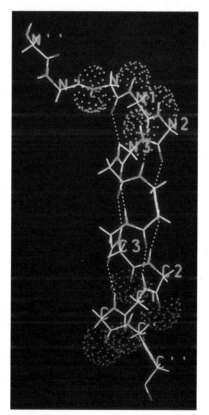

Plate XXII.

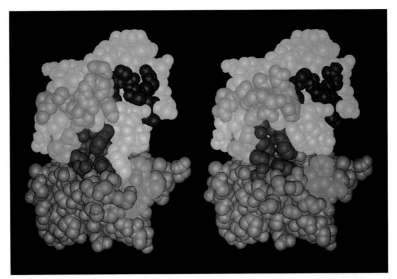

Plate XXIII.

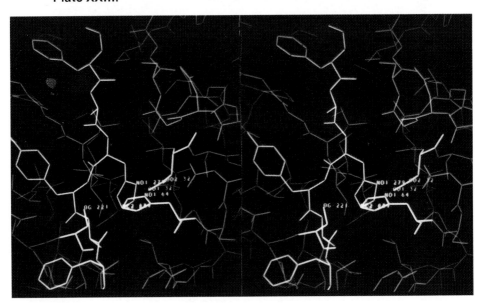

Plate XXIV.

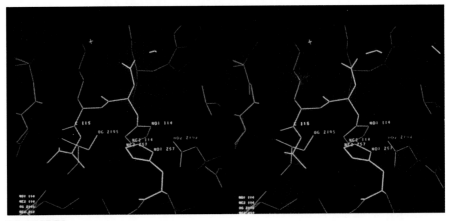

Plate XXV.

Index